The ASQ Certified Quality Engineer Handbook

THE ASQ CERTIFIED QUALITY ENGINEER HANDBOOK

Fifth Edition

Scott A. Laman, Editor

ASQExcellence
Milwaukee, Wisconsin

Published by ASQExcellence, Milwaukee, WI

Produced and distributed by Quality Press, ASQ, Milwaukee, WI

Publisher's Cataloging-in-Publication Data

Names: Laman, Scott A., editor.
Title: The ASQ certified quality engineer handbook , fifth edition / Scott A. Laman, Editor.
Description: Includes bibliographical references and index. | Milwaukee, WI: ASQExcellence, 2022.
Identifiers: LCCN: 2022947805 | ISBN: 978-1-63694-026-7 (hardcover) | 978-1-63694-028-1 (epub) | 978-1-63694-027-4 (pdf)
Subjects: LCSH Production management--Quality control--Handbooks, manuals, etc. | Reliability (Engineering)--Handbooks, manuals, etc. | BISAC BUSINESS & ECONOMICS / Quality Control | STUDY AIDS / Professional
Classification: LCC TS156 .A87 2022 | DDC 658.4/013--dc23

ASQ advances individual, organizational, and community excellence worldwide through learning, quality improvement, and knowledge exchange.

Bookstores, wholesalers, schools, libraries, businesses, and organizations: Quality Press books are available at quantity discounts for bulk purchases for business, trade, or educational uses. For more information, please contact Quality Press at 800-248-1946 or books@asq.org.

To place orders or browse the selection of all Quality Press titles, visit our website at: http://www.asq.org/quality-press.

Printed in the United States of America
26 25 24 GP 6 5 4 3

Quality Press
600 N. Plankinton Ave.
Milwaukee, WI 53203-2914
Email: books@asq.org
Excellence Through Quality™

Inspire Excellence

Table of Contents

List of Figures

List of Tables

Preface

The purpose of this book is to help people become better quality engineers, with American Society for Quality (ASQ) certification being a tool toward that end. For many purchasing this book, you probably have a good idea about what a quality engineer is and how you fit the bill with your strengths and experience. Congratulations and thank you for choosing this valuable vocation!

For others, let's begin with what quality engineering is. It is not just one field. Quality engineers can be found in product design, manufacturing, post-market surveillance, supplier development, and auditing, for example. Some of us work on the front end of new product development, crossing into reliability engineering and proactive design assurance. Others are continuous improvement and failure analysis experts, utilizing product and process performance information and solving problems identified during manufacturing and use. Some quality engineering disciplines are more technical, some are more interpersonal, and all have various levels of leadership and management.

Quality engineering crosses all demographics, generations, and educational backgrounds. It provides a unifying influence to an organization by its nature of using objective evidence, facts, and data. Few people come out of high school or college knowing that they want to be a Quality Engineer. However, occasionally someone does. More often, however, after several years of working and being exposed to many functions in an organization, a person will decide that quality engineering is what they want to do.

Much comes down to natural inclination and knowing yourself. Have you seen yourself migrate toward using mathematical tools and numbers? Do you consider yourself to have excellent attention to detail, the ability to think and present logically and clearly, and the capability of identifying problems and helping solve them? Can you discern when to take a strong stand on an issue for compliance or safety, and when there may be a gray area involved or give-and-take needed to optimize an outcome? Have others pointed out any of these characteristics in you?

With the foundation built on your natural abilities and interests, your education, and your experiences, ASQ certification can formally get your arms around what has proudly become your professional identity. Think of it as a present, a gift to yourself and by extension to your organization and professional network. In that way, the package is the certified quality engineer (CQE) body of knowledge (BoK), consisting of seven major areas:

- Management and leadership

- The quality system

- Product, process, and service design

- Product and process control

- Continuous improvement

- Quantitative methods and tools

- Risk management

The bow and ribbon on the package are the certification itself, prestigious peer recognition for passing a difficult exam to demonstrate that you really do understand and are ready to apply this broad and comprehensive body of knowledge.

Every five to seven years, the body of knowledge of an ASQ certification is reevaluated and updated. A comprehensive process is followed, and at the end we move right into producing the references and study guides to help people prepare for the updated exam. A group of people begin to update the exam question bank by deleting, adding, and revising questions as necessary. At the same time, a separate, independent group of people begin updating ASQ training and certification preparation materials, of which this handbook is one.

The process to update a handbook is somewhat involved and takes an army of people, who you will see listed in the Acknowledgments. Quality Press provides a gap assessment between the old and new bodies of knowledge and handles logistics such as contracts and agreements. If there is one part of the process that stands out as most important, it is the selection of authors, which for this book are a collection of renowned experts in their fields and experienced contributors to other publications. Editing then becomes a matter of taking the individual contributions of the authors, fitting their content into the handbook in the logical sequence per the body of knowledge, filling gaps with some writing yourself, and polishing it all to make it look consistent.

For this edition of *The ASQ Certified Quality Engineer Handbook*, the following is a summary of changes. These changes were made to cover the new body of knowledge comprehensively and clearly. It was also acknowledged that certain content, while still of value to quality professionals of all kinds, was no longer part of the body of knowledge for this certification. The following list is being provided to be thorough in communication and honest about what has been changed and removed.

- New content

  - Cost-benefit analysis and responsible, accountable, consulted, and informed matrix (RACI) as quality management system deployment techniques in Chapter 1

  - Assessing risks in audit planning and implementation in Chapter 2

  - Critical to quality as a design input in Chapter 3

  - Hazard analysis and use failure mode and effects analysis as reliability/safety/hazard assessment tools in Chapter 3

  - Overall equipment effectiveness (OEE) as a Lean tool in Chapter 5

  - 5 Whys as a corrective action tool in Chapter 5

- Data automation and database integration as data collection methods in Chapter 6

- An entirely new chapter 7 on risk management

- Restructured content

  - Risk management tools were moved from Chapter 7 to Chapter 3 as part of reliability/safety/hazard assessment tools.

  - Continuous improvement tools and methodologies were aligned with the body of knowledge in Chapter 5.

  - Quality function deployment (QFD) was moved from Chapter 1 to Chapter 3.

Regarding this book's writing style, attempts were made to simplify and reduce the number of words needed to make the point. Microsoft Word was very helpful to identify opportunities for improvement in this area. For example, using the CQE BoK philosophy of Lean, simply replacing the approximately 100 previous usages of "in order to" and "a number of" with "to" and "several" made an impact on word count and readability.

Ultimately, this book was built upon the foundation laid by an outstanding group of editors of previous editions, who are mentioned in the next section.

I hope you find this edition to be helpful in preparing for the certification exam and as a reference to help you succeed in your profession.

Acknowledgments

First, thank you to the giants in quality engineering who laid the foundation to this book by serving as editors of previous editions.

- Roger W. Berger

- Donald W. Benbow

- Ahmad K. Elshennawy

- H. Fred Walker

- Connie M. Borror

- Sarah E. Burke

- Rachel T. Silvestrini

Next, the Quality Press editorial staff was tremendously helpful in providing guidance and removing roadblocks, some of which seemed significant enough hurdles that this project could have been derailed. Simple advice ranged from determining the scope of the content (what should be in and out of the book) to reducing manuscript file size. A breakthrough at one critical point was the suggestion to use skilled people to produce the equations and mathematical symbols, which I was stuck on but apparently is simple *if* you know how to do it.

- Lillian McAnally, Managing Editor, Quality Press

- Erica Barse, Associate Editor, Quality Press

This project, and editing a book is certainly a project by any measure, could not have been completed if I were not surrounded by an incredibly knowledgeable group of authors, who each took on an area of new content in their area of expertise. They also provided guidance during the project to optimize communications and information flow. This is also a call out to a few of the ASQ Technical Communities. The certified quality engineer exam does not have a sponsoring division like some exams do. Therefore, to obtain the assistance needed to determine contributing authors, I reached out to leadership in ASQ divisions whose focus is on areas including in the CQE BoK. The Audit Division, the Quality Management Division, and the Statistics divisions all provided at least one author, who are listed below followed by the subject(s) each contributed.

- Matthew A. Barsalou, BorgWarner Systems Engineering GmbH – Critical to quality, control chart selection

- Andrew Davison, Genesys Spine – Assessing audit risks, 5 Whys, and auditing standards

- Denis Devos, Devos Associates Inc. – Cost-benefit analysis and responsible, accountable, consulted, and informed matrix

- Harish Jose, Bausch + Lomb Synergetics – Overall equipment effectiveness

- Dr. Michael Mladjenovic, The Sensei Group – Data automation and database integration

- Jayet Moon, Terumo Medical Corporation – Risk management and tools

Two graduate students from the Georgia Institute of Technology produced the mathematical content and at times went above and beyond by finding editing improvements.

- Sweta Senthil

- Manav Sheth

Others provided additional sets of eyes and risk management subject matter expertise in the form of pre-submission reviews.

- Barry Craner, CQA-Associates

- Veronica Cavendish-Stephens, Auchincloss-Stephens International

Now it gets more personal. Over the years, there have been many people who have believed in me and given me a chance to advance in quality engineering when at each step of the way, someone else told me that the next step was not possible. It has been a journey. Thank you to …

- Stephen Uliana, Mitsubishi Chemical Advanced Materials, for providing my first quality engineering opportunity at Quadrant Engineering Plastic Products and for supporting my initial, brash career venture into attaining ASQ certifications.

- Jeffrey P. Lewis, Globus Medical, for being the hiring manager to provide my first so-titled quality engineering position at Arrow International (now Teleflex).

- Scott McKently, Owens & Minor, for promoting me into my first and second quality engineering management positions at Teleflex.

- Robert Z. Phillips, Siemens Healthineers, for providing support and stretch opportunities at Teleflex to prepare me for continued growth.

- Julius Aviza for providing additional new opportunities at Teleflex that led to my job growing into the quality systems area including medical device management representative responsibilities.

- Michael Byrnes, ASQExcellence, who identified me to edit *The ASQ Certified Medical Device Auditor Handbook* a couple years ago, which led to a similar opportunity with this handbook.

The company Teleflex was mentioned several times above. I would like to acknowledge the organization as a whole for recognizing the importance of individual development plans and for fully supporting ASQ certifications and activities that lead to personal growth that can be translated to the job. It is a win for all and not taken for granted.

Finally, I would like to thank my wife, Krista, for patiently tolerating my work on this book at every opportunity for several months. That support was essential.

List of Acronyms

AHP: analytical hierarchy process

AIAG: Automotive Industry Action Group

AND: activity network diagram

ANOVA: analysis of variance

AQL: acceptable quality limit

AQP: advanced quality planning

ARL: average run length

ASN: average sample number

ASQ: American Society for Quality

ASTM: American Society for Testing and Materials

ATE: automated test equipment

ATI: average total inspection

BoK: body of knowledge

cdf: cumulative density function/cumulative distribution function

CL: center line

CLA: center line average

CM: configuration management

CMM: coordinate measuring machines

COPQ: cost of poor quality

COQ: cost of quality

CQE: certified quality engineer

CSA: Canadian Standards Association

CtQ: Critical to Quality

df: degrees of freedom

dFMEA: design failure mode and effects analysis

DMAIC: define, measure, analyze, improve, control

DMRCS: define, measure, reduce, combine, select

DoD: Department of Defense

DOE: design of experiments

DPMO: defects per million opportunities

DPU: defects per unit

DR: discrimination ratio

EC: earliest completion time

ECP: engineering change proposal

EEO: equal employment opportunity

8D: eight disciplines

ES: earliest start time

ESS: environmental stress screening

ESSEH: Environmental Stress Screening of Electronic Hardware

ELT: extract, load, transform

ETL: extract, transform, load

F: Fahrenheit

FMEA: failure modes and effects analysis

FMECA: failure modes effects and criticality analysis

FS: free slack

FT: fault tree

GD&T: geometric dimensioning and tolerancing

HACCP: hazard analysis and critical control points

IATF: International Automotive Task Force

IoT: Internet of things

IQ: installation qualification

IQR: inter-quartile range

IRR: internal rate of return

ISO: International Organization for Standardization

IT: information technology

JIT: just-in-time

K: Kelvin

LC: latest completion time

LCL: lower control limit

LRM: linear responsibility matrix

LS: latest start time

LSC: least squares circle

LSL: lower specification limit

LSS: Lean-Six Sigma

LTPD: lot tolerance percent defective

MA: moving average

MAP: measurement assurance protocol

MBNQA: Malcolm Baldrige National Quality Award

MCC: minimum circumscribed circle

MIC: maximum inscribed circle

MMC: maximum material condition

MRB: material review board

MRP: manufacturing resource planning

MRS: minimum radial separation

MS: mean square

MSA: measurement systems analysis

MTBF: mean time between failures

MTTF: mean time to failure

MTTR: mean time to repair

MZC: minimum zone circle

NAVAIR: Naval Air Systems Command

NAVMAT: naval material command

NDT: nondestructive testing

NIST: National Institute of Standards and Technology

NMCM: not-mission capable equipment due to maintenance

NPV: net present value

OC: operating characteristic

OEE: Overall Equipment Effectiveness

OEM: original equipment manufacturer

OQ: operational qualification

PC: peak count

PCB: printed circuit board

PDCA: plan–do–check–act

pdf: probability density function

PDPC: process decision program chart

PDSA: plan–do–study–act

pFMEA: process failure mode and effects analysis

PII: personally identifiable information

PLC: programmable logic controller

pmf: probability mass function

PPAP: part production approval process

ppm: parts per million

PPQ: process performance qualification

PQ: process qualification

PTR: precision-to-tolerance ratio

PVC: process value chain

QE: quality engineer

QFD: quality function deployment

QIS: quality information system

QMS: quality management system

R&D: research and development

R&R: repeatability and reproducibility

RACI: responsible, accountable, consulted, and informed

RCDQ: reactive customer-driven quality

RCI: rapid continuous improvement

RFID: radio frequency identification

RMS: root mean square

ROI: return on investment

RPN: risk priority number

RQL: rejectable quality level

RRM: resource requirements matrix

RTY: rolled throughput yield

SAE: Society of Automotive Engineers

SCADA: supervisory control and data acquisition

SDWT: self-directed work team

s.e.: standard error

SI: Systems International

SIPOC: suppliers, inputs, process, outputs, customers

SMED: single minute exchange of dies

SNR: signal-to-noise ratio

SPC: statistical process control

SQA: supplier quality assurance

SQM: supplier quality management

SQP: strategic quality planning

SS: sum of squares

SWOT: strengths, weaknesses, opportunities, threats

TPM: total productive maintenance

TQM: total quality management

TS: total slack

uFMEA: use failure mode and effects analysis

UCL: upper control limit

USL: upper specification limit

VOC: voice of the customer

VSM: value stream map

WBS: work breakdown structure

WIP: work in process

Certified Quality Engineer (CQE) Body of Knowledge

The topics in this Body of Knowledge include subtext explanations and the cognitive level at which the questions will be written. This information will provide useful guidance for both the Exam Development Committee and the candidate preparing to take the exam. The subtext is not intended to limit the subject matter or be all-inclusive of the material that will be covered in the exam. It is meant to clarify the type of content that will be included on the exam. The descriptor in parentheses at the end of each entry refers to the maximum cognitive level at which the topic will be tested. A complete description of cognitive levels is provided at the end of this document.

I. **Management and Leadership (17 Questions)**

  A. **Quality Philosophies and Foundations**

    Describe continuous improvement tools, including lean, six sigma, statistical process control (SPC), and total quality management. Understand how modern quality has evolved from quality control through statistical process control (SPC) to total quality management and leadership principles (including Deming's 14 points). (Understand)

  B. **The Quality Management System (QMS)**

    1. **Strategic planning**

    Identify and define top management's responsibility for the QMS, including establishing policies and objectives, setting organization-wide goals, and supporting quality initiatives. (Apply)

    2. **Deployment techniques**

    Define, describe, and use various deployment tools in support of the QMS such as:

    a. Benchmarking

    Define the concept of benchmarking and why it may be used. (Remember)

    b. Stakeholder

    Define, describe, and use stakeholder identification and analysis. (Apply)

c. Performance

Define, describe, and use performance measurement tools such as cost-benefit analysis. (Apply)

d. Project management

Define, describe, and use project management tools, including Gantt charts and the responsible, accountable, consulted and informed matrix (RACI). (Apply)

3. **Quality information system (QIS)**

Identify and describe the basic elements of a QIS, including who will contribute data, the kind of data to be managed, who will have access to the data, the level of flexibility for future information needs, and data analysis. (Understand)

C. **ASQ Code of Ethics for Professional Conduct**

Determine appropriate behavior in situations requiring ethical decisions. (Evaluate)

D. **Leadership Principles and Techniques**

Analyze various principles and techniques for developing and organizing teams and leading quality initiatives. (Analyze)

E. **Facilitation Principles and Techniques**

1. **Roles and responsibilities**

Describe the facilitator's roles and responsibilities on a team. (Understand)

2. **Facilitation tools**

Apply various tools used with teams, including brainstorming, nominal group technique, conflict resolution, and force-field analysis. (Apply)

F. **Communication Skills**

Identify and distinguish between specific communication methods that are used for delivering information and messages in a variety of situations across all levels of the organization. (Analyze)

G. **Customer Relations**

Define, apply, and analyze the results of customer relation tools such as customer satisfaction surveys. (Analyze)

H. **Supplier Management**

1. **Techniques**

Apply various supplier management techniques, including supplier qualification, certification, and evaluation. (Apply)

2. **Improvement**

Analyze supplier ratings and performance improvement results. (Analyze)

3. **Risk**

Understand business continuity, resiliency, and contingency planning. (Understand)

I. **Barriers to Quality Improvement**

Identify barriers to quality improvement, analyze their causes and impact, and implement methods for improvement. (Analyze)

II. **The Quality System (18 Questions)**

A. **Elements of the Quality System**

1. **Basic elements**

Interpret the basic elements of a quality system, including planning, control, and improvement, from product and process design through quality cost systems and audit programs. (Evaluate)

2. **Design**

Analyze the design and alignment of interrelated processes to the strategic plan and core processes. (Analyze)

B. **Documentation of the Quality System**

1. **Document components**

Identify and describe quality system documentation components, including quality policies and procedures to support the system. (Understand)

2. **Document control**

Evaluate configuration management, maintenance, and document control to manage work instructions and quality records. (Evaluate)

C. **Quality Standards and Other Guidelines**

Apply national and international standards and other requirements and guidelines, including the Malcolm Baldrige National Quality Award (MBNQA), and describe key points of the ISO 9000 series of standards. [Note: Industry-specific standards will not be tested.] (Apply)

D. **Quality Audits**

1. **Types of audits**

Describe and classify the various types of quality audits such as product, process, management (system), registration (certification), compliance (regulatory), first, second, and third party. (Apply)

2. **Roles and responsibilities in audits**

Identify and define roles and responsibilities for audit participants such as audit team (leader and members), client, and auditee. (Understand)

3. **Audit planning and implementation**

Describe and apply the stages of a quality audit, from audit planning, including assessing risks through conducting an audit. (Apply)

4. Audit reporting and follow-up

Apply the steps of audit reporting and follow up, including the need to verify corrective action. (Apply)

E. Cost of Quality (COQ)

Identify and apply COQ concepts, including cost categorization, data collection, reporting, and interpreting results. (Analyze)

F. Quality Training

Identify and apply key elements of a training program, including conducting a needs analysis, preparing curricula and materials, and determining the program's effectiveness. (Apply)

III. Product, Process, and Service Design (21 Questions)

A. Classification of Quality Characteristics

Define, interpret, assess, and classify quality characteristics for new and existing products, processes, and services. [Note: The classification of defects is covered in IV.B.3.] (Evaluate)

B. Design Inputs, Techniques, and Review

1. Inputs

Classify design inputs such as customer needs, regulatory requirements, critical to quality, and risk assessment into robust design using techniques such as failure mode and effects analysis (FMEA). (Analyze)

2. Techniques

Apply Design for X (DFX), Design for Six Sigma (DFSS), and requirements traceability. (Apply)

3. Review

Identify and apply common elements of the design review process, including roles and responsibilities of participants. (Apply)

C. Technical Drawings and Specifications

Interpret specification requirements in relation to product and process characteristics and technical drawings, including characteristics such as views, title blocks, dimensioning and tolerancing, and geometric dimensioning and tolerance symbols (GD&T). (Evaluate)

D. Verification and Validation

Interpret the results of evaluations and tests used to verify and validate the design of products, processes and services, such as installation qualification (IQ), operational qualification (OQ), and process qualification (PQ). (Evaluate)

E. Reliability and Maintainability

1. Predictive and preventive maintenance tools

Describe and apply the tools and techniques used to maintain and improve process and product reliability. (Apply)

2. **Reliability and maintainability indices**

   Apply indices such as mean time to failure (MTTF), mean time between failure (MTBF), mean time to repair (MTTR), availability, and failure rate. (Apply)

3. **Reliability models**

   Identify, define, and distinguish between the basic elements of reliability models such as exponential, Weibull, and bathtub curve. (Apply)

4. **Reliability/safety/hazard assessment tools**

   Define, construct, and interpret the results of failure mode and effects analysis (FMEA), design FMEA (dFMEA), process FMEA (pFMEA), use FMEA (uFMEA), failure mode, effects, and criticality analysis (FMECA), and hazard analysis. (Analyze)

IV. **Product and Process Control (23 Questions)**

   A. **Methods**

   Implement product and process control methods such as control plan development, critical control point identification, and work instruction development and validation. (Analyze)

   B. **Material Control**

   1. **Material identification, status, and traceability**

      Define and distinguish between these concepts, and describe methods for applying them in various situations. (Analyze)

   2. **Material segregation**

      Describe material segregation and its importance, and evaluate appropriate methods for applying it in various situations. (Evaluate)

   3. **Material classification**

      Assess and classify product and process defects and non-conformities. (Evaluate)

   4. **Material review board (MRB)**

      Describe the purpose and function of an MRB and evaluate nonconforming product or material to make a disposition decision in various situations. (Evaluate)

   C. **Acceptance Sampling**

   1. **Sampling concepts**

      Apply the concepts of producer and consumer risk, and related terms, including operating characteristic (OC) curves, acceptable quality limit (AQL), and lot tolerance percent defective (LTPD). (Apply)

   2. **Sampling standards and plans**

      Identify, interpret, and apply ANSI/ASQ Z1.4 and Z1.9 standards for attributes and variables sampling. (Analyze)

3. **Sample integrity**

Identify and apply techniques for establishing and maintaining sample integrity. (Apply)

D. **Measurement and Test**

1. **Measurement tools**

Select and describe appropriate uses of inspection tools such as gage blocks, calipers, micrometers, optical comparators, and coordinate measuring machines (CMM). (Analyze)

2. **Destructive and nondestructive tests**

Identify when destructive and nondestructive measurement test methods should be used and apply the methods appropriately. (Apply)

E. **Metrology**

Apply metrology techniques such as calibration, traceability to calibration standards, measurement error and its sources, and control and maintenance of measurement standards and devices. (Apply)

F. **Measurement System Analysis (MSA)**

Calculate, analyze, and interpret repeatability and reproducibility (Gage R&R) studies, measurement correlation, capability, bias, linearity, precision, stability and accuracy, using MSA quantitative and graphical methods. (Evaluate)

V. **Continuous Improvement (26 Questions)**

A. **Quality Control Tools**

Select, construct, apply, and interpret the following quality control tools:

1. Flowcharts

2. Pareto charts

3. Cause and effect diagrams

4. Control charts

5. Check sheets

6. Scatter diagrams

7. Histograms (Analyze)

B. **Quality Management and Planning Tools**

Select, construct, apply, and interpret the following quality management and planning tools:

1. Affinity diagrams and force field analysis

2. Tree diagrams

3. Process decision program charts (PDPC)

4. Matrix diagrams

     5. Interrelationship digraphs

     6. Prioritization matrices

     7. Activity network diagrams (Analyze)

C. **Continuous Improvement Methodologies**

Define, describe, and apply the following continuous improvement methodologies:

     1. Total quality management (TQM)

     2. Kaizen

     3. Plan-do-check-act (PDCA)

     4. Six sigma (Analyze)

D. **Lean tools**

Define, describe, and apply the following lean tools:

     1. 5S

     2. Value-stream mapping

     3. Kanban

     4. Visual control

     5. 8 Wastes

     6. Standardized work

     7. Takt time

     8. Single minute exchange of die (SMED)

     9. Overall equipment effectiveness (OEE) (Evaluate)

E. **Corrective Action**

Identify, describe, and apply elements of the corrective action process, including problem identification, failure analysis, root cause analysis, 5 Whys, problem correction, recurrence control, and verification of effectiveness. (Evaluate)

F. **Preventive Action**

Identify, describe and apply various preventive action tools such as error-proofing/poka-yoke and robust design and analyze their effectiveness. (Evaluate)

VI. **Quantitative Methods and Tools (34 Questions)**

A. **Collecting and Summarizing Data**

1. **Types of data**

Define, classify, and compare discrete (attributes) and continuous (variables) data. (Apply)

2. **Measurement scales**

Define and describe nominal, ordinal, interval, and ratio scales. (Understand)

3. **Data collection methods**

Describe various methods for collecting data, including tally or check sheets, data coding, automatic gaging, data automation, database integration, and identify the strengths and weaknesses of the methods. (Apply)

4. **Data accuracy and integrity**

Identify factors that can influence data accuracy such as source/ resource issues, flexibility, versatility, inconsistency, inappropriate interpretation of data values, and redundancy to ensure data accuracy and integrity. (Apply)

5. **Data visualization techniques**

Apply and interpret data visualization techniques using dashboards, and select the appropriate metrics for dashboards. (Apply)

6. **Descriptive statistics**

Describe, calculate, and interpret measures of central tendency and dispersion, apply the central limit theorem, and construct and interpret frequency distributions, including simple, categorical, grouped, ungrouped, and cumulative. (Evaluate)

7. **Graphical methods for depicting distributions**

Apply and interpret diagrams such as probability plots for normal and other distributions. [Note: Histograms are covered in V.A.] (Analyze)

B. **Quantitative Concepts**

1. **Terminology**

Define and apply quantitative terms, including population, parameter, sample, statistic, random sampling, and expected value. (Analyze)

2. **Drawing statistical conclusions**

Distinguish between numeric and analytical studies. Assess the validity of statistical conclusions by analyzing the assumptions used and the robustness of the technique used. (Evaluate)

3. **Probability terms and concepts**

Describe concepts such as independence, mutual exclusivity, multiplication rules, complementary probability, and joint occurrence of events. (Apply)

C. **Probability Distributions**

1. **Continuous distributions**

Define and distinguish between these distributions such as normal, uniform, exponential, lognormal, Weibull, Student's t and F. (Analyze)

2. **Discrete distributions**

Define and distinguish between these distributions such as binomial, Poisson, hypergeometric, and multinomial. (Analyze)

D. **Statistical Decision-Making**

1. **Point estimates and confidence intervals**

Define, describe, and assess the bias of estimators. Calculate and interpret standard error, tolerance intervals, and confidence intervals. (Evaluate)

2. **Hypothesis testing**

Define, interpret, and apply hypothesis tests for means, variances, and proportions. Apply and interpret the concepts of significance level, power, type I, and type II errors. Define and distinguish between statistical and practical significance. (Evaluate)

3. **Paired-comparison tests**

Define and use paired-comparison (parametric) hypothesis tests, and interpret the results. (Apply)

4. **Goodness-of-fit tests**

Define and use chi-square and other goodness-of-fit tests, and understand the results. (Apply)

5. **Analysis of variance (ANOVA)**

Define use, and interpret ANOVA and interpret the results. (Analyze)

6. **Contingency tables**

Define and use contingency tables to evaluate statistical significance. (Apply)

E. **Relationships Between Variables**

1. **Linear regression**

Calculate simple linear regression models. Illustrate hypothesis tests for regression statistics. Use linear regression models for estimation and prediction. (Apply)

2. **Simple linear correlation**

Calculate the correlation coefficient and its confidence interval, and illustrate a hypothesis test for correlation statistics. (Apply)

3. **Time-series analysis**

Define, describe, and use time-series analysis, including moving average to identify trends and seasonal or cyclical variation. (Apply)

F. **Statistical Process Control (SPC)**

1. **Objectives and benefits**

Identify and explain the objectives and benefits of SPC. (Understand)

2. **Common and special causes**

Describe, identify, and distinguish between these types of causes. (Analyze)

3. **Selection of variable**

Identify and select variable characteristics for monitoring by control chart. (Analyze)

4. **Rational subgrouping**

   Define and apply the principles of rational subgrouping. (Apply)

5. **Control charts**

   Identify, select, construct, and use various control charts, including $\bar{x}$ - R, $\bar{x}$ - s, individuals and moving range (ImR or XmR), moving average and moving range (MAMR), p, np, c, and u. (Analyze)

6. **Control chart analysis**

   Read and interpret control charts and use rules for determining statistical control. (Evaluate)

7. **Short-run SPC**

   Identify and define short-run SPC rules. (Understand)

G. **Process and Performance Capability**

   1. **Process capability studies**

      Define, describe, calculate, and use process capability studies, including identifying characteristics, specifications and tolerances, developing sampling plans for such studies, and establishing statistical control. (Analyze)

   2. **Process performance vs. specifications**

      Distinguish between natural process limits and specification limits, and calculate percent defective, defects per million opportunities (DPMO), and parts per million (ppm). (Analyze)

   3. **Process capability indices**

      Define, select, and calculate C_p, C_{pk}, C_{pm}, and C_r, and evaluate process capability. (Evaluate)

   4. **Process performance indices**

      Define, select, and calculate P_p and P_{pk}, and evaluate process performance. (Evaluate)

H. **Design and Analysis of Experiments**

   1. **Terminology**

      Define terms such as dependent and independent variables, factors, levels, response, treatment, error, and replication. (Understand)

   2. **Planning and organizing experiments**

      Identify the basic elements of designed experiments, including determining the experiment objective, selecting factors, responses, and measurement methods, and choosing the appropriate design. (Analyze)

   3. **Design principles**

      Define and apply the principles of power and sample size, balance, replication, order, efficiency, randomization, blocking, interaction, and confounding. (Apply)

4. **Full-factorial experiments**

Construct full-factorial designs and use computational and graphical methods to analyze the significance of results. (Analyze)

5. **Two-level fractional factorial experiments**

Construct two-level fractional factorial designs and apply computational and graphical methods to analyze the significance of results. (Analyze)

VII. **Risk Management (21 Questions)**

A. **Risk Fundamentals**

1. **Risk terminology**

Define, describe, and apply risk terminology such as risk, risk management, severity, occurrence, detection, and risk-based thinking. (Analyze)

2. **Types of risk management**

Understand and apply various types of enterprise (strategic, software, business, regulatory, medical, audit), operational (supplier, supply chain, safety, project, manufacturing, operations, service, quality system), and product (design, process, use, safety) risk management. (Apply)

B. **Risk Planning and Assessment**

1. **Risk management plan**

Analyze and interpret a risk management plan and its components (objectives, risk criteria, stakeholder identification, and team member roles/responsibilities) to identify and prioritize risks. (Analyze)

2. **Risk assessment**

Apply categorization methods and evaluation tools to assess risk such as failure mode and effects analysis. Identify and apply evaluation metrics including the use of risk matrices, risk priority numbers, and acceptability criteria. (Analyze)

C. **Risk Treatment, Control, and Monitoring**

1. **Identification and documentation**

Identify risks, gaps, and controls and document with tools such as a risk register. (Analyze)

2. **Risk management system evaluation**

Apply auditing techniques and testing of controls to evaluate a risk management system. (Apply)

3. **Risk treatment strategies**

Understand and apply risk treatment strategies, such as avoid, mitigate, transfer, and accept. (Analyze)

4. **Risk monitoring**

   Apply risk monitoring techniques such as, complaint tracking, trending, and post-market surveillance. (Analyze)

5. **Mitigation planning**

   Apply and interpret risk mitigation plan. (Analyze)

LEVELS OF COGNITION BASED ON BLOOM'S TAXONOMY—REVISED (2001)

In addition to content specifics, the subtext for each topic in this BOK also indicates the intended complexity level of the test questions for that topic. These levels are based on "Levels of Cognition" (from Bloom's Taxonomy—Revised, 2001) and are presented below in rank order, from least complex to most complex.

Remember

Recall or recognize terms, definitions, facts, ideas, materials, patterns, sequences, methods, principles.

Understand

Read and understand descriptions, communications, reports, tables, diagrams, directions, regulations.

Apply

Know when and how to use ideas, procedures, methods, formulas, principles, theories.

Analyze

Break down information into its constituent parts and recognize their relationship to one another and how they are organized; identify sublevel factors or salient data from a complex scenario.

Evaluate

Make judgments about the value of proposed ideas, solutions, by comparing the proposal to specific criteria or standards.

Create

Put parts or elements together in such a way as to reveal a pattern or structure not clearly there before; identify which data or information from a complex set is appropriate to examine further or from which supported conclusions can be drawn.

Chapter 1
Management and Leadership

The two main themes of Chapter 1 are a broad perspective on the quality profession and the human element in quality. Areas such as strategic planning and leadership may require additional training and years of experience before full competency is achieved. In the same vein, developing communication skills and removing barriers to quality improvement could take a lifetime. After a careful study of this chapter, you should have a clear idea of the elements upon which the profession of quality engineering is based.

The quality profession has both a human element and a technical element, and Chapter 1 examines the human element of quality from several different perspectives. First, definitions of quality are discussed, followed by a review of the history of quality. The contributions of the leading experts over the past 80 years are noted, starting with Walter Shewhart and highlighting his two greatest successors, W. Edwards Deming and Joseph M. Juran. Some major quality programs discussed are statistical process control, total quality management, lean philosophy, and Six Sigma. No matter whether the quality program is one that is discussed here or something else, a successful organization will have a system for managing its quality. One way to view the quality management system is to break it into three parts: strategic planning of the vision and goals, deployment techniques for converting the vision/goals into reality, and an information system to collect, analyze, and report the data. Deployment techniques used for selecting and managing projects include return on investment (ROI) and Gantt charts. Heavy emphasis is also given to performance measurement tools. Next, professional ethics is discussed, including the ASQ Code of Ethics and legal constraints on the quality engineer.

Leadership, facilitation, and communication skills are all interrelated. For the organization to achieve its goals in a positive and efficient manner, leaders must translate vision and goals into tangible activities. Executive direction and indirect or "soft" leadership known as facilitation unleash the energy and motivation of mid- and lower-level employees. Communication skills are critical to effective leadership and facilitation, as well as to individual career success.

The final three sections of Chapter 1 address the role of quality in dealing with customers, suppliers, and barriers to improvement. Two typical techniques for addressing the role of quality are supplier surveys, which tell us what one can expect from suppliers, and customer surveys, which tell us what our customers think of us. Finally, the section on barriers reinforces the idea that quality improvement is a constant struggle, and that the various ideas of this book must be applied again and again to maintain momentum toward that elusive but unobtainable goal of perfection.

QUALITY PHILOSOPHIES AND FOUNDATIONS

Describe continuous improvement tools, including lean, six sigma, statistical process control (SPC), and total quality management. Understand how modern quality has evolved from quality control through statistical process control (SPC) to total quality management and leadership principles (including Deming's 14 points). (Understand)

Body of Knowledge I.A

This section covers the meaning of quality and provides a brief history of quality. The pioneers of the quality engineering movement are highlighted: Walter A. Shewhart, W. Edwards Deming, and Joseph M. Juran. Also introduced are several continuous improvement methods.

What Is Quality?

Quality means different things to different people in different situations. As Henry Ford said, "Quality means doing it right when no one is looking." Some additional informal descriptions and results of quality include the following:

- Quality is inversely proportional to variability

- Quality is not a program; it is an approach to business

- Quality is a collection of powerful tools and concepts that are proven to work

- Quality is defined by customers through their satisfaction

- Quality includes continual improvement and breakthrough events

- Quality tools and techniques are applicable in every aspect of business

- Quality is aimed at perfection; anything less is an improvement opportunity

- Quality increases customer satisfaction, reduces cycle time and costs, and eliminates errors and rework

Additionally, typical elements used to assess quality include totality of features, essential characteristics, ability to satisfy needs, conformance to requirements, degree or grade of excellence, free of deficiencies, and meeting/exceeding

Table 1.1 Comparing the impact quality can have.

99.74% good = 3 sigma	99.9998% good = 6 sigma
20,000 lost articles of mail per hour	Seven lost articles of mail per hour
Unsafe drinking water for almost 15 minutes each day	One minute of unsafe drinking water every seven months
5,000 incorrect surgical operations per week	1.7 incorrect surgical operations per week
Two short or long landings at most major airports each day	One short or long landing every five years
200,000 wrong drug prescriptions each year	68 wrong drug prescriptions per year
No electricity for almost seven hours each month	One hour without electricity every 34 years

customer expectations. Garvin (1987) discusses eight dimensions of quality, and Montgomery (2013) adds three more regarding service and transactional organizations. These dimensions include performance, reliability, durability, serviceability, aesthetics, features, perceived quality, conformance to standards, responsiveness, professionalism, and attentiveness.

Quality is not just for businesses; it is also for nonprofit organizations such as schools, healthcare and social services, and government agencies. Results, performance and financial, are the natural consequence of effective quality management. Table 1.1 compares the consequences and impact of quality management at two different quality levels, three sigma (99.74% good) and six sigma (99.9998% good).

The above quality descriptors show that quality is difficult to define, and no one definition can be all-inclusive. The word *quality* is highly nuanced and allows many interpretations. For example, Merriam-Webster's definition of *quality* is "an inherent or distinguishing characteristic"[1] and is one of many distinctly different definitions from the same authority. The reader quickly comes to realize that most of the definitions are quite specialized and not pertinent to the practice of quality engineering. According to ISO 9000:2015, section 3.6.2, *quality* is defined as "the degree to which a set of inherent characteristics of an object fulfills requirements."

This definition is quite interesting, first because it is published by ISO, an international standards organization, and second because it specifically rebuts the definition that Joseph Juran used throughout his career: "quality = fitness for use." In contrast, Philip Crosby used the definition "quality = conformance to specifications." There probably never will be an ultimate definition of this all-important word, as the definition is constantly evolving.

The views of eight well-known quality experts appeared in the July 2001 issue of *Quality Progress*. Although these experts differ on details and nuances, some common themes appear in all their different quality philosophies:

1. Quality improvement is a never-ending process

2. Top management commitment, knowledge, and active participation are critical

---

[1]http://dictionary.reference.com/search?q=quality.

3. Management is responsible for articulating a company philosophy, goals, measurable objectives, and a change strategy

4. All employees in the organization need to be active participants

5. A common language and set of procedures are important to communicate and support the quality effort

6. A process must be established to identify the most critical problems, determine their causes, and find solutions

7. Changes in company culture, roles, and responsibilities may be required

History of Quality

The quality profession has a long history, which has greatly accelerated over the past 80 years. Joseph M. Juran (1988) traced the practice of the quality profession back to the ancient Egyptians and the building of the pyramids. For centuries, quality was intrinsically associated with craftsmanship, and each craftsman controlled all aspects of the final product of his craft. This changed dramatically with the Industrial Revolution.

Modern quality practices originated in two stages: mass inspection in the early 1900s and the control chart around 1930. Mass inspection became commonplace because of Frederick Taylor's *Scientific Management*. Workers stopped checking the quality of their work and instead passed it on to specially trained inspectors. Although inspection is a vital element of quality, Walter Shewhart's invention of the process control chart really initiated the quality profession. Awareness of worker motivation and attitudes as contributors to quality became prevalent in the early 1930s because of Elton Mayo's Hawthorne studies for Western Electric.

The next big push for quality emerged during World War II when suddenly people's lives could be destroyed by poor-quality products. At the same time, hundreds of American companies were called on to manufacture goods to the most exacting requirements. Many quality control techniques, such as acceptance sampling and process control charts, which were merely encouraged before the war, became mandatory as part of the defense effort. Two of the leading practitioners of the quality profession—W. Edwards Deming and Joseph M. Juran—established their professional credentials during this time. Both later went to Japan to teach statistical and management tools. The Japanese excelled in developing quality methods, and in the 1970s, Americans made repeated trips to Japan to explore Japanese successes and to bring home proven Japanese methods.

The American Society for Quality Control, now known as the American Society for Quality (ASQ), was established soon after World War II when Martin Brumbaugh saw that great benefits would be attained if he could unify various local quality control societies into one national organization. As he struggled with this task, he recognized the superb skills of George Edwards, who was then head of inspection engineering at Bell Telephone Laboratories. Edwards became the first president of the society and helped establish policies that guide its operation to this day.

The first three awards the society created to recognize these three pioneers of quality were the Brumbaugh Award, the Shewhart Medal, and the Edwards Medal.

Table 1.2   A timeline of quality methods.

1700–1900	Quality is largely determined by the efforts of an individual craftsman. Eli Whitney introduces standardized, interchangeable parts to simplify assembly.
1875	Frederick W. Taylor introduces "Scientific Management" principles to divide work into smaller, more easily accomplished units—the first approach to dealing with more complex products and processes. The focus was on productivity. Later contributors were Frank Gilbreth and Henry Gantt.
1900–1930	Henry Ford, inventor of the assembly line, provides a further refinement of work methods to improve productivity and quality; Ford developed mistake-proof assembly concepts, self-checking, and in-process inspection.
1901	First standards laboratories established in Great Britain.
1907–1908	AT&T begins systematic inspection and testing of products and materials.
1908	W. S. Gosset (writing as "Student") introduces the t-distribution—results from his work on quality control at Guinness Brewery.
1915–1919	WWI—British government begins a supplier certification program.
1919	Technical Inspection Association is formed in England; this later becomes the Institute of Quality Assurance.
1920s	AT&T Bell Laboratories forms a quality department—emphasizing quality, inspection and test, and product reliability. B. P. Dudding at General Electric in England uses statistical methods to control the quality of electric lamps.
1922	Henry Ford writes (with Samuel Crowtha) and publishes *My Life and Work*, which focused on elimination of waste and improving process efficiency. Many Ford concepts and ideas are the basis of lean principles used today.
1922–1923	R. A. Fisher publishes series of fundamental papers on designed experiments and their application to the agricultural sciences.
1924	W. A. Shewhart introduces the control chart concept in a Bell Laboratories technical memorandum.
1928	Acceptance sampling methodology is developed and refined by H. F. Dodge and H. G. Romig at Bell Labs.
1931	W. A. Shewhart publishes *Economic Control of Quality of Manufactured Product*—outlining statistical methods for use in production and control chart methods.
1932	W. A. Shewhart gives lectures on statistical methods in production and control charts at the University of London.
1932–1933	British textile and woolen industry and German chemical industry begin use of designed experiments for product/process development.
1933	The Royal Statistical Society forms the Industrial and Agricultural Research Section.
1938	W. E. Deming invites Shewhart to present seminars on control charts at the U.S. Department of Agriculture Graduate School.

(continued)

Table 1.2 A timeline of quality methods. (Continued)

1940	The U.S. War Department publishes a guide for using control charts to analyze process data.
1940–1943	Bell Labs develops the forerunners of the military standard sampling plans for the U.S. Army.
1942	In Great Britain, the Ministry of Supply Advising Service on Statistical Methods and Quality Control is formed.
1942–1946	Training courses on statistical quality control are given to industry; more than 15 quality societies are formed in North America.
1944	*Industrial Quality Control* begins publication.
1946	The American Society for Quality Control (ASQC) is formed as the merger of various quality societies. The International Standards Organization (ISO) is founded. Deming is invited to Japan by the Economic and Scientific Services Section of the U.S. War Department to help occupation forces in rebuilding Japanese industry. The Japanese Union of Scientists and Engineers (JUSE) is formed.
1946–1949	Deming is invited to give statistical quality control seminars to Japanese industry.
1948	Genichi Taguchi begins study and application of experimental design.
1950	Deming begins education of Japanese industrial managers; statistical quality control methods begin to be widely taught in Japan.
1950–1975	Taiichi Ohno, Shigeo Shingo, and Eiji Toyoda develop the Toyota Production System, an integrated technical/social system that defined and developed many lean principles such as just-in-time production and rapid setup of tools and equipment. Kaoru Ishikawa introduces the cause-and-effect diagram.
1950s	Classic texts on statistical quality control by Eugene Grant and A. J. Duncan appear.
1951	A. V. Feigenbaum publishes the first edition of his book *Total Quality Control*. JUSE establishes the Deming Prize for significant achievement in quality control and quality methodology.
1951+	G. E. P. Box and K. B. Wilson publish fundamental work on using designed experiments and response surface methodology for process optimization; focus is on chemical industry. Applications of designed experiments in the chemical industry grow steadily after this.
1954	Joseph M. Juran is invited by the Japanese to lecture on quality management and improvement. British statistician E. S. Page introduces the cumulative sum (CUSUM) control chart.
1957	J. M. Juran and F. M. Gryna's *Quality Control Handbook* is first published.
1959	*Technometrics* (a journal of statistics for the physical, chemical, and engineering sciences) is established; J. Stuart Hunter is the founding editor. S. Roberts introduces the exponentially weighted moving average (EWMA) control chart. The U.S. manned spaceflight program makes industry aware of the need for reliable products; the field of reliability engineering grows from this starting point.

Table 1.2   A timeline of quality methods. (Continued)

1960	G. E. P. Box and J. S. Hunter write fundamental papers on 2^{k-p} factorial designs. The quality control circle concept is introduced in Japan by Kaoru Ishikawa.
1961	National Council for Quality and Productivity is formed in Great Britain as part of the British Productivity Council.
1960s	Courses in statistical quality control become widespread in industrial engineering academic programs. Zero defects (ZD) programs are introduced in certain U.S. industries.
1969	*Industrial Quality Control by the ASQC* ceases publication, replaced by *Quality Progress* and the *Journal of Quality Technology* (Lloyd S. Nelson is the founding editor of *JQT*).
1970s	In Great Britain, the NCQP and the Institute of Quality Assurance merge to form the British Quality Association.
1975–1978	Books on designed experiments oriented toward engineers and scientists begin to appear. Interest in quality circles begins in North America—this grows into the total quality management (TQM) movement.
1980s	Experimental design methods are introduced to and adopted by a wider group of organizations, including the electronics, aerospace, semiconductor, and automotive industries. The works of Taguchi on designed experiments first appear in the United States.
1984	The American Statistical Association (ASA) establishes the Ad Hoc Committee on Quality and Productivity; this later becomes a full section of the ASA. The journal *Quality and Reliability Engineering International* appears.
1986	Box and others visit Japan, noting the extensive use of designed experiments and other statistical methods.
1987	ISO publishes the first quality systems standards, ISO 9001, ISO 9002 and ISO 9003. Motorola's Six Sigma initiative begins.
1988	The Malcolm Baldrige National Quality Award is established by the U.S. Congress. The European Foundation for Quality Management is founded; this organization administers the European Quality Award.
1989	The journal *Quality Engineering by the ASQC* appears.
1990s	ISO 9001 certification activities increase in U.S. industry; applicants for the Baldrige award grow steadily; many states sponsor quality awards based on the Baldrige criteria.
1995	Many undergraduate engineering programs require formal courses in statistical techniques, focusing on basic methods for process characterization and improvement.
1997	Motorola's Six Sigma approach spreads to other industries.
1998	The American Society for Quality Control becomes the American Society for Quality (see www.asq.org), attempting to indicate the broader aspects of the quality improvement field.

(continued)

Table 1.2 A timeline of quality methods. (Continued)

2000s	ISO 9001:2000 standard is issued. Supply-chain management and supplier quality become even more critical factors in business success. Quality improvement activities expand beyond the traditional industrial setting into many other areas, including financial services, health care, insurance, and utilities. Organizations begin to integrate lean principles into their Six Sigma initiatives, and lean Six Sigma becomes a widespread approach to business development.

Source: Reprinted from D. C. Montgomery, *Introduction to Statistical Quality Control*, 7th ed. (Hoboken, NJ: John Wiley & Sons, 2013).

In time, the society created numerous other awards, each honoring a specific hero of the profession and recognizing outstanding achievement in a particular area of the profession. These awards include the Crosby Medal, Feigenbaum Medal, Juran Medal, Deming Medal, and Ishikawa Medal, among others.

Table 1.2 provides a detailed timeline that shows the development and progression of formal methods and practice in quality engineering. Management and statistics are the most critical aspects of the quality control and engineering movement. In the remainder of this section, the influences of the three people who have arguably had the biggest impact on the quality movement are discussed: Shewhart, Deming, and Juran. Shewhart, Edwards, Juran, and Deming all worked for and learned from the Bell System in one way or another. Edwards and Shewhart retired as Bell System employees. Both Juran and Deming went on from the Bell System to become world-famous consultants and authors.

Walter A. Shewhart

The industrial age was approaching its second century when a young engineer named Walter A. Shewhart altered the course of industrial history by bringing together the disciplines of statistics, engineering, and economics. He referred to his greatest achievement, the invention of the process control chart, as "the formulation of a scientific basis for securing economic control." The Shewhart control chart is sometimes referred to as a process behavior chart.

Shewhart wanted statistical theory to serve the needs of industry. He exhibited the restlessness of one looking for a better way. A man of science who patiently developed his and others' ideas, he was an astute observer of the world of science and technology. While the literature of the day discussed the stochastic nature of both biological and technical systems, and spoke of the possibility of applying statistical methodology to these systems, Shewhart actually showed how it could be done. In that respect, the field of quality control can claim a genuine pioneer in Shewhart. His book *Economic Control of Quality of Manufactured Product*, published in 1931, is regarded as a complete and thorough exposition of the basic principles of quality control.

Called on frequently as a consultant, Shewhart served the War Department, the United Nations, the government of India, and others. He was active with the National Research Council and the International Statistical Institute. He was a fellow of numerous societies and in 1947 became the first honorary member of ASQ. Many consider the Shewhart Medal, given for outstanding technical contributions to the quality profession, to be the most prestigious award ASQ offers.

As of 2016, 67 people have been awarded the Shewhart Medal in recognition of their contributions to the quality profession.

W. Edwards Deming

Deming became the best-known quality expert in the United States. He delivered his message on quality not only throughout the United States but also around the world. In recognition of his valuable contribution to Japan's postwar recovery, the Union of Japanese Scientists and Engineers established an annual award for quality achievement called the Deming Prize.

Deming (1982) emphasized that the keys to quality are in management's hands—85% of quality problems are due to the system and only 15% are due to employees. The heart of his quality strategy is the use of statistical quality control to identify special (erratic, unpredictable) causes and common (systemic) causes of variation. Statistical tools provide a common language for employees throughout a company and permit quality control efforts to be widely diffused. Each employee assumes considerable responsibility for the quality of his or her own work. Those in traditional quality control functions are then able to take more proactive roles in the quality improvement effort.

Deming introduced statistical quality control to the Japanese in the early 1950s when Japan was recovering from World War II and trying to overcome a reputation for poor workmanship. Deming's guidance was instrumental in transforming "made in Japan" from a liability to an asset. Deming asserted that there was no point in exhorting employees to produce higher-quality work because the changes needed to improve quality were almost always outside the workers' control, such as having the right tools, training, and materials. Instead, management had to accept responsibility for quality. Based on his experience, Deming developed a 14-point set of requirements called *Deming's 14 points*, shown in Figure 1.1. He also described *seven deadly diseases* of the workplace, including emphasis on short-term profits, use of personnel performance evaluations (which he labeled "management by fear"), and mobility of management (management as a profession independent of the product/service or commitment to the organization).

Joseph M. Juran

Juran, like Deming, built his quality reputation in America and then took his expertise to Japan in the 1950s. The two complemented each other well in Japan, as Deming showed the use of statistical tools and Juran taught the techniques of managing for quality. Juran originated the concept of "the vital few" and the "useful many" (originally "trivial many"). He called this concept the Pareto principle, which is now implemented in the well-known Pareto diagram. An economist, Vilfredo Pareto, had noticed the phenomenon, but it was Juran who applied it to quality improvement.

Juran recognized that improving quality requires a completely different approach from what is needed to maintain existing quality. He demonstrated this idea in his book *Managerial Breakthrough*, first published in 1964, and later condensed his ideas into the Juran trilogy:

1. Quality control: monitoring techniques to correct sporadic problems (analogous to special causes)

1. Create consistency of purpose toward improvement of products and services, with a plan to become competitive and to stay in business. Decide to whom top management is responsible.

2. Adopt the new philosophy. We are in a new economic age. We can no longer live with commonly accepted levels of delays, mistakes, defective materials, and defective workmanship.

3. Cease dependence on mass inspection. Require instead statistical evidence that quality is built-in to eliminate need for inspection. Purchasing managers have a new job and must learn it.

4. End the practice of awarding business on the basis of price tag. Instead, depend on meaningful measures of quality, along with price. Eliminate suppliers who cannot qualify with statistical evidence of quality.

5. Find problems. It is management's job to work continually on the system (design, incoming materials, composition of material, maintenance, improvement of machines, training, supervision, retraining).

6. Institute modern methods of training on the job.

7. Institute modern methods of supervision of production workers. The responsibility of foremen must be changed from sheer numbers to quality. Improvement of quality will automatically improve productivity. Management must prepare to take immediate actions on reports from foremen concerning barriers such as inherited defects, machines not maintained, poor tools, fuzzy operation definitions.

8. Drive out fear, so that everyone may work effectively for the company.

9. Break down barriers between departments. People in research, design, sales, and production must work as a team, to foresee problems of production that may be encountered with various materials and specifications.

10. Eliminate numerical goals, posters, and slogans for the workforce, asking for new levels of productivity without providing methods.

11. Eliminate work standards that prescribe numerical quotas.

12. Remove barriers that stand between the hourly worker and his right to pride of workmanship.

13. Institute a vigorous program of education and retraining.

14. Create a structure in top management that will push every day on the above 13 points.

Figure 1.1   Deming's 14 points.

2. Quality improvement: a breakthrough sequence to solve chronic problems (analogous to common causes)

3. Quality planning: an annual quality program to institutionalize managerial control and review

Juran served the quality profession well when in 1951 he created the monumental *Juran's Quality Handbook*, now in its seventh edition (Defeo 2016). Juran's contributions are extensive and varied. He defined quality as "fitness for use by the customer." He emphasized the need for top managers to become personally involved for a quality effort to be successful and for middle and lower-level managers to learn the language and thinking of top management—money, for example—to secure their involvement. Juran's universal process for quality improvement requires studying symptoms, diagnosing causes, and applying remedies. He repeatedly emphasized that major improvement could be achieved only on a project-by-project basis. The basis for selecting projects was the Return on Investment (ROI), now a major aspect of Six Sigma.

Continuous Improvement Tools

In the seven decades since World War II ended, great quality leaders have emerged. Besides those mentioned previously, the following individuals have become famous for their contributions. Philip Crosby popularized the concept of zero defects and established the Crosby Quality College. Kaoru Ishikawa, who helped sponsor Deming's seminars in Japan, created quality circles and invented the cause-and-effect diagram, also called the Ishikawa diagram. Armand Feigenbaum coined the term "total quality control" and tirelessly preached its fundamentals around the world. Genichi Taguchi, a Japanese engineer, developed a unique system for designing industrial experiments to establish robust systems. Eliyahu Goldratt created an improvement system built around the theory of constraints. Other notable contributors to the profession include George Box, Eugene Grant, Jack Lancaster, Frank Gryna, Richard Freund, and Dorian Shainin.

The most notable continuous improvement methodologies (all of which include the use of various quality tools) in quality engineering are the following:

- Statistical process control

- Total quality management

- Lean

- Six Sigma

Statistical process control (SPC) is considered one of the major areas of statistical technology useful in quality improvement. The main tool in SPC is the control chart, which has been widely adapted and is utilized by all practitioners of quality engineering. Process control and improvement are discussed in Chapter 4, while Chapter 6 covers SPC in detail.

Total quality management (TQM) is based on the principles of Feigenbaum, Deming, and Juran. The exact origin of TQM has been debated, but TQM as a process improvement methodology received the most use and attention in the mid-1980s and early 1990s before being mostly replaced by lean and Six Sigma methods. TQM is a structured approach to managing quality improvement methods within an organization. While it is important as a continuous improvement tool, its lack of recent success is attributed to insufficient effort on the technical aspects associated with improving and maintaining quality in an organization. TQM is further discussed in Chapter 5.

Lean philosophy, discussed in detail in Chapter 5, is exemplified by its terse name: get the job done as simply as possible. It was originally called lean manufacturing but has migrated into many different service industries. A good example of lean philosophy is *just-in-time* (JIT), where a process is managed so that parts arrive just prior to their actual integration into the assembly.

Six Sigma, a widely used quality philosophy, combines and exploits the strengths of other approaches to the extent that it now dominates all others. There are journals, conferences, study groups, and consulting firms devoted solely to Six Sigma. Six Sigma combines effective communication, organization of effort, financial accountability, and strong techniques to enable organizations to make sustained improvements over a period of time. Improvements such as cost reduction, quality improvement, cycle time reduction, improved morale, greater profits, and so forth, are all attainable through Six Sigma, but these improvements require a great deal of dedicated work, dedication to the process, and continuous training and learning. See Chapter 5, for more about Six Sigma.

THE QUALITY MANAGEMENT SYSTEM (QMS)

In this section, aspects of the quality management system (QMS) are discussed, including strategic planning, deployment techniques, and the quality information system.

Strategic Planning

> Identify and define top management's responsibility for the QMS, including establishing policies and objectives, setting organization-wide goals, and supporting quality initiatives. (Apply)
>
> **Body of Knowledge I.B.1**

Strategic planning usually begins with an analysis phase. The strengths and weaknesses of the organization are assessed and forecasts are generated to predict how market opportunities and competitive threats will change during the time period covered by the study. This analysis is sometimes called a SWOT (strengths, weaknesses, opportunities, and threats) analysis. Ideally, strategic planning for quality will address each aspect of the SWOT analysis.

The strengths of the organization can be leveraged to create or sustain a competitive advantage. The weaknesses of the organization should be addressed through appropriate measures such as training initiatives to develop strategic skills or process improvement efforts. The opportunities available to the organization can be identified through various marketing research techniques. Key outputs of the marketing research may include estimates of the size and growth rate of the market and clearly articulated customer expectations, desires, and perceptions. This information should drive new product development efforts.

Finally, the business environment should be assessed, with emphasis on potential threats to the success of the organization. Threats can come from direct competitors offering similar products, indirect competitors offering substitute products or services (e.g., butter vs. margarine), suppliers of critical proprietary components, and even from distributors that can influence the purchase decisions of the final customers.

After the SWOT analysis is complete, the organization can develop strategic quality plans. As the strategy is being formulated, management should evaluate

---

Strategic Planning Effectiveness Tests

1. Does the plan adequately address strengths, weaknesses, opportunities, and threats (SWOT)?

2. Will the plan result in a significant competitive advantage in the marketplace?

3. Is this advantage sustainable?

4. Does the vision statement inspire a sense of mission and purpose among employees?

5. Are the goals and objectives SMART (specific, measurable, achievable, realistic, and time-based)?

6. Are the goals and objectives aligned throughout the organization?

7. Have adequate resources been allocated to achieve the plan?

8. Are organizational structures, systems, and processes appropriate to execute the plan?

9. Is a review/reporting system in place to monitor the execution of the plan?

10. Does the strategic planning team include representatives from all key stakeholders?

Figure 1.2   Ten effectiveness tests for strategic quality plans.

whether the plans will ensure the success of the organization. To discern the effectiveness of strategic quality plans, management should employ a series of sequentially ordered effectiveness tests, shown in Figure 1.2 and discussed in more detail below:

1. Does the strategy adequately address all four SWOT elements? Leverage the organization's strengths; remedy the weaknesses. Exploit the opportunities in the market; minimize the potential impact of external threats. It also may be prudent to prepare contingency plans that can be implemented quickly in response to threatening actions from competitors. It is crucial for this stage of the planning process to be data-driven. The analysis should be comprehensive, including product quality, finance, purchasing, human resources, marketing and sales, delivery, customer service, and the internal processes that drive these activities. The notion that quality improvement is limited to the factory floor is obsolete. When management begins to apply quality disciplines and statistical methods to assess advertising campaigns and HR initiatives, the transformation is under way. The organization is poised to establish strategic quality plans.

2. Will the strategic plan result in a significant competitive advantage in the marketplace? Incremental improvements in quality may not be sufficient to ensure success. Furthermore, the advantage must be recognized and valued by the customer. Engineering and manufacturing can create superior products, but that may not help the organization succeed if the customers do not know about the products. Other activities must be involved in the strategic planning process. For example, marketing is responsible for raising customer awareness of product enhancements and influencing purchase decisions through advertising or promotions. Keep in mind that the current strengths of

an organization may only generate passing interest among customers. For example, a product may have best-in-class durability, but customers may be more interested in appearance, availability, or ease of use. In such cases, consider strategic initiatives that will strengthen the organization's ability to maximize customer satisfaction throughout the purchase and ownership experience. Such market research tools as conjoint analysis and the Kano quality model can measure how product or service features influence customer purchase behavior. Companies that use market research to help select targets for creating a competitive advantage are more likely to thrive in the marketplace.

3. Is the competitive advantage sustainable? Can your competitors quickly and easily imitate your strategy? Will they respond with counteroffensives that weaken your position? Will your competitors' strategic efforts pay off a year from now and undermine your leadership in the market? Some consultants recommend avoiding cost reduction as a primary strategy because price is one of the easiest things to imitate in the market. Both you and your competitors will lose if a price war erupts. Anyone can reduce costs by using cheaper components or reducing staff in service or support activities. The risk of this approach is that customers may perceive deteriorating quality, which damages the organization's reputation and results in lost sales. Insisting on a strategy that will deliver outstanding quality through continuous improvement is much more likely to generate a sustainable competitive advantage. The popularity of the Six Sigma movement and its impressive success stories demonstrate that it is possible to embark on a major strategic quality improvement initiative and reap substantial benefits on the bottom line.

4. Does the vision inspire and motivate your employees? The vision should be customer focused and provide a clear, succinct view of the desired future state of the organization. A major strategic effort will require dedication and commitment. Resources may be stretched to achieve the vision. If the vision is too difficult to achieve, employees may become discouraged and give up. If the vision is too easy to achieve, your competitors may implement something better, and you will be playing catch-up.

5. Goals and objectives are established to direct the efforts of the organization and measure whether the vision is being achieved. Are the goals and objectives SMART?

   — **Specific.** State what is expected in precise terms.

   — **Measurable.** Demonstrate progress through quantitative rather than qualitative or subjective measures.

   — **Achievable.** The goal can be achieved with available resources if appropriate actions are taken.

   — **Realistic.** A reasonable, sensible person would accept the goal after considering the degree of difficulty and the probability of success.

— **Time-based.** Deadlines serve a useful purpose. Companies that are first to market with new innovations frequently enjoy a significant, sustainable advantage over their competitors. For more information on innovation and competitive advantage, see Porter and Stern (2001), Hockman and Jensen (2016), and Box and Woodall (2012).

6. Are the goals and objectives aligned throughout the organization? Goals and objectives must be in harmony with each other. As goals are cascaded through an organization and broken down into manageable tasks to be performed by various departments or individuals, unity of purpose and alignment of priorities must be maintained to avoid conflicts.

7. Are resources (staffing, equipment, financing, etc.) adequate to achieve the plan? Can the additional workload be absorbed? Are the skill levels of the employees sufficient? Has the timeline been reviewed by affected participants to ensure that there are no scheduling conflicts? Project management techniques may be helpful.

8. Are organizational structures, systems, and processes suitable for executing the plan? Is a departmental reorganization necessary to streamline the flow of work and facilitate concurrent activities? Is a research and development (R&D) effort necessary to upgrade designs or manufacturing equipment capability?

9. Is a review and reporting system in place to periodically assess progress? These reviews should be conducted by management at a high enough level within the organization to marshal additional resources as needed when the program is in danger of falling behind schedule. Key program milestones should have clearly defined expectations to ensure consistency and excellence in the execution of the activities. Checklists are a simple yet effective means of communicating the expectations.

10. Does the strategic planning team include the participation of experienced professionals from all affected work groups? Do the team members fully understand the strategy, and have they bought into it? The benefits of a cross-functional planning effort cannot be overemphasized. Consider an analogy to the product development process: manufacturing personnel contribute expert advice during the early stages of product design and thereby avoid costly, time-consuming delays and redesigns. Ford Motor Company's advanced quality planning process lists the use of a cross-functional team as the number one expectation for executing many of the quality disciplines within a product development effort.

The importance of establishing the right strategy is critical to the success of an organization. Countless years of sincere toil have been wasted by implementing poorly developed strategies. Excellent execution will not ensure success unless the plan is also excellent. Juran argues that a structured planning process results in products that perform better and have a shorter development cycle from concept to customer (Juran and Godfrey 1999).

Management must explore strategic quality initiatives that go beyond mere incremental improvement: Drive the philosophy of continuous improvement throughout the organization and create a culture of innovation. Look beyond the factory floor for breakthroughs in all systems, such as R&D, product development, marketing, human resources, and purchasing. Strive for quality initiatives that add value for the customer and establish a sustainable competitive advantage.

Deployment Techniques

Quality improvement does not just happen; it must be planned, supported, and monitored just like any other process. Planning requires ways to identify the specific initiatives to be undertaken, while support and monitoring require methods for tracking and communicating progress. Establishing goals is not enough. Goals must be supported by measurable objectives that are in turn supported by action plans that delineate how and when the objectives are to be achieved and by whom. There must be measurable objectives to know what the projected results should be. In addition, a means for measuring the attainment of these objectives must be established. Similarly, action plans provide more specific information about attaining objectives. An example of the hierarchical relationships between strategies, goals, objectives, and action plans is as follows:

Organizational strategy: Continually build and retain a loyal customer base.

Organizational goal: Deliver all products to all customers 100% on time.

Organizational objective: Given current capacity, improve delivery dates of all future customer orders from 35% to 75% on-time delivery by February of the current year and to 100% by August of the current year.

Functional objectives: The quality department will assign a quality engineer to convene a cross-functional process improvement team by November 1 of the current year. The team will utilize lean manufacturing techniques to reduce cycle time and will continue its efforts until the production process has achieved 100% on-time delivery performance.

Action plans: Detailed plans state how and when the objective will be achieved and by whom. Action plans may resemble mini project plans or may be more complex project planning documents as needs dictate. In either case, action plans influence planning and scheduling.

Deployment techniques in support of the QMS include benchmarking against competitors, feedback from stakeholders, performance assessment via metrics, and project management. These are all discussed in this section as well as additional information regarding deployment such as policy considerations and useful tools.

Benchmarking

Define the concept of benchmarking and why it may be used. (Remember)

Body of Knowledge I.B.2.a

Benchmarking is a process in which organizations compare their performance with that of their competition or with best practices found internally or in outside organizations. It was pioneered by Xerox in the late 1970s in response to growing pressure in the photocopy industry. Benchmarking is now recognized as an important input to strategic planning. It can be applied to any business process or function, such as optimizing inventory levels or improving service delivery.

Benchmarking can help an organization identify new ideas and methods to improve operational effectiveness. It can help break through institutional barriers and resistance to change because some other organization has already demonstrated that the new methods are more effective. Once these best practices are identified, the organization can develop plans to adopt them. In this way, benchmarking can become an integral part of the continuous improvement process.

Internal benchmarking is used to compare performance between plants or divisions. Competitive benchmarking is used to assess performance relative to that of direct competitors within an industry. Internal and competitive benchmarks are useful in identifying gaps in performance. For example, automotive manufacturers use customer surveys to compare quality and customer satisfaction. Poor performance must be addressed to ensure survival in the marketplace. However, competitive benchmarking may not identify the best practices needed to close the gap in performance. Furthermore, although benchmarking internally or among competitors may identify incremental improvement opportunities, it is not likely to identify breakthroughs leading to world-class performance.

Collaborative benchmarking requires cooperation between two or more organizations. Each organization freely shares information about its best practices in exchange for information about other best practices from a partner. Suppose, for example, Wal-Mart wishes to team with Dell Corporation. Wal-Mart offers to share information on forecasting consumer demand, and Dell reciprocates by sharing insights on how it minimizes order-to-delivery times. With collaborative benchmarking, the key is to identify the very best performer. Use trade associations, publications, financial analysis, market research, or other tools to find the leader.

External benchmarking may identify the best opportunities, but it requires a significant investment of time and effort. It may be useful to employ internal benchmarking first because it will generate quicker results. Internal successes should receive recognition, which can help convince skeptics that the process works. The benchmarking team also will gain valuable experience and be better prepared for pursuing external benchmarking partners. A typical benchmarking project includes the following:

- **Planning.** Identify what is to be benchmarked. Establish the objectives for the study. If the scope is too narrow, the benefits will be limited. If the scope is too broad, the task may become unmanageable and the probability of successfully implementing the best practices will diminish. Select the team members and search for target organizations to benchmark.

- **Data collection.** Develop a mutually acceptable protocol with the partner, including a code of conduct, confidentiality agreements, and performance measures to be analyzed. Data sharing may include information about procedures, standards, software, training, and other supporting systems. The key is to gain enough understanding and direction to replicate the best practice within your organization.

- **Analysis.** Assess the data for accuracy and credibility. Determine current performance levels and identify gaps. Explore the feasibility of implementing the best practice. Some practices are not readily transferable—is adaptation necessary? Forecast the expected improvement.

- **Implementation.** Obtain the support of key stakeholders. Use project management techniques and action plans to initiate the change. Monitor performance. Document activities and communicate progress.

Benchmarking is not a precise discipline, and common pitfalls include lack of commitment, insufficient planning, comparing processes that are not sufficiently similar to generate useful insights, and measuring processes that have little potential for significant gains. A well-executed benchmarking project will help in both deploying strategic plans and suggesting modifications to future strategic plans. But real leadership means not just catching up with other industry leaders but surpassing them. Benchmarking can never accomplish that.

Stakeholder Analysis

> Define, describe and use stakeholder identification and analysis. (Apply)
>
> **Body of Knowledge I.B.2.b**

Congruence between policy and results is evaluated through audits that periodically check for conformance. The stakeholders need to be clearly identified and their differing needs must be met. If adaptation of a policy must occur, it must remain within the original intent if the policy is to remain credible to the stakeholders. Frequent feedback from all stakeholders helps to quickly identify and correct any disparity. Performance measures, discussed below, must take into account the differing needs and perceptions of each stakeholder group. Stakeholders include the following:

- Stockholders, the owners of the company. Their role is often passive and their needs are primarily of a financial nature. They expect the company to maintain its credibility in the financial markets and hope for growth in earnings and share price.

- The executive group, including the board of directors and the top tier of managers. They must acknowledge and serve the other stakeholders. Conversely, the health of any organization is critically dependent on its decision making and deployment.

- Employees other than top management. This critical group of stakeholders has little direct impact on policy but all other groups depend on them to carry out the policy efficiently and promptly. The quality of any organization's end product depends on how well the employees are recruited, trained, and supervised.

- Suppliers and customers. These two groups are concerned with external inputs and outputs. Suppliers must adhere to contractual requirements and therefore can insist on fair and prompt payment for their goods and services. Customers are paramount stakeholders; if customers do not want the organization's products, this organization will eventually cease to exist. The "Customer Relations" and "Supplier Management" sections later in this chapter deal with customer relations and supplier management, respectively.

- The community at large. Communities, neighbors, environmental regulators, law enforcement agencies, chambers of commerce, legislatures, and similar bodies often are indirect stakeholders. Individually their impact is relatively slight, but if a major issue arises, the concerns of a community can have an overwhelming influence. This stakeholder group is especially critical when plant openings or closings are being planned. The community often is concerned about treatment of minorities, public service (or the absence thereof), and environmental abuses.

Performance

> Define, describe and use performance measurement tools such as cost-benefit analysis. (Apply)
>
> Body of Knowledge I.B.2.c

The strategic plan is a vision with broad goals and objectives for the organization to achieve. Management at all levels is charged with implementing the strategic plan. Metrics must be developed to monitor activities and track progress toward achieving the goals and objectives. But before discussing numbers and types of metrics, it is important to emphasize that the metrics should reflect the strategic vision. Some authors use the word "linkage" to describe the connection between strategic goals and performance metrics. An organization is on the right path if people two or three levels down from top management in the organization can articulate how their activities support a strategic objective.

Once the strategic plan is finalized, management must cascade the goals and objectives down through the organization and identify specific tasks with time-lines, methods, and responsibilities. This is not a trivial task. Considerable care should be taken to select appropriate measures. Stakeholders and subject matter experts within the organization should be involved in the selection process. Team participation is more likely to result in performance measures that are aligned with strategic objectives. Participation also fosters ownership of the metrics. Some managers go a step further and link the objectives to annual employee performance evaluation programs or to bonus programs.

For a clear example of how to cascade performance measures, look to the field of reliability engineering. When designing a system, reliability targets are established for the system as a whole. When designing the components of the system, more stringent reliability targets must be established for each component so that the system as a whole continues to meet the overall performance target. This process, called reliability allocation, is a highly technical process that should be performed by someone with expertise in reliability. Unfortunately, management science has not progressed to the same level of discipline as the reliability field. Nevertheless, the basic concepts still apply. When cascading a high-level objective down to operations, one must allocate tasks and apportion the targets to ensure that the organization as a whole will meet the objectives.

Performance measures should be:

- Linked to strategic objectives

- Rigorous, objective, quantifiable, and standardized

- Achievable, realistic, and time-based

- Assigned to appropriate personnel who are held accountable and who are empowered with some level of control to influence outcomes

In general, there should only be a "vital few" performance metrics. Use your judgment and avoid using too many metrics, which may dilute the results. Automate data collection and calculations if possible. Spend more time making decisions than generating reports. Select measures that are resistant to problematic behavior. In the following subsections, performance metrics are discussed as well as two tools for assessing performance: the balanced scorecard and the dashboard.

Performance Metrics

Most of the guidelines for performance measures are self-evident, but the recommendation to select measures that are resistant to problematic behavior warrants explanation. Suppose an organization faces stiff competition in a commodity market. Cost reduction is a key strategic initiative. When the objective is cascaded to plant operations, the maintenance department decides to support the objective by postponing costly equipment overhauls. This "problematic" behavior may help in the short run but could cause a catastrophe in the future. How can this be avoided? One solution is to use combined metrics. For example, a maintenance productivity metric could be created:

$$\text{Maintenance productivity} = \frac{\Delta^R \text{MTTF}}{(\Delta^R \text{Maintenance budget})(\Delta^R \text{MTTR})}$$

In this metric, bigger is better. The symbol Δ^R is applied to each variable and refers to the ratio of the variable in period t divided by the variable in period $t - 1$. This little math trick results in a dimensionless equation that is "normalized" to a value of 1.0 when there is no change in the variable from one period to the next. If the productivity value is greater than 1, performance is improving; if it is less than 1, performance is deteriorating. Since maintenance spending is in the denominator, less spending is encouraged because it will increase the productivity metric. But the productivity metric can also be increased by increasing the equipment mean time to failure (MTTF) or by decreasing the mean time to repair (MTTR). If the maintenance department starts scrimping on the budget, breakdowns will probably occur more frequently and repair times may increase. Declining performance will offset the benefit of reduced spending in the metric. Thus, this combined metric encourages appropriate behavior.

The point of this illustration is not to advocate specifically for a maintenance productivity metric but to suggest that a little creativity can overcome inherent weaknesses in traditional performance measures.

Balanced Scorecard

Robert Kaplan and David Norton introduced the balanced scorecard in 1992. Kaplan and Norton argued that most strategic plans were unbalanced because one stakeholder group—the stockholders—was overemphasized. They proposed a "balanced" scorecard with four perspectives:

1. Financial fundamentals

2. Business processes

3. Customer

4. Learning and growth

Financial measures include traditional indicators such as cash flow, sales, and ROI. Business processes include manufacturing measures such as yield and rework, along with support activities such as order processing. Customer measures may include trends in customer satisfaction or average customer service wait times. The learning and growth perspective recognizes the human element in an organization and looks at softer measures such as participation in employee suggestion programs and training.

The balanced scorecard provides a framework to translate the strategic plan into specific tasks that can be managed by frontline employees. In a typical scorecard, the objective is listed along with associated measures, targets for performance, and initiatives that will drive the organization to achieve the objective.

Cost-benefit Analysis

Cost-benefit analysis (CBA) estimates the strengths and weaknesses of alternative courses of action to determine the best use of investment. It is used for business and policy decisions and project investments. The analysis can determine if an investment makes sense by judging how much the benefits outweigh the costs and provide a way to compare investments by assessing the total expected costs and expected benefits of each.

Cost-benefit analysis attempts to determine all the costs and benefits of an investment and express these in present-day dollars. A means of doing this calculation is using the Net Present Value (NPV) calculation as described below. Then it is a straightforward comparison of the benefits vs costs based on some established threshold or criteria for making the decision. Because the future value of money (based on future inflation and interest rates) and the future benefits of an action are unknown, probabilistic techniques such as uniform, gamma and normal distributions, based on the user's assumptions about future uncertainty, are often used in the NPV model.

Project Management

Define, describe and use project management tools, including Gantt charts and the responsible, accountable, consulted and informed matrix (RACI). (Apply)

Body of Knowledge I.B.2.d

Quality engineers often become involved in project, either as a project team member or as a project leader. Several proven techniques and tools are available to assist in cost-effective project management. The first is proper project selection. The following subsections cover project tools, project planning techniques, how to monitor and measure project activities, documentation, and strategies for policy deployment.

Project Tools

Projects must be prioritized to select those having the most merit. Projects should be evaluated for their fit with overall business needs, financial payoff, and potential risks. Exceptions will be made for legal mandates, consumer safety, and customer demands. Only projects that are optional should be prioritized.

Major projects involve risk of loss. Risk assessment involves identifying potential problems that could occur, their impact, and what, if any, actions should be taken to offset them (e.g., taking countermeasures, purchasing risk insurance, or developing contingency plans). For complex projects, it may be prudent to apply a formal risk assessment tool such as a failure modes and effects analysis (FMEA) or simulation.

If the benefits of a project are uncertain and multiple outcomes are possible, then a decision tree can help estimate the expected value of gain or loss (see Example 1.1). A decision tree lists the potential outcomes and assigns a probability to each branch. The financial payout for each outcome is shown at the end of the branch. A few simple rules apply to the creation of a decision tree:

- At each branch point, the probabilities must sum to 1.0.

- The expected value for each branch is calculated by multiplying all the probabilities along the branch by the financial payout.

- Add the expected payout for all the outcomes within a decision branch.

- Choose the decision with the highest payout.

There are many other financial methods for justifying projects. Three very common methods are the following:

- Payback period. The number of years it will take to recover the investment from net cash flows.

- Net present value (NPV). NPV takes the time value of money into account. NPV involves finding the present value of each cash flow (yearly) discounted at the cost of capital percentage used by the organization, summing the discounted cash flows, and determining if the project is a candidate for approval based on positive NPV (see Example 1.2).

- Internal rate of return (IRR). A discount rate that causes the NPV to equal zero. If the IRR is greater than the minimum required by the organization for typical capital investments, the project is a candidate for acceptance.

The payback period is widely used because it is easy to calculate and simple to understand. In the decision tree example (Example 1.1), the payback period for installing a new machine is less than one year, which implies a very high ROI. But a major weakness of the payback period is that it does not give any insight into the magnitude of future savings, that is, savings after the initial investment has been recovered.

EXAMPLE 1.1

A quality engineer is considering several options to fix a problem with a production machine. The machine is starting to wear out, so it has excessive variation and approximately 1% of production must be scrapped. He can replace the machine with a proto-type machine. There is an 80% chance the new machine will eliminate the variability problem and it will probably increase capacity by 2%. The second choice is to over-haul the machine, with a 60% chance of improving the yield. The third choice is to perform selected repairs. This choice has the lowest initial investment but also is least likely to solve the variability problem. This problem is summarized in the decision tree in Figure 1.3. The probabilities associated with the choices are shown in brackets.

Currently, the variation problem generates scrap worth $50,000 per year. A 2% increase in capacity would be worth an additional $100,000 profit per year. Therefore, the financial payout changes depending on whether the scrap is eliminated and the capacity is increased.

Continued

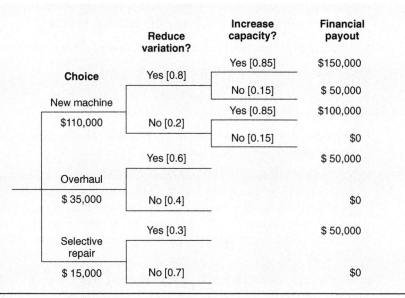

Figure 1.3   Decision tree for production machine.

The expected value (EV) for a decision is given by the equation:

$$EV = \sum x\, p(x)$$

where x is the financial payout, and $p(x)$ is the associated probability of the outcome. Expected value calculations are discussed in more detail in Chapter 6. Sum all the values within the decision branch. Therefore, the expected value of the new machine is:

EV = (0.8)(0.85)$150,000 + (0.8)(0.15)$50,000 + (0.2)(0.85)$100,000 + (0.2)(0.15)$0
EV = $125,000

Note that the expected value of the new machine is less than the maximum payout because there is a chance the new machine will not work perfectly. One can calculate the expected value for the other options using the same approach.

For the overhaul: EV = (0.6)$50,000 + (0.4)$0 = $30,000
For the repairs: EV = (0.3)$50,000 + (0.7)$0 = $15,000

Finally, subtract the initial investment, shown in Figure 1.4, from the expected value to get the *net* return.

New machine = $125,000 – $110,000 = $15,000
Overhaul machine = $30,000 – $35,000 = ($5,000)
Selective repairs = $15,000 – $15,000 = $0

In the first year, money will be made on the new machine, break even using repairs, but lose money if the overhaul is selected. (Note: when evaluating projects, always consider the savings in future years, not just the first year.) At the end of the first year, experience will be gained with the option that was implemented. The probability assumptions can be updated and the decision tree exercise repeated in subsequent years.

NPV and IRR rectify this deficiency. Both methods give more accurate information, provided that suitable estimates of future cash flows can be obtained. The major difference between the two methods is that IRR generates an interest rate that balances all future cash flows against the present outlay, while NPV generates a dollar amount of present and future cash flows. With both calculation methods, bigger is better. Many companies have an internal hurdle rate, such as an IRR greater than 10% or 20%, that projects must achieve to be considered. The company probably could not consistently earn such a high return on stocks or bonds, yet it requires projects to clear this hurdle. One reason for this conservatism is the difficulty of getting accurate estimates of future cash flows.

A final cautionary word about project estimating: sometimes things do not work out as planned. Assumptions may be misleading, probabilities may be optimistic, and factors beyond your control may come into play, such as unexpected changes in the market, new legislative policies, or changes in regulatory requirements. If you enter the calculations in a spreadsheet, it is easy to make adjustments and perform a sensitivity analysis. Sensitivity analysis allows you to evaluate how the projected results would be affected by changes in the estimated inputs (e.g., probabilities of success or potential risks). For example, how much would the NPV change if the probability of success decreased by 10%? For more details and examples see Park (2007) in References.

EXAMPLE 1.2

The NPV method converts all future cash flows to today's dollars at a specified interest rate. It is easy to calculate using a spreadsheet. From the decision tree example above, enter the initial investment and the expected values of the payouts for year 1, year 2, and so on. In year 3, the warranty expires and performing repairs begins. After year 5, the machine is starting to wear out, and by year 7, the machine is ready to be overhauled or replace d. Note: the NPV example shown here can be understood without reference to the decision tree in Example 1.1.

	A	B	C	D
1	Year	Cash flow New machine	Cash flow Overhaul	Comments
2		0.10	0.10	Interest rate
3	1	($110,000)	($35,000)	Initial investment
4	2	$125,000	$30,000	First year, expected value
5	3	$125,000	$30,000	Second year
6	4	$110,000	$15,000	Offset savings, paying for repairs
7	5	$110,000	$15,000	$15,000 in repairs
8	6	$105,000	$10,000	Machine is starting to wear out

Continued

| 9 | 7 | $ 98,000 | $8,500 | Variability increasing, yield decreasing |
| 10 | 8 | $ 62,000 | $2,400 | Time to replace machine? |

To calculate the NPV, use the formula:

$$NPV = \sum_{t=1}^{N} \frac{R_t}{(1 + i)^t}$$

where R_t is the cash flow in year t, and i is the interest rate.

The interest rate should be the prevailing rate for raising cash in capital markets (that is, a bank loan). Ten percent is typical. The NPV function assumes that the initial investment is made at year 0 and the first payout is at the end of year 1. The results are surprising:

NPV, new machine = $379,136
NPV, overhaul = $ 46,200

The net return for the new machine option in the first year was $15,000. But when you consider the life of the investment, the return is enormous. The overhaul option loses money in the first year but proves to generate positive cash flows in subsequent years. The selective repair option has zero NPV—it is a basic maintenance strategy.

Project Planning and Estimation

The success of a project is significantly impacted by the effectiveness of project planning. A typical project-planning sequence for a larger project, often identified in the project charter, is as follows:

1. Statement. This first step is where the kernel of an idea or the basic concept visualized is translated into a clear statement of the problem, deficiency, or opportunity to be realized. Careful definition at this point helps later to clarify the scope of the project.

2. Project justification. Risk analyses and assessment (payback period, NPV, IRR, ROI, return on assets, and benefits/cost) are performed, and a go/no-go decision is made.

3. Drafts of mission statement, project scope, and project objectives. These documents clarify the overall direction of the project, what it is to accomplish, the breadth and depth of the project, and the measurable objectives by which progress and completion are to be measured.

4. Stakeholder requirements. Stakeholders consist of two groups: (1) those with a direct commitment to the project team, for example, a process manager who provides a skilled person to serve on a process improvement team working to reduce machine downtime, and (2) those without involvement but who can influence project results, for example, the purchasing department that selects the vendor for a new machine.

A macro-level process map may be used to identify areas from which potential team members should be selected.

5. Project team formation. Team members should be selected based on the need to represent a stakeholder group and/or specific skill sets required. Stakeholder groups not represented on the project team should have opportunities to provide input. Some members may be required on an as-needed basis only. Whenever possible, the interests, values, and personality profiles of individuals nominated should be considered. The Myers-Briggs Type Indicator (http://www.myersbriggs.org) can be a useful tool for building a team with complementary interpersonal skills and interests.

6. Finalized mission statement, project scope, project objectives, and project charter. Team members refine the original drafts. A benchmarking study may be appropriate to better define target outcomes. Items that are out of scope of the current project are also identified to prevent "scope creep."

7. Contractual requirements and deliverables. All requirements and outputs of the project are identified, defined, and documented.

8. Work breakdown structure (WBS). Project work is further defined by breaking the work down into a hierarchy of work categories (families of like work clusters) down to the task level. Boxes on a WBS may be annotated with "person/work unit responsible," "resources required," "cost estimates," various other cross-references, and so on. See Figure 1.4 and the discussion below for more on WBS.

9. Gantt chart. Major project steps or task clusters are listed vertically on a timeline chart with each item's estimated start-to-finish time depicted as a bar across the chosen time intervals (weeks, months, quarters). As the project progresses, the same chart may be used to plot the actual time expended next to the estimated time. Major milestones are shown as points along the time bar. See Figure 1.5 and the discussion below for a more detailed example.

10. Time-dependent task diagram (AND). Depending on the size, complexity, and duration of the project, it may be necessary to plot the time dependencies of each task to each other task. An activity network diagram (AND) depicts the interrelationships of each task or task cluster in the project. Typically, AND is used for shorter-term, simpler projects.

11. Resource requirements matrix (RRM). An RRM delineates the various types of resources needed (e.g., personnel, facilities, equipment, materials, consultants, etc.), quantity, when needed, and cost.

12. Linear responsibility matrix (LRM). An LRM, used for larger projects, defines the interfaces: who has what responsibility for what tasks, and to what degree (e.g., primary, secondary, resource only, need to know).

13. Responsible, accountable, consulted, and informed matrix (RACI). Responsible persons do the work to complete the task, there may be

Figure 1.4   Work breakdown structure (partial).

more than one. The Accountable role is answerable for the accurate completion of the task, and may issue the work to those Responsible, there can be only one Accountable person. Consulted are those whose opinions are sought. Informed are those kept up-to-date on task progress, often champions and others in leadership positions. See Figure 1.6 for an example RACI chart.

14. Project budget. A detailed itemized budget is prepared based on the time and cost estimate prepared by the team.

15. Measurements. Define quantifiable measurements to track both project progress and achievement of project objectives. Determine and document the progress-monitoring process, methods for analyzing data gathered, reporting protocols, and checkpoints for initiating corrective action.

16. Approved. Final approval of the project and authorization for implementation project plan is given.

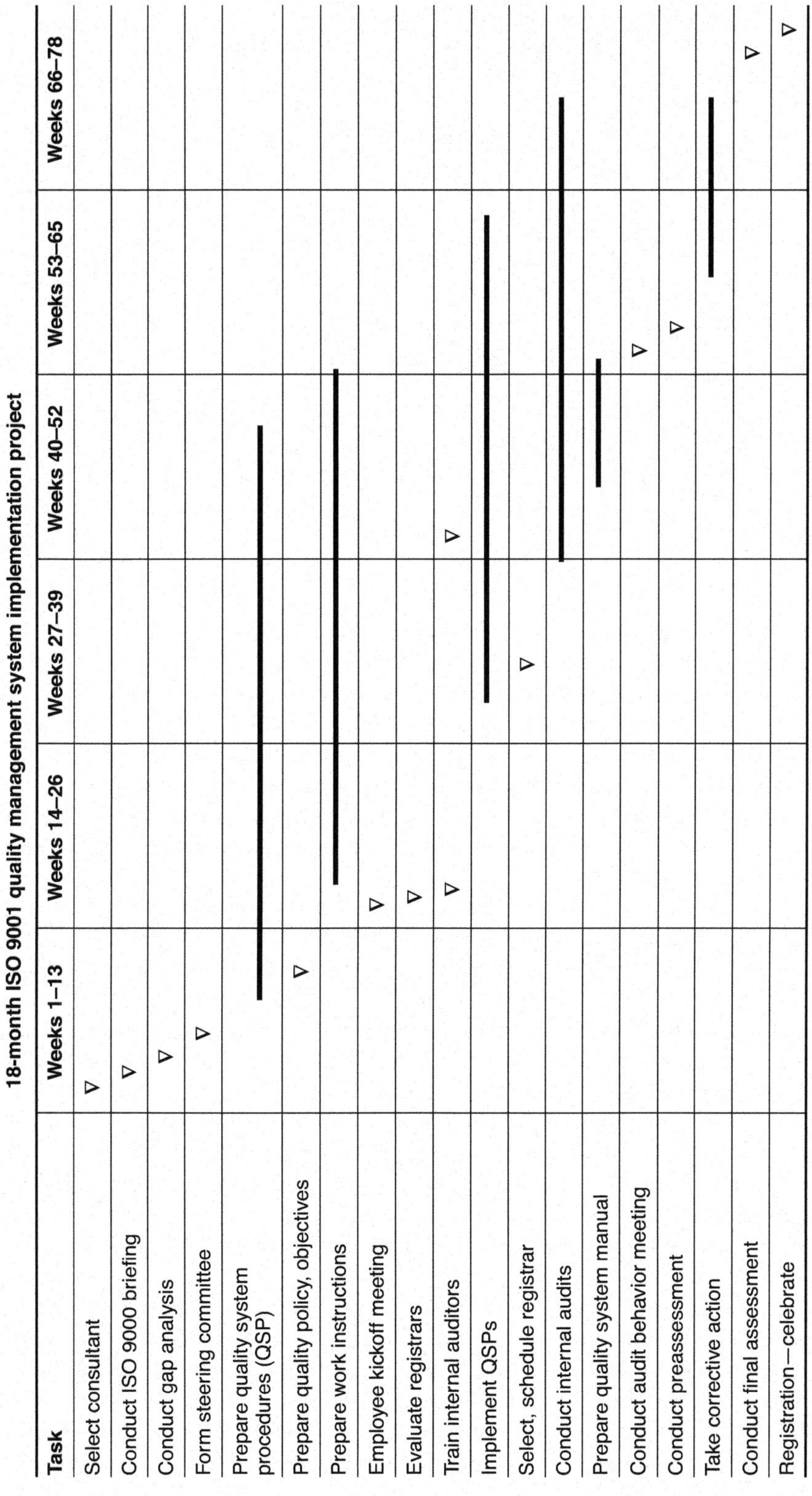

18-month ISO 9001 quality management system implementation project

Task	Weeks 1–13	Weeks 14–26	Weeks 27–39	Weeks 40–52	Weeks 53–65	Weeks 66–78
Select consultant	▷					
Conduct ISO 9000 briefing	▷					
Conduct gap analysis	▷					
Form steering committee	▷					
Prepare quality system procedures (QSP)	━━━━━━━━━━━━━━━━━━━					
Prepare quality policy, objectives	▷					
Prepare work instructions		━━━━━━━━━━━━━━				
Employee kickoff meeting		▷				
Evaluate registrars		▷				
Train internal auditors		▷		▷		
Implement QSPs			━━━━━━━━━━━━━━━━━			
Select, schedule registrar			▷			
Conduct internal audits				━━━━━━━━━━━━━━━━━━		
Prepare quality system manual				━━━━	▷	
Conduct audit behavior meeting					▷	
Conduct preassessment					▷	
Take corrective action					━━━━━━━━━	
Conduct final assessment						▷
Registration—celebrate						▷

Figure 1.5 Gantt chart example.

R = Responsible, A = Accountable, C = Consulted, I = Informed

TASK	Marketing	Project Mgt	Engineering	QA
Define Product Specification	R + A		C	
Define Project Scope & Resources	A	R	C	C
Build Product Prototype	I	A	R	
Test Product Prototype	I	A	C	R
Coordinate Approvals	R	A	R	R
Product Design Approval and Release	A	I	R	

Figure 1.6   RACI example.

WBS and Gantt charts are useful project management tools from a project-planning standpoint. Figure 1.4 shows a three-level WBS under development. A WBS allows determination of the many activities that must occur during the project. The numbering scheme in Figure 1.4 may seem unduly complex at first, but the consistent use of multiple decimal points allows nesting of levels and facilitates changes to dynamic projects. The project budget details the anticipated expenditures over time for each category of expense. Depending on the size of the project, budgets may be prepared for successive levels of the project (usually paralleling the WBS hierarchy).

Figure 1.5 is a Gantt, or milestone, chart showing the major implementation phases and their relative timing for an ISO 9001 implementation. The Gantt chart is one of the earliest planning tools, dating back to the early years of the twentieth century. Solid bars indicate activities that require an elapsed period of time, while triangles denote events that occur at specific points in time. The figure is fairly simple; computerized Gantt charts created in programs such as Visio can involve multiple layers and interactions of activities.

RRMs are essentially spreadsheets that lay out the requirements over time against the activities in the project. RRMs may be compiled for facilities, equipment, materials, contract/consulting services, personnel, and so on. Understanding the project life cycle can also help in estimating the resources required. The five stages of a project are (1) concept, (2) planning, (3) design, (4) implementation, and (5) evaluation and closeout.

Follow the old adage: plan your work, work your plan. Work planning requires a clear understanding of the overall goal and objectives, also referred to as outcomes to be achieved (the "what"). The planning process must also take into account how the initiative relates to other projects (e.g., sharing of resources) and therefore often requires input from, or participation by, multiple stakeholders. Figure 1.7 shows an action plan format that can be used to document the plan.

Action plan

Objective/plan title:	Plan no.: _____
Description	Date initiated: _____
	Date needed: _____
	Approval: _____
	Team (L): _____
	Team (M): _____
	Team (M): _____
	Team (M): _____
	Team (M): _____

Major outcomes desired/required:

Scope (Where will the solution/implementation be applied? What limitations exist?):

By what criteria/measures will completion and success of project be measured?

Assumptions made that may impact project (resources, circumstances outside the project):

Describe the overall approach to be taken:

When should the project be started in order to meet the date needed/wanted?:

Estimate the resources required (time and money):

Outline the tentative *major* steps to be taken, a projected *start* and *complete date* for each step, and the *person to be responsible* for each step. (Use the back of this sheet to sketch your time line.)

Figure 1.7   Action plan format example.

Source: © 2000 R. T. Westcott & Associates (Reprinted with permission of R. T. Westcott & Associates).

After the plan has been documented, activities can be associated with a schedule. Figure 1.8 shows a format for an implementation schedule. A Gantt chart may be added to show the timing of each step in the schedule and would allow for activities to overlap one another.

Periodic work review meetings are held to provide the following:

- An opportunity for the project leader and the sponsor of the project to discuss progress

- A summary of performance (presuming day-to-day feedback was given), evaluation of progress, determination of actions to correct/improve performance, and renegotiation of such activities as may be necessary

- An assessment documentation relative to the work objectives

- An effective time for the manager to reinforce work done well, assuming the work climate is conducive to frank, open, two-way discussion and problem solving

- An effective time for the sponsor to provide input on the project and assist with elevating to upper management any issues/concerns regarding the project

The specific time to review progress is a matter of preference. Different objectives or projects may be reviewed at different time intervals depending on complexity,

Action plan implementation schedule

Step no.	Activity/event description	Depends on step	Start date	Finish date	Person responsible

Figure 1.8   Action plan implementation schedule example.

Source: © 2000 R. T. Westcott & Associates (Reprinted with permission of R. T. Westcott & Associates).

time span of work, competency level of performer, criticality of work outcomes, disruptions in due dates, resource shortages, and so on. As a rule of thumb, work reviews should be scheduled at least once a month for objectives spanning more than a three-month period, in addition to project milestones. It is never appropriate to wait until just before the planned achievement date to review progress on work objectives. Also, a review should be conducted any time the project deviates from the plan.

Monitoring and Measuring Project Activity and Results

Critical project performance measures include timeliness, budget variance, quality, scope, and resource usage. Project measurements must then be determined and a system for tracking, monitoring, and reporting progress is established.

In medium to large projects, milestones (critical checkpoints) are established in the planning stage and the project is monitored against these milestones. Thorough periodic project reviews are conducted, including assessment of schedules against the critical path, expenditures against budgets, resource utilization against plans, implementation results achieved, a possible reevaluation of risks, and any major issues impacting project continuance. Based on these reviews, the project may be continued as planned, modified, put on hold, or canceled. A similar review is conducted to evaluate the results when the project is completed.

Project Documentation

Documenting the project throughout the process will make it easier to complete the project and potentially any associated paperwork required to close out the project. If the team has not documented every aspect of the project, begin to document as soon as you can to capture details such as the following while they are still available:

- Assumptions, risks, and rationale for selecting the project
- Decisions made to initiate project and approvals
- Detailed plans for design and implementation
- Design and/or implementation changes
- Major obstacles encountered and how they were resolved
- Details of implementation (e.g., measurements established)
- Progress reports and resulting decisions
- Risk log
- Budget information
- Scope changes
- Final evaluation of project results
- Results of post-project audits

All documentation is valuable in planning and estimating new projects and in avoiding previous mistakes. Likewise, the documented knowledge base is a tool for training those new to project management. Documentation can also be useful in the development of new policies or employment of old policies to support future and ongoing projects.

Policy Deployment

Policies provide direction to guide and determine present and future decisions. They indicate the principles to be followed or what is to be done, but not specifically how it is to occur. For example, a quality policy should summarize the organization's view on the meaning and importance of quality as it relates to competitiveness, customers, suppliers, employees, and continual improvement.

To ensure consistency and understanding throughout the organization, policies need to be integrated with the strategic plan, then deployed through appropriate initiatives and performance checks. Projects must be justified and scheduled. Performance must be measured and reported. An organization's policies should be actionable. Some situations may call for temporary adaptation of the policy to meet unanticipated needs. A documented and deployed quality policy provides the following:

- A written guide to managerial action, lending stability to the organization

- Consideration of quality problems and their ramifications

- A basis for auditing practices against policy

Deployed policies cascade throughout the organization, directly impacting each functional area and indirectly affecting events, activities, and outcomes depending on those functions. If policies do not have this effect, they are not fulfilling their purpose. Each function and person impacted by the organization's policy must align their objectives and procedures to support the policy.

Quality Information System (QIS)

Identify and describe the basic elements of a QIS, including who will contribute data, the kind of data to be managed, who will have access to the data, the level of flexibility for future information needs, and data analysis. (Understand)

Body of Knowledge I.B.3

A *quality information system* (QIS) is a collection of data, rules, and equipment that creates information about quality in a systematic way. A QIS will collect, store, analyze, and manage quality-related data from customers, suppliers, and internal processes. It will generate information in the form of printed reports, screen displays, and signals sent to mechanical devices. Depending on the degree of automation, it may give answers to questions posed by humans, or it may have built-in action rules. Above all, if it is well done it will enhance profit and productivity. In some industries, a QIS is required by law; for example, the Federal Drug Administration requires pharmaceutical companies to maintain a QIS.

The first requirement in studying QISs is to understand what, exactly, a "system" is. The word is used in many different contexts. For example, this book discusses management systems, information systems, strategic planning systems, and quality systems, for starters. The essence of a system is this: it ties several components together that act in common with each other. Systems that quality engineers are interested in are dynamic and goal oriented. They have inputs, outputs, operating rules (procedures or transformational processes), data storage, and boundaries. They are designed by people to achieve specified goals. Computerized information systems are explicitly designed, usually by cross-functional teams.

A QIS is both a quality system and an information system. It is naïve to speak of *the* QIS, because an effective organization will have numerous quality systems, which may be manual, computerized, or a hybrid of the two, with both manual and computer elements. A well-designed information system allows information generated at one level or in one part of the organization to be used for many different purposes.

QISs may be used to:

- Initiate action (e.g., generating a shop order from a customer's order)

- Control a process (e.g., controlling the operation of a laser cutting machine within given specification limits)

- Monitor a process (e.g., real-time production machine interface with control charting)

- Record critical data (e.g., measurement tool calibration)

- Create and deploy operating procedures (e.g., an ISO 9001–based quality management system)

- Manage a knowledge base (e.g., capturing, storing, and retrieving needed knowledge)

- Schedule resource usage (e.g., personnel assignments)

- Archive data (e.g., customer order fulfillment)

- Store quality processes and procedures

- Document required training

The importance of information systems becomes apparent when looking at their impact on various aspects of quality management. Both process management and problem solving require accurate and timely information. Contrast the following two cases. One information system in a plant might be hardwired into manufacturing and testing equipment, with monitors displaying real-time information complete with alarms and action signals; it could have options for graphic display of statistical and trend analysis for quick intervention. Another system in the same plant could tie executives, project teams, and off-site employees together through an intranet; organizational objectives and milestones appropriate for each level and function could be displayed as both text and graphics, along with actual performance and gaps. These two QISs are quite different.

Good information systems are critical to cross-functional collaboration, since access to distributed information is required for groups and employees to make quicker and better decisions. For example, some projects can be carried out largely through computerized discussions and transmission of documents. Often this enables highly skilled team members to participate regardless of their physical location and can also reduce the amount of time required for the project.

The modern quality engineer must be competent in the selection, application, and use of hardware and software technology appropriate to the tasks and responsibilities assigned. Consideration should be given not only to the functionality of the system for the task, but also issues such as required user skills, compatibility with other systems, and information security. Furthermore, if the quality system is of any magnitude, the quality engineer must understand project and data management techniques and must be a good team member.

Industry 4.0 refers to the fourth industrial revolution of manufacturing and partially focuses on data management and analysis in a system. This revolution is characterized by four trends: big data, advanced analytics, human-machine interfaces, and digital-to-physical transfer (3D printing) (Baur and Wee 2015). Some associate Industry 4.0 with some of its large-scale data exchange capability. Organizations, particularly those in the manufacturing technology sector, make use of the data exchange system (see B. Lydon, "Industry 4.0—Only One-Tenth of Germany's High-Tech Strategy," April 4, 2014[2]). Refer to Brettel et al. (2014) in References for additional information on Industry 4.0.

PLC and SCADA Systems

The widespread use of microcomputers and programmable logic controllers (PLCs) has transformed the factory floor. There is a growing trend toward distributed measurement and control, where PLCs have built-in programs and logic to control machines and processes. Fewer and fewer technicians are turning dials or opening and closing valves to control processes. These tasks are now controlled by PLCs; however, many PLCs do not have a human interface such as a monitor or keyboard. The PLCs are widely distributed throughout the plant, making manual data collection time-consuming and cumbersome. Furthermore, PLC language is not user-friendly. These drawbacks have given rise to large-scale supervisory control and data acquisition (SCADA) systems (e.g., Systems, Applications, and Products [SAP], a system used in many industries). Other automatic data extraction and data exchange programs have been built for industry-specific needs.

The SCADA system interfaces with all the PLCs through a network. The SCADA system periodically polls the PLC memory registers to collect data. The system includes a human interface, usually in a central location such as a control room, to monitor the processes, generate alarms, and allow the operator to intervene or issue an override as necessary. The SCADA system typically includes real-time trend charts and graphic displays of the current status of the equipment. The system also provides for data storage in a database program, which allows for rapid retrieval of data for subsequent analysis and reporting.

---

[2]http://www.automation.com/automation-news/article/industry-40-only-one-tenth-of-germanys-high-tech-strategy.

What is the role of a quality engineer in the creation of a large-scale SCADA system? The information system should be viewed as no different from a manufacturing system. The quality engineer should be involved from the earliest planning stages to ensure that user and system requirements are thoroughly documented. It may be appropriate and beneficial to apply some of the advanced quality planning disciplines discussed in Chapter 3 even though the "product" is a software system. For example, customer requirements should be fully understood, even if the "customer" is an hourly employee who will use the system to monitor and adjust the process. The quality engineer should participate in creating the user requirements; after all, the quality engineer is typically considered the local expert in data analysis and reporting. The required reports and methods to display and summarize the data are discussed in the next subsection.

QIS Tools

Although there are many ways to design information systems, the larger they get, the more fraught with risk of failure they become. The quality engineer can render a real service to the employer by studying strategy and tactics of systems development. Two useful tools are the information systems strategy matrix and the V model. The need for a strategy was emphasized by Pearlson and Saunders (2004), who produced an information systems strategy matrix, as shown in Figure 1.9.

The matrix shown in Figure 1.9 displays the following four categories: hardware, software, networking, and data. Other categorizations could also be used. This basic example demonstrates the kinds of analysis required. Another tool to consider is the V model. The V model starts on the left side at the top of the V (see Figure 1.10) with high-level user requirements and cascades down through functional specifications and detailed design requirements. On the right side of the V, test protocols are developed, executed, and documented to verify that the design specifications have been met. The quality engineer should be involved in this process to ensure quality and data integrity during the execution of the project.

Tasks that seem trivial, such as naming conventions, can have a huge impact down the road. Large, real-time control systems may have hundreds of PLCs and thousands of sensors. Imagine the complexity of creating a downtime report for

	What	Who	Where
Hardware	List of physical components of the system	Individuals who use it, individuals who manage it	Physical location
Software	List of programs, applications, and utilities	Individuals who use it, individuals who manage it	What hardware it resides on and where that hardware is located
Networking	Diagram of how hardware and software components are connected	Individuals who use it, individuals who manage it, and the company from which service is obtained	Where the nodes are located, where the wires and other transport media are located
Data	Bits of information stored in the system	Individuals who own it, individuals who manage it	Where the information resides

Figure 1.9 Information systems strategy matrix.

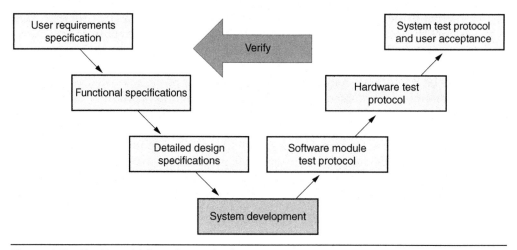

Figure 1.10   The V model for software development.

the packaging area of the plant. Every machine and sensor in the area must be included in the database query. A good naming convention will allow a group of variables to be captured within a single query statement that includes a "wild card." If a naming standard is not used or is poorly executed, then the user has no choice but to individually specify each sensor and PLC when the database query is created.

Similar care and consideration should be given when creating the test protocols. How much data should be collected? How often will the samples be collected? If the sampling duration is too short, or the elapsed time between samples is too long, then it may not be possible to detect variation that is directly caused by the PLC control system. Is there a difference between the process target and the actual steady-state process average? What about including process upsets in the test protocol? Does the controller overshoot the target during initial recovery?

Further ideas to improve the success of system development projects are reported by Long and Gryna (1999), who drew the following conclusions:

- Carefully define the scope of the QIS and what it is expected to accomplish. From the very beginning emphasize operational benefits, not technical specifications. It may be wise to develop a pilot project that can be used to show what really does work and what does not. Getting some benefits in a short period of time builds confidence not only in the system itself, but also in the competence of the system developers.

- Be sure that the goal of the QIS supports the goal of the business. (This point was discussed earlier in this chapter when discussing strategic planning.) Once the goal is set, use well-proven project management techniques.

- Get advance agreement on who will do what and when. Get buy-in to clearly understood milestones. Do not simply delegate the project to the information technology (IT) folks; keep quality engineers and sponsors fully engaged in the development.

- Concentrate on user expectations and how they are being realized. Focus attention on the overall performance of the system rather than specific metrics. Ongoing discussion and comparison between the users and the developers is an important key to success.

- Publish regular progress reports and keep the language in user terms. A common trap in large-scale information systems projects is to get bogged down in technical metrics and jargon; the user may cross their fingers and hope for the best without really understanding what is going on. A corollary of this is to be sure that the end user has the technical competency to understand what is being said. Reports cannot be oversimplified in order to avoid confusing the uneducated.

Repeatedly stress the anticipated benefits that were specified at the outset and do not abandon original goals under pressure. The exception to this guideline occurs if it becomes evident that the original specifications cannot be met. The top-level sponsors must then be fully briefed and participate in the revised benefit statement. This action should be viewed as a last resort and is in a sense a salvage operation.

Productivity improvement is perhaps the most frequently cited reason for investing in an information system. The investment can be considerable because the infrastructure requires hardware, networks, sensors, customized software, and information systems support personnel. Estimating the payback can be a challenge. The payback estimates may include optimistic forecasts and tenuous assumptions. Some people focus on the human benefits such as automating periodic reports. Relief from mundane tasks will free up personnel to pursue other important tasks. But much larger gains usually can be achieved by using the information system to improve production processes. A well-designed information system can identify opportunities that probably would be missed by even the most conscientious and determined analyst using a manual or paper-based data system. At many facilities, a 1% gain in production yield is a realistic assumption and will generate a much larger return than a few hours saved per month generating manual reports. Electronic QISs can be used effectively for traceability and ensuring quality of production.

QIS Example

To illustrate the tremendous value of a QIS, consider this case study regarding a highly automated packaging plant in Texas. Equipment breakdowns plagued the facility for the first year of production. Downtime was so excessive that the plant was operating below the break-even point. Management decided to make a major investment in a new information system. Over the course of the next year, nearly every machine in the facility was linked through a network to a database. Sensors were added to monitor key production processes. Automatic feedback systems were installed and gradually tuned to achieve stability in the most complex processes. Customized reports were created to distill vast amounts of data into usable information. The reports summarized and prioritized the current status so that management could quickly allocate resources where they were most needed. One such report is shown in Figure 1.11. The report executes automatically at the end of

Equipment Exception Report
7/2/16 3:00 PM to 7/2/16 10:00 PM

Concern	Number of faults	Concern		Number of faults
Critical / misc machine alarms	4	**Annealing oven faults**		1
No. 2 compressor, low oil pressure	3	Shop 1, zone 5, high temperature		1
No. 2 compressor, oil temperature	1			
Cooling hood jams	23	**Coating sprayer alarms**		260
Prior shift	This shift			
Shop 1: 14	**19**	Shop 1:	No spray alarm	**157**
Shop 3: 7	2	Shop 3:	No spray alarm	89
Shop 2: 3	2	Shop 2:	No spray alarm	14
Inspection conveyor jams	34	**Discharge conveyor jams**		11
Shop 3, loop A Check detector	23	Shop 2, loop A	Check detector	6
Shop 2, loop C Leak test	4	Shop 3, loop A	Leak test	2
Shop 3, loop A Leak test	3	Shop 3, loop A	Scanner	1
Carton forming faults	12	**Carton packer faults**		18
CF 2 Case not at madrel	11	Shop 1, north packer	Missing jars	13
CF 2 In flight jam	1	Shop 1, north packer	Elevator jam	2
		Shop 2, west packer	No glue	1
Downtime summary (minutes)	285	**Throughput % of budget**		0
Shop 3 Total downtime	**146**		Shop 3	**94.6%**
Shop 1 Total downtime	83		Shop 2	98.1%
Shop 2 Total downtime	56		Shop 1	98.4%

Figure 1.11 Current status report example.

each production shift. It analyzes data from nearly 700 machines, identifies the top three concerns in each functional area, and prints a one-page summary.

The quality department and the maintenance department worked together to develop the format. The general manager participated in establishing the equipment performance standards needed to support the balanced scorecard objectives. If performance does not meet the objectives, then the report highlights the total with a large, bold font. Management and maintenance employees can quickly identify concerns and focus their process improvement efforts accordingly.

The team designing this system took several months and gave a great deal of thought to balancing the automatic collection and processing of data with the human interpretation of information. It would have been easier to design a completely closed-loop control system, but this would have precluded human intervention and thoughtful study of what the processes were saying. At the same time, the data on which the daily and weekly reports were based were massive and it was essential that the data be condensed and summarized before being presented to management.

The plant achieved a dramatic improvement in throughput in less than six months after implementing this QIS. The report shown in Figure 1.12 (and others like it) helped drive a transformation in quality and productivity. By the end of the second year, the plant achieved best-in-class quality and its profit margin was over 10%, exceeding the original performance target.

This example is only one type of the tremendous number and variety of QISs now being implemented. Bar codes, voice entry, optical character recognition, and local area and wide area networks are among the host of new technologies available for cost-effective automation of quality systems. Other technologies include knowledge management, audiovisual presentations, individual learning programs, decision support systems, computerized conferencing, systems modeling, automated online reference services, and so on. quality engineers should carefully study computerized information systems techniques and possibilities. QIS is an area that will continue to revolutionize all aspects of life, both organizational and personal.

ASQ CODE OF ETHICS FOR PROFESSIONAL CONDUCT

Code of Ethics

Determine appropriate behavior in situations requiring ethical decisions. (Evaluate)

Body of Knowledge I.C

All professions are bound by specific codes of ethics, and one mark of any profession is publishing and upholding standards of conduct. ASQ has adopted the code of ethics shown in Figure 1.12.[3]

Quality engineers must be aware of legal issues, such as equal employment opportunity (EEO) laws and other guidelines. Another example of how the legal system impinges on quality engineers is the Sarbanes-Oxley legislation. Because of several instances of large-scale corporate fraud at the turn of the century, the US Congress passed this law, sometimes called Sarbox or SOX, which mandates several stringent requirements for corporate financial reporting that can be understood as quality assurance techniques applied to the corporate financial system. Sarbox enhances the role of quality engineering because it carries the same concept from the quality arena to the financial arena.

Whether your work is governed by EEO laws, Sarbox, or other relevant statutes, the point to remember is that your behavior must always be such that no embarrassment comes to the supplier, your employer (subordinates, peers, or

---

[3]See https://asq.org/about-asq/conferences-events-policies/code-of-ethics.

CODE OF ETHICS

Introduction

The purpose of the American Society for Quality (ASQ) Code of Ethics is to establish global standards of conduct and behavior for its members, certification holders, and anyone else who may represent or be perceived to represent ASQ. In addition to the code, all applicable ASQ policies and procedures should be followed. Violations to the Code of Ethics should be reported. Differences in work style or personalities should be first addressed directly with others before escalating to an ethics issue.

The ASQ Professional Ethics and Qualifications Committee, appointed annually by the ASQ Board of Directors, is responsible for interpreting this code and applying it to specific situations, which may or may not be specifically called out in the text. Disciplinary actions will be commensurate with the seriousness of the offense and may include permanent revocation of certifications and/or expulsion from the society.

Fundamental Principles

ASQ requires its representatives to be honest and transparent. Avoid conflicts of interest and plagiarism. Do not harm others. Treat them with respect, dignity, and fairness. Be professional and socially responsible. Advance the role and perception of the Quality professional.

Expectations of a Quality Professional

A. **Act with Integrity and Honesty**
    1. Strive to uphold and advance the integrity, honor, and dignity of the Quality profession.
    2. Be truthful and transparent in all professional interactions and activities.
    3. Execute professional responsibilities and make decisions in an objective, factual, and fully informed manner.
    4. Accurately represent and do not mislead others regarding professional qualifications, including education, titles, affiliations, and certifications.
    5. Offer services, provide advice, and undertake assignments only in your areas of competence, expertise, and training.

B. **Demonstrate Responsibility, Respect, and Fairness**
    1. Hold paramount the safety, health, and welfare of individuals, the public, and the environment.
    2. Avoid conduct that unjustly harms or threatens the reputation of the Society, its members, or the Quality profession.
    3. Do not intentionally cause harm to others through words or deeds. Treat others fairly, courteously, with dignity, and without prejudice or discrimination.
    4. Act and conduct business in a professional and socially responsible manner.
    5. Allow diversity in the opinions and personal lives of others.

C. **Safeguard Proprietary Information and Avoid Conflicts of Interest**
    1. Ensure the protection and integrity of confidential information.
    2. Do not use confidential information for personal gain.
    3. Fully disclose and avoid any real or perceived conflicts of interest that could reasonably impair objectivity or independence in the service of clients, customers, employers, or the Society.
    4. Give credit where it is cue.
    5. Do not plagiarize. Do not use the intellectual property of others without permission. Document the permission as it is obtained.

Figure 1.12 ASQ Code of Ethics.

management), the customer, or yourself. You must be polite and diplomatic and show respect to all persons. In the final analysis, you must be honest with yourself that you have acted fairly and legally, and you should have a good feeling about the things you have been involved with, including resolving ethical dilemmas.

Ethical Dilemmas

Ethical dilemmas arise often when dealing with technology, in federal and state legislation, and in management activities. How technology is applied and the consequences of the application often call for ethical decisions. Some have equated the definition of quality and ethics with "do the right thing."

Another area of concern is managing personally identifiable information (PII), which includes phone numbers, addresses, social security numbers, credit card numbers, and so on. There should be industry and organization policies along with government regulations to ensure this type of information is protected from abuse. These policies should include the need to encrypt, safeguard, and remove these data from computer databases as required. For example, in the medical industry these policies are known as the Health Insurance Portability and Accountability Act (HIPAA), and in academia, the Family Educational Rights and Privacy Act (FERPA).

A case in point is the ongoing need for guidelines governing ethical behavior in the application of computers, e-commerce, e-business, and other new technologies. Some of the issues demanding critical attention are the following:

1. Misusing employers' computers for personal gain or pleasure

2. Destroying others' property (e.g., injecting a virus or wiping out files)

3. Using or condoning the use of computers for fraudulent activities

4. Violating individual and company rights to privacy and confidentiality

5. Omitting safeguards that protect users and data

6. Infringing on copyrights and trademarks

7. Failing to maintain a sufficient level of accuracy and completeness implied when data are collected and stored in computer databases

8. Failing to make critical information known to appropriate decision makers in time to prevent a negative outcome

9. Failing to capture, manage, and make available critical knowledge to those who need it

10. Failing to upgrade computer technology

11. Managing retrieval of data files from old or different software programs/versions

12. Dealing with global employees, businesses, and markets

13. Dealing with legal requirements (including safety and environmental regulations) of different governmental groups across geographic boundaries

14. Ensuring the usage quality of the new technology itself, and ensuring that people are trained to use the new technology

Another area of concern to the engineer is the Occupational Safety and Health Administration (OSHA). Both federal-level agencies and state-level agencies monitor organizations to ensure compliance with the respective rules and regulations. Some of the more common sets of rules and regulations are the following:

OSHA, Labor (*Randall's Practical Guide to ISO 9000* provides a more comprehensive list of regulations)

29 CFR 1910.95, Occupational Noise Exposure (Ear Protection)

29 CFR 1910.120, Hazardous Waste Operations and Emergency Response

29 CFR 1910.132, Personnel Protective Equipment

29 CFR 1910.133, Eye and Face Protection

29 CFR 1910.147, The Control of Hazardous Energy (Lockout/Tagout)

29 CFR 1910.1200, Hazard Communication

Engineers also find themselves involved with ethical issues usually handled by management, such as interviewing potential new employees for the organization. Without the proper training, engineers could put themselves and their employers at great risk for lawsuits by asking inappropriate questions. Engineers conducting interviews should keep the following guidelines in mind:

- Ask only job-related questions

- Do not ask about age, race, national origin, marital status, or religion

- Focus on the competencies and skills for the job in question

- Avoid any small talk that is not related to the job

The ASQ Code of Ethics emphasizes that quality engineers are professionals and must act accordingly. Federal law and employer rules create additional requirements for compliance. You must understand all of the above and more as it is presented to you.

LEADERSHIP PRINCIPLES AND TECHNIQUES

> Analyze various principles and techniques for developing and organizing teams and leading quality initiatives. (Analyze)
>
> **Body of Knowledge I.D**

Leadership is an essential part of any quality initiative. Robbins and Judge (2012) define leadership as "the ability to influence a group toward the achievement of goals." While there are many different leadership approaches involving personality and situation, the literature has indicated several theories of leadership that may help in understanding these approaches. Robbins and Judge (2012) detail two main theories of leadership:

- Trait theory of leadership: personality and social, physical, and intellectual traits may play a role in differentiating leaders from nonleaders

- Behavioral theory of leadership: specific behaviors may differentiate some leaders from nonleaders

See the text by Robbins and Judge (2012) for further details on leadership theory and traits and discuss some important principles for leaders in the quality field to keep in mind.

The leader's role is to establish and communicate a vision and to provide the tools, knowledge, and motivation necessary for those individuals or teams that will collaborate to bring the vision to life. This can apply to an entire organization as well as to a specific department or work group. For example, the leader of the quality engineering function is responsible for helping shape the policies for the quality technologies that will be deployed throughout the organization and for ensuring that department personnel are sufficiently qualified to support the use of the technologies.

A leader may or may not hold an officially designated leadership position. Often, someone in a work group will emerge as a leader because of their knowledge, skills, experience, and/or abilities. Further, teams often include facilitators, another leadership role. The facilitator's purpose is to provide support to the team's effort while at the same time allowing the team to maintain ownership of its decisions.

A good leader always tries to understand where the other person is coming from, what makes them act the way they do—in other words, understanding what motivates others. Good leaders recognize and apply Maslow's hierarchy of needs. This principle asserts that people are driven by their needs and wants and that all human needs can be roughly placed in a hierarchy. Higher-level needs are not relevant until lower-level needs are satisfied; however, once a need is met, it no longer motivates behavior. The five levels are (1) physiological (hunger, thirst, sleep), (2) safety and security (protection from the elements and predators), (3) socialization, (4) ego, and (5) self-actualization. Many people never get their ego needs fully satisfied and thus do not experience self-actualization needs, but all the great thinkers and leaders of the ages are in fact self-actualized. When trying to lead less cooperative followers, it often helps to think about what need level they are working on.

Leadership of the quality engineering function involves defining and carrying out projects that support the organization's strategic plan, as well as providing the resources for and overseeing day-to-day quality engineering activities. While some of these activities may be performed by an individual, in today's complex environment they are often conducted in a team setting. Examples include working with an advanced quality planning team to analyze repeatability and reproducibility (R&R) of a new measurement system, and working with a software engineer to implement a new automated SPC online package.

Developing, Building, and Organizing Teams

Since around 1980, quality concepts and team concepts have moved in tandem through the economy. Teamwork is now vital in government, space exploration, healthcare, education, and most profit-oriented businesses. Compared to a generation or two ago, control of a project or process has shifted from a single individual to the team level.

The Need for Teams

The drive for excellence includes better deployment of people at all levels. Workers at all levels now expect to have some say in designing and implementing change, and only through change can quality improve. Managing an organization through teams has become recognized as a core competency of business.

There are many types and purposes of teams, each requiring different structures, skills, resources, and support. Leaders of an organization must therefore be clear about what they are trying to accomplish to ensure that the appropriate team processes are utilized for their situation.

A team-based environment might be initiated as part of the strategic plan or as a response to a specific problem encountered by the organization. Regardless of the reason, there should be a process for planning and carrying out the team-based initiative. This process is often done through a steering committee that focuses on driving business improvement. A member of management—called the sponsor—also typically is identified and takes responsibility for initiating and guiding a team. The sponsor usually is the individual with ownership of the process or area where the team's actions are focused.

Types of Teams

Three major types of teams are widely used:

1. Process improvement team. These are temporary teams whose mission is to develop a new process or improve an existing process. These teams are often cross-functional, consisting of representatives from multiple departments involved in the process under study. The management sponsor typically selects the team leader and will negotiate with other area managers to identify other team members appropriate for the project mission. Figure 1.13 shows how teams should be integrated within the organizational hierarchy.

2. Work group. These teams consist of the personnel who work in a particular department or process area. Their mission is the ongoing monitoring and improvement of process performance, and they typically meet on a regular basis (e.g., weekly) to review indicators and identify any actions required. The work group leader is usually the individual with supervisory responsibility for the process area. The team also may initiate a process improvement team, especially when the improvement requires interfacing with other departments that are suppliers or customers of the work group. Organizations committed

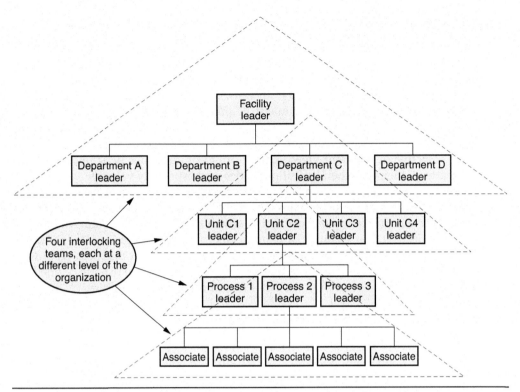

Figure 1.13   Linking team structure.

to applying work group–based improvement from top to bottom can use an interlocking team structure that includes all members of the organization.

3. Self-directed work team (SDWT). An SDWT is a group of individuals who have broader and deeper day-to-day responsibility for management and improvement of their process area. SDWT members are highly trained in subjects such as quality, safety, maintenance, and scheduling, and in some cases also carry out human resource functions. These teams are highly empowered to make their own decisions, although of course there are still limits, such as spending authority.

Whether and to what extent an organization utilizes teams is usually dependent on factors such as the rate of change in its industry, the culture of the organization, the predominant management style, employee education levels, and where the company's product or service is in the maturity cycle.

Some teams are less formally structured, such as an ad hoc group organized to address a customer complaint or a virtual team that wants to compare the process used for design reviews by several different facilities. Regardless, many of the following considerations will influence the success of the team and the satisfaction of its members.

Selecting Team Members

The primary determination of who will participate in a team effort is whether the person is involved in the process to be improved. However, when selecting team members, other issues often are considered. For example, a process improvement team might not be very effective if all team members have the same personality style (e.g., as measured by a personality evaluation instrument such as the Myers-Briggs Type Indicator/MBTI; see http://www.myersbriggs.org). Some teams intentionally include someone from outside the process area who can provide a more objective or different viewpoint. Supplier or customer personnel often are invited to participate when their input is deemed especially valuable.

Selection of team members for organizational management and improvement is vital, just as it is for a sports team. The many different activities to be carried out call for certain roles and responsibilities, which then require a certain set of skills and/or mind-set. For example, a team needs to analyze process data, minimize disruptive conflict, monitor meeting time effectiveness, and maintain records of activities. Specific roles, such as a timekeeper and a scribe, are usually defined for individuals who will carry out the latter two of these responsibilities.

Support Mechanisms Required for Team Success

Team-based improvement requires more than creating teams; it requires providing them with adequate support to ensure success. Examples of support include:

- Equipment. Face-to-face teams need meeting space, equipment (such as tables, chairs, projectors, and whiteboards), and access to computer hardware and software to document meeting minutes, analyze process data, and prepare presentation materials. Virtual teams can utilize software such as Microsoft Teams.

- Training. Unless an organization is extremely lucky, most employees who become involved in teams will not have all of the necessary skills to participate effectively in a team. Such skills may include how to plan and effectively manage meetings, how to analyze processes and data, and how to make group decisions based on consensus. The organization must therefore determine the specific skills required and the current skill levels of employees, and provide opportunities to close the gap.

- Management sponsor. The sponsor role is a vital leadership function that goes beyond simply launching a team. It also includes staying in contact with the team leader to ensure sufficient progress and resolving any conflicting issues with other parts of the organization. The sponsor typically has authority to cross organizational boundaries that team members would need to negotiate and can therefore resolve some types of issues quicker. The sponsor is also ultimately responsible for effective implementation of the team's recommendations.

- Systems change. Setting up a new team in an organization that is not adequately designed for this way of working is a prescription for failure. An organization is a system, meaning that if one part is changed, other parts will be affected. If the primary management style is autocratic and people are rewarded for competition versus cooperation, teams are unlikely to be an effective mechanism. Before beginning the team process, leadership must consider what other systemic changes will be necessary to align the various parts of the organization. How team success will be recognized and rewarded is especially important.

Team Development

Each new team is a new mini-organization. The team will therefore progress (and often regress) through the traditional stages of group development (Tuckman 1965), which are described briefly here:

- Stage 1: Forming. When team members first begin to meet, each member brings their individual identity and the perspective of their own environment (e.g., functional process area). Even for members who have participated in other teams, each team is a unique experience and individuals often approach it cautiously, uncertain of how they will perform in the new situation. During the forming stage, a team usually clarifies its mission, specifies roles that need to be carried out and who is to perform them, and defines rules of acceptable behavior, often called norms.

- Stage 2: Storming. During this phase, team members realize the size of the task before them. They still think primarily as individuals and often attempt to shape decisions to their own advantage rather than considering the impact on other team members. Arguments, testing the leader's authority, and attempts to change the team's mission are typical behaviors during the storming stage.

- Stage 3: Norming. In this phase, the individuals begin to shift their focus from personal concerns to that of helping the team meet the challenge at hand. Interpersonal conflicts and the tug of external loyalties have less of an impact as team members realize their interdependence. They are more willing to discuss differences of opinion to understand them and how they might impact team success.

- Stage 4: Performing. At this stage, the team has matured to the point where it is working as a smooth cohesive unit. Team members trust each other and have a good understanding of each other's strengths and weaknesses and how they support the mission and are now able to work through group conflict. There is a greater appreciation of the importance of the team's processes and members are more satisfied with being part of the team. During this phase, the team typically makes significant progress toward achieving its goals.

Although these stages indicate a logical sequence that occurs over time, actual progress by a particular team will vary greatly. For example, a team that has progressed to stage 3 or 4 may fall back to stage 1 or 2 if team members find that some previous assumptions about one another are not true or if team membership changes because of a job transfer. Some teams may not progress beyond the earlier stages due to a short project duration or if they are unable to successfully resolve group dynamics issues.

A fifth stage, adjourning, was added to the original small-group development process in 1977 (Tuckman and Jensen 1977). This final stage represents team disbandment. While team members often feel happy due to the success of the team's accomplishments, there can also be a sense of sadness due to the "death of the team."

Team development can be enhanced by making sure that team members have a basic understanding of how to (1) interact in positive ways, (2) deal with difficult people or situations, (3) contribute to accomplishing the team's goals, and (4) give or receive constructive feedback. A facilitator can help ensure that the team is aware of its progress by commenting during meetings. Special interventions are also sometimes useful. Examples include simulations or outdoor adventures that allow the group members to become more familiar with one another's styles, strengths, and weaknesses, and to become more effective at working with and through their differences.

Leading Quality Initiatives

A quality engineer is frequently called on to lead particular quality initiatives. Such projects might involve improving an existing product or service, working to resolve supplier performance issues, addressing product field performance failures, implementing new measurement technology, or obtaining ISO 9001 quality system registration.

The following list offers several recommendations for leadership of such initiatives. Most are appropriate whether or not the project is a team-based initiative, because, by definition, most initiatives will influence others in the organization (and/or the supply chain), and the roles of others should therefore be taken into account throughout the project.

- Ensure that the project mission is clear, including expected results, timing, limitations, and reporting structure and methods. Obtain supporting data used to indicate the value of the project and determine how the project is related to the bigger picture (e.g., strategic plan, other projects, and/or day-to-day operations).

- Determine who the other players in the project will be and make contact with them individually. Learn of their interest in and commitment to the project.

- Define the technical process and the time schedule to be used to carry out the initiative. For example, a problem-solving project might use a seven-step problem-solving process, while a Six Sigma project might use the DMAIC process (see Chapter 5).

- Execute the project according to the process defined in the previous step, involving others as appropriate and keeping management informed.

- Evaluate outcomes of the project against the original mission. Ensure that all people involved receive appropriate recognition for their contributions.

Most of these steps are basic to effective project management. However, a significant portion of the impact of such initiatives also will be related to the quality of leadership demonstrated throughout the project. Following are some useful guidelines:

- Ensure that all involved understand the mission, the goals, and the project objectives and how the team fits with the bigger picture.

- Understand that all people and organizations involved will have their own priorities, perspectives, and skills. Learn what they are, recognize the validity of the differences, and find ways to integrate them effectively.

- Be aware of your own strengths and weaknesses and how they can affect project success. Find ways to learn from and utilize the skills of others to compensate. Also, provide as many opportunities as possible for other project personnel to utilize their full capability and to develop new skills.

- Understand all of the team members' strengths, weaknesses, and personalities to successfully lead the team.

- Communicate, communicate, communicate. People tend to fill gaps in their understanding with their own bias or fears, and that's how rumors start. Keep the gaps to a minimum.

- Be a role model by emphasizing and demonstrating the importance of high-quality work.

Additionally, a quality engineer will frequently be called on for technical advice regarding particular methods for process analysis, such as conducting a process FMEA (see Chapter 3). Although the quality engineer may not be in a leadership role, they must still understand these principles. For more information, see Snee and Hoerl (2012) and the many references within their article on leadership, leadership skills, and statistical leadership.

FACILITATION PRINCIPLES AND TECHNIQUES

Concurrent with the development of teams was the emergence of the facilitator as a key organizational player. Whereas the old-fashioned boss would simply tell workers what was to be done, the facilitator must understand the objectives and constraints of the team, as well as its needs.

In an ideal world there would be no need for facilitators. Everyone would have the skills necessary for their roles and would work effectively with everyone else. However, it is not an ideal world since all of us are continually learning. The role of facilitator is therefore a valuable one since it allows special additional skills to be readily available to the team.

Facilitator Roles and Responsibilities

Describe the facilitator's roles and
responsibilities on a team. (Understand)

Body of Knowledge I.E.1

A facilitator's primary mission is to ensure that a team is successful, but this must be done in a way that ensures that the team, not the facilitator, is responsible for the outcome. A successful facilitator is one that is continually working himself or herself out of the role by helping the team develop higher and higher levels of competency.

The facilitator is termed a marginal role since facilitators are not actually members of the team with which they are working. However, facilitators are usually present at most or all the team's meetings, and their role is to provide support that helps the team work better. Simple examples of this support include notifying the team when it has veered from the meeting agenda, jumped to a conclusion without any supporting data, or not allowed all team members to voice their opinions.

Facilitators usually take one of two types of roles within a team. One is that of meeting manager, where the facilitator guides the team through the agenda. The other role is that of observer, where the facilitator sits quietly to the side and simply comments when it seems necessary or useful to further team progress. The observer role also provides the opportunity to gain information that can be used to coach the team leader in team process skills.

An important distinction, though, is that facilitators do not discuss content issues, only process issues. For example, if a team were trying to reduce the amount of time patients spend in the waiting room of a healthcare clinic, the facilitator would not interject comments such as, "Should we change the patient scheduling process?" since it is relative to technical content of the subject matter. However, at the appropriate time the facilitator might ask, "What are some additional ways that the time could be reduced?" since it only involves ensuring that the team has taken a broad view of potential opportunities.

It is not necessary that facilitators be someone from outside the team. The team leader or a specific team member who has sufficient skills and experience may also take on the role of facilitator. In this case, the facilitator is allowed to contribute content, because the person is in fact a bona fide member of the team. The ultimate objective, of course, is for all teams to be fully capable of working without the need for anyone in a designated facilitation role. Each member simply pays attention to both content and process issues and ensures that the team works effectively.

Because a facilitator tries to help the team be more effective, there is a wide range of issues to consider. Here is a list of just a few of the items that facilitators must pay attention to:

- Meeting agenda. Is there an agenda for each meeting, and does the team follow it?

- Communication. Do team members listen to and discuss each other's opinions, or does each simply state his or her own? Are discussions on a positive note or does negativity sap people's energy? Does everyone have the opportunity to speak, does the team leader appear to give more attention to some members than others, or do some individuals dominate?

- Technical process model. Have the team members engaged in procedural conflict: negotiating the where, when, how, and why issues, such as defining the steps they will take to carry out the project (e.g., a seven-step problem-solving model, if appropriate), or are they simply wandering around with no defined direction?

- Conflict. Is there interpersonal or procedural conflict between group members that prevents them from working together effectively? Is all conflict being suppressed, causing ideas to be withheld? Is substantive conflict—for example, deferring consensus when discussing ideas to get to the best ideas—encouraged?

- Decision-making. Does the team make decisions based on data, or does it jump to conclusions? Is consensus used when the decision is one that requires everyone's commitment?

- Follow-up. Does the group identify action items, then ensure that they are carried out?

An effective facilitator must have a broad range of capabilities. Three of the most important are the following:

- Meeting management skills. A facilitator should know how to run meetings in a manner that effectively uses the time available. In many ways, meetings are like mini-projects, with a mission (purpose of the meeting), technical process (meeting agenda), and boundaries (meeting duration). In addition, since meetings consist primarily of discussion, the ability to communicate effectively is vital.

- People skills. Since each person brings his or her own background, skills, and priorities to meetings, the ability to understand and work with different perspectives is critical for a facilitator. An understanding of psychology (both individual and social) and methods for change (e.g., from the field of organization development) is therefore valuable.

- Technical process analysis skills. Improvement of processes involves analysis of processes. An understanding of the seven basic quality control tools, the seven management tools, SPC, and design of experiments gives a facilitator a wide range of tools that can be introduced at an appropriate time. (These tools are all discussed in Chapters 5 and 6.) Perhaps the most important knowledge for facilitators is also the most difficult to obtain: understanding themselves. It is difficult to understand others if you do not understand yourself, because you may make interpretations using filters of which you are unaware. An effective facilitator must be able to determine whether a particular intervention is being done because of the needs of the team or because of the needs of the facilitator.

When facilitators believe that the team should change the way it is working, they can select from several different ways of bringing this matter to the attention of the team. The method the facilitator chooses will often depend on a combination of the facilitator's personal style and level of comfort with the team, and the team's responses to previous interventions. Following are some of the different ways to intervene:

- Tell the team. The easiest way is simply to tell the team what it is doing wrong or what it needs to do differently. For minor issues, this is a quick and probably safe intervention; however, it may cause more resistance with some teams since it can be interpreted as being authoritative.

- State observations. A slightly more discreet way of intervening is for the facilitator to simply state what he or she is seeing that the team may want to do differently. This puts the information in front of the team, allowing them to decide whether to pay attention to it.

- Have the team explore. Another choice is to ask the team members to think about what they are doing at the moment (and perhaps frame the context of the issue, for example, whether it is relative to communications or agenda issues). Although this method takes more time, it causes the team to take more ownership of the intervention, so that learning is more likely to be internalized.

Perhaps it is clear from some of the above discussion, but it is worth emphasizing again: it is vital for the team to have ownership of decisions that are made regarding content and, when possible, those regarding team processes. A facilitator who gets glory from making such decisions for the team simply reduces the likelihood of the team learning from and being committed to the team process.

There are, however, situations when facilitators have a higher level of involvement than what has been presented here. For example, with kaizen blitz teams, which typically last three to five days, acceleration of the improvement process comes about partially due to reducing concerns over how decisions are made. The facilitator in such projects usually has much more authority to specify the direction the team will take.

Facilitation Tools

> Apply various tools used with teams, including brainstorming, nominal group technique, conflict resolution, and force-field analysis. (Apply)
>
> **Body of Knowledge I.E.2**

Facilitation tools are useful for idea generation. One of the main purposes of idea generation is to encourage creative thinking. Robbins and Judge (2012) discuss the three components of creativity: expertise, creative-thinking skills, and intrinsic task motivation. The tools outlined in this section can help facilitate creative thinking and improve creative thinking skills.

Most people are familiar with brainstorming as a means of generating many ideas in a short period of time to identify solutions to problems. Other facilitation tools include nominal group technique, conflict resolution, and force field analysis. All these tools are detailed below, with the exception of force field analysis, which is discussed in Chapter 5.

Brainstorming

Groups and teams can use both structured and unstructured brainstorming methods. For unstructured brainstorming, a topic is agreed on and written in front of the group. The leader/facilitator then asks for ideas to be randomly called out and all are recorded without any discussion. When the flow of ideas stops, the list is reviewed and discussed, which may result in the elimination or combination of ideas.

A structured brainstorming approach involves a round-robin process whereby each person in the group is asked to state one idea. If a person has none, he or she passes and the next person is asked, and so on. When everyone has passed on a round, the brainstorming is complete. A similar process can be used by posting several sheets of paper around the room with a topic or problem written at the top of each. Each team member goes to a sheet and writes down ideas that come to mind, then the members rotate repeatedly until all have contributed to each sheet. Another alternative is to simply circulate sheets of paper among the group.

Another method of brainstorming, called Crawford slip, is especially useful when the team is working on a particularly sensitive topic or when the team does not yet have a high level of trust. All the team members are asked to record their ideas on pieces of paper that are then given to a trusted individual (e.g., the facilitator) who compiles all the items into a single list (e.g., on a whiteboard). The anonymous nature of this method helps people feel freer to include their ideas, and the team often finds that several members had the same idea, which begins to build cohesiveness.

Nominal Group Technique

Nominal group technique is one way of processing lists of brainstormed items. It involves using the following steps to reduce a large list to a shorter one:

1. Ask each participant to rank the items in numeric order (e.g., in a list of eight items, 1 is best and 8 is worst).

2. Record the ranks of all participants beside each item.

3. Total the rankings for each item. Those with the lowest totals are the preferred options.

Table 1.3 shows an example applied by a group of course participants who were trying to decide where to go for lunch. Of the four choices, Marlow's received the lowest total (therefore the highest priority), making it the group's first choice.

Another way to narrow down a list of items is to have the group select from the list only those that they prefer. The number they are to select is usually approximately one-half of the total number. After all participants have made their selection, the facilitator asks how many participants voted for each option and records this. The Pareto principle will usually work, with some of the options getting very few votes; they are then dropped from the list. The voting process is then repeated until the desired number of items remains. Table 1.4 shows multivoting on a larger version of the lunch selection problem. Five people are voting, and in the third round of voting Grunge Café finally emerges as the winner by a 4:1 margin.

Conflict Resolution

Most people identify conflict as a problem to be solved, as something that is inevitable, and as something that is undesirable in teams. Further, many believe conflict only comes about when two or more people have ideas that appear to be totally different and where it is perceived that a choice must be made between them. In

Table 1.3 Nominal group technique ranking table.

| Restaurant | Individuals and rankings | | | | | |
	Tom	Joe	Mary	Sue	Terry	Total
Marlow's	1	2	3	1	2	9
Grunge Café	3	1	1	2	3	10
Stew & Brew	2	4	2	4	4	16
Fancaé	4	3	4	3	1	15

Table 1.4 Multivoting.

	First vote (select 4)	Second vote (select 3)	Third vote (select 1)
Pizzas R Us	2		
Marlow's	4	3	
Alice's Restaurant	1		
Grunge Café	5	5	4
Mom's Diner	0		
Stew & Brew	3	2	
Fancaé	5	5	1

reality, however, two kinds of conflict, substantive conflict and procedural conflict, can actually enhance teamwork. A third kind, affective or interpersonal conflict, results when team members "allow personal feelings to negatively affect group interaction" (Burnett 2005), such as when hidden biases surface, normally inconsequential behaviors become irritants, or past slights or unresolved issues spill over into team interaction.

Kilmann and Thomas (1977) detail several styles of conflict resolution, including competing, avoiding, accommodating, collaborating, and compromising. Dealing directly with conflict means that a facilitator or other team member either reminds the team of its common goal or puts the grievances on the table in as neutral a fashion as possible to defuse the situation or negotiate a compromise that will allow the team to function. Not all conflict can be avoided, but one way to minimize conflicts is to clearly identify roles and responsibilities in the team early in the process.

By engaging in substantive conflict, teams actively work at avoiding hasty consensus (such as jumping on the first idea instead of waiting for possibly better alternatives or making a decision before everyone has had a chance to give input). Teams can use three strategies to defer consensus:

- Elaborate key ideas by adding details, examples, or explanations. Remember that one good idea can spark several other good ideas, which means the team has more choices.

- Consider alternatives by adding to an idea or exploring an idea that has not been previously considered. One team member might add details to help another explain a suggestion or might restate the idea so that everyone understands.

- Voice disagreements to strengthen the product or process. Remember that disagreeing does not mean you do not like someone; in fact, disagreeing about ideas can mean that you are sufficiently engaged to notice strengths and weaknesses (Gillette et al. 1993).

Negotiation is key to resolving procedural conflict, especially when a team is first convened, at specific points in reaching an objective or goal, and at the beginnings of project meetings. As the name suggests, procedural conflict has to do with how the group runs, and requires participants to be very clear; participants should write down and maintain group memory documents that keep track of where and when the team will meet, who will take on certain roles (such as team leader, recorder, time manager, devil's advocate), what procedures and tools the team will use (such as consensus versus voting), and the anticipated time line for meeting the team's objectives. All these issues are important and some may need to be renegotiated on an ongoing basis to keep the group running smoothly.

The following guidelines incorporate each of the three kinds of conflict:

- Encourage people to exchange ideas freely before coming to a decision

- Treat the discussion as a problem to be solved instead of an attack on a person

- Take the time to attend to housekeeping issues such as regular breaks, room temperature, and sufficient supplies of necessary items (paper, pens, tissues)

- Consider, and keep records of, the benefits and drawbacks of each option

- Keep the team's goals, objectives, and common interests on the front burner, especially when tempers run high

One difficulty is getting everyone on the team to understand what the other team members are saying and why it is important to them. When everyone understands and is willing to share their values and the assumptions underlying their positions, asking team members to restate in their own words what has been said helps ensure true understanding.

Time is also an ally for conflict resolution. If the issue is over a decision that can be delayed, the time between subsequent discussions may allow the players to not only cool off but also think over both their own positions and those of other team members. When all is said and done, many of the skills related to conflict are also communication skills.

COMMUNICATION SKILLS

> Identify and distinguish between specific communication methods that are used for delivering information and messages in a variety of situations across all levels of the organization. (Analyze)
>
> **Body of Knowledge I.F**

The term "communicate" comes from the Latin *communicat(us)*, meaning to impart or make common. When people communicate, they try to establish a common ground. Every communication interaction is unique in terms of purpose, context, mode of communication, and people involved. Communication skills are critical for success, whether measured by promotion or by higher-quality processes and products. Robbins and Judge (2012) point out that "communication can be thought of as a process" and "must include both the transference and the understanding of meaning." When thinking about communication from both a communicator standpoint and a receiver standpoint, it may be helpful to keep in mind best practices associated with both parties. Some of these best practices are detailed below.

In the quality field, effective communication is essential for everyone to understand and have a sense of ownership of the common vision. Every employee must be aware of objectives and necessary actions that are required for successful quality initiatives within the organization. Common goals are a unifying factor in virtually all successful teams. The communication skills needed to accomplish complex goals and objectives should involve some understanding of communication theory and practice. They also require the communicator to consider the various tools and methods available for communication as well as the audience receiving the communication.

Communication can be achieved on an individual level (one-on-one), from an individual to a group, or in a group or team environment. Methods of communication include verbal, visual, and written. Regardless of the setting or the method used, it is important to try to be as transparent and as clear as possible.

Verbal or oral communication can be achieved by using a variety of methods or conveying the information in a variety of ways. Types of oral communication include, but are not limited to, interviews, formal speeches, conversation, debate, directives, briefings (in person or via telecommunication), and public announcements. Telecommunication using Skype or Teams has become popular. In the absence of attendees, sometimes the telecommunications are recorded and saved for viewing asynchronously. While video recordings or even YouTube videos can be considered a form of visual communication, also consider graphics, photographs, and images as visual communication methods. Written communication ranges from the very informal text, instant message, or tweet to the formal technical report or peer-reviewed publication.

All forms of communication convey a message to the receiver. Quality engineers rely heavily on the discovery and organization of data, facts, and evidence—systematically collecting, analyzing, and organizing the material. Descriptive statistical methods involving data visualization are an important part of the data analysis process. There are many visual displays of information presented throughout this handbook. Some of the displays involve a combination of visual and written communication, such as the FMEA diagrams. Careful thought and consideration should be involved when choosing an appropriate graphical technique to study, understand, and present data. For example, pie charts can be very informative when a population or sample can be grouped into proportions, but they are not appropriate graphical choices for use in every analysis.

Technical communication of results often includes all forms of communication. PowerPoint presentations are regularly used when one person is relaying technical information to a group of listeners. When creating PowerPoint presentations, pay attention to details such as numbering the slides, using large and legible fonts (especially for any graph or axes titles), clearly detailing and explaining the main message of the presentation, and including an outline of the talk.

To be successful, quality engineers should master both discussion skills and presentation skills. The ability to analyze and organize information and present it orally will consistently reap rewards. Clear, concise, and unambiguous writing is also an essential skill. Practicing presentations ahead of time as well as seeking out constructive feedback from peers and superiors is essential.

Feedback is an important component of the communication interaction. It provides the opportunity for clarification and in-depth understanding. There are five main categories of feedback that occur in communication exchanges:

1. Evaluation. Making judgment about the worth, goodness, or appropriateness of the statement

2. Interpretation. Paraphrasing or perception checking as a means of clarification

3. Support. Confirming behavior that encourages the sender to continue to communicate

4. Probing. Attempting to gain additional information, continue the discussion, or clarify a point

5. Understanding. Trying to discover what the sender of the message intends or means by the message

Being an active listener and supplying adequate feedback, including asking relevant questions, are important. This is especially true when communicating as part of a team. Group communication skills require some additional considerations, such as what your role is in the group, when to talk, when to listen, and how to resolve issues in the event of a conflict or confrontation. Successful quality engineering implementation requires the development of effective teams, and effective communication is an important aspect.

Leaders of the quality engineering teams and leaders of an organization should pay careful attention to communication details. Leaders must establish a vision, communicate that vision to those in the organization, and provide the tools and knowledge necessary to accomplish the vision. Therefore, good leaders understand and employ efficient and effective communication to achieve this goal. Remember that leadership is needed at all levels of the organization.

To accomplish a stated goal, all members involved in reaching that goal must understand and be committed to achieving that goal. One way to achieve understanding and commitment is to include all members in the complete process. Members of effective teams feel some ownership of programs and projects when they understand goals, objectives, and/or mutually well-understood expectations and are given access to needed information and resources.

To create understanding and commitment, leaders employ skills such as clear formulation of a concept, emphasis of key points, repetition, and summarization. Multiple channels are absolutely vital to convey our message in the intricate information in today's world. Every listener/reader is bombarded with communication from myriad sources all day long (and most of the night).

CUSTOMER RELATIONS

> Define, apply, and analyze the results of customer relation tools such as customer satisfaction surveys. (Analyze)
>
> **Body of Knowledge I.G**

Customers can be found both internally and externally to the organization, and you must find some way of communicating with your customers on a regular basis. In studies conducted over several years, Collins and Porras (1997) point out that the best-of-the-best companies (visionaries) in their respective industries have developed systems that transcend dependence on any single leader or great idea to build an enduring, great human institution that has lasted and will last for decades. Many of these companies stumbled along the way but somehow found a way to come back, providing the customer or client the products or services that are wanted and/or needed. The secret seems to be to try a lot of things, keeping those that work and stopping those that do not, and continually check back with the customer to see if anything has changed, and starting the process over, in a typical Plan-Do-Study-Act cycle.

Customer Needs and Wants

Your organizational objective should be to ensure that customers want and need your products or services. As Perry (1998) states, "Staying in direct, face-to-face contact with customers, in their world, is the surest way to combat organizational myopia." Far too often a system is developed and people in that system "expect" customers to conform to the way things are done by the supplier organization. This occurs everywhere from the corner grocery store to other retail outlets, from schools to manufacturing organizations. How often have you seen cartoons with the central theme of "if it wasn't for the unrealistic customers, this would be a great place to work"?

The quality engineer's job (either manufacturing or service-based) is to help the organization see that customers are the reason for its existence, versus the other way around. Hayes (2008) provides details on effective methods to measure customer satisfaction and loyalty through surveys or questionnaires. These methods now include online surveys as well. Particular attention should be paid to potential measurement error in these types of surveys as response rates tend to be low. Regardless, the goal should be to receive measurements that accurately represent customers' attitudes.

This work, however, should go beyond just collecting a sample of information (surveys, focus group meetings, plant visits, and so on). Everyone has seen the customer survey cards at hotels and restaurants that ask about customer satisfaction. But what is the validity of such an effort when considering issues such as response rate and nonrandomness of response? A four-stage model for evaluating training events devised by Kirkpatrick (2006; discussed in more detail in Chapter 2) would categorize this kind of data-gathering effort—and its validity—as reaction, or level-one evaluation. Some consider these tools to be "smiley sheets," a pejorative term referencing the halo effect, which results from the glow of the moment of the event or because the participant wants the researcher to feel good. The real question for the quality engineer should be, "What do my customers think after using the product or service for some period of time in actual real-world settings, and what are they telling other people about my organization?"

Customer Value Analysis

Gale and Wood (1994) describe seven tools of customer value analysis:

1. The market-perceived quality profile (an "indicator of how well you are performing overall for customers in your targeted market")

2. The market-perceived price profile (a weighted indicator of how customers perceive different competitors' performance on given price attributes)

3. The customer value map (a "map that reveals a sizable cluster of business units receiving premium prices that are not fully supported by superior perceived quality")

4. The won/lost analysis (an analysis of those factors that won or lost the sale)

5. The head-to-head area chart of customer value (a "chart of customer value displaying where you do well and where you do worse against a single competitor")

6. The key events timeline (a chronological list of the events that changed the market's perception of performance on each quality attribute, yours and your competitor's)

7. A what/who matrix ("a method for tracking who is responsible for the actions that will make success in customer value possible")

Using these tools will "enable an organization to navigate strategically even in confusing times." Numerous factors represent value to different customers under a variety of situations. The characteristics shown in Table 1.5 illustrate different perspectives of what the customer considers important.

Customer-driven Quality

A growing number of approaches focus on greater understanding of and interaction with customers. The two types of customer-driven quality, reactive and planned, are proving to be successful in improving quality but still do not guarantee customer satisfaction (Foster 1998). *Reactive customer-driven quality* (RCDQ) responds to customer requirements after the fact. *Planned customer-driven quality*, on the other hand, is anticipatory and proactive in that it assesses customer needs and seeks methods for satisfying those needs before the fact. Any organization wanting to meet customer expectations is pursuing a moving target. The reactive nature of the RCDQ approach will cause the supplier to fall behind the moving target.

Planned customer-driven quality is best accomplished using some form of strategic quality planning (SQP). This is not necessarily the same as the strategic planning process, however, and is one reason that the Malcolm Baldrige National Quality Award changed the name of the SQP category to strategic planning, to

Table 1.5   Customer perspectives of value.

Characteristics—product (examples)	Performance Reasonable price Durability Safety	Serviceability Ease/flexibility of use Simplicity of design, aesthetics Ease of disposal
Characteristics—service (examples)	Responsiveness Reliability Competence Access Courtesy Communication (sensitivity, genuine interest/concern)	Credibility/image Confidentiality/security Understanding the customer Accuracy/completeness Timeliness

counter the sense that some quality professionals had too narrow a focus on company competitiveness in the marketplace.

With any given effort to become a customer-driven company, an organization should study how it is perceived by its customers, which is related to organizational practices. One list of top 10 key characteristics of customer-focused companies includes:

1. Total consumer experience. The ability to look at the customer from all angles of how the organization's products and services are experienced in the real world. Look for every possible point of contact with the customer to collect information on what is happening in the field.

2. Product hits. Use of the Kano model to continually delight the customer with new products and services, some of which the customer may not even have known that they wanted.

3. Consumer loyalty. Building a sustained momentum over time to the point where the customer will use only your product or service—even waiting, if necessary, to get the "real thing."

4. Retailing and distribution. Creating a win–win–win for your organization, distributors, and customers. Your distribution system is a customer as well.

5. Brand process. The creation of recognized products or services that are sought after in the marketplace.

6. Logistics. Providing JIT and just what is needed/wanted in the marketplace at point of usage.

7. Build to demand. Creating a lean process that is capable of rapid changeovers to give the customers the needed products and services as they want them (JIT). This process has to be built into the entire system, from suppliers, through production, to the ultimate customer.

8. Consumer knowledge system. Continuous information gathering of customers' expectations and wants that feed into the system; used to look for continual improvement opportunities.

9. E-commerce. Becoming interactive and offering distribution, selling, and constant communication with customers online.

10. Growth. Continually improving with faster service, better value, and higher quality to create a culture that uses creativity and innovations to improve customer satisfaction.

To summarize, there is no sure way to always satisfy or delight customers, because one cannot talk to every individual customer and because customers are constantly changing their minds about what they need or expect. So one must find ways to continually talk with many customers using the techniques that are available. With today's technology this should become easier, but will the quality engineer be able to ensure that the information received is good enough to make sound predictions? The challenge is to keep the process both simple and informative. (See the "Quality Information Systems" section earlier in the chapter for more details on QISs.)

SUPPLIER MANAGEMENT

Many years ago, companies worked under the assumption that engineers designed products and specified requirements, suppliers provided materials, manufacturing built the products, and quality control inspected the product after it was made to ensure quality. This approach was inherently wasteful. Since the 1940s, the use of quality standards for suppliers has gradually evolved into a system that ensures quality products that meet requirements with only a limited amount of inspection by quality control personnel. MIL-Q-9858, BS 5750, industry-specific (starting in the early 1960s), and ISO 9000 standards (see Chapter 2) have each made their contribution. For example, in the automotive industry, the Automotive Industry Action Group (AIAG) manages the *Production Part Approval Process Manual* (2006), a standard that supplies a list of several elements of the manufacturing process to ensure suppliers meet their customer's requirements (e.g., design records, change documents, FMEA, and control plans). In the aerospace industry, AS9102B (2014), managed by the Society of Automotive Engineers (SAE), details requirements for first article inspection, a method to document requirements of aerospace parts between customers and suppliers.

Quality assurance personnel now spend greater effort ensuring that quality is built into products and that conformance is achieved during production. The lines are becoming more blurred as Six Sigma programs help everyone in the organization become concerned about quality and defect prevention. The same team cooperation and close communication used internally are now being applied to supplier relations. The goal is to ensure that purchased items and materials conform to requirements without the need for extensive inspection upon receipt by the purchaser and that continual improvement is being practiced (Johnson and Webber 1985).

Suppliers also can be found both internally and externally to the organization. It is important to find an effective way of communicating with all your suppliers on a regular basis and to put together an effective process and practice for supplier quality management (SQM). SQM practices may differ by industry. AlMaian et al. (2016) discuss the importance of SQM in the construction industry and discuss methods for quantitative analysis when faced with the problem of too little data due to time and budget constraints. In this section, high-level techniques, improvement, and risk for SQM are covered.

Techniques

> Apply various supplier management techniques, including supplier qualification, certification, and evaluation. (Apply)
>
> **Body of Knowledge I.H.1**

At the superficial level, surveys, audits, and inspection all have the same goal: they provide internal or external customers with a degree of confidence (but not absolute assurance) that the quality of the product or process is what it should be. However, each of these tools has its own distinctive characteristics.

Audit

As defined by ISO 9000:2015, an *audit* is a "systematic, independent and documented process for obtaining objective evidence and evaluating it objectively to determine the extent to which the audit criteria are fulfilled. The fundamental elements of an audit include the determination (3.11.1) of the conformity of an object according to a procedure carried out by personnel not being responsible for the object audited." Audits of a supplier's systems or processes can only be performed at the supplier's facility. Audits of a supplier's product may be performed at either the supplier's facility or the customer's facility.

A *system audit* is a documented activity performed on a management system to verify, by examination and evaluation of objective evidence, that applicable elements of the quality system are suitable and have been developed, documented, and effectively implemented in accordance with specified requirements (Russell 2013). A system audit examines everything within the system: the processes, products, services, and supporting groups (e.g., purchasing or customer service).

A *process audit* is an analysis of elements of a process and appraisal of completeness, correctness, conditions, and probable effectiveness. A process audit in this context is usually a manufacturing process or service delivery process as opposed to something like a calibration process or a supplier qualification process. It is done to ensure that the processes are working within established limits. Unlike a system audit, a process audit covers only a small portion of the total system and therefore often takes less time to complete than a system audit. Furthermore, "a process audit checks the adequacy and effectiveness of the process controls established by procedures, work instructions, flowcharts, and training and process specifications" (Russell 2013).

A *product audit* is "an examination of a particular product or service (hardware, processed material, software) to evaluate whether it conforms to requirements (that is, specifications, performance standards, and customer requirements)" (Russell 2013). The product audit verifies that the system and processes used to produce the product are capable of producing a product that conforms to the established specifications/requirements. Product audits are performed after the product has been completed and has passed final inspection; therefore, this method should not be confused with the term "inspection," which concerns the acceptance or rejection of the product or lot. In a product audit, the product or service is examined in terms of form, fit, and function after it has passed final inspection. Put another way, the product audit reviews that everything that was supposed to happen to the product being held in your hand was in fact properly executed.

Audits can also be used to assess change control of products and configuration management programs. A product audit is used to ensure configured products or services meet specifications and perform as required. A process audit can also be used on the configuration process to verify the process is appropriate and maintained (Russell 2013).

Sampling Inspection

Inspection is a process of measuring, examining, testing, gauging, or otherwise comparing a unit with the applicable requirements. Sampling inspection is somewhat comparable to surveys and audits, while 100% inspection is somewhat comparable to production line operation because every item is subjected to it. (See Chapter 4 for inspection and sampling.)

One hundred percent inspection is required in certain highly critical processes and in processes that produce unavoidable defects, such as semiconductor fabrication. Generally, 100% inspections done by people are not completely effective. Thus, in today's industrial environment, 100% inspections are nearly always automated. Several types of sampling inspection include the following:

Acceptance sampling is sampling where decisions are made to accept or reject a product or service based on the results of inspected samples.

Skip-lot inspection is an acceptance sampling plan in which some lots in a series are accepted without inspection because the sampling results for a stated number of immediately preceding lots met stated criteria. Explanation of this methodology is found in American National Standard, ANSI/ASQ S1-2012.

Incoming inspection is the inspection of purchased parts at the customer's facility, after the shipment of parts from the supplier, to ensure supplier compliance with specifications and contractual agreements.

Source inspection is the inspection of purchased parts at the supplier's facility by a customer representative to ensure supplier compliance with specifications and contractual agreements.

Survey

The *survey* can be defined as a broad overview of a supplier's system and/or processes that is used to evaluate the adequacy of that system or processes to produce quality products (Laford 1986). A *system survey* is used to assess whether the supplier has appropriately controlled systems that will adequately prevent the manufacture of nonconforming products. A *process survey* is used to evaluate whether a supplier has controls in place to ensure that the process will manufacture quality products. Process controls include proper tooling, equipment, inspection, and so on.

The primary purpose of a survey of a supplier or potential supplier is to ascertain whether the supplier has adequate financial resources (evaluated by purchasing), adequate manufacturing capabilities (evaluated by manufacturing engineering), and adequate quality systems (evaluated by the quality assurance group). Although a supplier survey and a supplier audit may be almost the same, a distinction is often drawn as a survey is conducted prior to a formal contractual relationship, and audits are performed after a formal, contractual relationship is in place between the parties.

In preparing for the survey, the team leader should obtain as much information about the supplier as possible. The purchasing agent can provide copies of the supplier's annual reports, credit investigation, Dun & Bradstreet reports,

Internet searches, certifications, and so on. A facilities and equipment list should be obtained for review by manufacturing engineering, and a copy of the supplier's quality manual must also be reviewed prior to the survey.

The survey team may be made up of members from purchasing, manufacturing, and quality control, plus various specialists in the areas of nondestructive testing, product design, or other special processes. At times, the team may consist of only the quality professional. In the latter case, the purchasing agent usually has previously evaluated the supplier's financial status.

It is important that the team meet prior to arriving at the supplier's facility. Based on the premise that the team has reviewed all pertinent materials, the pre-survey meeting is held to (1) ensure that all of the team members agree on the theme and purpose of the survey, (2) ensure that the roles and responsibilities of each team member are understood by the others, (3) draft a preliminary survey agenda, and (4) select the team leader.

The team leader must not overlook the obvious, such as the supplier's current address, name of host individual to contact, correct time and date for the survey, and so on. It is important that the team leader verify that the supplier is ready for the survey. Often it is appropriate to advise the supplier of the proposed agenda, allowing supplier representatives to prepare for the visit.

To quantify the results of a survey, there must be a formalized approach for collecting data and evaluating the systems observed. The primary method of quantification is for the survey team to use a checklist to record survey results. Checklists commonly used cover both procurement and manufacturing/quality aspects of a supplier's organization.

The manufacturing/quality checklists often are broken into the following categories:

1. Drawing and specification control

2. Purchased material control

3. Measuring and test equipment control

4. Process control and product acceptance

5. Material storage area, packing, shipping, and record retention control

6. Quality program management

7. Statistical process control

8. Strength summary of system survey

9. Corrective action summary of system survey

10. Summary report

The manufacturing/quality categories may be expanded as needed. An amplification of the listed categories can be found in Laford (1986) in References.

The supplier procurement checklist often is broken down into the following categories:

1. General information

2. Product information

3. Facilities and equipment information

4. Sales, shipping, and payment information

The supplier procurement checklist categories may be expanded as needed. An amplification of the list can be found in Laford (1986).

The use of scoring (numerical, alphabetical, or other regularly sequenced scores) in a checklist further enhances quantification and validity of judgments. Many professional evaluators prefer to have the supplier also score a copy of the checklist to better compare the customer's viewpoint with that of the supplier's.

The opening conference is get-acquainted time. The survey team members should explain why they are there, what they are going to attempt to do, and, in a general way, the sort of results they expect. Each team member should explain his or her role in the survey and in the customer's organization. The team leader also should briefly explain the nature of the customer's products or services. It is essential that all levels of supplier management understand the scope and purpose of the survey (Vendor-Vendee Technical Committee 1977).

Each supplier representative present should explain his or her role in the supplier organization. At this time, the supplier representatives also should briefly describe the nature of the products manufactured and present an overview of the company and systems used. The opening conference also is a good time for the survey team to brief the supplier on the intended products to be purchased.

A brief plant tour will acquaint the survey team with the supplier's overall operations. Following the plant tour, the team members can proceed to their respective areas for evaluation. Each area should be evaluated in detail in accordance with the checklist and point scores recorded. It is imperative that each area be evaluated in the actual area and not in the conference room or manager's office. Furthermore, by being in the appropriate area, verbal statements of compliance and quality procedures can be verified by witnessing the action being performed. The survey team should discuss any negative findings with the supplier escort who was present during the finding to reconfirm the facts prior to the closing conference with supplier top management.

Prior to the closing conference, the survey team must meet to compile the report for that conference (this is not the final report). During the closing conference, the team leader should review each category, expressing the strengths and weaknesses observed. At this time it may be possible to estimate corrective actions required for deficiencies found if they have not already been addressed.

The closing conference must be kept on a positive note, with a win–win attitude on both sides, which requires careful attention to communication strategies and can challenge the team leader's communication skills. In the closing conference, the team leader should focus on the major deficiencies found, if any, and detail appropriate corrective actions. This should be followed by a brief mention of any minor deficiencies observed. All can be lost if the survey team presents an extensive list of minor observations with a few major deficiencies intertwined.

If at all possible, the survey team should leave a draft copy of the survey report with the supplier. By doing so, any questions can be cleared up immediately. It is much more difficult to clarify misunderstandings when a copy of the final report is received a month or more later.

The end product of the survey or quality program evaluation should be an understandable final report. A good report effectively communicates the findings, using the original observations to support the conclusions. The report must be an honest, objective summation of the team's efforts.

The report should detail the following:

1. All individuals present and their correct titles

2. The areas evaluated

3. Any major deficiencies requiring written corrective action

4. Any minor deficiencies

5. A summary that states the conclusion, for example, approval, conditional approval (corrective actions that should be addressed), or disapproval

6. A closing statement expressing appreciation for the supplier's assistance and cooperation

Survey follow-up is carried out to ensure that a supplier that did not qualify at the time of the survey visit has taken satisfactory corrective action. The customer may have to judge whether a follow-up visit is warranted. A report from the supplier, accompanied by suitable documentation of corrective actions taken, may be adequate.

Evaluation

Rating a supplier's capabilities involves rating or evaluating (1) the supplier's system (financial, manufacturing, and quality) and (2) the supplier's delivered product. Other considerations to take into account include the amount of effort, time, and cost necessary to replace a supplier, the ability of the supplier to deliver material on time, the location in the world of the supplier's manufacturing facility, and the importance of the material to the producer's product.

The rating of a supplier's system usually begins with the initial supplier survey (as discussed above). Often, the initial survey is followed up with a periodic supplier resurvey, called a systems audit. The audit provides the customer with an opportunity to evaluate the supplier's systems over time so that any deterioration is noticed immediately.

The rating of a supplier's delivered product basically takes the form of recording, in some predetermined manner, the results of incoming inspections and the results of rejections within the customer's manufacturing process. It also can include failures caused by the supplier's delivered products that appeared during the customer's manufacturing cycle or while the product was in service.

Supplier rating elements and formulas are as diverse as companies are. The common aspects are quality, price, and delivery.

The quality factor usually includes quality lot rating, quality part rating, comparison with competition, complexity analysis, and economic conditions, where

$$\text{Quality lot rating} = \frac{\text{Number of lots rejected}}{\text{Number of lots inspected}}$$

and

$$\text{Quality part rating} = \frac{\text{Number of parts rejected}}{\text{Number of parts inspected}}$$

The delivery factor usually includes a timeliness rating and completeness rating. The timeliness rating is based on the due date of the lot minus some demerit (e.g., 10%) for each day the lot is early or late beyond some specified grace period or window (e.g., due date ± two working days). It is important to note that if the supplier chooses the freight carrier, the system can base the due date on the date the lot is received on the customer's dock. If the customer chooses the freight carrier, however, the due date should be measured by the date shipped from the supplier.

$$\text{The completeness rating} = \frac{\text{Number of parts actually received}}{\text{Number of parts scheduled to be received}}$$

An overall rating, for example, can be derived by assigning percentages to the aforementioned aspects of quality, price, and delivery and taking a weighted average.

Quality rating = 0.40(Quality lot rating) + 0.60(Quality part rating)
Price rating = 0.40(Comparison level) + 0.30(Complexity level) + 0.30(Economic condition)
Delivery rating = 0.50(Timeliness rating) + 0.50(Completeness rating)

The next step is to assign weights to the three main factors. For example:

Overall supplier rating = 0.40(Quality rating) + 0.30(Price rating) + 0.30(Delivery rating)

This generic example can be expanded into an elaborate computerized system. It also can be tailored for use by smaller businesses that may still have manual systems.

Improvement

Analyze supplier ratings and performance improvement results. (Analyze)

Body of Knowledge I.H.2

The purchasing organization usually tracks and monitors suppliers. A special supplier quality assurance (SQA) group may be formed to work with the buyer to look at suppliers' performance. Some common supplier information includes:

- Defective parts per million (ppm)
- Cost adjustment requests
- Delivery date slippages
- Performance improvement
- Adherence to quality system requirements

Using metrics such as the above, a QIS can generate reports such as supplier profiles by select criteria. Suppliers can be ranked by defective ppm, improvement, or similar metrics. Preferred suppliers can then be selected using quantitative data instead of guesswork and politics.

Ideally, suppliers are treated like partners in satisfying customers. This requires a mature organization with objective information. Communication skills, careful fact gathering, and a good QIS are all needed to achieve this goal. You and your suppliers should keep constant communication open on many fronts to ensure that everything is working well to delight the ultimate customer.

Risk

> Understand business continuity, resiliency, and contingency planning. (Understand)
>
> **Body of Knowledge I.H.3**

Standards and specifications are documents containing criteria that must be met, and these documents become legally binding by reference on the purchase order. They define what is being purchased from the supplier. They can be in the form of engineering drawings, catalog descriptions, or other documentation. The purchaser need not always develop original specifications. Commercial quality specifications are available and range from detailed engineering drawings (which may include references to process specifications, such as reliability verifications and inspection requirements) to off-the-shelf items (which are defined by the characteristics on the manufacturer's data sheet or catalog). Such commercial specifications help simplify the procurement process.

It is important that the applicable standard or specification document be incorporated into the purchase order so that there is no doubt that the requirements are to be met. If they are not incorporated, there is no basis for enforcing compliance. This helps to ensure business continuity and minimize risk associated with the supplier materials or items.

It is important to include contingency plans related to supplier purchases. See Chapter 7 for detailed information regarding risk management, which can be applied to suppliers as well as internally.

BARRIERS TO QUALITY IMPROVEMENT

> Identify barriers to quality improvement, analyze their causes and impact, and implement methods for improvement. (Analyze)
>
> **Body of Knowledge I.I**

An organization with a properly implemented total QMS will have fewer nonconformities, reduced rework and scrap, lower inventory levels, reduced cycle times, greater employee satisfaction, and increased customer satisfaction. Organizations that are not able to overcome the barriers or obstacles to quality improvement will not experience these benefits. In a study by Salegna and Fazel (2000), managers of TQM companies ranked 12 obstacles to implementing quality. These barriers or obstacles follow in order of importance:

1. Lack of time to devote to quality initiatives. Frequently, managers are too busy with their regular activities to take on an additional activity such as quality. Initially, senior management must provide time for employees to devote to the quality initiative. Once a program is well established, the quality activity will become part of the employees' activities.

2. Poor intra-organizational communication. All organizations communicate with their employees in one manner or another. Communications deliver the organization's values, expectations, and directions, provide information about developments, and allow feedback from all levels. The organization must encourage and provide the means for two-way communication so that information flows up as well as down the ladder.

3. Lack of real employee empowerment. Too often, empowerment is merely lip service. Individuals should be empowered to make decisions that affect the efficiency of their process or the satisfaction of their customers. Teams need to have the proper training and, at least in the beginning, a facilitator.

4. Lack of employee trust in senior management. In many organizations, this obstacle will not be a problem because senior management has created an atmosphere of trust in its relationship with the employees. In other organizations, this atmosphere will have to be developed by management being honest with the employees.

5. Politics and turf issues. Differences between departments and between individuals create problems. The use of multifunctional teams will help break down long-standing barriers. Restructuring to make the organization more responsive to customer needs may be needed. An example of restructuring is the use of product or customer support teams whose members are permanently reassigned from the areas of quality, production, design, and marketing.

6. Lack of a formalized strategic plan for change. A formalized plan for change is necessary because individuals resist change. They become accustomed to performing a process in a particular way and it becomes the preferred way. Management must understand and utilize these basic concepts of change:

   — People change when they want to and to meet their own needs

   — Never expect anyone to engage in behavior that serves the organization's values unless an adequate reason (why) has been given

— For change to be accepted, people must be moved from a state of fear to one of trust

It is difficult for individuals to change their own behavior, and it is much more difficult for an organization. Honest two-way communication with respectful feedback increases the chances of success.

7. Lack of strong motivation. The building of a motivated workforce is, for the most part, an indirect process. Management at all levels cannot cause an employee to become motivated; they must create a conducive environment for individuals to become motivated.

8. View of quality program as a quick fix. Frequently, the quality program is viewed as a quick fix. Quality improvement is a race that does not have a finish. Management must constantly and forever improve the system so that quality and productivity are continually and permanently improved and costs reduced.

9. Drive for short-term financial results. Too often, organizations focus their efforts on the quarterly financial results. Quality improvement requires an organization to have a strong future orientation and a willingness to make long-term commitments.

10. Lack of leadership. For any organizational effort to succeed, there must be leadership. Leadership requires a substantial commitment in terms of both management time and organizational resources.

11. Lack of customer focus. Organizations need to understand the changing needs and expectations of their internal and external customers. Effective feedback mechanisms are necessary for this understanding.

12. Lack of a company-wide definition of quality. This obstacle is the least of the 12 and is easy to correct. Experienced quality professionals recommend that all areas of the organization be involved in writing the definition.

Overcoming these barriers to change can be difficult. Some ways of overcoming the barriers outlined here are self-explanatory. For example, if there is a lack of leadership in an organization, especially leadership interested in quality, then change will not occur unless new leadership is established. Other ways of dealing with barriers can be accomplished with change management. A *change agent* is someone responsible for managing change activities (Robbins and Judge 2012). Change agents can be successful when making changes regarding structure, technology, physical setting, and people. A change agent who is interested in improving quality in an organization can be very effective. To overcome a lack of time, a strategic process for selecting quality projects should be implemented and supported by leadership, and time for supporting quality projects should be built into the employees' work day. This type of strategic planning is a fundamental principle in many continuous improvement methodologies, including Six Sigma.

Chapter 2
The Quality System

A quality system is the enabling mechanism behind the quality assurance and improvement functions of any organization. It is a statement of commitment to quality and tells how quality is to be achieved. The term "system" implies functional elements, attributes, and relationships. Chapter 1 explained quality management and leadership. In this chapter, the quality system, its elements, and how they are documented are discussed. Also introduced are recognized standards that define or recommend quality systems, as well as quality audits. Quality is intrinsically related to cost, so the most prominent quality cost systems are explained. Finally, since training can be considered a quality system, an overview of the role of the quality engineer in quality training is provided.

ELEMENTS OF THE QUALITY SYSTEM

The basic elements of a quality system are planning, control, and improvement. These elements span the entire process and are present regardless of the type of organization or industry implementing quality initiatives. In this section, these elements are briefly introduced these elements along with the basic design of the strategic plan used to ensure that implementation of these elements is successful.

The elements of the quality system pertain to all functions in the organization. Four functions are described below with a brief discussion of how quality applies to each.

1. Quality in marketing. The marketing function is an important source of information regarding the implied and stated needs of the customer, actual field performance, and the degree of customers' satisfaction with the product. Such information will help identify product problems relative to expectations and initiate corrective measures. Consequently, the marketing function is required to define and document the requirements for a quality product, provide the organization with a formal statement or outline of product requirements, and establish an information feedback system for monitoring field performance on a continuous basis.

2. Quality in specification and design. With the customers' needs clearly identified, the design function provides the translation of these needs into technical specifications. Formal plans should be prepared and documented for identifying critical stages of the design process and

assigning responsibility for each. Design reviews should be conducted at the end of each stage to identify problem areas and initiate corrective actions. All necessary measures should be taken to ensure clear and definitive statements of the design requirements. Methods for evaluating conformance during production should also be specified. Design verification and validation through prototype testing or other techniques is required. Provisions should be made for periodic evaluation of the design in light of field performance data.

3. Quality in purchasing. The standard requires that all purchasing activities be planned and controlled by documented procedures. Successful purchase of supplies begins with clear definition of the requirements. A close working relationship with vendors and subcontractors is required to facilitate and secure continuous quality improvements. Procedures must be established for evaluating the capability of the vendors. In some cases, the vendor is required to establish a demonstrated capability of meeting design requirements. If incoming inspection is to be performed, the costs involved should be considered and the vendor should be notified of the results.

4. Quality of processes. This element stipulates the requirements of operation under controlled conditions. The operation of processes and the operating conditions should be specified by documented work instructions. Process capability studies are recommended to determine the effectiveness of the process and to identify the need for improvements (see Chapter 6 for more information).

Basic Elements

> Interpret the basic elements of a quality system, including planning, control, and improvement, from product and process design through quality cost systems and audit programs. (Evaluate)
>
> **Body of Knowledge II.A.1**

The elements of a quality system are the activities used to ensure customer satisfaction. Typically, these activities depend on the type of organization, its structure, the market, and the particular type of product or service provided. The basic elements of a quality system (planning, control, and improvement) are relevant from product and process design through quality cost systems and audit programs.

Quality-related activities start with identifying customer needs and extend throughout the life cycle of the product, as depicted in Figure 2.1. The procedures and work instructions followed within each of these functional areas to achieve the stated quality objectives represent elements of the quality system. It is important

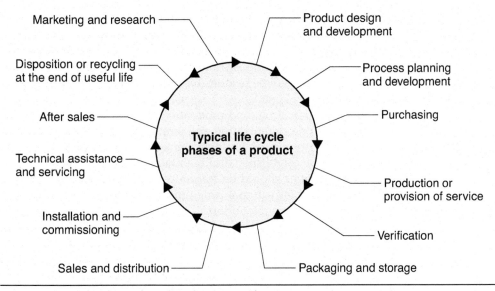

Figure 2.1 Product life cycle and quality system elements.
Source: Adapted from ANSI/ISO/ASQC Q9004-1-1994. Used with permission.

to note that the suitability and effectiveness of the system as a whole are determined by the attributes of these individual elements and their relationships. Top management must establish, document, and maintain such systems with the overall objectives in mind.

System elements closely correspond to the various phases in the traditional product life cycle depicted in Figure 2.1. In other words, a quality system must cover all the activities that affect product or service quality. ISO 9004:2018 (2018) organizes quality management in the following elements: managing for the sustained success of an organization, strategy and policy, resource management, process management, monitoring, measurement, analysis, review, improvement, innovation, and learning. These elements are critical for managing quality and for the long-term success of an organization. In the following subsections, planning, improvement, and control of the quality system are discussed.

Planning

Planning a quality system is critical to address risks and opportunities in an organization. As described in ISO 9001:2015 (2015), there are three main goals of planning for a quality system: planning actions to address risks and opportunities, planning to achieve quality objectives, and planning changes. Planning for risks and opportunities (1) gives assurance that the quality system can achieve its intended results, (2) enhances desirable effects, (3) prevents or reduces undesired effects, and (4) achieves improvements. Addressing risks includes avoiding risks, taking risks to pursue an opportunity, eliminating risk, reducing risk, sharing risk, or accepting risk. Risk management is discussed in more detail in Chapter 7. Planning for opportunities may include adopting new practices, launching new products, opening new markets, seeking new customers, building partnerships, and using new technology.

Organizations should plan how to achieve quality objectives. These objectives should be documented and be consistent with policy, measurable, relevant, monitored, communicated, and updated as needed; they should also take into account any requirements. Organizations should identify what will be done, what resources will be needed, who will be responsible, when items will be completed, and how the results will be evaluated.

Employee training, qualification, and motivation are key factors in developing the human resources of an organization and emphasizing quality awareness among them. Documented procedures for identifying and providing training programs at all levels should be established and maintained. Periodic assessment of personnel skills and capabilities should be considered. Recognition of proper job performance and the use of motivational programs are ways in which management can support quality improvement efforts.

Organizations should plan for when changes will be required to the quality system. As discussed in ISO 9001:2015, the organization should consider the purpose of the changes and their potential consequences, the integrity of the quality system, the availability of resources, and the allocation of responsibilities.

Finally, procedures are needed for identifying the safety aspects of products and processes. These aspects are best identified and considered during the design phase of the product life cycle. Further, the rule of strict liability has created a need to plan for field failures and their legal implications. These procedures may include documenting prototype and product design evaluation testing for safety, providing adequate operational instructions with warnings against known hazards, and developing contingency plans for product recall. Failure modes and effects analysis (FMEA), fault tree analysis, and hazard function analysis are all valuable tools for assessing risk (see Chapter 3 for details).

Control and Improvement

Control of processes is a central element in achieving conformance to design requirements. The type and sensitivity of the control technique depend on the quality characteristic involved or generated, the nature and stability of the process, and its potential capability. Control should extend over the material and parts used, tooling and any shop aids utilized, and environmental conditions. Proper identification of materials from the time of receipt to product delivery and installation is required. Statistical techniques for monitoring process variables are a crucial and extremely important element of the quality system. The analytical techniques used to measure, control, and improve quality throughout the product life cycle include design of experiments, estimation, tests of significance, control charts, and sampling inspection. All of these techniques are discussed in detail in Chapter 6. The control chart is one of the most useful techniques for understanding whether a process is in statistical control and how it is behaving with respect to tolerance limits required by the process.

Control charts are useful for studying a process over time and can be used for both variable critical-to-quality measures (e.g., the diameter of an arterial stent) and attributes (e.g., whether the stent contains a defect). Defects can be labeled as nonconformities. Documented procedures for dealing with nonconforming units should be established and maintained. These procedures include steps for the identification, segregation, and review of the nonconformities. The objective is to avoid the unintended use of such units and the consequent dissatisfaction of internal and external customers. Product verification addresses the allocation of test and inspection points in the process for the purpose of verifying conformance. Verification of incoming materials and products at various stages of the process prevents the unnecessary cost of further processing nonconforming units. Final product verification is performed to prevent shipping nonconforming units to customers.

In addition to the process and output being in control, all measuring systems used in the development, production, and installation of products should be controlled. Documented procedures should be established to maintain the measuring process in a state of statistical control. The procedure includes initial calibration against a reference standard as well as periodic recall for adjustment and recalibration, and may be extended to all vendors.

Post-production activities, including procedures for product storage, delivery, and installation activities, can prevent deterioration of product quality, secure proper identification, and safeguard against improper installation. Also, the quality system should allow for feedback of information regarding field performance, customer satisfaction, and the initiation of corrective actions.

A quality system should define the responsibility and authority for instituting corrective actions. These actions should be planned after identifying the root causes of the problem. Actions to eliminate these causes may involve a variety of functions such as design, purchasing, production, and quality control. The objective should be to prevent the recurrence of these causes and improve quality. Corrective action is required to monitor the effect of actions and ensure a high quality is obtained.

Quality records are records that indicate the results of implementing the system and provide subjective means for evaluating its effectiveness. An organization is required to establish and maintain documented procedures for identification, collection, storage, retrieval, and disposition of these records. Analysis of the quality records can help identify trends in quality performance, as well as the need for and effectiveness of corrective actions, and thus is useful for improvement. In addition, records should indicate authorized changes to the quality manual and any modifications made in the procedures or work instructions. Documentation systems are discussed in the "Documentation of the Quality System" section of this chapter.

Design

> Analyze the design and alignment of interrelated processes to the strategic plan and core processes. (Analyze)
>
> **Body of Knowledge II.A.2**

The design of the quality system should be related to the strategic plan and core processes within an organization. This means that quality initiatives and plans should be part of the management system. Montgomery (2013) argues that the effective management of quality involves successful execution of three activities: quality planning, quality assurance, and quality control/improvement.

Quality planning is a strategic activity that involves identifying the needs of the customer. This activity relies on the combined efforts of management, employees, and customers (internal and external). Determining how the needs of the customers will be achieved should be included in the quality plan.

Quality assurance is the set of activities associated with achieving and maintaining products and/or services that meet the needs of both the business and the customer. Documentation during this activity is important for successful quality efforts. Documenting is discussed in detail in "Document of the Quality System."

Quality control/improvement activities are those used to ensure, improve, and maintain a level of quality that is appropriate for the organization. These activities often involve statistical methods such as statistical process control (SPC), design of experiments, and acceptance sampling. All of these statistical methods are discussed in detail in Chapter 6 of this handbook. Continuous improvement methods such as Six Sigma and lean, among others, can also be utilized in a quality system. See Chapter 5 for details on these and other continuous improvement methodologies.

DOCUMENTATION OF THE QUALITY SYSTEM

It is important to have appropriate and detailed documentation of the quality system in use. ISO 9000 defines a *document* as "information and the medium on which it is contained." Documented information includes any goals, policies, procedures, and other meaningful data required to be controlled and maintained by the organization and the medium on which it is contained. A common document is a specification, which states any requirements. As discussed in ISO 9000:2015, specifications may be related to processes or products. Regular checks to ensure that the documentation is up to date and still pertains to the existing practice are important. A *quality plan* is "the specification of the procedures and associated resources to be applied when and by whom to a specific object" (ISO 9000:2015). Quality plans often reference sections in the quality manual. The quality manual and supporting documentation are discussed in more detail in the following section, along with document components and document control.

Document Components

> Identify and describe quality system documentation components, including quality policies and procedures to support the system. (Understand)
>
> **Body of Knowledge II.B.1**

Plans for achieving customer satisfaction and ensuring that the quality of products or services is documented in a quality manual are sometimes referred to as the quality program, which represents the first of two major system efforts: documentation and implementation. A *quality manual* is the "specification for the quality management system of an organization" (ISO 9000:2015). Compliance, accuracy, and clarity are critical characteristics of documentation. Although there are several ways to structure quality system documentation within or under a quality manual, one generic method is to create a structure of four tiers—also known as the documentation hierarchy or pyramid—as illustrated in Figure 2.2. Starting from the top, these tiers are policies, procedures, work instructions, and quality records.

The first tier represents policies, which may begin with an overall organizational quality policy statement explaining what the company stands for and what its commitments are. This may be the opening statement of the quality manual, indicating the management policy and objectives for quality. There may also be policy statements or brief documents for each of the requirements of applicable standards. Such policies may be contained within the quality manual or be separate documents.

The second documentation tier is procedures and provides an overview of how a company conducts its business. Direct yet simple statements indicate who is responsible for what in achieving the requirements. In some cases, the procedures will be in the quality manual, but more often they will be distributed, often online.

The third tier represents work instructions, which spell out the how-to in a clear manner. An organization may choose to include detailed work instructions or exclude proprietary information. Work instructions are documented in many ways, depending on the function at hand.

Finally, the fourth tier shows the results obtained by implementing the quality system. These results are documented and maintained to form quality records. These records provide subjective evidence that the system has been implemented

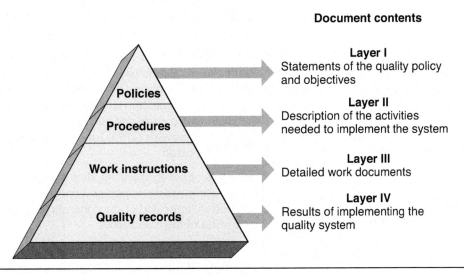

Document contents

Layer I
Statements of the quality policy and objectives

Layer II
Description of the activities needed to implement the system

Layer III
Detailed work documents

Layer IV
Results of implementing the quality system

Policies

Procedures

Work instructions

Quality records

Figure 2.2   Tiers of the quality documentation hierarchy.

and is effective. Records must be maintained for a specified time in a protected format retrievable for analysis.

A simple way to remember the distinction between documents and records would be that a blank controlled form or template is a document, but once that form or template is used to record data or results, then it becomes a record. Records should have unique numbers just as quality system documents do.

The documentation of a quality management system need not be partitioned into four separate parts to include the four tiers; this is only a model. The structure of the quality management system documentation is best selected based on the nature of the organization and applicable standards and requirements. In a small organization, a separation between the work instructions and the procedures may not be necessary, as it would be for a large organization. However, if the tiers are separated, it is important to provide cross-references or links between the tiers to ensure effective documentation. Identifying the "parent/child" relationships between tiers of documents is essential to trace connections within the quality system. For example, the parent document for a local design control work instruction may be the global design control procedure, which itself may be the child document of a global design control policy, a policy that may be its own separate document or be contained in the quality manual. ISO 10013:2021 is a great resource that provides much more guidance on methods to structure and document information in a quality management system.

Document Control

> Evaluate configuration management, maintenance, and document control to manage work instructions and quality records. (Evaluate)
>
> **Body of Knowledge II.B.2**

Upon the completion of the quality manual, a final review to determine its competence, accuracy, and clarity is undertaken. Top management should endorse the contents of the reviewed copy and authorize its release. The quality manual should be communicated and distributed in total or by section to intended users throughout the organization. Proper distribution and control can be aided, for example, by a dedicated document control function. Parsowith (1995) identifies the following four requirements for proper document control:

1. A process is in place for the *generation of documents* that includes the writing of the policies and procedures, drawings and specifications or other required documentation, approval of the contents of the documents, and the distribution of the documents

2. *Documentation* fulfilling the needs of contractual or process requirements is available at all locations in which these functions are performed

3. A process is in place for the *control of revisions* to or redistribution of documents using the same system as the original document distribution

4. A process is in place for the *identification* and *removal* of obsolete documents to ensure against unintended use

QUALITY STANDARDS AND OTHER GUIDELINES

> Apply national and international standards and other requirements and guidelines, including the Malcolm Baldrige National Quality Award (MBNQA), and describe key points of the ISO 9000 series of standards. [Note: Industry-specific standards will not be tested.] (Apply)
>
> **Body of Knowledge II.C**

The concept of national standards, which spelled out requirements for how things were to be done in the production of goods and services, grew hand-in-hand with the industrialization of national economies. One of the first national standards was a boiler standard, issued late in the nineteenth century by the American Society of Mechanical Engineers. Over time, different nations adopted standards that, while entirely appropriate to their own national needs, were in conflict with those of other nations, which meant that a company would have to either customize its operations to different national standards (which could become very inefficient and expensive) or forfeit the opportunity to do business in some countries.

These conflicts between different national standards naturally gave rise to the concept of international standards. Around the beginning of the twentieth century, when electricity became a powerful force in many different countries, an international standards organization, the International Electrotechnical Institute, was established. This organization provided precedence for the later establishment of the International Organization for Standardization, familiarly known as ISO. In the 1970s and 1980s, as global commerce became a matter of interest to more than a hundred countries and thousands of companies, a major cooperative effort of international quality professionals led to the ISO 9000 family of standards. ISO is an independent, nongovernmental international organization based in Geneva, Switzerland, with a membership of over 160 national standards bodies (https://www.iso.org/home.html).

There has been some critique of the effectiveness of the ISO 9000 series and of industry-specific standards because of their focus on formal documentation of the quality system. Montgomery (2013) argues that with the primary focus on documentation, not enough attention is always paid to quality improvement and that ISO certification does not guarantee quality products are produced.

The ISO 9000 Family

ISO 9000:2015 refers to both a family of three related standards and one of the standards in that family. The purpose of this family is "to assist organizations, of all types and sizes, to implement and operate effective quality management systems"; the family consists of three standards: quality management vocabulary, requirements, and guidelines for performance.

- *ISO 9000: Quality management systems—fundamentals and vocabulary* provides the fundamental concepts, principles, and terminology of quality management systems

- *ISO 9001: Quality management systems—requirements* specifies the needed requirements for an organization to provide products that aim to enhance customer satisfaction

- *ISO 9004: Quality Management – Quality of an Organization – Guidance to Achieving Sustained Success* suggests ways to improve organizational performance and customer satisfaction beyond the requirements of ISO 9001

The ISO 9000 standards are based on seven quality management principles:

1. **Customer focus.** Understand customer needs, meet their requirements, and strive to exceed their expectations

2. **Leadership.** Establish unity of purpose and direction and create conditions in which people are engaged in achieving the organization's quality objectives

3. **Engagement of people.** Recognize, empower, and enhance competence to help people at all levels have a sense of ownership and involvement in achieving quality objectives

4. **Process approach.** Understand how interrelated processes combine and affect each other to optimize the system

5. **Continual improvement.** Maintain the ideal of continually improving all aspects of the organization to maintain current performance, to react to internal and external conditions, and to create new opportunities

6. **Evidence-based decision making.** Facts, evidence, and data analysis provide better objectivity and confidence in decision making

7. **Relationship management.** All relevant, interested parties influence performance, including suppliers, customers, providers, employees, investors, society as a whole, and so on

ISO standards are reviewed every five years and revised if needed. These revisions are made to adapt to changing environments, to reflect increasingly complex organizations in the global market, and to ensure that new standards reflect the changing needs of all interested parties. The latest edition of the ISO 9000 family was published in September 2015 with ISO 9001:2015 replacing ISO 9001:2008, which replaced ISO 9001:2000 (which itself replaced ISO 9001:1994). The major changes from ISO 9001:2005 to ISO 9001:2015 are summarized by Cianfrani and West (2015) in *ISO 9001:2015 Explained*.

The following sections are overviews of the three standards that make up what is commonly referred to as the ISO 9000 family.

ISO 9000:2015 Fundamentals and Vocabulary

This document is the language foundation for the entire worldwide system of development, implementation, auditing, and registration of ISO 9001:2015. It proposes a well-defined quality management system (QMS) "based on a framework that integrates established fundamental concepts, principles, processes, and resources related to quality, in order to help organizations realize their objectives. Its aim is to increase an organization's awareness of its duties and commitment in fulfilling the needs and expectations of its customers and interested parties, and in achieving satisfaction with its products and services."

The standard contains definitions of terms based on many person-years of research and consultation. In all, 146 concepts and their associated terms are organized in conceptual order in the following 14 categories: person or people, organization, activity, process, system, requirement, result, data, information and document, customer, characteristic, determination, action, and audits.

The standard differentiates between a concept and a term as follows: a *concept* is a unit of knowledge created by a unique combination of characteristics; a *term* is the verbal designation of the concept as it applies to a specific field of study.

Two criteria apply to all of the ISO 9000 terms and definitions:

1. Avoid technical language in technical descriptions

2. Employ a coherent and harmonized vocabulary that is understood by all actual and potential users

Because the standards are translated into many different languages, it is critical that all users have the same understanding of what the terms mean. This goal has been accomplished by having representatives from more than 100 countries intimately involved in polishing the definitions. A good example of the need for this kind of language-specific polishing is the term "interested party." In English, a more common term would be "stakeholder." However, in some languages, a literal translation of "stakeholder" is "someone holding a stick." Many such conflicts and ambiguities have been resolved over the years.

ISO 9001:2015 Requirements

This document is the set of requirements that organizations must satisfy to achieve ISO 9001 registration or certification. Such registration is required in some industries and highly regarded in many others. Over 140 countries have ISO 9001 registration programs. Many people inadvertently refer to this key document as "ISO 9000:2015." Remember: ISO 9000 refers to a family of three documents (9000, 9001, and 9004); ISO 9001 refers to the requirements document. ISO 9001:2015 is the only standard in the 9000 family that allows an organization to be certified. When a new edition is published, an organization wishing to remain ISO 9001 certified must update its QMS so that it conforms to the new standard. The organization must then seek certification to the new standard; there is a grace period to allow time for organizations to make all necessary changes.

ISO 9001:2015 has several major changes compared with the previous edition. First, the structure of this standard was changed so that it follows the same overall structure as other ISO management system standards (called High-Level Structure). This restructuring was implemented to make it easier for organizations to unify multiple management systems.

In addition to making the standard more user-friendly for service- and knowledge-based organizations, other major changes include emphasis on the following (ISO 9001:2015):

- Leadership engagement

- Organizational risks and opportunities in a structured manner

- Addressing supply chain management more effectively

- Understanding the organization's context: "one size does not fit all"

- Process-oriented approach

- Preventive action and risk identification and mitigation

- Seeking opportunities for improvement

- Managing processes in a planned manner

ISO 9001:2015 also updates various terminology used in previous editions of this international standard (e.g., ISO 9001:2008). For example, "products" has been updated to "products and services," and "purchased product" has been updated to "externally provided products and services." These changes were made to improve alignment with other management systems standards. Note that there is not a requirement for an organization to apply the structure and terminology of the standard to the organization's QMS. The standard serves as the list of requirements, not a model for documenting the organization's policies and objectives.

The standard has 10 major parts, or clauses. The first three are general clauses:

1. Scope. This tells what organization(s), location(s), process(es), product(s), and so on, are covered

2. Normative references. These cite other standards that, by being listed, constitute provisions of the ISO 9001 standard

3. Terms and definitions. Here, reference is made to ISO 9000, which contains all definitions applicable to ISO 9001

The remaining seven are technical clauses and are listed here as they appear in the standard. For further details, consult the standards themselves. The seven technical clauses (clauses 4–10) are the following:

4. Context of the organization

   4.1. Understanding the organization and its context

   4.2. Understanding the needs and expectations of interested parties

4.3. Determining the scope of the quality management system

4.4. Quality management system and its processes

5. Leadership

   5.1. Leadership and commitment

   5.2. Policy

   5.3. Organizational roles, responsibilities and authorities

6. Planning

   6.1. Actions to address risks and opportunities

   6.2 Quality objectives and planning to achieve them

   6.3 Planning of changes

7. Support

   7.1 Resources

   7.2 Competence

   7.3 Awareness

   7.4 Communication

   7.5 Documented information

8. Operation

   8.1 Operational planning and control

   8.2 Requirements for products and services

   8.3 Design and development of products and services

   8.4 Control of externally provided processes, products and services

   8.5 Production and service provision

   8.6 Release of products and services

   8.7 Control of nonconforming outputs

9. Performance evaluation

   9.1 Monitoring, measurement, analysis and evaluation

   9.2 Internal audit

   9.3 Management review

10. Improvement

   10.1 General

   10.2 Nonconformity and corrective action

   10.3 Continual improvement

**ISO 9004:2018 Quality Management – Quality of an Organization –
Guidance to Achieving Sustained Success**

Whereas ISO 9001 is compliance based, ISO 9004 is improvement based. All the great ideas in ISO 9004 are guidelines, not requirements. There is some controversy in the field of quality on the usefulness of ISO 9004 and it has not been widely adopted. The developers of the ISO 9000 family made ISO 9001 and ISO 9004 completely compatible in structure, so it is easy to follow any of the following three paths:

1. **Path A.** You have no present wish to be certified to ISO 9001 requirements, but you want to install a powerful QMS now, with the option to go for ISO 9001 certification later. So, you build your present quality system on the guidelines of ISO 9004. The actions you take to follow the ISO 9004 guidelines will not cause you trouble if you later seek ISO 9001 certification.

2. **Path B.** You are presently certified to ISO 9001 but want to upgrade to a more powerful system that leads to performance improvement. Without making any changes in your present QMS, you can start to selectively apply the ISO 9004 guidelines.

3. **Path C.** You are not certified but want to become certified and also want to put quality improvement procedures in place that are not required for registration. You can work with ISO 9001 and ISO 9004 simultaneously, devoting to each the resources you deem appropriate to achieving your goals.

ISO 9004:2018 replaces ISO 9004:2009, and the major changes to the newer edition are as follows:

- alignment with the concepts and terminology of ISO 9000:2015 and ISO 9001:2015;

- focus on the concept of "quality of an organization";

- focus of the concept of "identity of an organization."

Like ISO 9001, ISO 9004:2018 relies on the principles of quality management mentioned earlier. Whereas compliance with 9001 raises the issue of corrective action, the 9004 guidelines suggest how and where to go further in improving performance.

ISO 9004 contains one annex (not present in 9001) in the form of a self-assessment tool that identifies a specific process for self-improvement. Westcott (2003) expands on this approach, helps management develop plans to implement ISO 9004, and provides some case studies of successful implementation. The best place to start, of course, is with the ISO 9004 standard itself.

Other Quality Standards

There exist several industry-specific standards that may have an impact on the quality management system. The automobile, telecommunications, and biomedical industries have all created industry-specific standards that emulate ISO 9001 but impose additional requirements. The American automobile industry took the lead in creating its own industry standard with QS-9000. This standard was replaced by ISO 16949:2009. In October 2016, the International Automotive Task Force (IATF) revised this standard as IATF 16949:2016. IATF 16949:2016 is not a stand-alone quality management standard; rather, it is intended to be used in conjunction with ISO 9001:2015 to define the QMS requirements for automotive-related products. The IATF 16949:2016 standard is now mandatory for many original equipment manufacturers (OEMs). The telecommunications quality standard is TL 9000 and the biomedical quality standard is ISO 13485:2016.

These standards, as well as other pertinent publications, are available from ASQ Quality Press by phoning 800-248-1946 or visiting the website http://www.asq.org/quality-press. Commentary and offers of assistance on all three of these standards can be found by entering the standard number into a Web browser search engine. For an overview of quality standards, see Boulanger, Johnson, and Luko (2012).

Malcolm Baldrige National Quality Award

The Malcolm Baldrige National Quality Award (MBNQA), another quality management approach, emphasizes results rather than procedures or requirements. Congress established this award in 1987 to recognize US organizations for their achievements in quality and business performance and to raise awareness about the importance of quality and performance excellence as a competitive edge. The award is named in honor of Malcolm Baldrige, who was secretary of commerce at the time of his death in 1987. The award is not given for specific products or services. Awards may be given annually in each of these categories: manufacturing, service, small business, education, healthcare, nonprofit, and government.

While the Baldrige Award and the Baldrige recipients make up the very visible centerpiece of the US quality movement, a broader national quality program has evolved around the award and its criteria. A report, *Building on Baldrige: American Quality for the 21st Century*, by the private Council on Competitiveness said, "More than any other program, the Baldrige Quality Award is responsible for making quality a national priority and disseminating best practices across the United States."

The US Commerce Department's National Institute of Standards and Technology (NIST) manages the MBNQA program in close cooperation with the private sector. Since its inception, the MBNQA has received over 1600 applications. As of 2015, over 100 organizations from a wide variety of industries have received the award, with seven organizations winning the award twice.

The MBNQA is awarded according to these criteria for performance excellence:

1. Leadership. Examines how senior executives guide the organization and how the organization addresses its responsibilities to the public and practices good citizenship.

2. Strategic planning. Examines how the organization sets strategic directions and how it determines key action plans.

3. Customer and market focus. Examines how the organization determines requirements and expectations of customers and markets, and how it builds and maintains strong, lasting relationships with customers.

4. Measurement, analysis, and knowledge management. Examines the management, effective use, and analysis of data and information to support key organization processes and the organization's performance management system.

5. Human resource focus. Examines how the organization enables its workforce to develop its full potential and how the workforce is aligned with the organization's objectives.

6. Process management. Examines aspects of how key production/delivery and support processes are designed, managed, and improved.

7. Business/organizational performance results. Examines the organization's performance and improvement in its key business areas: customer satisfaction, financial and marketplace performance, human resources, supplier and partner performance, and operational performance. This category also examines how the organization performs relative to competitors.

Further information about the MBNQA, including procedures for ordering the criteria, is available at http://www.nist.gov/baldrige.

QUALITY AUDITS

A *quality system audit*, as defined by *The ASQ Auditing Handbook*, is a "systematic, independent, and documented process for obtaining audit evidence and evaluating it objectively to determine the extent to which the audit criteria are fulfilled" (Russell 2013). It is a fact-finding process that compares actual results with specified standards and plans. It provides feedback for improvement. It differs from inspection, which emphasizes acceptance or rejection, and differs from surveillance, which is ongoing continuous monitoring.

Types of Audits

> Describe and classify the various types of quality audits such as product, process, management (system), registration (certification), compliance (regulatory), first, second, and third party. (Apply)
>
> **Body of Knowledge II.D.1**

Quality audits may be classified according to the party conducting them, their scope, and the audit method used. In general, three parties are involved in an audit: (1) the organization requesting the audit (the client), (2) the party conducting the audit (the auditor), and (3) the organization to be audited (the auditee).

When the auditor is an employee of the organization being audited (auditee), the audit is classified as an internal quality audit. For the purposes of maintaining objectivity and minimizing bias, internal auditors must be independent from the activity being audited. On the other hand, when the auditors are employees of the client or an independent organization or third party hired for the purpose, the audit is classified as an external quality audit. In this case, the auditors are clearly independent of the auditee and are in a position to provide the client with an unbiased, objective assessment. This type of audit is required to permit listing in a register or to meet mandatory quality requirements. However, the time required and costs involved in an external audit are much higher compared with internal audits.

Another way to classify quality audits is by scope and extent. An audit may be as comprehensive as needed or requested by the client. The most comprehensive type of audit is the quality system audit, which examines suitability and effectiveness of the system as a whole. This audit involves both the documentation and implementation aspects of the quality system. Reasons for initiating a system audit may range from evaluating a potential supplier to verifying an organization's own system. Audits of specific elements of a system, processes, products, or services are also possible. These audits are limited in scope and are typically referred to with a modifier preceding the term "quality audit." Examples include process quality audits and product quality audits.

The method by which the quality audit is conducted provides yet another way to classify audits. Audits may be conducted by location or function. A location-oriented audit provides an in-depth examination of all the quality-related activities within a given location. In a function-oriented audit, an activity is examined in all the locations where the activity is carried out.

It is important to note that these classifications are not mutually exclusive and that, in practice, cross-classifications of a quality audit are possible.

ISO 19011:2011 (second edition) was replaced by ISO 19011:2018 (third edition) and details guidelines for auditing management systems.

The main differences compared to the second edition are as follows:

- addition of the risk-based approach to the principles of auditing;

- expansion of the guidance on managing an audit program, including audit program risk;

- expansion of the guidance on conducting an audit, particularly the section on audit planning;

- expansion of the generic competence requirements for auditors;

- adjustment of terminology to reflect the process and not the object ("thing");

- removal of the annex containing competence requirements for auditing specific management system disciplines (due to the large number of individual management system standards, it would not be practical to include competence requirements for all disciplines); and

- expansion of Annex A to provide guidance on auditing (new) concepts such as organization context, leadership and commitment, virtual audits, compliance and supply chain.

This document provides guidance for all sizes and types of organizations and audits of varying scopes and scales, including those conducted by large audit teams, typically of larger organizations, and those by single auditors, whether in large or small organizations. This guidance should be adapted as appropriate to the scope, complexity, and scale of the audit program.

This document concentrates on internal audits (first party) and audits conducted by organizations on their external providers and other external interested parties (second party). This document can also be useful for external audits conducted for purposes other than third party management system certification.

Roles and Responsibilities in Audits

> Identify and define roles and responsibilities for audit participants such as audit team (leader and members), client, and auditee. (Understand)
>
> **Body of Knowledge II.D.2**

Each of the three parties involved in an audit—the client, the auditor, and the auditee—plays a role that contributes to its success. The client, the party that initiates the audit, selects the auditor and determines the reference standard to be used. The client, typically the end user of the audit results, determines the type of audit needed (system, process, product, etc.) as well as its time and duration.

The selected auditor, whether an individual or a group, needs to adhere to the role of a third party. That is, the auditor must maintain objectivity and avoid bias in conducting the audit. The auditor must comply with any confidentiality requirements mandated by the auditee. An experienced individual is appointed as lead auditor to communicate audit requirements, manage the auditing activities, and report the results. For rules, qualifications, and evaluation criteria for an auditor, see ASQ/ANSI/ISO QE19011:2018 or *The ASQ Auditing Handbook*.

Finally, the auditee has the responsibility of accommodating the audit, which entails providing the auditors access to the facilities involved and copies of all relevant documentation. The auditee is also expected to provide the resources needed and select staff members to accompany the auditors.

Audit Planning and Implementation

> Describe and apply the stages of a quality audit, from audit planning, including assessing risks through conducting an audit. (Apply)
>
> Body of Knowledge II.D.3

Proper planning is a key factor in achieving an efficient quality audit. Planning should be conducted with consideration of the client expectations. This includes the scope, depth, and time frame. The lead auditor has the responsibility of planning and conducting the audit and should be authorized to perform these activities.

Planning an audit, just like any other activity, should address the questions of what, when, how, and who. That is, what elements of the quality system are to be audited? Against what document or reference standard should the quality system be audited? The answers to both questions are determined by the client and should be communicated clearly to the auditee. A schedule of the audit activities needs to be prepared and communicated to both the client and the auditee. It is the lead auditor's responsibility to inform the client of any delays, report their reasons, and update the completion date of the audit.

The method of conducting the audit should also be addressed. Working documents need to be prepared, including checklists of the elements to examine, questions to ask, and activities to monitor. Some references provide generic checklists that can be used as templates. However, it is best to design a checklist to suit the audit at hand and its specific scope and objectives. Forms for collecting auditors' observations and the supporting evidence should also be included in the working document. Working documents typically are reviewed by an experienced auditor and approved by the lead auditor before implementation. It is recommended that the auditor explain the methods planned to the auditee. This should help the organization better prepare for the audit and ease the fear usually attached to the process.

The question of who will examine specific elements, processes, or products addresses the qualifications and experience of the individual auditors (assessors) needed. With the client expectations in mind, the lead auditor should assign the various tasks among his or her team.

An audit is usually conducted in three steps. The first step is a pre-examination or opening meeting with the auditee that marks the beginning of the process. During this meeting, the lead auditor introduces team members to the senior management of the auditee and explains the objectives of the audit and the methods used. The auditee is represented by selected members of the organization who facilitate and assist in the process and submit a documented description of the quality system or element to be examined. Issues regarding proprietary information typically are addressed and resolved before starting the audit.

The second step involves a suitability audit of the documented procedures against the selected reference standard. Observed nonconformities at this stage of the audit should be reported to both the client and the auditee for immediate action. The auditing process should pause to allow for corrective measures.

For the third step, the auditor examines the implementation of the quality system in depth. The auditor maintains records of all nonconformities observed and the supporting data. Provisions should be made in the audit plan to allow additional investigation of clues suggesting nonconformities revealed by the data collected. The auditee management should be made aware of and acknowledge all the nonconformities observed during the audit. When assessing audit nonconformities, it is recommended to use a risk-based approach. For example, when delineating between a major and minor nonconformance, this should be based on the level of risk and the analysis of audit objective evidence. In addition, audits may be requested based on identified risks from quality sources such as trending of corrective actions, nonconformance reports, complaints, or outputs from management reviews. When assessing process risk through audits, see Table 2.1 below, which provides a reference guide in identifying a risk-based audit approach to process auditing throughout the Quality Management System. This step concludes with a closing meeting with the auditee's management for a presentation of findings. In some cases, the auditor may be required to recommend corrective measures for improving the system. However, it is up to the auditee to plan and implement these measures in a way that best suits the organization.

Audit Reporting and Follow-up

> Apply the steps of audit reporting and follow up, including the need to verify corrective action. (Apply)
>
> **Body of Knowledge II.D.4**

A final report is submitted to the client indicating the facts of the audit and conclusions regarding the ability of the subject system, element, process, or product to achieve quality objectives. Proper planning and execution of the audit facilitates the preparation of this report and provides data to support its conclusions. The lead auditor is responsible for the accuracy of the report and the validity of its conclusions. The report should be submitted to the client, who in turn is responsible for providing a copy to the auditee.

The audit final report should include, at a minimum, the following:

1. Type of audit conducted

2. Objectives of audit

3. Identification of involved parties: auditor, auditee, and third party

4. Audit team members

Table 2.1 Risk-based audit approach.

Quality Management System Element	Risk-based Audit Approach	Documentation (example)
Management Responsibility	The risk-based approach is documented in the quality manual and QMS processes/procedures as applicable	• Quality manual
Management Review • Monitoring of Product • Monitoring of Process	The risk-based approach will drive: • Frequency of reporting at quality management review • Level of detail in quality management review meeting minutes • Actions resulting from quality management review	• Quality management review procedure
Human Resources • Competence • Training Effectiveness	The risk-based approach will drive: • Competency requirements for hiring (e.g., education and experience) • Level/type of training required (e.g., read and understand, formal classes or one-on-one hands-on training) • Training effectiveness evaluation (e.g., quiz assessment, hands-on demonstration, etc.)	• Training procedure • Employee training matrix
Product Realization • Design Controls • Risk Management	The risk management process will ensure the medical benefits of the product outweigh the risks associated with the product and its use, or foreseeable misuse. Outputs of the risk management process will be product design inputs.	• Design controls procedure • Risk management procedure • Validation procedure
Design Change	The risk-based approach will drive: • Level of evaluation/testing (e.g., human factors/usability, verification, validation, clinical investigations) • Regulatory requirements (e.g., notifications to notified body, competent authority, and regulatory filing/registrations) • Level of change approval (e.g., engineer, manager)	• Design controls procedure • Document control procedure

(continued)

Table 2.1   Risk-based audit approach. (Continued)

Quality Management System Element	Risk-based Audit Approach	Documentation (example)
Supplier Controls	The risk-based approach will drive: • Supplier evaluation criteria (e.g., self-assessment forms, audits, etc.) • Frequency of supplier evaluation or audit • Level of control exercised • Supplier corrective action report (SCAR) requirements • AQL for incoming inspection	• Purchasing procedure • Supplier qualification procedure • Supplier corrective action procedure • Receiving inspection procedure
Product Acceptance • Incoming Inspection • Final Acceptance	The risk-based approach will drive: • AQL, skip-lot, dock-to-stock incoming inspection/verification of purchased product • Final acceptance criteria	• Receiving inspection procedure • Statistical techniques procedure • Supplier corrective action procedure
Process Validation	The risk-based approach will drive: • The need and frequency of process validation/re-validation • Statistical techniques and sample sizes • Approval levels for process changes	• Validation procedure • Statistical techniques procedure
Nonconforming Materials	The risk-based approach will drive: • Decision to rework or scrap nonconforming materials • Evaluation of adverse effects/level of testing following rework (e.g., testing AQL and acceptance criteria)	• Control of nonconforming product procedure
Measuring Equipment	The risk-based approach will drive: • Frequency of calibration and/or preventive maintenance • Tolerance acceptance criteria • Corrective action for out-of-tolerance conditions	• Control of monitoring and measurement equipment procedure
Internal Audits	The risk-based approach will drive: • Audit frequency • Audit sampling sizes (e.g., number of records to be evaluated)	• Internal audit procedure • Third party inspection procedure

Table 2.1   Risk-based audit approach. (Continued)

Quality Management System Element	Risk-based Audit Approach	Documentation (example)
Field Safety	Risk-based approach will determine field safety corrective action to be taken for nonconforming materials or when an incident is reported through the complaint process (e.g., market withdrawal, recall), as well as the timing requirements.	• Complaint handling procedure • Distributed product risk analysis procedure • Corrections, removals, recall procedure • Post-market surveillance procedure • Medical device reporting procedure
CAPA	Risk-based approach will drive: • Prioritization of activities • Level of investigations to be performed • Timing for investigations/root cause determination and for implementation of corrections and corrective actions	• Corrective and preventive action (CAPA) procedure
Feedback and Complaints	Feedback and complaints will serve as inputs to the risk management and post-market surveillance processes	• Design controls procedure • Risk management procedure • Complaint handling procedure • Post-market surveillance procedure

5. Critical nonconformities and other observations

6. Audit standards and reference documents used

7. Determination of proper corrective action(s)

8. Duration of audit

9. Audit report distribution and date

10. Audit results and recommendations

11. Audit-related records

Should the auditee initiate improvement efforts to correct nonconformities, the three parties should agree on a follow-up audit to verify the results. The plan, audit, report, and improve cycle may be repeated whenever systems and/or requirements change. The results attained provide a measure of the effectiveness of the audit. Improvement efforts also should be directed to identifying and eliminating the root causes of reported nonconformities and identifying the corrective action(s) to be taken. Root causes represent the main reason behind the occurrence of a nonconformance or an undesirable condition or status. These corrective actions may then be validated by performing tests, inspections, or even more audits.

COST OF QUALITY (COQ)

Identify and apply COQ concepts, including cost categorization, data collection, reporting, and interpreting results. (Analyze)

Body of Knowledge II.E

To achieve the most effective improvement efforts, management should ensure that the organization has ingrained in its operating principles the understanding that quality, speed, and cost are complementary, and not conflicting, objectives. Traditionally, recommendations made to management were choices between quality, speed, and cost, where they could pick two of the three. Experience throughout the world has shown, and management is beginning to see, that this is not true. Good quality leads to increased productivity and reduced quality costs, and eventually to increased sales, market penetration, and profits.

The facts about quality management and quality costs show that the real value of a quality program is determined by its ability to contribute to customer satisfaction and profits. Quality cost techniques provide tools for management in its pursuit of customer satisfaction, quality improvement, and profit contributions.

The purpose of cost of quality (COQ) techniques is to provide a tool to management for facilitating quality program and quality improvement activities. Quality cost reports can be used to point out the strengths and weaknesses of a quality system. Improvement teams can use COQ reports to describe the monetary benefits and ramifications of proposed changes. Return-on-investment (ROI) models and other financial analyses can be constructed directly from quality cost data to justify proposals to management. Improvement team members can use this information to rank problems in order of priority. In practice, quality costs can define the activities of quality program and quality improvement efforts in a language that management can understand and act on: dollars. Any reduction in quality costs will have a direct impact on gross profit margins and can be counted immediately as pretax profit.

The Economics of Quality

The expression "the economics of quality" has contributed to some confusion surrounding the true business and economic value of quality management. Some people believe there is no economics of quality; that is, it is never economical to ignore quality. At the other extreme are those managers who believe it is uneconomical to have 100% quality.

Whether for manufacturing or service, a quality cost program will lend credence to the business value of the quality management program and provide cost justification for the corrective actions demanded. Quality cost measurements provide guidance to the quality management program much as the cost accounting system does for general management. Quality cost measurements define and quantify those costs that are directly affected, both positively and negatively, by the quality management program, thus allowing quality to be managed more effectively.

Simply stated, *quality costs* are a measure of the costs specifically associated with the achievement or nonachievement of product or service quality, including all product or service requirements established by the company and its contracts with customers and society. More specifically, quality costs are the total of the costs incurred by (1) investing in the prevention of nonconformances to requirements (prevention costs), (2) appraising a product or service for conformance to requirements (appraisal costs), and (3) failure to meet requirements (failure costs). Quality costs represent the difference between the actual cost of a product or service and what the reduced cost would be if there were no possibility of substandard service, failure of products, or defects in their manufacture.

Every company lives with significant costs that fit this description. Unfortunately, significant chunks of quality costs are normally overlooked or unrecognized simply because most accounting systems are not designed to identify them. As this is generally the case, it is not too difficult to understand why top management of most companies is more sensitive to overall cost and schedule than to quality. The interrelationship of quality, schedule, and cost is likely to be unbalanced in favor of schedule and cost, and often unwittingly at the expense of quality. This imbalance will continue to exist as long as the real COQ remains hidden among total costs. In fact, such a condition can easily set the stage for a still greater imbalance whenever the rising, but hidden, true COQ grows to a magnitude that can significantly affect a company's competitive position.

When the COQ rises without constraint, or is tolerated at too high a level, failure to expose the condition is a sign of ineffective management. Yet, it is entirely possible for this condition to exist without top management's awareness. A quality cost program can provide specific warnings of oncoming dangerous quality-related financial situations. An argument for needed quality improvement is clear when a company suddenly finds itself in serious, expensive quality trouble.

On the premise that any dollar expenditure that could have been avoided will have a direct negative effect on profits, the value of clearly identifying the COQ should be obvious. Achieving this clarity of identification, however, is more easily said than done. A real danger lies in finding and collecting on a small portion of the costs involved and assuming it represents the total. There are as many ways of hiding costs in industry as there are people with imagination. This is an all-too-natural phenomenon in organizations that are never fully charged with all inefficiencies (because some inefficiencies are hidden and not measured) and thus are able to maintain an illusion of effective management.

Goal of a Quality Cost System

The goal of any quality cost system is to facilitate quality improvement efforts that will lead to opportunities to reduce operating costs. The strategy for using quality costs is quite simple: (1) directly attack failure costs in an attempt to drive them to zero, (2) invest in the right prevention activities to bring about improvement, (3) reduce appraisal costs according to results achieved, and (4) continually evaluate and redirect prevention efforts to gain further improvement.

This strategy is based on the premise that:

- For each failure there is a root cause

- Causes are preventable

- Prevention is generally cheaper

In a practical sense, real quality costs can be measured and then reduced through the proper analysis of cause and effect. As failures are revealed through appraisal actions or customer complaints, they are examined for root causes and eliminated through corrective action. The further along in the operating process that a failure is discovered (and thus the nearer to product or service use by the customer), the more expensive it is to correct. Usually as failure costs are reduced, appraisal efforts also can be reduced in a statistically sound manner. The knowledge gained from this improvement can then be applied, through prevention activities or disciplines, to all new work. By minimizing quality costs, quality performance levels can be improved.

Management of Quality Costs

Managing quality costs begins with a general understanding and belief that improving quality performance and improving quality costs are synonymous (the economics of quality). The next step is recognizing that measurable quality improvement also can have a tangible effect on other business measures, such as sales and market share. The caveat, however, is that quality costs must be measured and must reflect cost or lost opportunities to the company.

It should be further understood that COQ is a comprehensive system, not a piecemeal tool. There is a danger in responding to a customer problem only with added internal operations, such as inspections or tests. For service operations, this could mean more operators. While this may solve the immediate customer problem, the added costs may, in fact, destroy profit potential. A comprehensive quality management program will force the analysis of all associated quality costs, making these added internal costs appear clearly as just one step toward the ultimate resolution: prevention of the root cause of the problem. Quality costs should, therefore, become an integral part of any quality management program and, in turn, any quality system or quality improvement activity. Overall quality cost data will point out the potential for improvement and provide management with the basis for measuring the improvement accomplished.

Quality Cost Categories

To manage quality costs, they must be categorized. The three major categories commonly used are prevention costs, appraisal costs, and failure costs.

Prevention costs are the costs of all activities specifically designed to prevent poor quality in products or services. Examples are the costs of quality planning, training programs, and quality improvement projects.

Appraisal costs are the costs associated with measuring, evaluating, or auditing products or services to ensure conformance with quality standards and performance requirements. These include the costs of inspection, testing, product or service audits, process audits, and calibration of measuring and test equipment.

Failure costs are those costs resulting from products or services not conforming to requirements or customer needs. They are usually divided into two types, internal and external. *Internal failure costs* occur prior to delivery or shipment of the product or furnishing of a service to the customer, such as the costs of scrap, rework, material review, and so on. *External failure costs* occur after delivery of the product and during or after furnishing of a service to the customer. Examples include the costs of processing customer complaints, customer returns, warranty claims, and product recalls. See Table 2.2 for an example list of quality cost elements by category.

Total quality cost is the sum of these costs (prevention, appraisal, and failure) and represents the difference between the actual cost of a product or service and what the reduced cost would be if there were no possibility of substandard service, failure of products, or defects in their manufacture. It is, according to Joseph Juran, "gold in the mine," waiting to be extracted (Juran and Godfrey 1999). When you zero in on the elimination of failure costs and then challenge the level of appraisal costs, you will not only be managing COQ but mining gold.

Quality Cost Implementation

To implement a quality cost program, the need for the program must first be determined. This need should be presented to members of management in a way that will justify the effort and interest them in participating. One way to do this is by establishing a simple trial program. For this purpose, only major costs need to be gathered and only readily available data need to be included. Much of the required data may already be available. If necessary, some of these costs may even be estimated.

When setting up the trial program, there is no need to do everything immediately. Select a program, facility, or area of particular interest to management. The results should be sufficient to sell management on the need for the program.

With management sold and the accounting department recruited to assist in the quality cost program, the specific quality costs to be collected must be determined. To do this, tasks must be classified as prevention, appraisal, or failure and listed together with the departments responsible for them. Remember that the quality department isn't the only department to incur quality costs. To determine the prevention costs in the effort to prevent poor quality, such tasks performed in the company should be listed together with the departments responsible for those tasks. In a like manner, appraisal cost elements are determined by listing those tasks associated with the inspection or test of products or services for the detection of poor quality. For failure costs, determine those costs that would not have been expended if quality were perfect. If quality were perfect, there would not be any rework, customer complaints needing response, or need for corrective action. Remember to also divide failure costs into internal and external categories.

Quality cost elements may differ from company to company and particularly from industry to industry. However, the overall categories of prevention, appraisal, and failure are always the same.

Table 2.2 Quality cost elements by category.

Code	Element	Code	Element
1.0	Prevention Costs	1.4.2.1	Design and Development of Quality Measurement and Equipment
1.1	Marketing/Customer/User	1.4.3	Operations Support Quality Planning
1.1.1	Marketing Research	1.4.4	Operator Quality Education
1.1.2	Customer/User Perception Surveys/Clinics	1.4.5	Operator SPC/Process Control
1.1.3	Contract/Document Review	1.5	Quality Administration
1.2	Product/Service/Design Development	1.5.1	Administrative Salaries
1.2.1	Design Quality Progress Reviews	1.5.2	Administrative Expenses
1.2.2	Design Support Activities	1.5.3	Quality Program Planning
1.2.3	Product Design Qualification Test	1.5.4	Quality Performance Reporting
1.2.4	Service Design Qualification	1.5.5	Quality Education
1.2.5	Field Trials	1.5.6	Quality Improvement
1.3	Purchasing Prevention Costs	1.5.7	Quality System Audits
1.3.1	Supplier Reviews	1.6	Other Prevention Costs
1.3.2	Supplier Rating		
1.3.3	Purchase Order Tech. Data Reviews	2.0	Appraisal Costs
1.3.4	Supplier Quality Planning	2.1	Purchasing Appraisal Costs
1.4	Operations (Manufacturing or Service) Prevention Costs	2.1.1	Receiving or Incoming Inspections and Tests
1.4.1	Operations Process Validation	2.1.2	Measurement Equipment
1.4.2	Operations Quality Planning	2.1.3	Qualification of Supplier Product

Table 2.2 Quality cost elements by category. (*Continued*)

Code	Element	Code	Element
2.1.4	Source Inspection and Control Programs	3.0	Internal Failure Costs
2.2	Operations (Manufacturing or Service) Appraisal Costs	3.1	Product/Service Design Failure Costs (Internal)
2.2.1	Planned Operations Inspections, Tests, Audits	3.1.1	Design Corrective Action
2.2.1.1	Checking Labor	3.1.2	Rework Due to Design Changes
2.2.1.2	Product or Service Quality Audits	3.1.3	Scrap Due to Design Changes
2.2.1.3	Inspection and Test Materials	3.1.4	Production Liaison Costs
2.2.2	Set-Up Inspections and Tests	3.2	Purchasing Failure Costs
2.2.3	Special Tests (Manufacturing)	3.2.1	Purchased Material Reject Disposition Costs
2.2.4	Process Control Measurements	3.2.2	Purchased Material Replacement Costs
2.2.5	Laboratory Support	3.2.3	Supplier Corrective Action
2.2.6	Measurement (Inspection and Test) Equipment	3.2.4	Rework of Supplier Rejects
2.2.6.1	Depreciation Allowances	3.2.5	Uncontrolled Material Losses
2.2.6.2	Measurement Equipment Expenses	3.3	Operations (Product or Service) Failure Costs
2.2.6.3	Maintenance and Calibration Labor	3.3.1	Material Review and Corrective Action Costs
2.2.7	Outside Endorsements and Certifications Control	3.3.1.1	Disposition Costs
2.3	External Appraisal Costs	3.3.1.2	Troubleshooting or Failure Analysis Costs (Operations)
2.3.1	Field Performance Evaluation	3.3.1.3	Investigation Support Costs
2.3.2	Special Product Evaluations	3.3.1.4	Operations Corrective Action
2.3.3	Evaluation of Field Stock and Spare Parts	3.3.2	Operations Rework and Repair Costs
2.4	Review of Test and Inspection Data	3.3.2.1	Rework

(continued)

Table 2.2 Quality cost elements by category. *(Continued)*

3.3.2.2	Repair	4.0	External Failure Costs
3.3.3	Reinspection/Retest Costs	4.1	Complaint Investigations/Customer or User Service
3.3.4	Extra Operations	4.2	Returned Goods
3.3.5	Scrap Costs (Operations)	4.3	Retrofit Costs
3.3.6	Downgraded End-Product or Service	4.3.1	Recall Costs
3.3.7	Internal Failure Labor Losses	4.4	Warranty Claims
3.4	Other Internal Failure Costs	4.5	Liability Costs
		4.6	Penalties
		4.7	Customer/User Goodwill
		4.8	Lost Sales
		4.9	Other External Failure Costs

Source: ASQ Quality Costs Committee, *Principles of Quality Costs: Principles, Implementation, and Use,* 3d ed., edited by Jack Campanella (Milwaukee, WI: ASQ Quality Press, 1999).

Quality Cost Collection

Now that the specific costs to be collected have been decided, a method to collect them must be developed. Collection of quality costs should be the responsibility of the controller. The finance and accounting department is the cost collection agency of the company. In addition, having the controller collect the costs adds credibility to the data.

If top management is properly sold on the program, the controller will be charged with the task of heading this effort. With the help of the quality manager, the controller should review the list of costs to be collected, determine which of these are already available under the existing accounting system, and decide where additions to the existing system are needed. Sometimes, the simple addition of new cost element codes to the present charging system is sufficient. However, if necessary, the present system could be supplemented by separate inputs designed specifically for this purpose.

Ideally, a complete system of cost element codes would be generated. The system could be coded in such a way that the costs of prevention, appraisal, and internal and external failures could be easily distinguished and sorted (see Table 2.1). Then, these codes could be entered into the labor cost collection system, together with the hours expended against the cost element or task represented by the code. The labor hours could later be easily converted to dollars.

Scrap is an exception to this system of collecting quality costs as they are incurred. All work needs to be inspected, rejected, and dispositioned first. In many companies, the existing scrap reporting documents are forwarded to estimating, where the costs of expended labor and material are estimated to the stage of completion of the scrapped items.

The accounting department should provide all collected quality costs to the quality function in a format suitable for analysis and reporting. Of course, training programs will be necessary to ensure that all personnel are informed as to how to report their quality cost expenditures. The training should be repeated periodically, and the collection system should be audited on a regular basis.

Quality Cost Summary and Analysis

Quality costs can be summarized in many ways, such as by company, division, facility, department, or shop. They may be summarized by program, type of program, or all programs combined. The best way to summarize these costs is according to the specific needs of the organization.

Analysis can include comparison of the total quality cost with an appropriate measurement base. Some commonly used bases are sales, cost input, and direct labor. The base selected will depend on what is appropriate for the needs of the organization. Comparing quality costs with a measurement base will relate the COQ to the amount of work performed. An increase in quality costs with a proportionate increase in the base is normal. It is the non-proportionate change that should be of interest. The index "total quality cost over the measurement base" is the factor analyzed. The goal is to bring this index to a minimum through quality improvement. The index may be plotted so that trends representing present status in relation to past performance and future goals may be analyzed.

Other methods of analysis include study of the effect that changes in one category have on the other categories and on the total quality cost. For example, was the increase in prevention costs effective in reducing failure costs? And was this reduction in failure costs sufficient to cause a reduction in total quality costs? This technique can provide insight into where the quality dollar can most wisely be spent. Increases in failure costs must be investigated to determine where costs must be expended to reverse a trend and reduce the total quality cost. Losses must be defined, their causes identified, and corrective action taken to preclude recurrence.

Other existing quality systems, such as a defect reporting system, can be used in conjunction with the quality cost program to identify significant problems. The defect reporting system can help define the causes of scrap, rework, and other failure costs. While the losses are distributed among many causes, they are not uniformly distributed. A small percentage of the causes will account for a high percentage of the losses. This concept is the Pareto principle, where these causes are the vital few as opposed to the trivial many. Refer to Chapter 5 for more information on the Pareto principle and Pareto charts. Concentration on prevention of the vital few causes will achieve maximum improvement at a minimum of cost. This quality improvement tool will have the effect of improving quality while reducing costs.

Quality Cost Reporting

There are almost as many ways to report quality costs as there are companies reporting them, because how they are reported depends on who they are reported to and what the report is trying to say. The amount of detail included in the quality cost report generally depends on the level of management the report is geared to.

To top management, the report might be a scorecard depicting the status of the quality program through a few carefully selected trend charts—where the quality program has been and the direction it is heading. Savings over the report period and opportunities for future savings might be identified. To middle management, the report might provide quality cost trends by department or shop to enable identification of areas in need of improvement. Reports to line management might provide detailed cost information, perhaps the results of a Pareto analysis identifying specific areas where corrective action would afford the greatest improvement. Scrap and rework costs by shop also provide valuable information when included in reports to line management.

Using Quality Costs

Once the quality cost program is implemented, it should be used by management to justify and support improvement in each major area of product or service activity. Quality costs should be reviewed for each major product line, manufacturing area, service area, and cost center. The improvement potential that exists in each individual area can then be looked at and meaningful goals can be established. The quality cost system then becomes an integral part of quality measurement. The proper balance is to establish improvement efforts at the level necessary to effectively reduce the total COQ. As progress is achieved, adjust improvement efforts to where total quality costs are at the lowest attainable level. This approach prevents unheeded growth in quality costs and creates improved overall quality performance, reputation, and profits.

Another benefit to be gained from a quality cost program is its ability to be used as a budgeting tool. As costs are collected against quality cost elements, a history of costs is generated. This history can then be used to determine the average cost per element. In other words, depending on how detailed the elements are that have been established, the organization can identify what it has been spending for various functions or tasks. This information can be used as the basis for future quotes and estimates. Budgets can be established for each element. Then, going full circle, the actuals collected against these elements can be bounced against the budget amounts to determine budget variances. Action can then be initiated to bring over- or underrunning elements into line.

The key factor in the reduction of quality costs is quality improvement, and a key factor in quality improvement is corrective action. Quality costs do not reduce themselves. They are merely the scorecard. They can tell you where you are and where your corrective action dollar will afford the greatest return. Quality costs identify targets for corrective action.

Once a target for corrective action is identified, through Pareto or other methods of quality cost analysis, the action necessary must be carefully determined. It must be individually justified on the basis of an equitable cost trade-off. You do not want to resolve a $500 problem with a $5000 solution. At this point, experience in measuring quality costs will be invaluable for estimating the payback on individual corrective action investments or quality improvement projects. Cost-benefit justification of corrective action and quality improvement projects should be a continuing part of the quality management program.

Some problems have fairly obvious solutions, such as the replacement of a worn bearing or a worn tool, which can be fixed immediately. Others are not so obvious, such as a marginal condition in design or processing, and are almost never discovered and corrected without the benefit of a well-organized and formal approach. Marginal conditions usually result in problems that can easily become lost in the accepted cost of doing business. Having an organized quality improvement program and corrective action system, justified by quality costs, will reveal such problems to management. The true value of corrective action is that you only have to pay for it once, whereas failure to take corrective action may be paid for repeatedly.

Quality Cost Principles and Lessons

Traditional quality cost methods have been around a long time. These principles still apply today and will apply for the foreseeable future. However, through our experiences with quality costs over time, we've identified some useful lessons learned that can be applied in the future.

The first lesson is that speaking the language of money is essential. For a successful quality effort, the single most important element is leadership by upper management. To gain that leadership, some concepts or tools could be proposed, but that is the wrong approach. Instead, management should first be convinced that a problem exists that requires its attention and action, such as excessive costs due to poor quality. A quality cost study, particularly when coupled with a successful pilot quality improvement project, is a solid way to gain management support for a broad quality improvement effort. Excessive costs and loss of sales revenue are both quality-related hot buttons for management.

The second lesson learned is that quality cost measurement and publication do not solve quality problems unless they are used. Improvement projects must be identified, clear responsibilities established, and resources provided to diagnose and remove the cause of problems, as well as other essential steps. New organizational machinery is needed to attack and reduce the high costs of poor quality. The third lesson is that the scope of traditional quality costs should be expanded. Traditionally, quality costs have emphasized the cost of nonconformities.

Important as this cost is, there is a need to estimate the cost of inefficient processes. This includes variation of product characteristics (even on conforming products), redundant operations, sorting inspections, and other forms of non-value-added activities. Another area to be considered is the cost of lost opportunities for sales revenue.

The fourth lesson is that the traditional categories of quality costs have had remarkable longevity. About 50 years ago, some pioneers proposed that quality costs be assigned the categories of prevention, appraisal, and failure. Many practitioners found the categories useful and even devised ingenious ways to adapt the categories beyond manufacturing, as in engineering design, and also to the service sector, as in financial services and healthcare. The principles still work today. The difference is in their additional applications.

Quality costs have expanded to become a principal management and quality improvement tool. Definitions and standards have been developed and refined along with techniques and methods for implementation. Quality cost principles and concepts have been expanded to include lessons learned over the past half century, with applications now including the software and service sectors. The quality cost program is the bridge between line and executive management. It provides a common language and a measurement and evaluation system that shows how quality pays in increased profits, productivity, and customer acceptance.

QUALITY TRAINING

> Identify and apply key elements of a training program, including conducting a needs analysis, preparing curricula and materials, and determining the program's effectiveness. (Apply)
>
> **Body of Knowledge II.F**

To keep an organization healthy, its people must be continually trained in new concepts and techniques. Frank Gryna epitomized the role of quality engineer as leader and trainer. In addition to the college students he helped educate and the adult workers he trained, he inspired hundreds of professionals to become passionate, skillful carriers of the quality torch as trainers. Gryna (1988b) stated, "The need is to extend training in quality-related matters to personnel in all functions." He stated that while U.S. companies (formerly) trained only quality-related specialists in quality, the Japanese, from the very beginning of their industrial renaissance in 1946, targeted all departments, and that "this difference in training contributed to a quality crisis" for the United States.

Training may be formal or informal, large scale or small. Although it is usually delivered by instructors in classrooms, training can be done through self-directed study with workbooks or as an online course. A powerful training method in the areas of intellectual skills and human relations is mentoring. A mentor provides guidance, inspiration, and motivation. Likewise, well-structured improvement projects can include a training component. Project leaders are given special instructions to ensure that team members learn various skills as they complete the project. For details on facilitation, see Chapter 1.

If the training task is small, it may involve only two people—for example, an apprentice working alongside a master. At the other extreme it may require a fully staffed training and development department with a budget in the millions. In some companies, such as McDonald's and Motorola, this department is called a corporate university, and it manages dozens of instructors delivering courses, seminars, exercises, and workshops year-round. The middle ground would be a quality engineer organizing a small training program or helping a task team build a larger one.

Regardless of the size of the training program, the same development process is used. Many training programs are organized in five phases, as follows:

1. Assess the need for training

2. Design a curriculum, or training plan

3. Develop the lesson plans and training materials

4. Implement the plan (i.e., deliver the instruction)

5. Evaluate effectiveness of the training

This is known as the ADDIE model, so-called because it uses the first letter of the first word of each phase. Some have proposed a seven-phase model—beginning with "customer identification" and ending with "maintain beneficial outcomes"—resulting in the CADDIEM model. Many other variations can also be used successfully.

If large-scale training is contemplated, spend more time than you think necessary in assessing the needs. Stay open-minded as to possibilities. A thorough needs analysis can prevent wasting large amounts of time and money on ineffective or inadequate training. For example, you might start out thinking a training program is needed, only to discover through needs assessment that your problem is solved by organizational realignment.

The methods of quality function deployment (QFD) are very suitable to needs assessment. One key QFD tool is the matrix chart, which can be used to organize the results of surveys and focus groups. See Chapter 3 for more details about QFD.

The curriculum flows naturally from the needs analysis. It states learning objectives and how they will be achieved in each training event, whether by lecturer, demonstration, role-play, or other method. Suppliers, customers, and even competitors may share their curriculum ideas. Training professionals will need to partner with subject matter experts in this phase because of its highly technical and subject-specific nature.

Once the curriculum is set, the lesson plans flow rather naturally. There are numerous issues to resolve, such as detailed content, sequencing, depth, breadth, review points, quizzes, and demonstrations.

Finding suitable materials is not a problem. However, selecting from the plethora of artifacts, paper and electronic media, simulations, workbooks, role-plays, and so on, might be a problem. Remember that training can be structured in many ways. Formal classrooms may be appropriate, but often the best training area is the workplace, with carefully designed instructional aids so that training occurs as the work is done. Creativity and imagination are definitely in order.

For developing intellectual skills such as facilitation and conflict resolution, role-playing is highly recommended. It is a good way to increase the learners' involvement in the process. Designing good role-plays can be time-consuming, but Stolovitch and Keeps (1992) explained how role-plays and simulations can be developed during the learning process in certain situations. Book discussion groups can focus management attention on timely issues with little or no development cost.

A rapidly growing body of training material is now available electronically, through video modules and online material. Many different organizations offer products and assistance in this exciting new area of training materials. Webinars hosted by companies and divisions of ASQ are also popular methods for on-the-job training. In addition, using search engines such as Google and Yahoo will yield many more electronic training materials.

Both technical competence and teaching skills are mandatory! An experienced quality engineer might need special "how to teach" training, since technical competence does not ensure teaching skill. "Train the trainer" programs can be anything from a colleague giving informal mentoring to an eight-week off-site course. Remember, students must respect both teaching ability and competence of the instructor for learning to take place.

Most training programs are directed toward adults. Knowles (1996) pointed out significant facts about how adults learn. Three of his conclusions are the following:

1. Adults decide for themselves what is and isn't important to learn. To ensure learning takes place, the trainer should state specifically what should be learned and how it relates to on-the-job performance.

2. Adults buy into training when it is supported on the job by supervisors and management.

3. Adults who are happy in their jobs are more receptive to training, and adults who are well trained for their jobs are happier employees.

According to Gryna (1988b), there are 10 reasons why training programs fail:

1. Cultural resistance by line managers

2. Doubt as to the usefulness of the training

3. Lack of participation by line managers

4. Technique rather than problem orientation

5. Inadequacy of leader/instructor

6. Mixing of participant levels

7. Lack of application during the course

8. Overly complex language

9. Lack of participation by the training function

10. Operational and logistical deficiencies

Consider reason #7 in more detail. To quote Gryna, "The ideal approach is to design the course so that the participants must apply the training during the course. One of the best learning experiences is the application of the material being taught. This was successfully done during World War II in the area of work-simplification programs. More recently, value engineering seminars often have a project included as part of the seminar. Quality circles also use the concept." In the years since Gryna published those words, the scope and effectiveness of training for quality in the United States have greatly increased.

Referring to the ADDIE model, evaluation (step 5) and needs analysis (step 1) are closely related. Both are learning experiences for the training team. It is very important for credibility to demonstrate that something useful has been accomplished. And if the outcome was poor, you need to know quickly to take immediate corrective action.

Some informal evaluation can occur while the course is under way. Especially if the instructor is new, a trusted colleague or mentor can help with discussions and role-play exercises and can visit with attendees during breaks. The single most prevalent (and probably most cost-effective) form of evaluation is the pre- and post-test of knowledge.

Attendee evaluation forms (rate the instructor, rate the course) have been widely used in the past, but this technique is not recommended as there is too much room for subjectivity. This is known as level 1 evaluation in Donald Kirkpatrick's (2006) hierarchy, shown with one additional level in Table 2.3. The fifth level is most informative but also quite difficult and expensive to achieve. Phillips (2003) discusses an ROI methodology for training and improvement programs.

In 1980, a company-wide training program at Tennessee Eastman Company evolved from concern about poor quality attitudes. The project was reported by Hill and McClaskey (1980; available at http://www.asq.org/qic). While this training study is rather dated, some aspects of the training program are still applicable over 40 years later and are highlighted here:

1. Determining the purpose. This phase involved upper and middle management, numerous operational units, and the training department. The stated purpose was not to create a training program but to improve overall quality performance. Only after several weeks of discussions and surveys was a training program decided on.

Table 2.3 Five different levels of evaluation.

Level	Name	Question	Techniques
1	Reaction	How did learners feel?	Post-instruction questionnaires or interviews. Learners report impressions of instructor, curriculum, facilities, and content.
2	Learning	What did learners retain?	Pretest and posttest, checking for gains in either knowledge or performance.
3	Behavior	Did learners change?	Assessors must collect data at the workplace to evaluate changes in skill and performance.
4	Organizational	Is the impact beyond the learner?	Large-scale surveys of morale, product quality, turnover, and so on, followed by executive conferences.
5	Return on investment	Is there an effect on the bottom line?	Analyze financial data carefully constructed by professionals. Six Sigma includes this element in program evaluation.

2. Developing alternatives that will achieve the purpose. Through the use of focus groups, brainstorming, and exchange of memos, several dozen alternatives were proposed. Seven were selected for further study; two of these were the following:

— Require position guides that include quality responsibilities

— Create a central quality organization to coordinate development and dissemination of information and requirements

3. Analyzing the alternatives. A set of five weighted criteria was developed, including such items as "chance of completion" and "flexibility of format." The alternative with the highest score was "teach about quality responsibilities."

4. Designing the selected program. Many elements were specified. Some typical design parameters were the following:

— Create awareness of quality responsibilities

— Cover total learning needs in quality awareness

— Be adaptable to specific needs

— Be used only by people requiring the knowledge

— Be portable and usable near work area

— Have a maximum length of two hours

After the design criteria were set, a survey was taken of all employees, with 40 potential courses listed. Using the survey, the task force proceeded to develop 16 new courses.

5. Implementing the solution. The team proceeded to write outlines and scripts, identify needed materials, and publish results, calling on others for help as needed. Teachers were selected and trained, a budget was set up, a cost tracking system was created, and the courses were put in place for delivery. The courses ran for several years with periodic updates.

6. Evaluating the results. Pre- and post-tests were regularly used to determine how much was learned.

In conclusion, it is important to keep in mind the distinction between training and education. *Training* is providing a skill and/or technique for immediate application in a job or related situation. *Education* is the development of knowledge and understanding in a topic. Education, rather than training, can enrich one's life in an unpredictable future.

Chapter 3
Product, Process, and Service Design

The five sections in this chapter cover the different elements that quality engineers use in quality initiatives involving products and processes. The areas covered in this chapter include classification of quality characteristics (as opposed to product defects, which are discussed in Chapter 4), design inputs and review elements, elements of technical drawings and specifications, design verification and validation to ensure fitness for use, and reliability and maintainability.

Basic definitions of reliability for both repairable and nonrepairable systems are presented. In addition, the basic relationships between the failure rate (hazard rate), probability density function, and reliability function are developed. Reliability estimations of simple systems made of series, parallel, or k-out-of-n components are obtained using the reliability of individual components. Maintainability of the systems is defined, and three widely used maintenance and repair policies—corrective maintenance, preventive maintenance, and predictive maintenance—are discussed. Conditions for the applicability of these policies are also discussed.

CLASSIFICATION OF QUALITY CHARACTERISTICS

> Define, interpret, assess, and classify
> quality characteristics for new and existing
> products, processes, and services. [Note: The
> classification of defects is covered in IV.B.3.]
> (Evaluate)
>
> Body of Knowledge III.A

Quality characteristics are features that describe the fit and function of a product or process and aid in differentiating between items of a given sample or population. To differentiate items from each other and/or to compare items with a standard, measurements and/or comparisons are used. Variables data are represented by direct measurement on a continuous scale. Attributes data are most often discrete data usually reported in the form of counts. The counts are classified by category, with the most common categories being pass/fail, go/no-go, and accept/reject.

(For more details on variables, attributes, and continuous and discrete data, see Chapter 6).

Measurement is the process of evaluating a property or characteristic of an object and describing it with a numerical or nominal value. A quality characteristic is referred to as a *variable* if it is measurable over a continuous scale. For example, in healthcare, a patient's temperature can be measured with an electronic thermometer. Other examples include measurements related to weight, length, diameter, or cost.

If the quality characteristic of interest can't be directly measured, then each item under inspection is often classified into one of two or more categories. For example, items inspected may be classified as conforming or nonconforming. Each product unit is assigned one of these two labels according to inspection operation results. It is then possible to derive a numerical measure of process quality using a quantitative scale. The numerical measure is achieved by calculating the *fraction nonconforming* as the ratio between the number of units labeled as nonconforming and the total number of units inspected. When the item inspected can be classified into one of exactly two possible categories, the binomial distribution is often appropriate to model this situation. (See Chapter 6 for more details on attributes data and the binomial distribution.)

Another commonly used attribute quality characteristic is the number of nonconformities (or number of defects) observed on an inspected item. In this situation, a single item inspected may have more than one nonconformity or defect. For example, a car door panel may have more than one scratch, dent, or discoloration. These would be considered nonconformities on the single item inspected, in this case, the car door panel. The number of nonconformities is often well modeled by the Poisson distribution. (See Chapter 6 for more details on the number of nonconformities and the Poisson distribution, respectively.)

Classification can be used for prioritization categories of quality characteristics and is also frequently used to describe defect seriousness, which is discussed in detail in Chapter 4. Desirability or consequence categories can also be used to indicate the levels of prioritization. These levels include minor, major, serious, and critical. Another prioritization classification method is to group changes or suggestions in the form of would have, could have, should have, or must have. ISO 9001:2015 gives the following verbal forms of improvement along with definitions:

- "Can" indicates a possibility or capability
- "May" indicates a permission
- "Should" indicates a recommendation
- "Shall" indicates a requirement

DESIGN INPUTS, TECHNIQUES, AND REVIEW

Design is a term that describes the thought processes, procedures, tools, documentation, and specifications associated with products and processes. Designs are developed to document and ensure compliance with customer expectations as they relate to operational capabilities and characteristics of products and processes. Whether for products or processes, designs progress through phases.

Design phases are linked to phases within the product/process development life cycle, wherein the product/process development life cycle typically includes the following:

- **Definition phase.** A problem or opportunity is clearly defined, documented, and refined, and consensus on the definition is reached among stakeholders.

- **Specification phase.** Specifications are set that lead to, or provide, a product or process desired by the customer. Specifications are commonly applied to characteristics that affect the form, fit, or function of a product or process. Specifications also are commonly applied to characteristics that affect the reliability of a product or process to function in a given environment, within a given range of temperature, or for a given period of time or cycle of operation.

- **Concept phase.** All possible solutions to solve the problem or exploit the opportunity are explored. Feasible solutions are identified, and nonfeasible solutions are dismissed.

- **Detailed design phase.** Specifications and the most feasible concept are used as the basis for development of detailed plans for a product or process design.

- **Prototype phase.** A working model of the detailed design is fabricated and tested in a laboratory or development environment for its ability to perform or operate as intended.

- **Production phase.** Following successful development, testing, and refinement of a prototype, production units of the design are produced in sufficient volume to satisfy customer demand. Unlike prototype units, which are produced in a laboratory or development environment, production phase units are produced with tools, equipment, methods, and procedures used on the shop floor or service delivery area, by regular production or service delivery personnel.

- **Distribution phase.** The product or process enters the supply chain for sale and distribution.

- **Normal use phase.** The product or process is released to the customer for use in its intended role or function. Products and processes require normal maintenance and repair (warranty and non-warranty), and customers frequently require technical assistance and support.

- **Obsolescence and disposal phase.** Products and processes lose their usefulness due to normal wear, catastrophic failure (planned or unplanned), introduction of enhancements to an existing design, or changes in technology. As products and processes become obsolete, the original designer must consider either how to provide enhancements that extend the life of the product/process or how to safely and ethically address disposal of the product/process.

How a design links with the product/process development life cycle (i.e., which specific design phases are used, and how the work of various design phases is related to the product/process development life cycle) depends completely on the model used as the basis for the design. It should be noted that there are numerous models or approaches for design, far too many to provide an exhaustive list in this book. One model for review of designs, however, is well developed, is sufficiently universal, and applies to products or processes: the Systems Engineering Technical Review Process as described in the United States Navy, Naval Air Systems Command (NAVAIR) Instruction 4355.19E (February 2015). The International Electrotechnical Commission (IEC) also has developed a standard on design review in IEC 61160 (September 2005).

Inputs

> Classify design inputs such as customer needs, regulatory requirements, critical to quality, and risk assessment into robust design using techniques such as failure mode and effects analysis (FMEA). (Analyze)
>
> **Body of Knowledge III.B.1**

Designs for products and processes are influenced by factors known as inputs. Inputs are simply requirements placed on products and processes that relate to the following:

- Customer needs and expectations (e.g., time of delivery, cost, performance characteristics)

- Regulatory agency guidance and law requirements (e.g., safety of end users, safety of production/service delivery personnel, use of hazardous chemicals, distribution to unauthorized personnel/vendors, control of sensitive technology)

- Patents and technology licensing (e.g., protections for existing designs owned by competitors)

- Product/process capabilities

- Product/process reliability

CtQs (Critical to Quality) are measurable requirements to achieve quality. Customers will seldom mention CtQs, yet they are essential to delivering a quality product or process output. An example of a CtQ is the diameter of a drilled hole in a component that goes into an assembly that is mounted in a machine. The customer will ask for the machine, but not the drilled hole. However, without the hole, the component can't be assembled and the machine will not function.

Often, CtQs will be identified when developing a new product or process. Alternatively, CtQs may be identified when seeking to improve the quality of a current product or process. In such cases, the CtQ identifies the critical characteristics that improve overall quality if they are improved.

The VOC (Voice of the Customer) must be understood before CtQs can be identified. The VOC describes what the customer wants and is necessary for the identification of CtQs (Seong-Ho et al. 2004). The VOC is captured through methods such as customer surveys (Cole 2011). Other options for capturing the VoC include feedback forms and focus groups (George et al. 2005). The VOC is used to identify CtQ (Critical to Quality) characteristics (Seong-Ho et al. 2004). The VOC describes what the customer needs.

The VOC is turned into CtQs using a CtQ tree (Critical to Quality tree), which goes from vague customer's wants and needs using the customer's own words to drivers of quality. The CtQ and ends with very specific CtQs, which are the required level of performance or specification needed to deliver what the customer wants or needs (Tague 2005).

The highest level of a CtQ tree is the VOC. The next level lists the quality drivers. The quality drivers are what is needed to achieve a high-quality product or process output. These drivers need to be present to ensure high quality. The third level is where the CtQs are listed. These are requirements to be fulfilled or specifications and one driver must have at least one CtQ but may have more.

The CtQs should be specific, unambiguous, and easy to understand. They must also be measurable in some form and they should have a direct relevance to the VOC. The CtQs must provide clear acceptance or rejection criteria. This could be in the form of a specification such as a length with a tolerance, or a criteria that must be fulfilled such as requiring an assembly manual to be present.

Figure 3.1 depicts a CtQ tree for a hotdog stand where the customers want a hotdog. The customers want a high-quality hotdog, but the quality of the hotdog is undefined and the drivers of quality must be determined. For a hot dog, these are the serving temperature, condiments, and speed and each of the drivers has at least one CtQ. For serving temperature, the hotdog must be stored hot enough to avoid

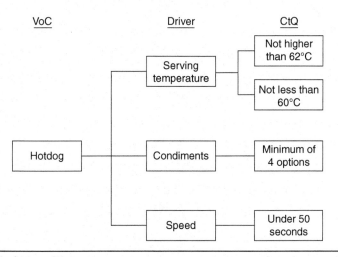

Figure 3.1 Critical to quality tree.

Table 3.1 VoC, driver, and CtQ examples.

VoC	Driver	CtQ
Comfort	Room temperature	18°C – 21°C
Durability	Material thickness	Minimum 2.3 mm
Food safety	Allergy information	Printed on menu
Affordable	Low cost	Less than $4.00 per unit
Fast service	Delivery time	Under 18 minutes
Productivity	Units per shift	Minimum 120
Convenience	Number of locations	At least 4
Cost	Scrap	Under 2%
Buffet dining	Options	At least 15 items
Customer satisfaction	Warranty claims	Less than 3 per year
Quick support	Waiting time	Less than 2 minutes
Reliable machine	Time between failures	Greater than 6 months

the growth of bacteria, but it should not be stored at a temperature high enough to burn a customer; therefore, there is a specification with an upper limit and a lower limit. To achieve customer satisfaction, there must be a sufficient number of condiments available, which was determined to be a minimum of four. Speed also matters as customers will not wait long, so there is an upper limit of 50 seconds.

A CtQ tree usually has three levels, but it is possible to create one with a fourth level. For example, "number of condiments" could have been listed between "condiments" and "minimum of 4 options." Such an approach can be used when dealing with a more complicated product or process.

Once identified, CtQs serve as good candidates for monitoring and improvement. The exact drivers and related CtQs will vary between products and processes. Table 3.1 lists examples of quality drivers and their CtQs.

In addition to CtQ, there are many variations on CtQ can be summarized as CtX. The X in CtX may be Critical to Satisfaction, Critical to Safety, Critical to Design, Critical to Customer, Critical to Cost, or Critical to Delivery.

Techniques

Apply Design for X (DFX), Design for Six Sigma (DFSS), and requirements traceability. (Apply)

Body of Knowledge III.B.2

The design inputs identified above translate into basic design concepts relevant to quality engineering, particularly when the nature of a design emphasizes a specific characteristic. When a specific characteristic is emphasized, the nature of the design may be considered "constrained," wherein the design input must either guide design efforts (such as the case with Design for Six Sigma) or constrain the product or process resulting from the design (such as the case with design for cost). In such cases, the design is referred to as "design for X," where X may be Six Sigma, cost, manufacturability, or reliability. Awareness of the basic design concepts and how they relate to the design process is included within the CQE BoK and is addressed as follows:

> Design for Six Sigma. Design for Six Sigma (DFSS) is not to be confused with the well-known DMAIC (define, measure, analyze, improve, control) approach to Six Sigma. While DMAIC Six Sigma focuses on solving problems in existing products or processes, DFSS focuses on eliminating problems before they occur.

> Design for Reliability. Design for Reliability (DFR) is an approach to design that focuses on development of products and processes able to perform under specified conditions, in a specified environment, and for specified periods of time.

> Concurrent Engineering. Concurrent engineering is practice of the design function and associated activities by a team of engineers, technicians, management, and administrative personnel such that all aspects of the design phases are considered simultaneously.

> Requirements Traceability. Quality function deployment (QFD) is one framework for the design process that captures the voice of the customer via a series of matrices. Once captured, the VOC is used to guide design efforts to ensure that customer expectations are met.

Quality Function Deployment

Quality function deployment (QFD) is a powerful planning technique, perhaps the most comprehensive ever invented for quality planning. QFD is an overall concept that provides a means of translating customer requirements into the appropriate technical requirements for each stage of product development and production (i.e., marketing strategies, planning, product design and engineering, prototype evaluation, production process development, production, and sales). QFD is especially suited to large-scale products such as airplanes, automobiles, and major appliances because these products have heavy tooling, high design costs, and many optional features that must be selected and then produced or procured. QFD was introduced into American industry in the 1980s by the American Supplier Institute of Livonia, Michigan, which remains one of the organizations that actively promote its usage. QFD continues to be employed across a variety of organizations. Recently, Camgoz-Akdag, Pinar, and Nazli (2016) discussed the use of QFD for increasing customer satisfaction in the textile industry in Turkey.

Definitions and Concepts of QFD

Five key terms are associated with QFD (Sullivan 1986):

1. Voice of the customer (VOC). The customer's requirements expressed in their own terms.

2. Counterpart characteristics. An expression of the customer's voice in technical language that specifies customer-required quality.

3. Product quality deployment. Activities needed to translate the voice of the customer into counterpart characteristics.

4. Deployment of the quality function. Activities needed to ensure that customer-required quality is achieved; the assignment of specific quality responsibilities to specific departments. (Any activity needed to ensure that quality is achieved is a quality function, no matter which department performs it.)

5. Quality tables. A series of matrices used to translate the voice of the customer into final product control characteristics.

Sometimes it is possible to incorporate all the key relationships into a simple diagram known as the house of quality, so-called because it resembles a house with a pitched roof. Figure 3.2 shows such a diagram.

For comprehensive coverage of more than 30 planning tools grouped under QFD, see King (1987). A typical project will require only a few of those tools. The following QFD documents are most common:

1. Customer requirements planning matrix

2. Design matrix

3. Final product characteristic deployment matrix

4. Manufacturing/purchasing matrix

5. Process plan and quality control charts

6. Operating instructions

7. Human factor studies or surveys for capturing VOC

Application of QFD: The Basics

By applying QFD, customers' expectations are translated into directly related job requirements. The objective is improved customer satisfaction at acceptable cost. The basic relationship is displayed in the input–output matrix shown in Figure 3.3. This matrix, one of many in QFD, organizes the process of determining relationships between what the customer wants (usually described in nontechnical terms) and how the supplier satisfies these wants. Wants fall into three categories: must have, expected to have, and would like to have. Numerical measures are highly

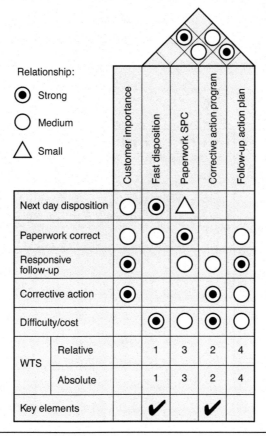

Figure 3.2   QFD house of quality diagram for a paperwork process.

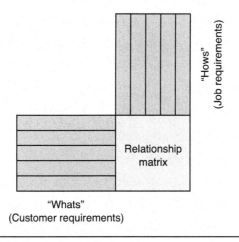

Figure 3.3   Input–output requirements matrix.

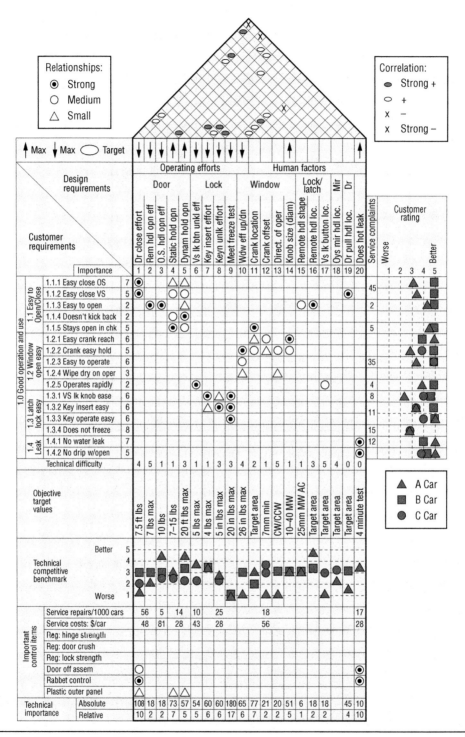

Figure 3.4 House of quality for a car door.

desirable. The wants must be specified in sufficient detail to ensure they are clearly understood. Customers may or may not be involved in setting the requirements; however, their satisfaction depends on identifying and meeting their wants.

The "hows" are the technical details of each job. The strength of each relationship may be strong, medium, or small, as shown in Figures 3.2 and 3.4. These symbols can be converted to weights, such as strong = 5, medium = 3, and small = 1. The weights will convert to scores indicating the importance of each job requirement. At the top of the requirements matrix, a correlation matrix is added to show the strength of the relationships among the different job requirements. A basic example is shown in Figure 3.2 for a paperwork improvement project, and a more complex example for a car door design is depicted in Figure 3.4.

QFD as a planning technique has significant benefits:

1. Product objectives based on customer requirements are not misinterpreted at subsequent stages

2. Particular marketing strategies or sales points do not become lost or blurred during the translation process from marketing through planning and on to execution

3. Important production control points are not overlooked

4. Efficiency is increased because misinterpretations are minimized

Review

Identify and apply common elements of the design review process, including roles and responsibilities of participants. (Apply)

Body of Knowledge III.B.3

Depending on the type and complexity of the design, any or all of the design reviews may be completed. The depth of detail, analysis, and documentation should increase as the design reviews progress toward completion. Design reviews are not intended for solving design-related problems but rather to verify completion of problem-solving activities by cross-functional teams. Discovery of too many design-related problems during a design review may indicate that a design review is being conducted prematurely.

Although the product development group is responsible for creating a design, no one group can provide all the necessary assurance that the design is adequate. Therefore, design reviews should be conducted periodically by a cross-functional team until the design and process are finalized. Quality and manufacturing should be active participants in the review process. Suppliers also should participate, if possible. Early sourcing commitments enable suppliers to attend the design reviews and contribute their expertise prior to investing in expensive tooling. Drawings should comply with applicable standards for drafting, dimensioning, and tolerances. At each review, the design must be considered from several different viewpoints:

- Reliability. Will the failure rate be sufficiently low?

- Quality engineering. Can the design be adequately inspected and tested?

- Field engineering. Are proper installation, maintenance, and user-handling features included in the design?

- Procurement. Can the necessary parts be acquired at acceptable costs, delivery schedules, and quality levels?

- Materials engineering. Will the selected materials perform as expected?

- Tooling engineering. Is the equipment capable of meeting the specified tolerances on a consistent basis?

- Packaging engineering. Can the product be shipped without damage?

- Outside consultants. Have appropriate outside consultants been called for when necessary?

- Customer. Should a customer representative participate in the design reviews for military applications and original equipment manufacturers?

- Other design engineers. Are other design engineers needed when there are tight tolerances to mating components or critical system interfaces?

Design reviews are often done at various stages of the life cycle of the product, particularly in the Department of Defense (DoD). Several types of reviews are discussed here, but many more are often done throughout the life cycle of the product or system. The systems requirements review is a technical review to ensure all system and performance requirements are defined, consistent, and testable. The preliminary design review assesses the maturity of the preliminary design of a system or product. This review establishes baselines to ensure the product is ready to move into the next phase of development. The critical design review is a technical review that assesses the maturity of the product or system design and remaining risks. This review determines whether the system is ready to move into prototype development. The production readiness review examines the system to determine whether the design is ready to move into production without incurring unacceptable risks. Finally, the in-service review ensures the product or system is operating with managed risk. The goal of this review is to understand the quality of the deployed product and provide a summary of any risks related to the product (*Defense Acquisition Guidebook*, 2017).

TECHNICAL DRAWINGS AND SPECIFICATIONS

> Interpret specification requirements in relation to product and process characteristics and technical drawings, including characteristics such as views, title blocks, dimensioning and tolerancing, and geometric dimensioning and tolerance symbols (GD&T). (Evaluate)
>
> **Body of Knowledge III.C**

It is expected that drawings have dimensions that provide detailed information about sizes, shapes, and the location of different components and parts. It is also expected that part and component dimensions show acceptable variation. To produce any part or component to an exact dimension is nearly impossible, except by remote chance. Variations in materials, machines, manufacturing parameters, and humans make it necessary that dimensions have acceptable variations. Such variation is referred to as *tolerance*. Higher quality requires tighter tolerances that, in turn, require more expensive and strict production and inspection procedures to obtain. There are two types of tolerances: unilateral tolerance and bilateral tolerance. Unilateral tolerance specifies allowable variation in a dimension from a basic or nominal size in one direction in relation to that basic size.

For example, $2.000^{+0.000/-0.005}$ inches describes an allowable variation only in the lower limit: unilateral tolerance. Specifications on a part with this tolerance will be 2.000 inches and 1.995 inches as desired upper and lower limits, respectively. On the other hand, $2.000^{+0.005/-0.005}$ inches describes a bilateral tolerance. It specifies a dimension with allowable variations in both directions of the basic size. Specifications on a part with such bilateral tolerance will be 2.005 inches and 1.995 inches as desired upper and lower limits, respectively.

Geometric Dimensioning and Tolerancing (GD&T)

Geometric tolerancing defines tolerances for geometric features or characteristics on a part. Figure 3.5 shows some of the geometric dimensioning symbols as defined in ANSI Y14.5M. Figure 3.6 illustrates the interpretation of a geometric tolerance on a drawing.

The limit dimensions of the simple cylindrical piece at the top of Figure 3.7 define the maximum and minimum limits of a profile for the work. The form or shape of the part may vary as long as no portions of the part exceed the maximum profile limit or are inside the minimum profile limit. If a part measures its maximum material limit of size everywhere, it should be of perfect form. This is referred to as the *maximum material condition* (MMC) and is at the low limit for a hole or slot, but at the high limit for parts such as shafts, bolts, or pins.

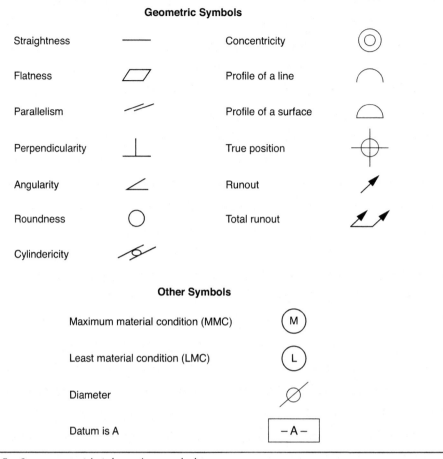

Figure 3.5 Some geometric tolerancing symbols.

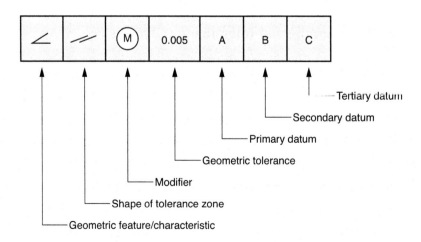

Figure 3.6 Interpretation of a geometric tolerance on a drawing.

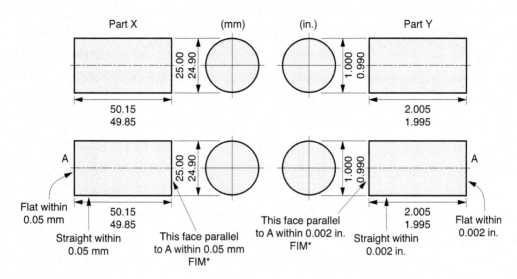

*FIM = Full indicator movement

Figure 3.7 Part drawing with and without tolerances of form.

Source: Reprinted with permission of the Society of Manufacturing Engineers, *Manufacturing Processes and Materials,* 4th ed., Copyright 2000.

If it is desired to provide greater control on the form than is imposed by the limit dimensions, then certain tolerances of form must be applied. In most cases, these tolerances appear in the form of notations on the drawing, as is illustrated at the bottom of Figure 3.7.

Positional Tolerances

Positional tolerancing is a system of specifying the true position, size, or form of a part feature and the amount it may vary from the ideal. The advantage of the system is that it allows the one responsible for making the part to divide tolerances between position and size as he or she finds best. The principles for two simple mating parts are illustrated in Figure 3.8. The basic dimensions without tolerances are shown at the bottom and right side of each part. Beneath the size dimension for holes or posts is a box with the notations for positional tolerancing. Several specifications are possible, but only one set is shown here as an example. The circle and cross in the first cell of the box is the convention that says the feature has a positional tolerance.

Part I in Figure 3.8 introduces the idea of the MMC utilized in most positional tolerancing. This is designated by the letter "M" in a circle and means that the smallest hole (12.70 mm or 0.500 in.) determines the inner boundary for any hole. The "Ø 0.20 mm (0.008 in.)" notation in the box specifies that the axis of any minimum-size hole must not be outside a theoretical cylinder of 0.20 mm (0.008 in.) diameter around the true position. A 12.50 mm (0.492 in.) diameter plug in true position will fit in any 12.70 mm (0.500 in.) diameter hole with its axis on the 0.20 mm (0.008 in.) diameter cylinder. Any hole that passes over such a plug is acceptable, provided that its diameter is within the high and low limits specified.

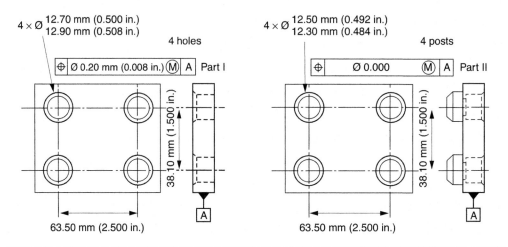

Figure 3.8 Two parts dimensioned with positional tolerances.

Source: Reprinted with permission of the Society of Manufacturing Engineers, *Manufacturing Processes and Materials*, 4th ed., Copyright 2000.

The letter "A" in the specification box designates that the theoretical cylinder bounding the hole axes must be perpendicular to the datum surface carrying the "A" flag. Features usually are referred to with three coordinate datum surfaces, but for simplicity, in this case, the holes are related only to each other and surface "A" and not to the sides of the part.

Part II of Figure 3.8 introduces the idea of zero MMC specified by "∅ 0.000" before the MMC symbol. This means the axis of the largest diameter post (12.50 mm [0.492 in.]) must be exactly in the true position, but smaller sizes of posts may vary in position as long as they do not lie outside the boundary set by the largest. Thus, if the posts are held to a tolerance smaller than the 0.20 mm (0.008 in.) specified, say to a tolerance of 0.05 mm (0.002 in.), the difference (0.15 mm [0.006 in.]) is then available for variations in post positions. The advantage of zero MMC is that only one limit of the feature, in this case the lower limit of the post diameter, needs to be checked along with position.

VERIFICATION AND VALIDATION

> Interpret the results of evaluations and tests used to verify and validate the design of products, processes and services, such as installation qualification (IQ), operational qualification (OQ), and process qualification (PQ). (Evaluate)
>
> **Body of Knowledge III.D**

Design verification as defined by ISO 9000:2015 is the "confirmation, through the provision of objective evidence, that specified requirements have been fulfilled." In other words, verification consists of a series of evaluations to ensure that the item is built to design and to specifications. The objective evidence may be the result of an inspection or may come from other forms of determination, such as performing alternative calculations or reviewing documents.

There are four potential verification methods: demonstration, inspection, analysis, and test. *Demonstration*, one of the simplest methods, is where the product or process is operated and visual confirmation is made to verify that the design requirements are met. Demonstration is appropriate only when quantitative evidence is not required for verification. Demonstration may use models, simulations, mockups, or the end product.

Inspection is another simple means of verification, where physical characteristics or materials or parts are examined to ensure requirements are met. Inspection requires the least number of resources and is typically used to verify a physical feature of the design. Inspection to ensure and control product quality, as performed in industry, is of two kinds: visual inspection and dimensional inspection. Visual inspection, by far the more common of the two, involves visual examination by human operators for conformity to aesthetic requirements. Less common, but equally important and generally more difficult to perform adequately, is dimensional inspection. Quality, of course, cannot be inspected into a product. Quality depends on engineering and manufacturing excellence, and inspection simply determines whether it exists. Better inspection is not the solution to large numbers of rejects. The solution must take the form of improvements in design or in the manufacturing process.

Visual inspection takes place, even if inadvertently, each time a part is handled during its manufacture. Parts such as bearing elements, which have critical aesthetic requirements, may be given a final visual inspection once manufacture is complete. Visual inspection is concerned primarily with gross appearance, the detection of surface flaws, and the recognition of patterns. These functions have, to date, attracted far less attention from developers of automatic inspection systems than the functions associated with dimensional inspection. Consequently, the human being currently is the most efficient general-purpose flaw-detection and pattern-recognition "instrument" available to the manufacturer. Human beings have highly developed sensing and data-processing faculties. Human operators are trainable and adaptive, although they are generally less reliable and experience more downtime than their automatic-equipment counterparts. Current research in artificial intelligence will surely cause this situation to change in the future.

Dimensional inspection refers to the measurement of lengths and angles and, in combination, of geometric shapes and may be accomplished automatically by a machine or manually by an operator. Measurements that are taken while the product is still undergoing manufacture have a greater value than those applied to the finished product, since the former constitute process control whereas the latter are merely process verification. Obviously, it is more expensive to correct or to scrap a bad product than it is to manufacture it properly in the first place.

Analysis uses mathematical models and other analytical techniques such as modeling and simulation to determine whether the design conforms to requirements. Finally, *test* is a designed experiment or activity to determine whether the requirements are met under controlled conditions (Defense Acquisition Guidebook 2017). This method of verification requires the most resources; it is described in more detail in Chapter 6. These verification activities should be done throughout the review process of a product or process.

Design validation is the "confirmation, through the provision of objective evidence, that the requirements for a specific intended use or application have been fulfilled" (ISO 9000:2015). In other words, validation ensures that the product or system operates as expected in its intended environment and as required by the customer. The objective evidence for validation may be the result of a test or some other form of determination. The test methods, sample sizes, and acceptance criteria should be clearly specified during conceptual planning of a product or process, and the design should be validated at each phase of the design review. When designing the tests, consider incorporating the following factors:

- Dimensional wear, material fatigue, assembly process variation
- Variation of critical characteristics throughout the range of the tolerances
- Contamination
- Environmental aging and extreme environmental conditions
- Extreme customer usage, such as maximum loads or long-duty cycles

Test results should be analyzed using appropriate statistical methods, including reliability analysis. Reliability testing falls into four major categories (details in Ebeling 2009 and Dodson and Nolan 1999):

- Environmental stress screening to determine the capability of the product under different operating conditions and to help eliminate infant mortality failures
- Reliability growth tests performed periodically between design conception and final production to track gains in reliability
- Reliability qualification tests to provide assurance that production units will meet requirements when they become available
- Production reliability acceptance tests to periodically verify that production units meet specified reliability requirements and are acceptable for use

A more detailed discussion of reliability and maintainability is provided in the "Reliability and Maintainability" section of this chapter. Test failures should be carefully examined to determine the failure modes. Unanticipated failure modes must be added to the design failure modes and effects analysis (DFMEA). Of course, corrective actions and design improvements must be pursued if the test results do not meet the quality goals.

Results of engineering evaluations, reliability tests, and other methods used to validate the design should be included in the design reviews. In addition, this information should be used to update the classification of quality characteristics. As is the case with many quality disciplines, the process of classifying characteristics should be iterative. Characteristics that are associated with unexpected failures may require reclassification as major or critical characteristics. Characteristics that perform as expected may be candidates for downgrading to minor characteristics. In all cases, involve the quality team in the discussions. There can be no substitute for the experience and process knowledge the team members bring to the design review process.

Process and product validation is broken down into several parts: installation qualification (IQ), operational qualification (OQ), and process qualification (PQ). IQ is done to establish that all systems and equipment have been installed correctly. OQ is performed to establish that the equipment control limits meet their respective requirements. PQ is done to establish that the process consistently produces acceptable products under normal operating conditions (Durivage 2016). A final stage often undertaken is the process performance qualification (PPQ), which demonstrates that the validated processes produce a product that meets its specifications. This phase accounts for the entire manufacturing process, not just one subprocess. For more information on product and process validation, see Durivage (2016) in References.

RELIABILITY AND MAINTAINABILITY

This section focuses on estimating and predicting reliability and defines other reliability measures for repairable systems, such as maintainability and availability. Other chapters in this handbook focus on quality as a static characteristic of a product at the time it is released to the user. However, because reliability is a time-dependent quality characteristic, traditional methods for quality control cannot be used to ensure product reliability and maintainability. Because reliability engineering is a broad field, it is impossible to cover the entire range of reliability topics in one section. Therefore, the focus is on reliability and maintainability definitions, analysis of failure data, design of systems for reliability, and maintainability. Reliability and maintainability as elements of product and process design will be discussed in four sections: predictive and preventive maintenance tools, reliability systems and measures, reliability models, and reliability, safety, and hazard assessment tools. The BoK includes a section on reliability, safety, and hazard assessment tools. While these are an important part of reliability and maintainability, they are also important tools for risk management and thus are discussed in detail in Chapter 7.

Predictive and Preventive Maintenance Tools

> Describe and apply the tools and techniques used to maintain and improve process and product reliability. (Apply)
>
> **Body of Knowledge III.E.1**

Reliability is defined as the probability that a product or service will operate properly for a specified time (design life) under the design operating conditions.

The main factors that lead to a system's failure include the system's design and configuration, the reliability of its components, the operating environment, and the interactions among environmental factors, manufacturing defects, and preventive and scheduled maintenance. Further, reliability cannot be measured at the release time of the product but can only be predicted (Elsayed 2000).

It is extremely important to consider reliability during the design phase of a product or service because minor, major, and catastrophic failures result in economic consequences such as repairs or replacements, the loss of production or interruption of service, and potentially severe economic losses and the loss of life. Examples of major failures are failure of a major link of a telecommunications network, failure of a power generating unit, or failure of software for an air traffic control system.

The consequences of catastrophic failures are much more severe than those of minor or major failures, and may include the loss of human life and significant economic losses. Examples of catastrophic failures are the explosions at the Chernobyl nuclear reactors site in the former USSR (Elsayed 1996), the explosion of the space shuttle *Challenger* in 1986, and the failure of the space shuttle *Columbia* in 2003.

Reliability also has a great effect on consumers' perception of a manufacturer. For example, consumers' experiences with automobile recalls, repairs, and warranties affect the manufacturer's future sales.

Three important functions that are the result of traditional calculus derivations help quantify reliability: the reliability function, the failure time distribution function (sometimes referred to as the probability density function), and the hazard rate function (or instantaneous failure rate).

Suppose N identical components are tested. During a specified time interval t, x failures and $(N - x)$ survivors are observed. Because reliability is defined as the cumulative probability function of success, then at time t the reliability $R(t)$ is:

$$R(t) = \frac{(N - x)}{N} \tag{3.1}$$

In other words, the *reliability function* (or survival function) at time t is the fraction of all components that have survived for a time greater than t. $R(t)$ is also used as the estimate of the probability that a randomly selected component will survive for a time greater than t. To describe the distribution of failures, the cumulative distribution function (cdf) of failure $F(t)$ can be defined as:

$$F(t) = \frac{x}{N} \tag{3.2}$$

(See Chapter 6 for more details on cdfs.) The cdf given in Equation (3.2) can be interpreted as:

- The probability that a randomly selected unit drawn from a population fails by time t, or

- The fraction of all units in the population that fail by time t.

In addition, $F(t)$ is the complement of $R(t)$ so

$$F(t) + R(t) = 1 \tag{3.3}$$

Equation (3.3) can be rewritten as:

$$R(t) = 1 - F(t) \tag{3.4}$$

or

$$F(t) = 1 - R(t) \tag{3.5}$$

Suppose N identical units are selected at random from a population described by $F(t)$. Then $NF(t)$ is the average (expected) number of failures through time t, and $NR(t)$ represents the average (expected) number of survivors through time t. That is, one would expect $NR(t)$ of the units to still be operational up to time t.

A probability density function (pdf) that represents the distribution of failure time can be found by taking the derivative of Equation (3.5):

$$f(t) = \frac{dF(t)}{dt} = -\frac{dR(t)}{dt} \tag{3.6}$$

The *hazard rate function* is defined as the limit of the failure rate as the time interval approaches zero. In other words, it provides an instantaneous rate of failure at some time t. The hazard rate function (also known as the instantaneous failure rate function) can be expressed as:

$$h(t) = \frac{\text{Number of failures per unit time}}{\text{Number of components tested per unit time}} = \frac{f(t)}{R(t)} \tag{3.7}$$

In some situations, failure times are placed into time intervals and the individual failure times are no longer preserved. In this case, the failure times become grouped data. The reliability, distribution function, failure density, and hazard rate are estimated from the grouped data.

Suppose it is desired to estimate the four quantities given in Equations (3.1), (3.2), (3.6), and (3.7) in terms of a reliability test where N identical units are tested. First, record the number of failed units (xi) and the number of survivors ($ni = N - xi$) at time ti (where $i = 1, 2, \ldots$). Next, $R(t)$, $F(t)$, $f(t)$, and $h(t)$ can be estimated as follows:

$$\hat{R}(t) = \frac{n_i}{N} \tag{3.8}$$

$$\hat{F}(t) = 1 - \hat{R}(t) \tag{3.9}$$

$$\hat{f}(t) = \frac{n_i - n_{i+1}}{N(t_{i+1} - t_i)}, \quad \text{for } t_i < t < t_{i+1} \tag{3.10}$$

$$\hat{h}(t) = \frac{n_i - n_{i+1}}{n_i(t_{i+1} - t_i)} = \frac{\hat{f}(t)}{\hat{R}(t)}, \quad \text{for } t_i < t < t_{i+1} \tag{3.11}$$

The caret ("hat") on each term indicates an estimated quantity. There are several methods for estimating these functions if the data are ungrouped, censored, ungrouped and censored, or grouped and censored. The reader is referred to Ebeling (2009) for a complete discussion and derivations of these quantities and more.

EXAMPLE 3.1

Suppose that 300 light bulbs are subjected to a reliability test. The manufacturer will release bulbs for distribution if the reliability of the bulbs is 0.75 at 2000 hours of usage. The observed failure during 1000-hour intervals are shown in Table 3.2.

Solution:

Using the previous equations, determine the four functions: reliability function, distribution function, probability density function (failure density), and the hazard rate function. The results are shown in Table 3.3.

To illustrate, consider the values for i=2, where 1000 < t < 2000:

Estimated reliability: $\hat{R}(t) = \dfrac{n_2}{N} = \dfrac{286}{300} = 0.95333$

Cumulative distribution function: $\hat{F}(t) = 1 - \hat{R}(t) = 1 - 0.95333 = 0.04667$

Failure density: $\hat{f}(t) = \dfrac{n_2 - n_3}{N(t_3 - t_2)} = \dfrac{286 - 269}{300\,(2000 - 1000)} = 0.0000567$

Hazard rate: $\hat{h}(t) = \dfrac{n_2 - n_3}{n_2(t_3 - t_2)} = \dfrac{286 - 269}{286\,(2000 - 1000)} = 0.0000594$

Table 3.2 Number of failures in the time intervals.

Upper bound (hours)	Number of failures, x
0	0
1000	14
2000	17
3000	21
4000	25
5000	31
6000	37
7000	40
8000	50
9000	65

Table 3.3 Reliability, cdf, failure density, and hazard rate for the light bulb example.

Interval	Upper bound	Failures in the interval	Survivors	Reliability	cdf	Failure density	Hazard rate
i	t_i	x_i	n_i	$\hat{R}(t)$	$\hat{F}(t)$	$\hat{f}(t)$	$\hat{h}(t)$
1	0	0	300	1.00000	0.00000	0.0000467	0.0000467
2	1000	14	286	0.95333	0.04667	0.0000567	0.0000594
3	2000	17	269	0.89667	0.10333	0.0000700	0.0000781
4	3000	21	248	0.82667	0.17333	0.0000833	0.0001008
5	4000	25	223	0.74333	0.25667	0.0001033	0.0001390
6	5000	31	192	0.64000	0.36000	0.0001233	0.0001927
7	6000	37	155	0.51667	0.48333	0.0001333	0.0002581
8	7000	40	115	0.38333	0.61667	0.0001667	0.0004348
9	8000	50	65	0.21667	0.78333	0.0002167	0.0010000
10	9000	65	0	0.00000	1.00000	—	—

These values can be easily calculated using a spreadsheet.

The reliability function in Figure 3.9 indicates that the bulbs exceed the level of reliability set by the manufacturers. The distribution function in Figure 3.10 shows how unreliability grows with the passage of time. The failure density function is displayed in Figure 3.11, and the hazard rate is displayed in Figure 3.12.

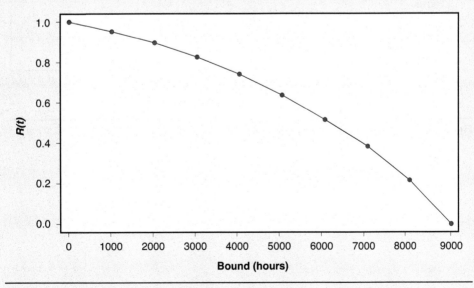

Figure 3.9 Reliability function versus time.

Continued

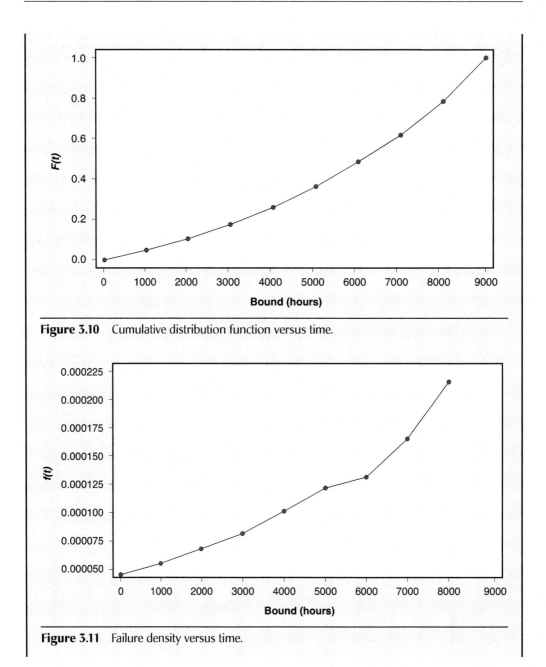

Figure 3.10   Cumulative distribution function versus time.

Figure 3.11   Failure density versus time.

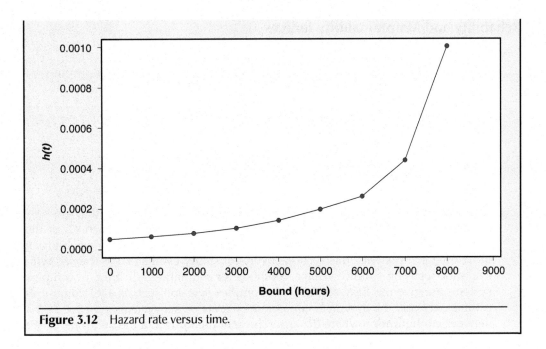

Figure 3.12 Hazard rate versus time.

EXAMPLE 3.2

Suppose the time-to-failure information given is no longer a set of data, but now is well modeled by a particular distribution. For example, suppose the failure time is well estimated or modeled by an exponential distribution with parameter λ (see Chapter 6 for details on the exponential distribution). For this distribution the cdf is given by

$$F(t) = 1 - e^{-\lambda t}$$

It can be shown that the pdf (failure density) is given by

$$f(t) = \lambda e^{-\lambda t}$$

Using the relationship $R(t) = 1 - F(t)$,

$$R(t) = e^{-\lambda t}$$

Finally, the hazard rate function can be shown to be

$$h(t) = \frac{f(t)}{R(t)} = \frac{\lambda e^{-\lambda t}}{e^{-\lambda t}} = \lambda$$

This result represents a *constant* failure rate. The exponential distribution is the only distribution with a constant failure rate function and whose application in reliability is discussed in more detail in the "Reliability Models" section.

Reliability and Maintainability Indices

> Apply indices such as mean time to failure
> (MTTF), mean time between failure (MTBF),
> mean time to repair (MTTR), availability, and
> failure rate. (Apply)
>
> **Body of Knowledge III.E.2**

A product is considered a system when it consists of components that are connected according to some design rules to produce the desired functions of the product. While the previous section discussed how to determine the reliability of individual components, this section covers reliability estimates for systems with a specific focus on simple systems. Methods for estimating reliability of complex systems are given in Elsayed (1996). In complex systems such as a telecommunications network, the system is composed of units or subsystems connected in a network configuration where the arcs represent the units and the nodes represent connection points along the paths. Reliability estimates of complex systems are often simplified into an aggregation of many simple systems.

This section discusses how to estimate the reliability of two kinds of simple systems (series systems and parallel systems) and addresses k-out-of-n systems and standby systems. Metrics for maintainability and availability are also discussed.

Series Systems

A typical series system is composed of n components (or subsystems) connected end to end. A failure of any component results in the failure of the entire system. A laser printer, for example, has several major components, such as a photoconductor drum, a laser beam, a toner station, and a paper feed system. The printer will fail if any of these components fails. The components are depicted graphically, with their respective reliabilities, in a block diagram in Figure 3.13.

Under the assumption that each of the component failures is independent, the reliability of the system is the product of the reliabilities of its components. The system reliability is expressed as:

$$R_s(t) = R_1(t)R_2(t) \ldots R_n(t) \tag{3.12}$$

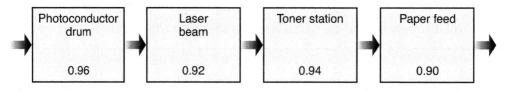

Figure 3.13 A typical series system.

where $R_i(t)$ is the reliability of the ith component (for $i = 1, 2, \ldots n$). Equation (3.12) assumes that the components are independent; that is, the degradation of one component does not affect the failure rate of the other components.

EXAMPLE 3.3

For Figure 3.9, the series reliability $R_s(t)$ is computed as follows:

$$R_s(t) = (0.96)(0.92)(0.94)(0.90) = 0.7472$$

The reliability of a series system is lower than its "weakest" component.

Parallel Systems

In a parallel system, components or units are connected in parallel so that the failure of one or more paths still allows the remaining path(s) to perform properly. The system fails when all units fail. Under the assumption of independence, the reliability of a parallel system $R_s(t)$ with n units can be estimated by:

$$R_s(t) = 1 - \left[F_1(t) F_2(t) \ldots F_n(t) \right] \tag{3.13}$$

or equivalently:

$$R_s(t) = 1 - \left[\left(1 - R_1(t)\right)\left(1 - R_2(t)\right) \ldots \left(1 - R_n(t)\right) \right] \tag{3.14}$$

where $F_i(t)$ is the probability of failure of the ith component and $R_i(t)$ is the reliability of the ith component (for $i = 1, 2, \ldots, n$). Equation (3.14) results from the relationship given in Equation (3.5); that is, $F_i(t) = 1 - R_i(t)$. If the components are identical and p is the probability that a component is operational (that is, $R_i(t) = p$ for all units), then the system reliability becomes

$$
\begin{aligned}
R_s(t) &= 1 - \left[F_1(t) F_2(t) \ldots F_n(t) \right] \\
&= 1 - \left[\left(1 - R_1(t)\right)\left(1 - R_2(t)\right) \ldots \left(1 - R_n(t)\right) \right] \\
&= 1 - \left[\left(1 - p\right)\left(1 - p\right) \ldots \left(1 - p\right) \right] \\
&= 1 - \left(1 - p\right)^n
\end{aligned}
\tag{3.15}
$$

The reliability block diagram of a parallel system is shown in Figure 3.10. The reader is referred to Ebeling (2009) or Tobias and Trindade (2011) for complete discussion of parallel systems.

Figures 3.13 and 3.14 show what is referred to as pure series and pure parallel systems, respectively. There are many situations where the design of the system is composed of combinations of series and parallel subsystems, such as parallel-series, series-parallel, and mixed parallel.

EXAMPLE 3.4

For Figure 3.10, the parallel system reliability is computed using Equation (3.14) (since the units are not identical):

$$R_s(t) = 1 - \left[\left(1 - R_1(t)\right)\left(1 - R_2(t)\left(1 - R_3(t)\right)\right]\right.$$
$$= 1 - \left[\left(1 - 0.95\right)\left(1 - 0.93\right)\left(1 - 0.91\right)\right]$$
$$= 0.99969$$

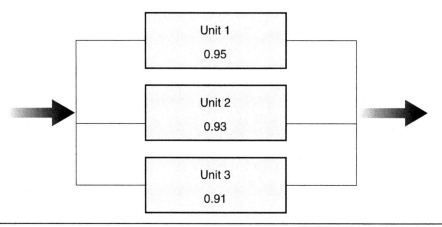

| Unit 1 |
| 0.95 |

| Unit 2 |
| 0.93 |

| Unit 3 |
| 0.91 |

Figure 3.14   A typical parallel system.

k-out-of-*n* Systems

Sometimes the system design requires, at a minimum, *k*-out-of-*n* functioning units for the system to operate properly. This is a direct application of the binomial distribution, where *p* represents the probability of success of a component (see Chapter 6 for complete details of the binomial distribution). Assuming the units are identical and independent, the system reliability in this case is given by:

$$R_s(t) = \sum_{i=k}^{n} {}_nC_i p^i (1-p)^{n-i} \tag{3.16}$$

where

$${}_nC_i = \frac{n!}{i!(n-i)!} \quad \text{and represents the number of ways } i \text{ units} \tag{3.17}$$
can be chosen from a group of *n* units.

$$n! = n(n-1)(n-2) \ldots (2)(1)$$

$$0! = 1$$

EXAMPLE 3.5

Suppose a system has four identical and independent components. System design requirements indicate that a minimum of two components must function for the successful operation of the system. What is the reliability of this system if each component has a reliability of 0.90?

Solution:

In this situation, $n = 4$, $k = 2$, and $p = 0.90$. Direct substitution into Equations (3.16) and (3.17) yields the following result:

$$R_s(t) = \sum_{i=2}^{4} {}_4C_i (0.90)^i (1-0.90)^{4-i}$$

$$= {}_4C_2 (0.90)^2 (1-0.90)^2 + {}_4C_3 (0.90)^3 (1-0.90)^1 + {}_4C_4 (0.90)^4 (1-0.90)^0$$

$$= 6(0.90)^2 (1-0.90)^2 + 4(0.90)^3 (1-0.90)^1 + 1(0.90)^4 (1-0.90)^0$$

$$= 0.9963$$

Standby Systems

Parallel systems are treated as redundant systems. Only one operational path is needed for the system to operate properly. Redundancy can take other forms, such as hot standby redundancy, where all units are operating in parallel at all times. Under this design, all units share the load equally.

In standby systems, the standby components function only upon the failure of the main component. The simplest form of a standby system is one where the components are assumed to be identical, the switch is assumed never to fail, and the standby component is also assumed never to fail while in standby status. Deviations from these assumptions present a variety of systems configurations whose analyses go beyond the scope of this section (see Tobias and Trindade [2011] or Ebeling [2009]). Figure 3.15 shows a standby system with perfect switching (i.e., the switch will turn on the standby component instantaneously upon the failure of the main component).

Standby system reliability with n standby components is given by

$$R(t) = e^{-\lambda t} \sum_{i=0}^{n} \frac{(\lambda t)^i}{i!} \tag{3.18}$$

where λ is the component failure rate and t is the time. If the system has only one standby component, the system reliability is given by

$$R(t) = e^{-\lambda t}[1 + \lambda t] \tag{3.19}$$

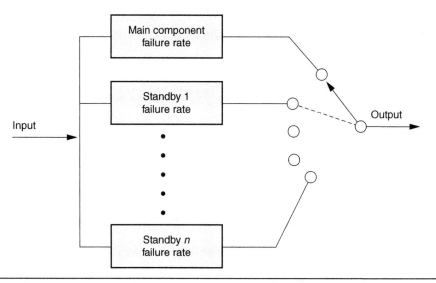

Figure 3.15 A standby system with *n* components in standby mode.

If the system has two standby components, the system reliability is given by

$$R(t) = e^{-\lambda t} \left[1 + \lambda t + \frac{(\lambda t)^2}{2!} \right]$$
(3.20)

Cold standby is another form of redundancy where the minimum number of units needed to properly operate the system share the load equally, and other units are available on a standby basis but can only share the load when one or more of the operating units fail. The third type of redundancy is called warm standby. This is similar to hot standby, but not all units share the load equally. Those carrying more than 50% of the load are the primary units, while the others are in a warm standby state. When a primary unit fails, the warm standby unit shares the load equally with the remaining primary units.

The following paragraphs present some important measures of reliability. The mean time to failure (MTTF) should not be confused with the mean time between failures (MTBF). The expected time between two successive failures is the MTTF when the system is nonrepairable. The expected time between failures, the MTBF, can be calculated when the system is repairable.

EXAMPLE 3.6

Suppose there is a standby system with three components in standby mode. All components are identical with a constant rate of failure of $\lambda = 0.02$. What is the system reliability at 75 hours of continuous operation?

Solution:
Substitute $n = 3$, $\lambda = 0.02$, and $t = 75$ in Equation (3.18):

$$R(75) = e^{-(0.02)(75)} \sum_{i=0}^{3} \frac{[(0.02)(75)]^i}{i!}$$

$$= e^{-1.5} \sum_{i=0}^{3} \frac{(1.5)^i}{i!}$$

$$= e^{-1.5} \left[\frac{(1.5)^0}{0!} + \frac{(1.5)^1}{1!} + \frac{(1.5)^2}{2!} + \frac{(1.5)^3}{3!} \right]$$

$$= e^{-1.5} [1 + 1.5 + 1.125 + 0.5625]$$

$$= 0.2231 [4.1875]$$

$$= 0.9344$$

First consider n identical nonrepairable systems and observe the times to failure for them. Assume that the observed times to failure are $t_1, t_2, \ldots, t_n$. The estimated MTTF is:

$$\text{MTTF} = \frac{1}{n} \sum_{i=1}^{n} t_i \tag{3.21}$$

For constant failure rate the MTTF is:

$$\text{MTTF} = \frac{1}{\lambda} \tag{3.22}$$

which can be interpreted as the reciprocal of the failure rate. It should be noted that this is only true for the constant failure rate model. The accurate method for estimating MTTF for discrete time intervals is given in Equation (3.21). MTTF can be estimated by using integration for continuous time functions.

Maintainability and Availability

Several measures of reliability have been presented for nonrepairable systems, including reliability function and MTTF. Other measures of reliability are defined for repairable systems, such as system availability (instantaneous, average uptime, inherent, operational, and achieved availabilities), mean time to repair (MTTR), and maintainability.

MTTR is defined as the average time to repair a failure, not including waiting time for parts or tools to start the repair. *Maintainability* is defined as the probability that a failed system is restored to its operational condition within a specified time.

Common to all these definitions is that the system is subject to repair or replacement upon failure. Availability at time t is defined as the probability that the system is properly operating at that time. The steady state availability is the long-term availability of the system ($t \rightarrow \infty$). The steady state availability A is defined as:

$$A = \frac{\text{MTBF}}{\text{MTBF} + \text{MTTR}} \qquad (3.22)$$

Maintenance actions or policies can be classified as corrective maintenance, preventive maintenance, and predictive maintenance (which is also called on- condition maintenance). Maintenance actions are dependent on many factors, such as the failure rate of the machine, the cost associated with downtime, the cost of repair, and the expected life of the machine.

A *corrective maintenance policy* requires no repairs, replacements, or preventive maintenance until failures occur, which allows for maximum run time between repairs. Although a corrective maintenance policy does allow for maximum run time between repairs, it is neither economical nor efficient, as it may result in a catastrophic failure that requires extensive repair time and cost.

A *preventive maintenance policy* requires maintaining a machine according to a predetermined schedule, whether a problem is apparent or not. On a scheduled basis, machines are removed from operation, disassembled, inspected for defective parts, and repaired accordingly. Actual repair costs can be reduced in this manner, but production loss may increase if the machine is complex and requires days or even weeks to maintain. Preventive maintenance also may create machine problems where none existed before. It is important to note that preventive maintenance is applicable only when the following conditions are satisfied:

1. The cost to repair the system after its failure is greater than the cost of maintaining the system before its failure.

2. The failure rate function of the system is monotonically increasing with time. Clearly, if the system's failure rate is decreasing with time, then the system is likely to improve with time and any preventive action or replacement is considered a waste of resources. Likewise, performing preventive maintenance when the failure rate is constant is improper, as replacing or maintaining the system before failures does not affect the probability that the system will fail in the next instant, given that it is now good (Jardine and Buzacott 1983).

The third repair policy is the *predictive maintenance policy*. Obviously, tremendous savings can result if a machine failure can be predicted and the machine can be taken off-line to make only the necessary repairs. Predictive maintenance can also be done when failure modes for the machine can be identified and monitored for increased intensity, and when the machine can be shut down at a fixed control limit before critical fault levels are reached.

Predictive maintenance results in two benefits. The first benefit is the result of taking a machine off-line at a predetermined time, which allows production loss to be minimized by scheduling production around the downtime. Since defective components can be predetermined, repair parts can be ordered and manpower scheduled for the maintenance accordingly. Moreover, sensors for monitoring the machines eliminate time spent on diagnostics, thus reducing the time to perform the actual repair. The second benefit is that only defective parts need to be repaired or replaced and the components in good working order are left as is, thus minimizing repair costs and downtime.

Three main tasks must be fulfilled for predictive maintenance. The first task is to find the condition parameter that can describe the condition of the machine. A condition parameter can be any characteristic, such as vibration, sound, temperature, corrosion, crack growth, wear, or lubricant condition. The second task is to monitor the condition parameter and to assess the current machine condition from the measured data. The final task is to determine the limit value of the condition parameter and its two components, the alarm value and the breakdown value. A running machine reaching the alarm value is an indication that the machine is experiencing intensive wear. At this point, the type and advancement of the fault must be identified to prepare the maintenance procedure. If a machine reaches the breakdown value, the machine must be shut down for maintenance. See Ebeling (2009) for a detailed discussion of availability and maintainability.

Reliability Models

> Identify, define, and distinguish between the basic elements of reliability models such as exponential, Weibull, and bathtub curve. (Apply)
>
> Body of Knowledge III.E.3

One of the earliest models of failure rate, the bathtub curve (see Figure 3.16), is so named because of its shape. The failure rate versus time can be divided into three regions. The first region is characterized by a decreasing failure rate with time and is conventionally referred to as the infant mortality phase or the early life region of the product, component, or system during its early period of use. Experience shows that the length (0 to T_1) of this region is about 10,000 hours (approximately one year) for most electronic components. The failures in this region are usually

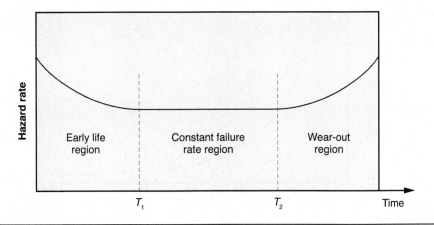

Figure 3.16 The general failure rate model (the bathtub curve).

attributed to defects in the manufacturing processes, assemblies, and shipping of the product.

The second region of the bathtub curve is the constant failure rate region, which is characterized by the inherent failure rate of the product's composite components. In this region, the failures occur randomly over time, as shown in Example 3.2. The third region is referred to as the wear-out region. It is characterized by an increasing failure rate over time. Most electronic components do not exhibit such a region, with the exception of electromechanical devices, such as relays. On the other hand, most, if not all, mechanical components that are subjected to rotating and alternating motions wear out with time. This is exemplified by the behavior of cutting tools, fatigue loading on structures, and wear-out due to friction between mating surfaces.

In Example 3.2, a case of constant failure rate was shown ("hazard rate" and "failure rate" are used interchangeably). This is the simplest failure model, as its pdf and reliability function can easily be shown in the following section, whereas other failure rate models (decreasing or increasing) are sometimes difficult to obtain from their corresponding functions.

The second region in the general failure rate model (bathtub curve) shows constant failure rate. Let λ be the constant failure rate. Thus $h(t) = \lambda$.

The reliability function and the pdf, originally derived in Example 3.2, are given in Equations (3.24) and (3.25), respectively:

$$R(t) = e^{-\lambda t} \tag{3.24}$$

$$f(t) = h(t)\, R(t) = \lambda e^{-\lambda t} \tag{3.25}$$

This is the standard exponential failure time distribution. The graphs of Equations (3.17) and (3.18), shown in Figures 3.13 and 3.14, are similar to those in Figures 3.10 and 3.11, which are obtained from actual failure data.

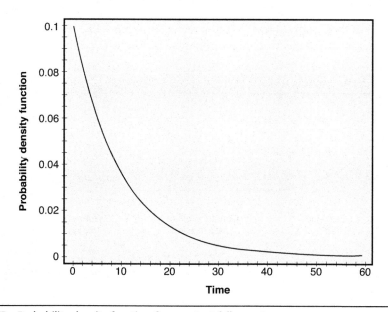

Figure 3.17 Probability density function for constant failure rate.

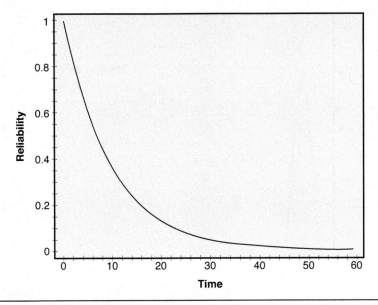

Figure 3.18 Reliability function for constant failure rate.

The first and third regions (the decreasing and increasing failure rate regions) of the general failure rate models can be described by time-dependent failure rate functions. The Weibull failure rate is the most widely used failure rate model that describes these regions. It is expressed as:

$$h(t) = \frac{\gamma}{\theta} t^{\gamma-1} \tag{3.26}$$

where γ and θ are the shape and scale parameters of the two-parameter Weibull distribution. For discussion of the Weibull distribution, see Chapter 6. The appeal of the Weibull hazard rate function comes from the fact that it can represent several other known functions. For example, when $\gamma = 1$, the Weibull hazard rate function becomes constant. When $\gamma = 2$, the resultant hazard function is linear with time and its pdf becomes the Rayleigh distribution. Indeed, Makino (1984) shows that the normal distribution can be approximated to Weibull when $\gamma = 3.43927$.

The reliability function and the pdf of the Weibull distribution are expressed respectively as:

$$R(t) = e^{\left(\frac{-t}{\theta}\right)^{\gamma}} \qquad t > 0 \tag{3.27}$$

and

$$f(t) = \frac{\gamma}{\theta}\left(\frac{t}{\theta}\right)^{(\gamma-1)} e^{\left(\frac{-t}{\theta}\right)^{\gamma}} \tag{3.27}$$

Figures 3.19 and 3.20 demonstrate the use of the Weibull failure model to describe decreasing and increasing failure rates. Of course, the constant failure rate is also included.

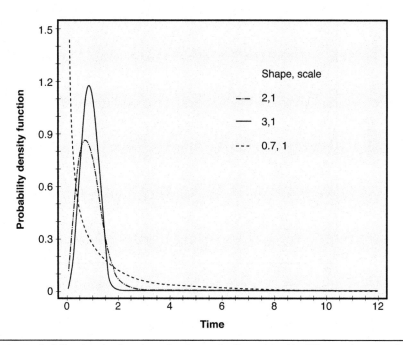

Figure 3.19   Probability density functions for the Weibull model with different shape and scale parameters.

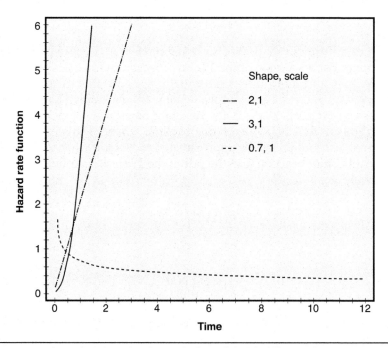

Figure 3.20   Hazard rate functions for the Weibull model with different shape and scale parameters.

Other probability distributions can be used to appropriately describe the failure times, including gamma, beta, log-logistic, lognormal, extreme value, and normal distribution (Elsayed 1996).

To be effective, a comprehensive reliability program must be based on data that are collected, verified and/or validated, analyzed, and used as the basis of decision making for design improvements and corrective action. At a minimum, reliability data must be thoroughly evaluated at key milestones such as the design phase and program reviews.

In the context of failure analysis and reporting, reliability data are most commonly evaluated in a closed-loop failure reporting and corrective action system. For purposes of this chapter, a closed-loop failure reporting and corrective action system provides the means to ensure that failures are not only documented and tracked over time but also analyzed to a sufficient depth to determine whether corrective action is required, and if so, what corrective action is necessary as determined by appropriate design engineers or a reliability review board.

Reliability/Safety/Hazard Assessment Tools

> Define, construct, and interpret the results of failure mode and effects analysis (FMEA), design FMEA (dFMEA), process FMEA (pFMEA), use FMEA (uFMEA), failure mode, effects, and criticality analysis (FMECA), and hazard analysis. (Analyze)
>
> **Body of Knowledge III.E.4**

During the design phase of the system, and when the system fails during operation, it is important to identify potential failures and their causes to eliminate critical failures (those that cause total interruption of the function or potential injuries to users) or develop appropriate methods to reduce their effects. Several approaches have proven to be effective in identifying potential failures: failure modes and effects analysis (FMEA), failure modes effects and criticality analysis (FMECA), and hazard analysis.

Hazard Analysis

The hazard-based approach to risk focuses specifically on safety risk, which is defined as the combination of the probability of occurrence of harm and the severity of that harm.

Thus, the focus here is on the harm and not on the failure mode. This doesn't mean the reliability focus of the FMECA is being de-emphasized. Instead, the scope of risk management is expanding to include all hazards that may lead to harm. This is important to understand since a perfectly reliable product without any failure mode may still potentially cause a harm to user or customer. Figure 3.21 shows that hazard-based risk management includes both failure mode and effects analysis (FMEA) and criticality analysis (CA).

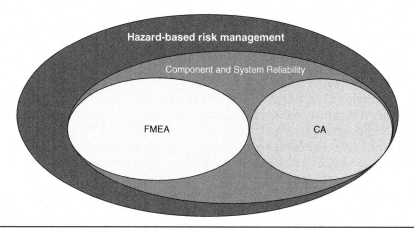

Figure 3.21   Hazard–based risk management.

Hazard analysis is a process to analyze the hazards and their consequences related to a product or process under study. The aim is to study the hazard, its causes, and hazardous conditions and effects such that the risks arising from them can be managed.

Let us begin by restating some relevant terminologies. Per ISO 14971:2019,

Hazard is the *"potential source of harm."*

Hazardous Situation is *"a circumstance in which people, property, or environment is/are exposed to one or more hazards."*

Risk is the *"combination of the probability of occurrence of harm and the severity of that harm."*

Figure 3.22 depicts the relationships among hazard, hazardous situation, impact (harm), and risk. The probability of a hazard leading to a hazardous situation is P1, and the probability of a hazardous situation leading to an impact is P2. Therefore, the probability of the risk itself, which is the combined probability of a hazard leading to a hazardous situation and the hazardous situation leading to harm (impact), is P1 × P2.

The main process involved in hazard analysis is shown in Figure 3.23.

Identify the Hazard

Hazard identification is the process of identifying and describing all significant system-specific hazards and hazardous situations. Some techniques for identifying hazards are the following:

- Checklists—going through a predefined generic list of hazards to identify which of them are applicable and documenting the rationale for their applicability.

- Questionnaire—a set of questions posed to subject matter experts, process owners, operators, and others to identify the applicable hazards. The answers to the questions are documented for the details of their applicablility and further analyzed and confirmed by the hazard identification team.

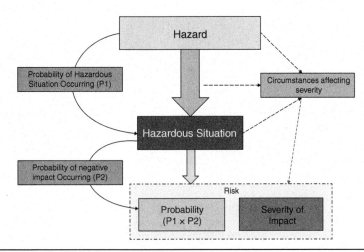

Figure 3.22 Relation among hazard, hazardous situation, impact (harm), and risk.

- Literature review—a review of any and all published literature and industry/trade publications of interest to document the applicable hazards on similar systems and check their applicability based on system and environment similarity.

- Brainstorming—a creative team-based technique of discussing the system and using checklists, questionnaires, or prompts to decide which hazards may apply to the system and how they can progress to hazardous situations.

- What-if techniques—analyzing the system by asking what-if questions to stimulate the brainstorming session. Certain guide words can be used to direct the team discussions for faster results.

- Review of internal and external information such as complaints, reports, and so on.

- Applicable standards and guidelines—review of national and international standards and guidelines by regulatory bodies to identify any recommended hazards or their sources.

Identify the Sequence of Events

Once the hazards are identified and their applicability is verified, identify the sequence of events that can transform the hazard into hazardous situations.

Identify the Hazardous Situation

For each sequence of events, identify all possible hazardous situations. One sequence of events could lead to multiple hazardous situations and vice versa.

Identify the Harm

Identify all possible harms from the hazardous situation. One hazardous situation could lead to multiple harms and vice versa.

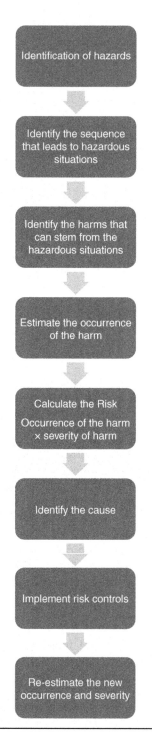

Figure 3.23   Hazard analysis process.

Estimate the Occurrence of the Harm

The process shown in Figure 3.24 is used to estimate the probability of the harm occurring due to a specific hazard. As denoted above, a sequence of events leads each hazard to become a hazardous situation and each hazardous situation to become a harm. Both of these steps have probabilities of their own.

Select a Scoring System

The risk scoring system includes scales for probability of occurrence and impact as well as any risk matrices for assessing risk levels. It is important to define and document these before proceeding with the risk ranking.

Estimate the Severity of the Harm

The severity of the harm is the measure of the impact or consequence. This must be graded using a severity scale.

Calculate the Risk

Calculate the risk as follows:

Risk (R) = the **probability** of the harm × the **severity** of the harm.

Identify the Cause

Identify the causes for the sequence of events or hazardous situations and in some cases for the hazard itself. Root cause analysis should be carried out where needed using tools such as 5 Whys and the Ishikawa diagram.

Implement Risk Control

Risk control is the process in which decisions are made and measures implemented by which risks are reduced to, or maintained at, specified levels. Based on the levels of the

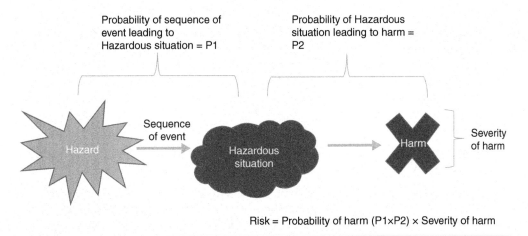

Figure 3.24 Probability path from hazard to harm.

risks, identify the ones that require mitigations or modifications. Once the new risk control measures are implemented, reestimate the occurrence value and the new severity. Recalculate the risk with the new occurrence and severity values, review the risk level, and document its acceptability.

Perform a Risk-Benefit Analysis

For the risks that remain in the unacceptable level, perform a risk-benefit analysis to see whether the benefits outweigh the risks for the system and its expected objective. If the benefits outweigh the risks, continue with the project; if the risks outweigh the benefits, redesign the product/process.

Failure Mode and Effects Analysis (FMEA)

Failure modes and effects analysis (FMEA) is a team-based problem-solving tool intended to help users identify and eliminate or reduce the negative effects of potential failures before they occur in systems, subsystems, product or process design, or the delivery of a service. FMEA can be used as a stand-alone tool or as part of a comprehensive quality program such as ISO 9000, ISO/TS 16949, advanced product quality planning and control plan (APQP), or Six Sigma. Accordingly, this section discusses terminology, theory, mechanics, and applications of FMEA as it applies to product designs, process designs, and systems.

Tague (2005) provides a list of when FMEA should be used:

- When a process, product or service is being designed or redesigned, after quality function deployment

- When an existing process, product or service is being applied in a new way

- Before developing control plans for a new or modified process

- When improvement goals are planned for an existing process, product or service

- When analyzing failures of an existing process, product or service

- Periodically throughout the life of the process, product or service

A word of caution: FMEA can be a powerful and effective tool for system, subsystem, product or process design, or service delivery improvement. However, FMEA cannot be used to identify combinations of failure modes, even when they are significant. Furthermore, FMEA is usually confined to analysis and evaluation of technical risks and not financial or strategic risks.

FMEAs Encountered by Quality Engineers

FMEA can be applied to the system, subsystem, design or process, or service delivery levels. A brief synopsis of each FMEA application is as follows:

- System FMEA. A system or subsystem is a collection of elements or components working together to accomplish a desired task or function. FMEA is applied at the system or subsystem level to identify potential failure modes and effects that could negatively impact system or subsystem performance. At the system or subsystem level, FMEA is focused at system or subsystem boundaries where potential failures are most likely to occur. The boundaries of interest for a system or subsystem FMEA include functional (i.e., expected outcomes assuming normal operation) or operational components (i.e., specific outputs expected as compared with tolerances, specifications, and timing).

- Design FMEA. A design—or more accurately, a product design—is a set of specifications that describe all aspects of a product (i.e., major functions, operating parameters and tolerances, materials, dimensions, and so on). FMEA is applied to product designs as early in the product design process as is feasible to identify potential failure modes that could result from a design flaw. Design FMEAs are a normal part of key milestones in the product development process, such as concept reviews, concept approvals, preliminary design reviews, and final design reviews.

- Process FMEA. A process design is a set of specifications that describe all aspects of a process (i.e., functional components, flow rates, process steps, equipment to be used, steps to be performed, operators or employees to be involved, etc.). Process design FMEA is applied to process designs at the earliest possible point to identify potential failure modes that could result from a design flaw. Process FMEAs are also a normal part of key milestones in the process development process.

- Service delivery FMEA. A service delivery is the completion of a set of tasks designed to meet one or more customer expectations. Service delivery FMEA is applied to service delivery designs to identify potential failure modes that, if experienced, would result in some level of dissatisfaction from customers. Service delivery FMEAs are also completed as early as possible in the design process and are a normal part of key milestones in the service delivery design process.

In most instances, the practicing quality engineer can be expected to work primarily on design and/or process FMEAs. Accordingly, this chapter focuses on design and process FMEAs and omits system/subsystem and service delivery FMEAs. Readers are encouraged to reference Stamatis (2003) for a detailed discussion of system/ subsystem and service delivery FMEAs.

Selecting a Standard for FMEA

There are two primary standards for FMEA: the military standard (MIL-STD 1629A) and the Society of Automotive Engineers standard (SAE J1739). Both standards are limited in scope to address only design and process FMEAs. These standards provide general FMEA forms and documents, identify criteria for the quantification of risk associated with potential failures, and provide very general guidelines on the mechanics of completing FMEAs. MIL-STD 1629A and SAE J1739 may be obtained by contacting the Department of the Navy (http://www.navy.mil) or the Society of Automotive Engineers (http://standards.sae.org), respectively.

Another useful reference is the manual *AIAG & VDA FMEA Handbook*, published by the Automotive Industry Action Group (AIAG). This manual is available at http://www.aiag.org.

FMEA can also be implemented in other fields, for example, healthcare. The Joint Commission recommends several resources and manuals on FMEA in healthcare, which can be found at http://www.jcrinc.com. The reader is encouraged to visit the Joint Commission at http://www.jointcommission.org or the Institute for Healthcare Improvement (IHI) at http://www.ihi.org for more information about FMEA and healthcare research and accreditation.

Planning for an FMEA

Planning for an FMEA involves a series of considerations that include, at a minimum, the following:

- Select appropriate applications for the analysis. An FMEA may be authorized by individuals at various levels within an organization or may be required by ISO 9000, QS-9000, APQP, Six Sigma methodologies, internal quality programs, or customer requirements. Whether authorized or required, an FMEA is expensive to complete and should be completed only in those instances where the benefits outweigh the costs.

- Identify and allocate resources. Resources include FMEA team members and a reporting structure, physical space to conduct the analysis and store documentation, time, and clerical/communications support.

- Define the scope. An FMEA can be conducted at a high level (i.e., the system level) or at a very detailed level (i.e., the component level or service delivery level). Since a high-level FMEA may lead to additional FMEAs at more detailed levels, it is very important to set the scope of the analysis before beginning.

- Establish expectations and deliverables. The team-based nature of completing an FMEA means FMEA team members will have dual or multiple responsibilities and reporting structures in addition to the FMEA team. It is critical, therefore, to clearly define performance expectations for all FMEA team members and to communicate those expectations directly to appropriate supervisory or managerial personnel in reporting structures outside the FMEA team. It is equally important that all FMEA team members understand what deliverables will result from the analysis and their respective roles in developing those deliverables.

- Establish milestones, due dates, and deadlines. Key milestones for an FMEA include receiving authorization for the analysis, establishing a reporting structure, allocating resources (particularly FMEA team members), gathering input for the analysis, completing the analysis, taking and monitoring corrective action, preparing documentation, and completing report-outs and debriefings. To ensure effectiveness, an FMEA should be conducted like a project from the perspective of establishing a schedule specifying due dates and deadlines for each of the major milestones.

- Establish a single point of responsibility. Although FMEA is a team-based analysis, sufficient practical experience supports the idea that assigning responsibility to a cross-functional team rather than a single individual is not the most effective policy. For a variety of reasons, a single person should be assigned the responsibility of FMEA team leader. That person must have authority to make decisions and allocate resources to complete the FMEA as planned.

FMEA Team Members

The belief that only the one or two people closest to a system, subsystem, product or process design, or service delivery should be assigned to an FMEA violates the very intent of the analysis. FMEA is intended to be completed by team members representing a broad cross section of expertise—technical and nontechnical. For example, an FMEA team should have representation from the following functional groups, as a minimum:

- Design engineering
- Manufacturing engineering
- Production
- Quality/reliability
- Purchasing/material control
- Sales and marketing
- Customers

It cannot be overemphasized that for an FMEA to be truly effective, the viewpoints and perspectives of every functional group mentioned above must be included—particularly customers. As Palady (1997) explains, "Excluding the customer's input from the FMEA will result in an incomplete list of the effects and low estimates of the severity."

Inputs and Outputs of an FMEA

To prepare for an FMEA, it is necessary to gather information from several sources. These data should be gathered prior to the initial FMEA team meeting to maximize the effectiveness of team members' time. Minimum inputs to an FMEA include the following:

- Process flowchart or functional block diagram
- Design specifications
- Customer requirements/specifications
- Testing data/results
- Data on similar process/design technology

- Warranty data

- Failure/rework data

- Design/configuration change data

- Prior FMEAs

- Results from quantitative analysis (DOE, SPC, process capability assessments, reliability assessments, etc.)

Outputs or deliverables from an FMEA include the following:

- FMEA documentation

- System, subsystem, design, process, and/or service delivery documentation

- Recommendation reports

- Corrective action reports

- Design changes

- Compliance reports

- Debriefings and presentations

Basic Steps in an FMEA

Complexity in an FMEA is directly related to the number of levels of analysis dictated by the situation or team members. At the most fundamental level, however, every FMEA consists of the same basic steps, including:

1. Identify a starting point for the analysis. The starting point will be a system, subsystem, product or process design, or service delivery system of interest. Identify boundaries of the system under analysis.

2. Gather all relevant inputs to support the analysis. Gathering inputs for an FMEA is a milestone to be completed prior to the initial FMEA meeting. It is far more effective, from both cost and efficiency perspectives, to have all team members at meetings participating in the analysis rather than leaving meetings to gather input. Other quality tools are frequently used during the completion of an FMEA. These other quality tools include, but are not limited to, cause-and-effect diagrams, process decision program charts, histograms, Pareto diagrams, run charts, force field analysis, fault tree diagrams, and root cause analysis. This step is used to analyze the structure and function of system and/or its components under analysis. This can be done by creating a functional block diagram, a process flow diagram or a boundary diagram.

3. Identify potential failure modes, such as:

   — Who would be impacted by a failure?

   — What would happen in the event of a failure?

   — When would the failure occur?

   — Where would the failure occur?

   — Why would the failure occur?

   — How would the failure occur?

4. Quantify the risk associated with each potential failure. Risk assessment is based on severity, occurrence, and, at times, detection of a potential failure. The risks should be evaluated in context of the risk acceptability criteria, which can be defined using RPN (Risk Priority Number), Risk Matrix, or though Action Priority Number (e.g. High, Medium, Low).

5. Develop a corrective action plan for mitigation of the most significant risks.

6. Repeat the analysis until all potential failures pose an acceptable level of risk. What constitutes an acceptable risk must be clearly defined by the individual or agent authorizing the FMEA.

7. Document results.

8. Report-out and/or present results.

Design FMEA (dFMEA) and Process FMEA (pFMEA)

Following the steps previously outlined that describe the planning functions preceding an FMEA, the analysis proceeds as the FMEA team completes appropriate documentation, such as the FMEA form. For purposes of this discussion, one form applicable to either a design or process FMEA will be described. Where the criteria change between a design FMEA and a process FMEA, both criteria will be provided. Figures 3.25 and 3.26 are blank FMEA forms applicable to design and process FMEAs. Each component of the forms is subsequently identified and described.

Figure 3.25 Blank design FMEA form.

Potential
Failure Mode and Effects Analysis
(Process FMEA)

FMEA number _____
Page _____ of _____
Prepared by _____

Item _____
Process responsibility _____
FMEA date (orig.) _____ (rev.) _____
Model year(s) vehicle(s) _____
Key date _____
Core team _____

Process function Requirements	Potential failure mode	Potential effect(s) of failure	Class	Potential cause(s)/ mechanism(s) of failure	Occur	Current design controls	Detec	R.P.N.	Recommended action(s)	Responsibility and target completion date	Action results				
											Actions taken	Sev	Occ	Det	R.P.N.

Figure 3.26 Blank process FMEA form.

The heading and documentation information of an FMEA is detailed below.

Product or process name	Provide the formal and/or commonly used (if different) name for the product or process.
Product or process description	Provide a brief description of the product or process that is meaningful to the FMEA team members.
FMEA number	Assign an FMEA number to each FMEA for tracking and documentation purposes. There are no standards for numbering FMEAs; however, a numbering system that links the FMEA to a specific period of time and product/process family is preferred.
Design/process owner	Identify the individual or team assigned primary responsibility for the design or process for tracking and documentation purposes. This individual or team is also identified for reference, if needed, during the FMEA.
FMEA team leader	Identify the individual assigned primary responsibility for completion of the FMEA for documentation purposes. This individual is also identified so as to establish a point of contact should any stakeholder need information during or after the FMEA.
FMEA team	List each member of the FMEA team along with any key responsibilities relative to the FMEA.
FMEA date	Provide the date(s) during which the FMEA is completed to help establish a chronology of events. Revision dates should be noted here as well.
FMEA risk assessment	Indicate the basis of the risk assessment. The FMEA risk assessment may be based on either actual failures or failure causes. It is important to document the team's decision to assess risk based on failures or causes to ensure that everyone evaluating the FMEA understands exactly how risk was assessed.

The analysis content and documentation of an FMEA is explained below.

DFMEA part name, number, and function, or PFMEA process function	Identify the product (i.e., part name, number, and function) or process (i.e., functions to be completed as part of the process).
Potential failure mode	List each of the potential failure modes associated with the design or process. Design failure modes may include dented, deformed, fractured, loosened, leaking, warped, and so on. Process failure modes may include overheating, inoperable, visual defect, and so on.

Potential effect of failure mode	For each potential failure mode, indicate the potential effect on customers or production/process personnel—it is entirely possible to have multiple effects for each potential failure mode.
Severity	Indicate the seriousness of the effect of the potential failure using the severity criteria defined in Tables 3.4 and 3.5. Note: The severity rating applies only to the effect of the potential failure.
Classification	Classify any special characteristics that may require additional process controls. SAE J1739 identifies classifications that include critical, key, major, and significant.
Potential cause of failure mode	For each potential effect of each failure mode, identify all possible causes—it is entirely possible to have more than one cause for each potential effect.
Occurrence	Indicate how frequently each failure is expected to occur using the occurrence criteria defined in Tables 3.6 and 3.7.
DFMEA design verifications or PFMEA process controls	For a design FMEA, identify the actions completed that ensure or verify the adequacy of the design. For a current process FMEA, identify the control currently in place that prevents a failure mode from occurring.
Detection	Indicate the ability of design verification or current process controls to detect a potential failure mode in the event that failure actually occurs. Use the detection criteria defined in Tables 3.8 and 3.9.
Risk priority number (RPN)	For each potential failure mode, multiply the severity (S), occurrence (O), and detection (D) assessments together. Since each scale (S, O, and D) ranges from 1 to 10, min(RPN) = 1 and max(RPN) = 1000.
Recommended actions	For each potential failure mode, list one or more recommended corrective actions. For further direction and guidance on prioritizing recommended corrective actions, refer to Chapter 5.
Individual/team responsible and completion date	For each recommended action, assign an appropriate individual or team and an expected completion date.
Actions taken	Provide a brief description of the actual actions taken and their respective action dates.
Resulting RPN analysis	Following each action taken, reiterate the severity, occurrence, and detection assessments and calculate a new resulting RPN. Actions taken based on RPNs and resulting RPNs continue until the risk assessment for each potential failure is "acceptable" to the customer and/or authorizing agent for the FMEA.

Table 3.4 Design FMEA severity criteria.

S	Effect	Severity Criteria	Corporate or Product Line Examples
10	Very High	Affects safe operation of the product, the health of users.	
9		Noncompliance with regulations.	
8	High	Loss of primary function necessary for normal operation during expected service life.	
7		Degradation of primary function necessary for normal operation during expected service life.	
6	Moderate	Loss of secondary function.	
5		Degradation of secondary function.	
4		Very objectionable appearance, sound, vibration, harshness, or haptics.	
3	Low	Moderately objectionable appearance, sound, vibration, harshness, or haptics.	
2		Slightly objectionable appearance, sound, vibration, harshness, or haptics.	
1	Very low	No discernible effect.	

Reprinted from Failure Mode and Effects Analysis FMEA Handbook (FMEAAV-1) 1st Edition, 2019. Manual with permission of AIAG (Automotive Industry Action Group) and VDA QMC (Verband der Automobilindustrie). AIAG and VDA QMC makes no representation or warranty as to the accuracy or usefulness of its materials when presented in contexts, with other materials, or for uses, other than as originally published by AIAG and VDA QMC.

Table 3.5 Process FMEA severity criteria.

S	Effect	Impact to Your Plant	Impact to Ship-to Plant (when known)	Impact to End user (when known)	Corporate or Product Line Examples
10	High	Failure may result in an acute health and/or safety risk for the manufacturing or assembly worker.	Failure may result in a health and/or safety risk for the manufacturing or assembly worker.	Affects safe operation of the product or operator.	
9		Failure may result in in-plant regulatory noncompliance.	Failure may result in in-plant regulatory noncompliance.	Noncompliance with regulations.	

Table 3.5 Process FMEA severity criteria. (Continued)

S	Effect	Impact to Your Plant	Impact to Ship-to Plant (when known)	Impact to End user (when known)	Corporate or Product Line Examples
8	Moderately high	100% of production run affected may have to be scrapped.	Line shutdown greater than full production shift; stop shipment possible; field repair or replacement required (Assembly to End User) other than for regulatory noncompliance.	Loss of primary function during expected service life.	
7		Product may have to be sorted and a portion (less than 100%) scrapped; deviation form primary process; decreased line speed or added manpower	Line shutdown from 1 hour up to production shift; stop shipment possible; field repair or replacement required (Assembly to End User) other than for regulatory noncompliance.	Degradation of primary function during expected service life.	
6	Moderately low	100% of production run may have to be reworked off line and accepted.	Line shutdown up to one hour.	Loss of secondary function.	
5		A portion of production run may have to be reworked off line and accepted.	Less than 100% of product affected; strong possibility for additional defective product; sort required; no line shutdown.	Degradation of secondary function.	
4		100% of production run may have to be reworked in-station before it is processed.	Defective product triggers significant reaction plan; additional effective products not likely; sort not required.	Very objectionable appearance, sound, vibration, harshness, or haptics.	

(continued)

Table 3.5 Process FMEA severity criteria. (Continued)

S	Effect	Impact to Your Plant	Impact to Ship-to Plant (when known)	Impact to End user (when known)	Corporate or Product Line Examples
3	Low	A portion of the production run may have to be reworked in-station before it is processed.	Defective product triggers minor reaction plan; additional defective products not likely; sort not required.	Moderately objectionable appearance, sound, vibration, harshness, or haptics.	
2		Slight inconvenience to process, operation, or operator.	Defective product triggers no reaction plan; additional defective products not likely; sort not required; requires feedback to supplier.	Slightly objectionable appearance, sound, vibration, harshness, or haptics.	
1	Very low	No discernible effect.	No discernible effect or no effect.	No discernible effect.	

Reprinted from Failure Mode and Effects Analysis FMEA Handbook (FMEAAV-1) 1st Edition, 2019. Manual with permission of AIAG (Automotive Industry Action Group) and VDA QMC (Verband der Automobilindustrie). AIAG and VDA QMC makes no representation or warranty as to the accuracy or usefulness of its materials when presented in contexts, with other materials, or for uses, other than as originally published by AIAG and VDA QMC.

Table 3.6 Design FMEA occurrence criteria.

O	Prediction of Failure Cause Occurring	Occurrence criteria - DFMEA	Corporate or Product Line Examples
10	Extremely high	First application of new technology anywhere without operating experience and/or under uncontrolled operating conditions. No product verification and/or validation experience. Standards do not exist and best practices have not yet been determined. Prevention controls not able to predict field performance or do not exist.	

Table 3.6 Design FMEA occurrence criteria. (Continued)

O	Prediction of Failure Cause Occurring	Occurrence criteria - DFMEA	Corporate or Product Line Examples
9	Very High	First use of design with technical innovations or materials within the company. New application or change in duty cycle / operating conditions. No product verification and/or validation experience. Prevention controls not targeted to identify performance to specific requirements.	
8	Very High	First use of design with technical innovations or materials on a new application. New application or change in duty cycle / operating conditions. No product verification and/or validation experience. Few existing standards and best practices, not directly applicable for this design. Prevention controls not a reliable indicator of field performance.	
7	High	New design based on similar technology and materials. New application or change in duty cycle / operating conditions. No product verification and/or validation experience. Standards, best practices, and design rules apply to the baseline design, but not the innovations. Prevention controls provide limited indication of performance.	
6	High	Similar to previous designs, using existing technology and materials. Similar application, with changes in duty cycle or operating conditions. Previous testing or field experience. Standards and design rules exist but are insufficient to ensure that the failure cause will not occur. Prevention controls provide some ability to prevent a failure cause.	
5	Moderate	Detail changes to previous design, using proven technology and materials. Similar application, duty cycle or operating conditions. Previous testing or field experience, or new design with some test experience related to the failure. Design addresses lessons learned from previous designs. Best Practices re-evaluated for this design but have not yet been proven. Prevention controls capable of finding deficiencies in the product related to the failure cause and provide some indication of performance.	

(continued)

Table 3.6 Design FMEA occurrence criteria. (Continued)

O	Prediction of Failure Cause Occurring	Occurrence criteria - DFMEA	Corporate or Product Line Examples
4	Moderate	Almost identical design with short-term field exposure. Similar application, with minor change in duty cycle or operating conditions. Previous testing or field experience. Predecessor design and changes for new design conform to best practices, standards, and specifications. Prevention controls capable of finding deficiencies in the product related to the failure cause and indicate likely design conformance.	
3	Low	Detail changes to known design (same application, with minor change in duty cycle or operating conditions) and testing or field experience under comparable operating conditions, or new design with successfully completed test procedure. Design expected to conform to Standards and Best Practices, considering Lessons Learned from previous designs. Prevention controls capable of finding deficiencies in the product related to the failure cause and predict conformance of production design.	
2	Very Low	Almost identical mature design with long term field exposure. Same application, with comparable duty cycle and operating conditions. Testing or field experience under comparable operating conditions. Design expected to conform to standards and best practices, considering Lessons Learned from previous designs, with significant margin of confidence. Prevention controls capable of finding deficiencies in the product related to the failure cause and indicate confidence in design conformance.	
1	Extremely Low	Failure eliminated through prevention control and failure cause is not possible by design.	

Table 3.7 Process FMEA occurrence criteria.

O	Prediction of Failure Cause Occurring	Type of Control	Prevention Controls	Corporate or Product Line Examples
10	Extremely High	None	No prevention controls.	
9	Very High	Behavioral	Prevention controls will have little effect in preventing failure cause.	
8				
7	High	Behavioral or Technical	Prevention controls somewhat effective in preventing failure cause.	
6		Best Practices: Behavioral or Technical		
5	Moderate		Prevention controls are effective in preventing failure cause.	
4				
3	Low	Best Practices: Behavioral or Technical	Prevention controls are highly effective in preventing failure cause.	
2	Very Low			
1	Extremely Low		Prevention controls are extremely effective in preventing failure cause from occurring due to design (e.g., part geometry) or process (e.g., fixture or tooling design). Intent of prevention controls - Failure Mode cannot be physically produced due to the Failure Cause.	

Reprinted from Failure Mode and Effects Analysis FMEA Handbook (FMEAAV-1) 1st Edition, 2019. Manual with permission of AIAG (Automotive Industry Action Group) and VDA QMC (Verband der Automobilindustrie). AIAG and VDA QMC makes no representation or warranty as to the accuracy or usefulness of its materials when presented in contexts, with other materials, or for uses, other than as originally published by AIAG and VDA QMC.

Table 3.8 Design FMEA detection criteria.

D	Ability to Detect	Detection Method Maturity	Opportunity for Detection	Corporate or Product Line Examples
10	Very Low	Test procedure yet to be developed.	Test method not defined.	
9	Very Low	Test method not designed specifically to detect failure mode or cause.	Pass-Fail, Test-to-Fail, Degradation Testing.	
8	Low	New test method; not proven.	Pass-Fail, Test-to-Fail, Degradation Testing.	
7	Low	New test method; not proven; planned timing is sufficient to modify production tools before release for production.	Pass-Fail Testing.	
6	Moderate	Proven test method for verification of functionality or validation of performance, quality, reliability and durability; planned timing is later in the product development cycle such that test failures may result in production delays for re-design and/or re-tooling.	Test-to-Failure.	
5	Moderate	Proven test method for verification of functionality or validation of performance, quality, reliability and durability; planned timing is later in the product development cycle such that test failures may result in production delays for re-design and/or re-tooling.	Degradation Testing.	
4	High	Proven test method for verification of functionality or validation of performance, quality, reliability and durability; planned timing is sufficient to modify production tools before release for production.	Pass-Fail Testing.	
3	High	Proven test method for verification of functionality or validation of performance, quality, reliability and durability; planned timing is sufficient to modify production tools before release for production.	Test-to-Failure.	

Table 3.8 Design FMEA detection criteria. (Continued)

D	Ability to Detect	Detection Method Maturity	Opportunity for Detection	Corporate or Product Line Examples
2	High	Proven test method for verification of functionality or validation of performance, quality, reliability and durability; planned timing is sufficient to modify production tools before release for production.	Degradation Testing.	
1	Very High	Prior testing confirmed that failure mode or cause cannot occur, or detection methods proven to always detect the failure mode or failure cause.		

Reprinted from Failure Mode and Effects Analysis FMEA Handbook (FMEAAV-1) 1st Edition, 2019. Manual with permission of AIAG (Automotive Industry Action Group) and VDA QMC (Verband der Automobilindustrie). AIAG and VDA QMC makes no representation or warranty as to the accuracy or usefulness of its materials when presented in contexts, with other materials, or for uses, other than as originally published by AIAG and VDA QMC.

Table 3.9 Process FMEA detection criteria.

D	Ability to Detect	Detection Method Maturity	Opportunity for Detection	Corporate or Product Line Examples
10	Very Low	No testing or inspection method has been established or is known.	The failure will not or cannot be detected.	
9		It is unlikely that the testing or inspection method will detect the failure mode.	The failure mode is not easily detected though random or sporadic audits.	
8	Low	Test or inspection method has not been proven to be effective and reliable (e.g. plant has little or no experience with method, gauge R&R results marginal on comparable process of this application, etc.).	Human inspection (visual, tactile, audible), or use of manual gauging (attribute or variable) that should detect the failure mode or failure cause.	
7			Machine-based detection (automated or semi-automated with notification by light, buzzer, etc.), or use of inspection equipment such as a coordinate measuring machine that should detect failure mode or failure cause.	

(continued)

Table 3.9 Process FMEA detection criteria. (Continued)

D	Ability to Detect	Detection Method Maturity	Opportunity for Detection	Corporate or Product Line Examples
6	Moderate	Test or inspection method has been proven to be effective and reliable (e.g. plant has experience with method, gauge R&R results are acceptable on comparable process of this application, etc.).	Human inspection (visual, tactile, audible), or use of manual gauging (attribute or variable) that will detect the failure mode or failure cause (including product sample checks).	
5			Machine-based detection (automated or semi-automated with notification by light, buzzer, etc.), or use of inspection equipment such as a coordinate measuring machine that will detect failure mode or failure cause (including product sample checks).	
4	High	System has been proven to be effective and reliable (e.g. plant has experience with method on identical process or this application), gauge R&R results are acceptable, etc.	Machine-based automated detection method that will detect the failure mode downstream, prevent further processing or system will identify product as discrepant and allow it to automatically move forward in the process until the designated reject unload area. Discrepant product will be controlled by a robust system that will prevent outflow of the product from the facility.	
3			Machine-based automated detection method that will detect the failure mode in-stream, prevent further processing or system will identify product as discrepant and allow it to automatically move forward in the process until the designated reject unload area. Discrepant product will be controlled by a robust system that will prevent outflow of the product from the facility.	
2		Detection method has been proven to be effective and reliable (e.g. plant has experience with method, error-proofing, verifications, etc.).	Machine-based detection method that will detect the cause and prevent the failure mode (discrepant part) from being produced.	

Table 3.9 Process FMEA detection criteria. (Continued)

D	Ability to Detect	Detection Method Maturity	Opportunity for Detection	Corporate or Product Line Examples
1	Very High	Failure mode cannot be physically produced as-designed or processed, or detection methods proven to always detect failure mode or failure cause.		

Reprinted from Failure Mode and Effects Analysis FMEA Handbook (FMEAAV-1) 1st Edition, 2019. Manual with permission of AIAG (Automotive Industry Action Group) and VDA QMC (Verband der Automobilindustrie). AIAG and VDA QMC makes no representation or warranty as to the accuracy or usefulness of its materials when presented in contexts, with other materials, or for uses, other than as originally published by AIAG and VDA QMC.

Figures 3.27 and 3.28, showing examples of design and process FMEAs, have been provided to help guide the reader through an actual analysis. The reader should note that the first column in the FMEA can be used to describe the item or component or it can describe the product or process function.

The function describes the intended use or expected useful characteristic of the system or component. The potential failure mode can correspond to failure of the function. Failures of the function can be derived from functional description and include:

- Loss of function (e.g., inoperable, fails suddenly)
- Degradation of function (e.g., performance loss over time)
- Intermittent function (e.g., operation randomly starts/stops/starts)
- Partial function (e.g., performance loss)
- Unintended function (e.g., operation at the wrong time, unintended direction, unequal performance)
- Exceeding function (e.g., operation above acceptable threshold)
- Delayed function (e.g., operation after unintended time interval)

The above list is reprinted from Failure Mode and Effects Analysis FMEA Handbook (FMEAAV-1) 1st Edition, 2019. Manual with permission of AIAG (Automotive Industry Action Group) and VDA QMC (Verband der Automobilindustrie). AIAG and VDA QMC makes no representation or warranty as to the accuracy or usefulness of its materials when presented in contexts, with other materials, or for uses, other than as originally published by AIAG and VDA QMC.

Sometimes, instead of functions, each potential failure mode of design feature of subcomponent or process step, can be analyzed in terms of requirement of that feature (Simon 2022). This is an exhaustive bottom up analysis which aims to equate the potential nonconformance of requirement with the failure effect.

Use FMEA (UFMEA)

UFMEA analyzes the uses and misuses of the product or process and identifies the use errors and their effects and consequences. The usability of the process or

Potential
Failure Mode and Effects Analysis
(Design FMEA)

System ___   Subsystem ___   X Component 01.03/Body closures (2)

Design responsibility Body engineering (3)

FMEA number 1234 (1)
Page 1 of 1
Prepared by A. Tate—X6412—Body engr (4)(7)

Model year(s)/vehicle(s) 199X/Lion 4dr/wagon (5)
Key date 9X 03 01 ER (6)
FMEA date (orig.) 8X 03 22 (rev.) 8X 07 14 (8)

Core team T. Fender—Car product dev., Childers—Manufacturing, J. Ford—Assy ops (Dalton, Fraser, Henley assembly plants)

Item / Function (9)	Potential failure mode (10)	Potential effect(s) of failure (11)	S e v (12)	C l a s s (13)	Potential cause(s)/ mechanism(s) of failure (14)	O c c u r (15)	Current design controls (16)	D e t e c (17)	R. P. N. (18)	Recommended action(s) (19)	Responsibility and target completion date (20)	Actions taken (21)	S e v	O c c	D e t	R. P. N. (22)
Front door L.H. H8HX-0000-A · Ingress to and egress from vehicle · Occupant protection from weather, noise, and side impact · Support anchorage for door hardware including mirror, hinges, latch, and window regulator · Provide proper surface for appearance items · Paint and soft trim	Corroded interior lower door panels	Deteriorated life of door leading to: · Unsatisfactory appearance due to rust through paint over time · Impaired function of interior door hardware	7		Upper edge of protective wax application specified for inner door panels is too low	6	Vehicle general durability test vah. T-118 T-109 T-301	7	294	Add laboratory accelerated corrosion testing	A Tate-Body Engrg 8X 09 30	Based on test results (Test No. 1481) upper edge spec raised 125mm	7	2	2	28
					Insufficient wax thickness specified	4	Vehicle general durability testing - as above	7	196	Add laboratory accelerated corrosion testing / Conduct Design of Experiments (DOE) on wax thickness	Combine w/test for wax upper edge verification A Tate Body Engrg 9X 01 15	Test results (Test No. 1481) show specified thickness is adequate. DOE shows 25% variation in specified thickness is acceptable	7	2	2	28
					Inapropriate wax formulation specified	2	Physical and Chem Lab test - Report No. 1265	2	28	None						
					Entrapped air prevents wax from entering corner/edge access	5	Design aid investigation with non-functioning spray head	8	280	Add team evaluation using production spray equipment and specified wax	Body Engrg & Assy Ops 8X 11 15		7	1	3	21
					Wax application plugs door drain holes	3	Laboratory test using "worst case" wax application and hole size	1	21	None						
					Insufficient room between panels for spray head access	4	Drawing evaluation of spray head access	4	112	Add team evaluation using design aid and buck and spray head	Body Engrg & Assy Ops	Evaluation showed adequate access	7	1	1	7

SAMPLE

Figure 3.27 Design FMEA example.

**Potential
Failure Mode and Effects Analysis
(Process FMEA)**

FMEA number ___1450___ (1)

Page ___1___ of ___1___

Item ___Front door L.H./H8HX-000-A___ (2)   Process responsibility ___Body engrg./assembly operations___ (3)   Prepared by ___J. Ford—X6521—Assy ops___ (4)

Model year(s) vehicle(s) ___199X/Lion 4dr/wagon___ (5)   Key date ___9X 08 26 Job #1___ (6)   FMEA date (orig.) ___9X 05 17___ (rev.) ___9X 11 06___ (7)

Core team ___A. Tate—Body engrg., J. Smith—OC, R. James—Production, J. Jones—Maintenance___ (8)

Process function (9)	Potential failure mode (10)	Potential effect(s) of failure (11)	S e v (12)	C l a s s (13)	Potential cause(s)/ mechanism(s) of failure (14)	O c c u r (15)	Current process controls (16)	D e t e c (17)	R. P. N.	Recommended action(s) (19)	Responsibility and target completion date (20)	Actions taken (21)	Action results (22)			
													S e v	O c c	D e t e c	R. P. N.
Manual application of wax inside door Requirements To cover inner door, lower surfaces at minimum wax thickness to retard corrosion	Insufficient wax coverage over specified surface	Deteriorated life of door leading to: • Unsatisfactory appearance due to rust through paint over time • Impaired function of interior door hardware	7		Manually inserted spray head not inserted far enough	8	Visual check each hour-1/shift for film thickness (depth meter) and coverage	5	280	Add positive depth stop to sprayer	MFG Engrg 9X 10 15	Stop added, sprayer checked on line	7	2	5	70
										Automate spraying	Mfg Engrg 9X 12 15	Rejected due to complexity of different doors on same line				
					Spray heads clogged • Viscosity too high • Temperature too low • Pressure too low	5	Test spray pattern at start-up and after idle periods, and preventative maintenance program to clean heads	3	105	Use Design of Experiments (DOE) on viscosity vs. temperature vs. pressure	Mfg Engrg 9X 10 01	Temp and press limits were determined and limit controls have been installed - control charts show process is in control Cpk=1.85	7	1	3	21
					Spray head deformed due to impact	2	Preventative maintenance programs to maintain head	2	28	None						
					Spray time insufficient	8	Operator instructions and lot sampling (10 doors / shift) to check for coverage of critical areas	7	392	Install spray timer	Maintenance 9X 09 15	Automatic spray timer installed - operator starts spray, timer controls shut-off control charts show process is in control Cpk=2.05	7	1	7	49

SAMPLE

Figure 3.28 Process FMEA example.

product is analyzed in detail to understand the errors that can occur during use and how they will impact the outcome of the intended function. As explained earlier in the chapter, FMEAs can be performed at different levels; the UFMEA is performed at a systems level. UFMEA usually considers the usability and human factors for the product, process, or service and considers the user interaction with the system as a whole at preset locations per design of the system. The flowchart in Figure 3.29 shows a workflow for UFMEA creation.

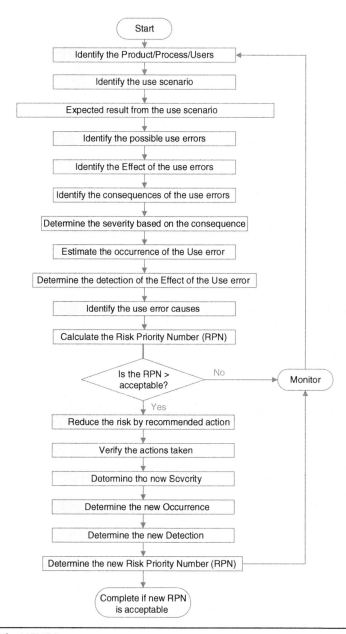

Figure 3.29 The UFMEA process.

Relationship between DFMEA and UFMEA

The failure modes in the DFMEA and the use errors in the UFMEA can be the failure effects in the PFMEA; the severity identified for the DFMEA and UFMEA failure effects should be the same for the PFMEA.

Failure Mode Effects and Criticality Analysis (FMECA)

MIL-STD 1629A defines two very important terms and concepts with respect to risk assessment. *Criticality* is "a relative measure of the consequences of a failure mode and its frequency of occurrences." *Criticality analysis* is "a procedure by which each potential failure mode is ranked according to the combined influence of severity and probability of occurrence" (MIL-STD-1629A 1980). Note that while this military standard was canceled in 1998, other industry standards for FMEA and FMECA exist—for example, AIAG FMEA-4, SAE J1739, and IEC 60812.

When criticality is considered in an FMEA, the name is changed to *failure mode effects and criticality analysis* (FMECA). FMECA can be a qualitative or quantitative assessment of risk that leads to a prioritization of corrective action based on severity (S) and occurrence (O) assessments. In the qualitative approach to risk assessment in FMECA, risk is categorized as frequent, reasonably probable, occasional, remote, or extremely unlikely. In the quantitative approach to risk assessment in FMECA, failure rate data, failure effect probability data, individual part failure data, and operating time data are required as input to one or more protocols as defined in Military Handbook 217.

The key result of an FMECA is a criticality matrix that ranks potential failures with respect to severity. The matrix then identifies a prioritization scheme for corrective actions based on the severity of potential failure modes. As displayed in an FMECA criticality matrix, potential failures plotted farther away from the matrix origin on a diagonal line represent higher potential risks of failure, and thus warrant increased need for corrective action.

Weighing of Constituent Risk Factors

As a general rule, the severity factor is weighed the highest, occurrence is second and detection should have the least weight. However, classic FMECA methods which rely of risk priority numbers (RPN) often weight them the same. This can lead to unintended data obfuscation and incorrect risk evaluations especially when detection is rated at extreme ends of the scale. To counter this, a Risk Matrix approach which assesses criticality based on just severity or occurrence can be used as in Chapter 7 or Moon (2020). Action Priority ratings can be assigned based on Severity and occurrence levels per Chapter 7 or AIAG VDA FMEA Handbook (2019).

EXAMPLE 3.7

Figure 3.30 shows an example of an FMECA for a traveling lawn sprinkler. Note that each hardware item is listed on a separate line. For each possible failure, its effect on the product is determined. Type of failure is also shown along with estimates for its probability of occurrence and for its seriousness (Gryna, Chua, and Defeo 2007). For additional discussion of FMECA, consult MIL-STD-1629A for guidance in completing a criticality assessment.

Designing for Quality

1 = Very low (<1 in 1000)
2 = Low (3 in 1000)
3 = Medium (5 in 1000)
4 = High (7 in 1000)
5 = Very high (>9 in 1000)

T = Type of failure
P = Probability of occurrence
S = Seriousness of failure of system
H = Hydraulic failure
M = Mechanical failure
W = Wear failure
C = Customer abuse

Product   HRC-1

Date   Jan. 14, 2017

By   S.M.

Component part number	Possible failure	Cause of failure	T	P	S	Effect of failure on product	Alternatives
Worm bearing 4224	Bearing worn	Not aligned with bottom housing	M	1	4	Spray head wobbles or slows down	Improve inspection
Zytel 101		Excessive spray head wobble	M	1	3	Spray head wobbles or slows down	Improve worm bearing
Bearing stem 4225	Excessive wear	Poor bearing/ material combination	M	5	4	Spray head wobbles and loses power	Change stem material
Brass		Dirty water in bearing area	M	5	4	Spray head wobbles and loses power	Improve worm seal area
		Excessive spray head wobble	M	2	3	Spray head wobbles and loses power	Improve operating instructions
Thrust washer 4226	Excessive wear	High water pressure	M	2	5	Spray head will stall out	Inform customer in instructions
Fulton 404		Dirty water in washers	M	5	5	Spray head will stall out	Improve worm seal design
Worm 4527	Excessive wear in bearing area	Poor bearing/ material combination	M	5	4	Spray head wobbles and loses power	Change bearing stem material
Brass		Dirty water in bearing area	M	5	4	Spray head wobbles and loses power	Improve worm seal design
		Excessive spray head wobble	M	2	3	Spray head wobbles and loses power	Improve operating instructions

Figure 3.30   Failure mode effects and criticality analysis.

Chapter 4
Product and Process Control

This chapter includes details on the following elements: product and process control methods, material control (including material identification, status, and traceability), material segregation, classification of defects, acceptance sampling (including sampling concepts, sampling standards and plans, and sample integrity), measurement and test (including measurement tools and destructive and nondestructive tests), metrology, and measurement system analysis (MSA).

METHODS

> Implement product and process control
> methods such as control plan development,
> critical control point identification, and work
> instruction development and validation.
> (Analyze)
>
> Body of Knowledge IV.A

In this section, product and process control methods, including control plans, critical control point identification, and work instructions, are presented. Such methods depend on the classification of quality characteristics and the results of validation tests (see Chapter 3 for more details). Characteristics that are critical to the operation of the process or the function of the product are subject to more intense monitoring and control.

Control plans are used to document and communicate the plan for monitoring and controlling the process. The control plan summarizes information from various sources into a single, handy document for quick reference on the production line. The format of the control plan is not important; standard spreadsheets are acceptable. However, the control plan should include the following elements:

- Station or operation number and process description

- Machinery, equipment, or fixtures

- Reference drawing numbers

- Product or process characteristic to be controlled (including tolerances)

- Evaluation method (gages, sensors, visual checks, etc.)

- Sample size and sample frequency

- Control method ($\bar{x}$ and R chart, check sheet, go/no-go, poka-yoke, etc.)

- Reaction plan to be followed when the control method detects a problem

The control plan is the final link in a seamless chain that begins with the design failure modes and effects analysis (FMEA) (refer to Chapter 3 for details on FMEAs). Potential failure modes that cannot be prevented through design are over to the process FMEA. Some failure modes can be prevented in the process through the use of poka-yokes or reduced to very low frequency through the use of designed experiments to optimize the process. Other failure modes can be detected with high confidence. Despite best efforts, some potential failures may still have unacceptable risk priority numbers (RPNs), and process controls must be added to monitor the process. The control plan should be checked to verify that all critical and significant characteristics identified during the design and process FMEAs are included.

At this point in the process, all nondestructive measurement systems listed in the control plan should have successfully passed the gage repeatability and reproducibility (R&R) requirement. Gage R&R studies are discussed in the "Measurement System Analysis (MSA)" section of this chapter. Sample sizes and sample frequencies should be based on statistically sound principles. Keep in mind that the sample frequency should be often enough to enable containment of suspect product prior to shipment to the customer. The quality engineer plays a critical role in selecting the control method that is best suited for the characteristic being monitored.

Perhaps the most important aspect of the control plan methodology is the reaction plan. The reaction plan lists the steps to be taken by the operator when the control method indicates a problem. For example, what should happen when the $\bar{X}$ chart goes out of control? Unfortunately, many references and training seminars do not adequately develop this concept. The examples simply state "adjust and recheck" or "recalibrate and recheck." Simplistic directions may lead to process tampering (overadjustment). In addition, opportunities for permanent corrective actions will be missed. (See Chapter 6 for a complete discussion of control charts.)

Good reaction plans include four critical elements: containment, diagnosis, verification, and disposition.

1. Containment. As soon as the problem is identified, quarantine and segregate all suspect product. This may include everything produced since the previous acceptable sample. A good inventory management system that uses the principle of "first in, first out" will simplify the task of containment should it ever be needed. Provide specific direction to the operator on how to accomplish containment. It also may be wise to intensify inspection until the problem is resolved.

2. Diagnosis. Determine the root cause of the failure. It may be necessary to repeatedly ask, "Why?" For example, if the failure occurred because the operator was not adequately trained, then ask, "Why was the

operator not properly trained?" Repeat this process until an appropriate root cause is identified that will lead to a permanent corrective action. Incorporate lessons learned from previous failures to facilitate the diagnostic process. Remember that in the heat of battle, common sense is not very common. Therefore, it is helpful to provide written guidance to the operator as to likely causes of the failure. In other words, specify the diagnostic steps and tests the operator should conduct during preliminary efforts to identify the root cause. If the root cause is still not identified, specify who should be called in to help, such as the product engineer or quality engineer.

3. Verification. Do not assume that the corrective action resolved the problem—prove it! Collect additional samples after the corrective change is implemented to verify that the problem is fixed. If possible, the reaction plan should specify how many additional samples are necessary before resuming normal operations.

4. Disposition. The obvious but nonetheless mandatory final step of the reaction plan is to determine an appropriate disposition for the material that was contained in the first step of the reaction plan. Typical dispositions include scrap, rework, sort, use as-is, and return to vendor. Written instructions are recommended for performing sorts or rework.

Figures 4.1 and 4.2 show an example of a control plan that was developed by a valve manufacturing company and incorporates many of the suggestions outlined above. The author uses code letters in the reaction plan section of the control plan. Detailed reaction plan instructions are provided on the second page.

Once the initial version of the control plan is released to production, the operators should take ownership of the document and treat it as a living document, constantly reviewing and updating it with new information. There also should be a feedback mechanism in the process; as new or unexpected failure modes are discovered on the line, update the control plan and feed the information back to update the FMEAs. Keeping the documentation current will facilitate the advanced quality planning (AQP) process during future programs.

Hazard analysis and critical control points (HACCP) is traditionally a food safety management system, but is commonly used in many other industries. A *critical control point* is a step or point in the process in which a major or serious failure of the product can be introduced. The goal of HACCP is to prevent known hazards and reduce the risk of them occurring at points in the production cycle. Rodriguez-Perez (2012) describes a 12-step process for successfully developing an HACCP plan:

1. Create an HACCP team

2. Fully describe the product (including specifications)

3. Determine the product's intended use

4. Create a process flow diagram (discussed in Chapter 5)

5. Confirm the flow diagram on-site

6. Identify and analyze hazards

Control plan number: CP714				Control plan revision level: C					Revision date: 12/01/2016	
Part/assembly number/rev: 714647-H & 714648-J				Product line: Soft start air dump valve					Originator: J. Hausner	
				Methods						
						Sample		**Control method**	**Reaction plan code**	
Sta #	**Process description**	**Machine tools/ equipment**	**Print no.**	**Characteristic specification**	**Evaluation measurement equipment**	**Size**	**Freq.**			
14	Machine needle bleed port on cover	Drill press	714648	0.060" min diameter	0.60 (minus) gage pin S/N 15-50-2118	1	1 per hour	Check sheet	A	
18	Pressure gage torque	Torque driver	714647 714648	20 ± 5 IN LB	Torque gage S/N 15-50-2019	5	1 per shift	$\bar{x}$ chart	Report issue to floor manager	
23	Body-cover screw torque	Torque driver	714647 714648	60 ± 15 IN LB	Torque gage S/N 15-50-2120	3 per screw	2 per shift	Separate $\bar{x}$ charts	Report issue to floor manager	
27	Solenoid assembly torque	Torque driver	209647 209648	14 ± 7 IN LB	Torque gage S/N 15-50-2019	5	1 per shift	$\bar{x}$ chart	Report issue to floor manager	
29	Final air test	Test tank	209647 209648	Functional test and leak check	Visual: ref. QA spec 203795 Functional: ref. assy instruction	1	100%	Go/no-go	A, B, C, D	
All	All	All	209647 209648	Workmanship	Visual	1	100%	Go/no-go	See note 2	

Note 1: At all times, quarantine one hour's worth of product before releasing to shipping. In the event of a final test failure, the last hour of production should be set aside for possible retest. This should be done on all final test failures with the exception of porosity.

Note 2: Compare suspect unit with visual accept/reject standards. If unit is unacceptable, stop the line and follow standard four-step reaction plan: (A) contain suspect units, (B) diagnose the root cause and implement corrective action, (C) verify that the corrective action is effective, (D) disposition suspect material (sort, scrap, rework, use as-is).

Figure 4.1   Control plan example: page 1.

Control plan number: CP714	Key contact: J. Hausner	Control plan revision level: C	Revision date: 12/01/2016
Part/assembly number/rev: 714647-H & 714648-J	Part name/description: Soft start air dump valve HG & HJ series	Product line: Airlogic control valve series	Originator: J. Hausner

Failure mode	Reaction plan	Code
Valve fails to open	Containment: Segregate nonconforming unit and previous hour of production for MRB. Disposition: Verify that wire leads and power supply are hooked up correctly. Verify needle port diameter > 0.060". If port diameter is under spec, switch to 100% inspection for the next 50 units and notify the product engineer (PE) if another failure is found. Replace drill bit if hole is not drilled through or burrs are present. Verify that piston ring is installed and free of nicks. Verify that needle valve is open at least one complete turn. Verify that the solenoid port resistor is installed. If other tests fail, check diameter of diaphragm. Contact the PE if additional diagnosis is required. Verification: Verify that corrective action eliminates problem. Disposition: Scrap nonconforming components. Rework assemblies as necessary and retest 100% of the previous hour of production.	
Valve fails to close	Containment: Segregate nonconforming product for MRB. Diagnosis: Verify that wire leads and power supply are hooked up correctly. Verify that flow control is open. Verify that diaphragm is installed correctly and check for voids in the seal bead. Verify that the dump hole is drilled completely through bonnet. Check that the fluid resistor is in place. Try another solenoid. If solenoid sticks open, quarantine current batch and switch to a new batch of solenoids. Contact PE if further diagnosis is required to determine cause. Verification: Verify that corrective action eliminates problem. Notify PE if another failure is found on the next 50 units. Disposition: Scrap nonconforming components. Rework assembly and retest.	
Body–bonnet leak	Containment: Segregate nonconforming product for MRB. Diagnosis: Verify torque. For torque adjustments, see Reaction Code "E" below. Ensure that diaphragm is installed correctly and that there are no voids present on the bead. Verify that the bead grooves on the bonnet and body are free of nicks or porosity and the diameters are within tolerance. Verify that the milled slot on the body is within tolerance. Contact PE if further diagnosis is required. Verification: Verify that corrective action eliminates problem. Disposition: Scrap nonconforming components. Rework assembly and retest. Contact line lead or PE if there are two or more consecutive failures or three failures within one hour.	
Leak at fittings	Containment: Segregate nonconforming product for MRB. Diagnosis: Verify that fittings are installed correctly and have the correct torque applied. Verify that the threads on the fitting and assembly are free of nicks or porosity. Contact PE if further diagnosis is required. Verification: Verify that corrective action eliminates problem. Notify PE if another failure is found on the next 50 units. Disposition: Scrap nonconforming components. Rework assembly and retest.	
Torque out of spec	Containment: Segregate nonconforming product for MRB. Diagnosis: Verify torque using another torque gage. For torque adjustments, take at least 10 samples and adjust torque gun if average is more than one standard deviation away from the nominal. Notify maintenance if average is close to nominal and there are any observations out of spec. Contact PE for further diagnosis. Verification: Measure a minimum of three subgroups and verify that the process is near nominal and in control. Disposition: If undertorque, retorque assembly. If overtorqued, replace screw(s) and retorque.	
SPC out of control, but parts in spec	Refer to QA/SPC procedure 231573. Comply with SPC procedure requirements. Document the root cause and corrective action in a note on the control chart.	

Figure 4.2 Control plan example: page 2.

7. Determine the critical control points

8. Establish critical limits for each critical control point

9. Establish a monitoring procedure

10. Establish corrective action

11. Verify the HACCP plan

12. Document the HACCP process

To determine critical control points, each step in the process is examined to see if any of the identified hazards could occur and if any control measures exist. The HACCP team assesses which steps in the process are critical control points. As Rodriguez-Perez writes, "If the hazard can be controlled adequately, and is not best controlled at another step, and is essential for process safety, then this step is a critical control point for the specified hazard." If there exists a step in the process where a hazard could occur and there are no control measures in place, this high-risk condition must be addressed.

Work instructions provide details for personnel who have direct responsibility for the operation of the process. The instructions must be documented and posted or readily accessible at the work site. Assembly instructions list each task to be performed in sequential order. Setup instructions list appropriate machine settings, such as feed rates, temperatures, and pressures. Setup instructions should also list any tasks or inspections that must be performed during production start-up to verify that the process is properly adjusted. Work instructions must be clear and understandable. Liberal use of sketches, charts, photographs, and other visual aids is strongly encouraged. The effort to eliminate opportunities for error in the process should include the work instructions. Therefore, organizations that produce a variety of similar products should consider creating unique instructions for each model, rather than using generic examples, look-up tables for bills of material, and cross-referenced setup instructions.

MATERIAL CONTROL

Material control addresses the raw materials, work in process (WIP), and final products and how they are physically controlled, identified, and tracked. The first step in control is classification; the last step is disposition.

Material control is based on identification and classification. Systems, components, nonconformities, and features are all subject to classification schemes, and only after a classification has been done can the appropriate control be applied. There are many different classification factors that should be considered, including:

- Volume of production

- Complexity

- Cost

- Expected lifetime

- Amount of maintenance required

- Risk to safety and/or the environment

If the product tends to be complex, expensive, and long-lived, then a great deal of effort must be expended in developing the material control scheme. Commodity-type products may require very little in the way of material control, but even the simplest products must be controlled in simple and inexpensive ways. Such issues as process selection, inspection method, amount of sampling, strictness of inspection, and control of deviating material must be decided with respect to the importance of each characteristic and each component. Every good quality engineer should spend time thinking about issues of relative importance and criticality. Think about the Pareto chart (see Chapter 5 for discussion of Pareto charts). Collect data and opinions so that even before production begins, a scheme of relative importance is clearly established.

This process requires careful study by several individuals. It is an exercise in clarification, in making distinctions, and in clearing up confusion. The task requires input from several sources of expertise to ensure that a balanced result is obtained. The people involved should include representatives of product design, safety, marketing, and field service.

Material Identification, Status, and Traceability

> Define and distinguish between these concepts, and describe methods for applying them in various situations. (Analyze)
>
> Body of Knowledge IV.B.1

Configuration management (CM) is defined in ANSI/EIA-649 (National Consensus Standard for Configuration Management) as a process for establishing and maintaining consistency of a product's performance, functional, and physical attributes with its requirements, design, and operational information throughout its life. The Department of Defense (DoD) created the handbook MIL-HDBK-61A(SE) (2001) to provide guidance for acquisition managers, logistics managers, and others responsible for CM. Material identification, status, and traceability can be achieved through CM. These three important items are discussed in this section.

Without product traceability, many manufacturers would be exposed to unacceptable risk, especially in the event of a recall. Modern technology has produced a wide array of identification methods. The physical application of markings and subsequent tracking by means of scanners and sensors provide many options. It is necessary to maintain records not only of items produced and their identification, but also of how the record-keeping system itself is operated and modified. The storage and retrieval of information is still a rapidly changing field.

One of the most effective identification methods is radio frequency identification (RFID). By using radio frequency tags, information can be provided about, for example, identification, tracking, and security. RFID technology has been used in supply chain management, inventory tracking, and the healthcare industry. In healthcare, RFID technology has been implemented for asset management (e.g., determining where mobile medical devices are at all times), patient care (e.g., determining where a patient is at all times while hospitalized), and inventory management (e.g., reducing the chance of inventory being out of stock at critical times).

To illustrate the mechanics of product identification, consider the case of the Sauer Danfoss Company in Ames, Iowa. This company makes moderately complex mechanical products that require 100% testing and periodic design modifications. The company improved its materials management system by creating a multifunctional task team of four people. The team collected data for two and a half years and finally decided to scrap the existing system for tracking material, which was dependent on manual entry on paper "move tags" and then manual keying into a computer database. Determination of current status required frequent physical count of all items.

The team switched to a system of using bar code and RFID technologies. Now, whenever an item of hardware moves, it is automatically accounted for, either by a bar code scanner or by an RFID receiver. A sophisticated database system automatically processes each scan and maintains a variety of characteristics about each unit, including:

- Model number

- Unit number

- Date produced

- Result of test

- Date of test

- Rework record

Product identification is vital when producing complex products, but is often unnecessary for mundane commodities. The StarLink corn seed recall in 2000 provides an example of the consequences of failure to identify and distinguish product.

StarLink was a form of seed corn that was approved for growing animal feed but not for human consumption. Inadequate controls were put in place when the seed corn was sold to farmers, and as a result the animal feed corn was inextricably intermixed with human-consumption corn at grain elevators throughout the Midwest. At the time they were delivering the corn, neither the farmers nor the grain elevator operators realized there was a problem. But later, consumer groups that were testing products made out of this corn detected the use of the unacceptable corn. A great outcry resulted, and many losses were incurred as both types of the intermixed corn had to be converted to animal feed.

Some companies use alternative product identification schemes. For example, a 10-digit alphanumeric product identification code can be used to allow traceability to a diverse set of factors, including the date of fabrication, the supplier of each subsystem, the product model, and the date of final assembly. Several things must be considered when setting up such a code, such as the amount of liability exposure, the number of levels of components and subcomponents, and the process design, which must incorporate the ability to trace products back to their point of creation and installation.

Traceability is an explicit part of the ISO 9000 and ISO/TS 16949 standards. See paragraph 8.5.2 in ANSI/ISO/ASQ 9001:2015, for example. Traceability is like a pedigree for a dog breed: it allows one to learn the history of any item. Commodity products such as nuts and bolts have limited needs for traceability, but even here, wise manufacturers will keep different lots segregated and identified as long as it is economically possible. Complex products such as automobiles must have multiple paths to trace back through many levels and many different sources. Sensitive material such as pharmaceuticals and food products must be traceable at all times. As an example of a traceability issue, consider the Heparin contamination in 2008. Heparin is a blood-thinning drug utilized during surgery to help prevent clotting. After reports of patient reactions, an investigation by the Food and Drug Administration led to the discovery of an ingredient in the drug that was the likely cause of adverse patient outcomes, including death.

The ISO 9001 standard requires product identification and traceability, where appropriate, for recall of nonconforming product, hazardous product, or product in conflict with laws, regulations, or statutes. Product identification must be provided when required by a customer. Properly identified items must have a unique number and are tracked by their location in the process. Differences between items and between lots must be distinguishable.

The place to start with traceability, that is, the ability to preserve the identity of the product and its origins, is when the process is first designed. Today, appropriate software and database designs are available. Training of workers may be required to create the proper climate and means to accomplish this.

Gryna (1988a) listed four reasons why traceability is needed:

1. Assure that only materials and components of adequate quality enter the final product, for example, sterility of drug materials, adequate metallurgical composition, and heat treatment of structural components

2. Assure positive identification to avoid mix-up of products that otherwise look alike

3. Permit recall of suspected product on a precise basis. Lacking traceability programs, huge recalls of automobiles and other products have been required in the past while the number of defectives in the recalled set was often quite small

4. Localize causes of failure and take remedial action at minimal cost

There are other uses of traceability, such as in inventory control and scheduling. Some of these uses also affect quality. For example, use of materials on a first-in, first-out basis reduces the risk of quality deterioration of perishable materials.

It is important to consider factors related to the product. For example, the following questions can help guide traceability:

- What is the cost of the product? A more expensive product requires more accountability over time, and thus better traceability.

- How long will the product last? If it is going to be around a long time, there is more concern about its origin, as new discoveries often are made of chemical characteristics and environmental effects. The discovery that asbestos was a carcinogen after its routine use for decades is a good example.

- Will the product be built into another product?

- Does the product have items or materials in it that have not been thoroughly evaluated over a long period of time?

- Is there a significant possible health hazard associated with the product?

- Are field modifications often required, with different replacement items required on different models? (Automobiles are a prime example.)

Ten items to consider in a traceability program are the following:

1. Product category

2. Product life

3. Unit cost

4. Recall or modification in the field

5. Product complexity

6. Level of downstream traceability

7. Documents providing traceability

8. Type of identification

9. Coded versus uncoded identification

10. Method of identification (e.g., tags, name plates, ink stamps)

The use of a tracing code is required for efficient operation (Feigenbaum 2004). This code is established at the beginning of material flow, and a traceability flowchart is established. The major activities on the flowchart include the following:

1. Critical component selection and listing by part number.

2. Vendor part coding (recording vendor name and date of receipt).

3. Coding internally manufactured parts, subassembly, assembly, and storage in a daily tally. At the end of the assembly line, each shipping container is date coded. This sequential coding procedure provides sufficient data to tie critical components to specific dates of receiving inspection, manufacturing, and final assembly.

4. Computerized shipping records, including date codes, customer name, and destination. Correlation of these data with tracing code numbers results in very effective traceability of critical components.

Material Segregation

> Describe material segregation and its importance, and evaluate appropriate methods for applying it in various situations. (Evaluate)
>
> **Body of Knowledge IV.B.2**

There are two major situations that demand disposition of nonconforming products. The first is when a product fails to pass inspection or a test and a decision regarding it must be made. This is the function of the material review board, discussed in the "Material Review Board (MRB)" section of this chapter. The second situation, considerably more serious, is when a problem develops after the product is out of the plant, on store shelves, in dealer showrooms, and in use by customers. Now a product recall may be required. In view of the very negative aspects of product recall, all the prior work concerning product traceability and product integrity will pay off quite handsomely in organizing the recall.

Material Classification

> Assess and classify product and process defects and non-conformities. (Evaluate)
>
> **Body of Knowledge IV.B.3**

In certain types of products, more than one defect could be present and a relatively small number of these minor defects could be acceptable to the customer. Product quality in these cases may be judged by the total number of defects or the number of defects per unit. Control charts for attributes are a tool that may be used for this purpose (see Chapter 6 for details). In such cases, the objective of inspection is to determine the number of defects or nonconformities present rather than to classify units as conforming or nonconforming.

"Defect" and "nonconformity" are two terms that may be used synonymously in many situations. However, in other situations, they have slightly different definitions. A *nonconformity* is defined as a failure of a quality characteristic to meet its intended level or state, occurring with severity sufficient to cause the product not to meet a specification. A *defect* is a nonconformity severe enough to cause the product not to satisfy normal usage requirements. Thus, the difference between the term "nonconformity" and the term "defect" is based mainly on perspective. The former is defined based on specifications, while the latter is defined based on fitness for use. The numerical result generated by inspection consists of the count of defects or nonconformities for each product unit. Often it is possible to classify the different types of defects according to their severity, and then assign a weight to each class based on the importance of the affected quality characteristic that relates to the product specifications. The selection of the weights should reflect the relative importance of the various defect categories and their likelihood of causing product failure or customer dissatisfaction. A typical seriousness classification includes four levels of defect seriousness:

1. Critical defects may lead directly to severe injury or catastrophic economic loss.

2. Serious defects may lead to injury or significant economic loss.

3. Major defects may cause major problems during normal use. A major defect will likely result in reducing the usability of the product.

4. Minor defects may cause minor problems during normal use.

See Montgomery (2013) for discussion of defect levels.

Material Review Board (MRB)

Describe the purpose and function of an MRB, and evaluate nonconforming product or material to make a disposition decision in various situations. (Evaluate)

Body of Knowledge IV.B.4

The material review board (MRB) is an appointed group of individuals with different backgrounds and expertise. Their assignment is to determine what corrective actions must be taken after nonconforming parts or components are discovered. In a larger sense, the purposes of the MRB are to determine the disposition of nonconforming parts, components, and subassemblies; determine the causes of the nonconformance of these items; and take the necessary corrective actions to prevent such nonconformance from taking place in future production.

The basic function of an MRB is to (1) review material that does not conform to standard, (2) determine what its disposition should be, and (3) drive the development of effective corrective action to prevent recurrence.

The MRB is a broad-based reviewing agency whose membership usually consists minimally of representatives from the following:

- Engineering. The cognizant designer is often the representative.

- Quality assurance. The representative is often from quality control engineering.

- Customers. The representative may be from the customer's organization (e.g., the government inspector) or from marketing. Note that customers can also represent an impacted group if "bad" material was used.

In some companies, the role of the MRB is solely one of judging fitness for use of nonconforming products. Bond (1983) discusses board composition, philosophy, and problem documentation.

In general, the MRB procedural steps can be summarized as follows: After a defect is discovered, verification by inspection may be needed. A complete description of any nonconformance is then initiated. A quality engineer picked by the MRB will review the facts and include the case in an appropriate tracking system. The MRB committee may then follow up with investigation and analysis. After the investigation and analysis, the case goes back to the quality engineer, who recommends the appropriate corrective action(s) and steps for implementation.

The term "standard repair" is common within the MRB framework. It signifies a procedure where a certain type of defect occurs time and again. A standard repair procedure is then initiated, documented, and implemented for such situations. Minor defects are most likely to be treated with a standard repair procedure. Within the context of defect classification, defects may further be classified as major or minor. Minor defects, unlike major ones, may not adversely affect the integrity of the part, component, or assembly.

In many cases, the MRB concludes that the lot containing nonconforming products should not be shipped as is. Then, along with inspection personnel, the MRB makes the decision to sort (100% inspection), downgrade, repair, rework, or scrap the nonconforming products. A decision to ship also may be authorized by the MRB. In such cases, a unanimous decision should be reached by all members. The decision should also create factual data and thus is an important source of information. A successful MRB program requires that the board not only make decisions about immediate disposition of rejected material, but also direct ongoing programs of root cause analysis to eliminate future rejections of the same type.

ACCEPTANCE SAMPLING

Acceptance sampling is a method for inspecting the product. Inspection can be done with screening (also called sorting or 100% inspection), in which all units are inspected, or with sampling. *Acceptance sampling* is the process of inspecting a portion of the product in a lot for the purpose of making a decision regarding classification of the entire lot as either conforming or nonconforming to quality specifications.

Whether inspection is done with screening or with sampling, the results of inspection can be used for different purposes as follows:

1. To distinguish between good lots and bad lots using acceptance sampling plans (as in incoming material inspection and final product inspection).

2. To distinguish between good products and bad products.

3. To determine the status of process control and if the process is changing. This is usually done in conjunction with control charts.

4. To evaluate process capability. In this case, inspection is used to determine if the process exhibits excessive variation and if it is approaching or exceeding the specification limits.

5. To determine process adjustment. Based on inspection results of process output, as depicted by a histogram, for example, the process mean may require adjustment and/or process variation may need to be reduced. A process might require adjustment even though all the units produced to date conform to the quality standards agreed on with the customer.

6. To rate the accuracy of inspectors or of inspection equipment by comparing the inspection results with corresponding standards. An inspection operation can result in two types of errors: (1) classification of a conforming unit as nonconforming and (2) classification of a nonconforming unit as conforming. The probabilities of both types of errors can be easily estimated using probability theory and other statistical methods.

7. To serve as a mechanism for evaluating vendors in terms of their products' quality. Vendors that consistently deliver high-quality products can receive preferred status involving reduced inspection and priority in bidding for new contracts, while vendors that do not stand up to quality requirements could be warned or discontinued altogether. This type of procedure is known as vendor qualification or vendor certification.

The last three uses of inspection might be seen as feedback about the production processes, the measurement processes, and the supplier.

Sampling provides the economic advantage of lower inspection costs due to fewer units being inspected. In addition, the time required to inspect a sample is substantially less than that required for the entire lot, and there is less damage to the product due to reduced handling. Most inspectors find that selection and inspection of a random sample is less tedious and monotonous than inspection of the complete lot. Another advantage of sampling inspection is related to the supplier/customer relationship. By inspecting a small fraction of the lot and forcing the supplier to screen 100% in case of lot rejection (which is the case for rectifying inspection), the customer emphasizes that the supplier must be concerned about quality. On the other hand, the variability inherent in sampling results in sampling errors: rejection of lots of conforming quality and acceptance of lots of nonconforming quality.

Acceptance sampling is most appropriate when inspection costs are high and when 100% inspection is monotonous and can cause inspector fatigue and boredom, resulting in degraded performance and increased error rates. Obviously, sampling is the only choice available for destructive inspection. Rectifying sampling, where sample units detected as nonconforming are discarded from the lot and either replaced with conforming units or repaired, is a form of acceptance sampling. Rejected lots are subject to 100% screening, which can involve discarding, replacing, or repairing units detected as nonconforming.

In certain situations, it is preferable to inspect 100% of the product. This would be the case for critical or complex products, where the cost of making the wrong decision would be too high. Screening is appropriate when the fraction nonconforming is extremely high. In this case, most of the lots would be rejected under acceptance sampling and those accepted would be so as a result of statistical variations rather than better quality. Screening is also appropriate when the fraction nonconforming is not known and an estimate based on a large sample is needed.

Sampling Concepts

> Apply the concepts of producer and consumer risk, and related terms, including operating characteristic (OC) curves, acceptable quality limit (AQL), and lot tolerance percent defective (LTPD). (Apply)
>
> **Body of Knowledge IV.C.1**

Sampling may be performed according to the type of quality characteristics to be inspected. There are three major categories of sampling plans: sampling plans for attributes, sampling plans for variables, and special sampling plans. It should be noted that acceptance sampling is not advised for processes in continuous production and in a state of statistical control. For these processes, Deming (1986) provides decision rules for selecting either 100% inspection or no inspection.

There are risks involved in using acceptance sampling plans. These risks are producer's risk and consumer's risk, and correspond with type I and type II errors, respectively, in hypothesis testing (type I and type II errors are discussed in Chapter 6). Producer's risk and consumer's risks are defined as follows:

- Producer's risk (α). The producer's risk for any given sampling plan is the probability of rejecting a lot that is within the acceptable quality level. This means that the producer faces the possibility (at level of significance α) of having a lot rejected even though the lot has met the requirements stipulated by the acceptance quality limit (AQL).

- Consumer's risk (β). The consumer's risk for any given sampling plan is the probability of acceptance (often 10%) for a designated numerical value of relatively poor submitted quality. The consumer's risk, therefore, is the probability of accepting a lot that has not met the requirements stipulated by the lot tolerance percent defective (LTPD) level, the poorest quality in an individual lot that should be accepted. The LTPD has a low probability of acceptance. In many sampling plans, the LTPD is the percent defective having a 10% probability of acceptance.

Single Sampling Plans and the OC Curve

A *single sampling plan* is one where the decision to either accept or reject the lot is based on the results of the inspection of a single sample of *n* items randomly selected from a submitted lot. A single sampling plan is defined by a sample number *n* and acceptance number *c*. If more than *c* items in the sample are determined to be defective, the lot is rejected. If c or fewer items in the sample are determined to be defective, the lot is accepted. Single sampling plans have the advantage of ease of administration, but due to the unchanging sample size, they do not take advantage of the potential cost savings of reduced or tightened inspection when incoming quality is either excellent or poor.

For continuing processes, sampling plans based on average quality protection have characteristics calculated from the binomial and/or Poisson distributions. For processes not considered to be continuing, sampling plans based on lot-by-lot protection have characteristics calculated from the hypergeometric distribution, which takes the lot size into consideration.

Sampling plans based on the Poisson and binomial distributions are more common than those based on the hypergeometric distribution. No matter which type of attribute sampling plan is being considered, an important evaluation tool is the operating characteristic (OC) curve.

The *OC curve* allows a sampling plan to be evaluated at a glance by graphically displaying the probabilities of accepting lots submitted at varying levels of percent nonconforming. The OC curve illustrates the risks involved in acceptance sampling. Figure 4.3 shows an OC curve for a single sampling plan with sample size n of 50 drawn from an infinite lot size, with an acceptance number c of 3.

As seen in the OC curve, if the lot were 100% to specifications, the probability of acceptance P_a also would be 100%. But if the lot were 13.4% defective, there would be approximately a 10% probability of acceptance.

There are two types of OC curves to consider: (1) type A OC curves and (2) type B OC curves. *Type A OC curves* are used to calculate the probability of acceptance on a lot-by-lot basis when the lot is not a product of a continuous process. These OC curves are calculated using the hypergeometric distribution.

Type B OC curves are used to evaluate sampling plans for a continuous process or for a process where a lot of size N is large. These curves are based on the binomial and/or Poisson distributions when the requirements for usage are met. In

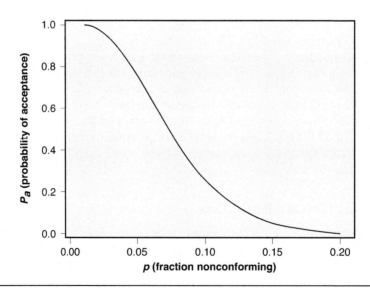

Figure 4.3   An operating characteristic (OC) curve for $n = 50$ and $c = 3$.

general, the ANSI/ASQ Z1.4-2003 (R 2018) standard OC curves are based on the binomial distribution for sample sizes through 80 and the Poisson approximation to the binomial for sample sizes greater than 80.

The Poisson approximation to the binomial was often employed for calculating the probability of acceptance (P_a) when the sample sizes of interest were quite large. This approximation was used because the computations needed to calculate the binomial probabilities were often impractical. With modern software, the binomial computations are no longer a problem. However, Poisson approximations are still sometimes used for the binomial distribution. This approximation is acceptable when $p < 0.1$.

In the examples that follow, it is assumed that the process of interest is continuous (in theory). Since the process is considered continuous, the lot size is not taken into consideration in the calculations of P_a. Suppose a sample of $n = 50$ is randomly selected from the lot. Furthermore, the lot is accepted if three or fewer nonconformities are found in the sample ($c = 3$). To create the OC curve, plot the probability of acceptance versus various values of p, the fraction nonconforming. Statistical software can readily create these curves.

The probability of acceptance P_a can be calculated using the binomial probability mass function (pmf) (see Chapter 6 for complete details on the binomial distribution and the cumulative distribution function [cdf]). The probability of acceptance is given by

$$P_a = P(d \le c) = \sum_{d=0}^{c} \left(\frac{n!}{d!(n-d)!} \right) p^d (1-p)^{n-d} \tag{4.1}$$

where

$d =$ the number of nonconforming items

$c =$ the acceptance number

$p =$ fraction nonconforming

The probability of acceptance of the lot for a single sampling plan with $n = 50$ and $c = 3$ can be found for values of p using Equation (4.1); the probabilities are shown in Table 4.1.

The OC curve can be constructed similarly to the one in Figure 4.3 for various values of p.

The probabilities of acceptance can also be calculated using the Poisson distribution (discussed in Chapter 6). The probability of acceptance is

$$P_a = P(d \le c) = \sum_{d=0}^{c} \frac{(np)^d e^{-np}}{d!} \tag{4.2}$$

where np is the mean of the binomial distribution and therefore the necessary parameter for the Poisson distribution. Tables providing probabilities for the binomial distribution can be found in Appendix I and in Appendix L for the Poisson distribution.

The OC curve is useful for several quantities of interest such as the AQL and LTPD. As part of the revision of ANSI/ASQC Z1.4-1993, "acceptable quality level" was changed to "acceptable quality limit" and is defined as the quality level that

Table 4.1 Probability of acceptance
for various levels of fraction
nonconforming.

p	P_a
0.01	0.9984
0.02	0.9822
0.03	0.9372
0.04	0.8609
0.05	0.7604
0.06	0.6473
0.07	0.5327
0.08	0.4253
0.09	0.3303
0.10	0.2503
0.15	0.0460
0.20	0.0057

is the worst tolerable process average when a continuing series of lots is submitted for acceptance sampling. This means that a lot that has a fraction defective equal to the AQL has a high probability (generally around 0.95, although it may vary) of being accepted. As a result, plans that are based on the AQL, such as ANSI/ASQ Z1.4-2003 (R2018), favor the producer in getting lots accepted that are in the general neighborhood of the AQL for fraction defective in a lot.

Lot Size, Sample Size, and Acceptance Number

For any single sampling plan, the plan is completely described by the lot size, sample size, and acceptance number. In this section, the effect of changing the sample size, acceptance number, and lot size on the behavior of the sampling plan will be explored along with the risks of constant percentage plans.

The effect on the OC curve for a single sampling plan caused by changing the sample size while holding all other parameters constant is shown in Figure 4.4. The probability of acceptance changes considerably as sample size changes. The probability of acceptance for the given sample sizes for a 10% nonconforming lot and an acceptance number of zero is shown in Table 4.2.

The effect of changing the acceptance number on a single sampling plan while holding all other parameters constant is shown in Figure 4.5. Another point of interest is that for $c = 0$, the OC curve is concave in shape, while plans with larger acceptance numbers have a "reverse s" shape. Figure 4.5 and Table 4.3 show the effect of changing the acceptance number of a sampling plan on the indifference quality level (50–50 chance of accepting a given percent defective).

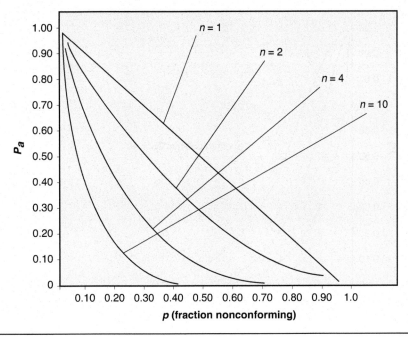

Figure 4.4 Effect on an OC curve of changing sample size (*n*) when accept number (*c*) is held constant

Table 4.2 Probability of acceptance for various *n*.

Sample size (*n*)	Probability of acceptance (P_a)
10	0.35
4	0.66
2	0.81
1	0.90

The parameter having the least effect on the OC curve for the single sampling plan is the lot size *N*. Figure 4.6 shows the changes in the OC curve for a sample size of 10, acceptance number of 0, and lot sizes of 100, 200, and 1000. For this reason, using the binomial and Poisson approximations, even when lot sizes are known (and are large compared with sample size), results in little error in accuracy. Some key probabilities of acceptance points for the three lot sizes are displayed in Table 4.4. The differences due to lot size are minimal.

Computing the sample size as a percentage of the lot size has a large effect on risks and protection, as shown in Figure 4.7. In this case, plans having a sample size totaling 10% of the lot size are shown. The degree of protection changes

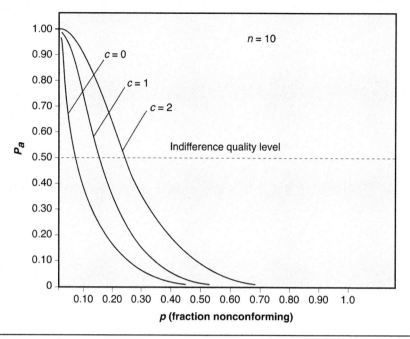

Figure 4.5 Effect of changing accept number (*c*) when sample size (*n*) is held constant.

Table 4.3 Fraction defective at indifference quality level.

Sample size (*n*)	Acceptance number (*c*)	Percent defective at indifference quality level
10	2	0.26
10	1	0.17
10	0	0.07

dramatically with changes in lot size, which results in low protection for small lot sizes and gives excessively large sample requirements for large lot sizes.

Sampling Standards and Plans

Identify, interpret, and apply ANSI/ASQ Z1.4 and Z1.9 standards for attributes and variables sampling. (Analyze)

Body of Knowledge IV.C.2

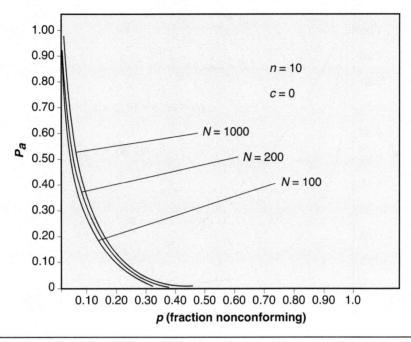

Figure 4.6 Effect of changing lot size (N) when acceptance number (c) and sample size (n) are held constant.

Table 4.4 Probability of acceptance for various lot sizes.

Fraction defective (p)	Probability of acceptance (P_a)	Lot size (N)
0.10	0.330	100
0.30	0.023	100
0.50	0.001	100
0.10	0.340	200
0.30	0.026	200
0.50	0.001	200
0.10	0.347	1000
0.30	0.028	1000
0.50	0.001	1000

Acceptance sampling by attributes generally is used for two purposes: (1) protection against accepting lots from a continuing process whose average quality deteriorates beyond an acceptable quality level, and (2) protection against isolated lots

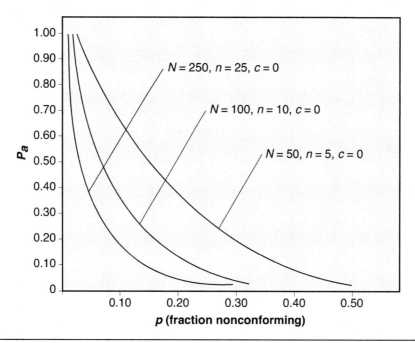

Figure 4.7 OC curves for sampling plans having the sample size equal to 10% of the lot size.

that may have levels of nonconformances greater than can be considered acceptable. The most common form of acceptance sampling is sampling by attributes. The most widely used standard of all attribute plans is ANSI/ASQ Z1.4. The following sections provide more details on the characteristics of acceptance sampling and discussion of military standards in acceptance sampling.

There are several types of attribute sampling plans available, with the most common being single, double, and multiple sampling plans. The type of sampling plan used is determined by ease of use and administration, general quality level of incoming lots, and average sample number.

Double and Multiple Sampling Plans

When using double sampling plans, a smaller first sample is taken from the submitted lot, and one of three decisions is made: (1) accept the lot, (2) reject the lot, or (3) draw another sample. If a second sample is to be drawn, the lot will either be accepted or be rejected after the second sample. Double sampling plans have the advantage of a lower total sample size when the incoming quality is either excellent or poor because the lot is either accepted or rejected on the first sample.

To calculate the OC curve for a double sampling plan, Equations (4.1) and (4.2) can again be utilized. To calculate probabilities of acceptance, some arbitrary points for p are chosen to cover the range of the OC curve. The fraction defective p is then multiplied by n_1 (the first sample) or n_2 (the second sample) to determine the expected value np.

The generalized formula for calculating the probability of acceptance (P_a) is:

$$P_a = p_0 + (p_1 p_2 + p_1 p_1 + p_1 p_0) + (p_2 p_1 + p_2 p_0) \tag{4.3}$$

where:

p_0 = probability of zero nonconformities in the first sample

$p_i p_j$ = probability of i nonconformities in the first sample times the probability of j nonconformities in the second sample for all i and j

---

EXAMPLE 4.1

A double sampling plan is to be executed as follows: take a first sample (n_1) of 75 units and set c_1 (the acceptance number for the first sample) at 0. The lot will be accepted based on the first sample results if no nonconformances are found in the first sample.

If three nonconformances are found in the first sample, the lot will be rejected based on the first sample results. If after analyzing the results of the first sample one or two nonconformances are found, take a second sample ($n_2 = 75$). The acceptance number for the second sample (c_2) is set to 3. If the combined number of nonconformances in the first and second samples is three or fewer, the lot will be accepted and if the combined number of nonconformances is four or more, the lot will be rejected. The plan is represented as shown in Table 4.5.

Table 4.5 Double sampling plan.

Sample size	Acceptance number (c)	Rejection number (r)
$n_1 = 75$	$c_1 = 0$	$r_1 = 3$
$n_2 = 75$	$c_2 = 3$	$r_2 = 4$

To determine the technique of plotting the OC curve, 3 points for p may be used (0.01, 0.04, and 0.08), although in practice 6–10 should be used. The points for the OC curve are calculated using the generalized equation for each fraction nonconforming (Equation (4.1), selected as shown in Table 4.6.

Table 4.6 OC curve calculations for double sampling plan.

Generalized equation values	$p = 0.01$	$p = 0.04$	$p = 0.08$
p_0	0.470587	0.04681	0.001923
$p_1 p_0$	0.167767	0.006848	0.000024
$p_1 p_1$	0.127096	0.021399	0.000157
$p_1 p_2$	0.0475	0.032989	0.000506
$p_2 p_0$	0.062701	0.010557	0.000078
$p_2 p_1$	0.0475	0.032989	0.000506
Totals for P_a	0.923151	0.151592	0.003195

Continued

These points are used to construct the OC curve for the double sampling plan, as shown in Figure 4.8.

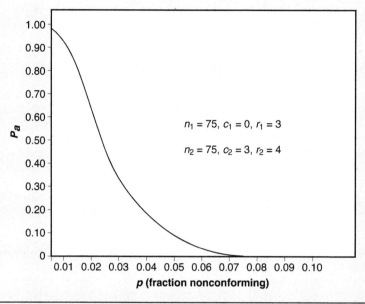

$n_1 = 75, c_1 = 0, r_1 = 3$

$n_2 = 75, c_2 = 3, r_2 = 4$

p **(fraction nonconforming)**

Figure 4.8 OC curve for double sampling plan where $n_1 = 75, c_1 = 0, r_1 = 3, n_2 = 75, c_2 = 3, r_2 = 4$.

Multiple sampling plans work in the same way as double sampling, but with an increase in the number of samples to be taken up to seven, according to ANSI/ASQ Z1.4. In the same manner that double sampling is performed, acceptance or rejection of submitted lots may be reached before the seventh sample, depending on the acceptance/rejection criteria established for the plan.

Average Sample Number

The *average sample number* (ASN) is a determination of the expected average amount of inspection per lot for a given sampling plan. The ASN for single sampling plans is a constant value that is equal to the single sample size for the plan. The ASN for double sampling plans is the sum of the first sample size plus the second sample size times the probability that a second sample will be required. The ASN is also a function of fraction nonconforming when working with a double sampling plan. The double sampling plan ASN formula is:

$$\text{ASN} = n_1 + n_2 P_2 \tag{4.4}$$

where:

n_1 = size of first sample

n_2 = size of second sample

P_2 = probability of requiring a second sample

EXAMPLE 4.2

The double sampling plan in the earlier section was

$$n_1 = 75 \qquad c_1 = 0 \qquad r_1 = 3$$
$$n_2 = 75 \qquad c_2 = 3 \qquad r_2 = 4$$

- A second sample is required if on the first sample one or two nonconformances are noted.

- If zero nonconformances are found in the first sample, the lot is accepted.

- If three or more nonconformances are found in the first sample, the lot is rejected.

Create the average sample number curve for this double sampling plan.

Solution:

Denote the probability of making a decision, accept or reject, on the first sample as $P(D_1)$. Then,

$$P(D_1) = P(0) + P \text{ (3 or more)}$$

$P(0)$ = the probability of zero nonconformances on the first sample

P (3 or more) = the probability of three or more nonconformances on the first sample.

$$P_2 = 1 - P(D_1), \text{ then, ASN} = n_1 + n_2 P_2$$

When using Equation (4.1) to calculate the probability of three or more nonconformances, remember that the probability of three or more nonconformances is given by:

(1 – probability of two or less nonconformances) in the sample

The average sample number will be plotted for several values of fraction nonconforming p and an ASN curve will be plotted. An example of the ASN calculation for the fraction nonconforming $p = 0.01$ is shown below. Several other points need to be plotted for other values of p. Figure 4.9 shows the ASN curve for this example.

When $p = 0.01$:

$P(0)$ = Probability of zero nonconformances in sample = 0.4706

P(3 or more) = Probability of three or more nonconformances in sample
= 0.0397

$P(D_1)$ = Probability of a decision on the first sample (using the above equation) = 0.4706 + 0.0397 = 0.5103

Then P_2 = probability of requiring a second sample = 1 – 0.5103 = 0.4897.

Thus the ASN is

ASN(0.01) = Average sample number for a lot quality $p = 0.01$

$$= n_1 + n_2(P_2)$$

$$= 75 + 75(0.4866) = 111.73$$

Continued

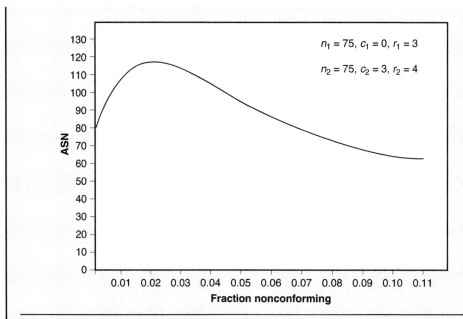

Figure 4.9 Average sample number curve for double sampling plan.

Values of ASN at different p values ASN(p) may be calculated in a similar way; the results are given below.

ASN(0.01) = 111.73	ASN(0.06) = 86.65
ASN(0.02) = 119.28	ASN(0.07) = 81.93
ASN(0.03) = 112.99	ASN(0.08) = 78.97
ASN(0.04) = 102.89	ASN(0.09) = 77.20
ASN(0.05) = 93.62	ASN(0.10) = 76.18

When comparing sampling plans with equal protection, double sampling plans will generally result in smaller average sample sizes when quality is excellent or poor. When quality is near the indifference level, double sampling plans will rarely result in greater ASN.

Attribute Sampling Plans

ANSI/ASQ Z1.4 is probably the most common standard for attribute sampling plans.

The wide recognition and acceptance of ANSI/ASQ Z1.4 could be due to government contracts stipulating the standard rather than its statistical importance. Producers submitting products at a nonconformance level within the AQL have a high probability of having the lot accepted by the customer.

When using ANSI/ASQ Z1.4, the characteristics under consideration should be classified. The general classifications are critical, major, and minor defects:

- Critical defect. A defect that judgment and experience indicate is likely to result in hazardous or unsafe conditions for the individuals using, maintaining, or depending on the product, or a defect that judgment and experience indicate is likely to prevent performance of the unit. In practice, critical characteristics are commonly inspected to an AQL of 0.40 to 0.65%, if not 100% inspected. One hundred percent inspection is recommended for critical characteristics if possible. Acceptance numbers are always zero for critical defects.

- Major defect. A defect other than critical that is likely to result in failure or to reduce materially the usability of the unit of product for its intended purpose. In practice, AQLs for major defects are generally about 1%.

- Minor defect. A defect that is not likely to reduce materially the usability of the unit of product for its intended purpose. In practice, AQLs for minor defects generally range from 1.5% to 2.5%.

Levels of Inspection

There are seven levels of inspection used in ANSI/ASQ Z1.4: reduced inspection, normal inspection, tightened inspection, and four levels of special inspection. The special inspection levels should be used only when small sample sizes are necessary and large risks can be tolerated. When using ANSI/ASQ Z1.4, a set of switching rules must be followed as to the use of reduced, normal, and tightened inspection.

The following guidelines are taken from ANSI/ASQ Z1.4:

- Initiation of inspection. Normal inspection level II will be used at the start of inspection unless otherwise directed by the responsible authority.

- Continuation of inspection. Normal, tightened, or reduced inspection shall continue unchanged for each class of defect or defectives on successive lots or batches except where the following switching procedures require change. The switching procedures shall be applied to each class of defects or defectives independently.

- Switching procedures. Switching rules are shown in Figure 4.10.

- Normal to tightened. When normal inspection is in effect, tightened inspection shall be instituted when two out of five consecutive lots or batches have been rejected on original inspection (i.e., ignoring resubmitted lots or batches for this procedure).

- Tightened to normal. When tightened inspection is in effect, normal inspection shall be instituted when five consecutive lots or batches have been considered acceptable on original inspection.

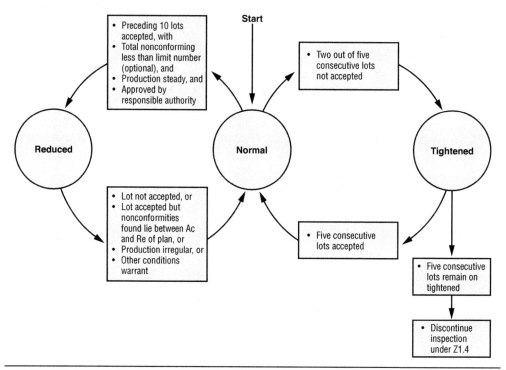

Figure 4.10 Switching rules for normal, tightened, and reduced inspection.

- Normal to reduced. When normal inspection is in effect, reduced inspection shall be instituted providing that all the following conditions are satisfied:

  a. The preceding 10 lots or batches (or more), as indicated by the note on ANSI/ASQ Z1.4 Table VIII, have been on normal inspection and none has been rejected on original inspection.

  b. The total number of defectives (or defects) in the sample from the preceding 10 lots or batches (or such other number as was used for condition (a) above) is equal to or less than the applicable number given in Table VIII of ANSI/ASQ Z1.4. If double or multiple sampling is in use, all samples inspected should be included, not "first" samples only.

  c. Production is at a steady rate.

  d. Reduced inspection is considered desirable by the responsible authority.

- Reduced to normal. When reduced inspection is in effect, normal inspection shall be instituted if any of the following occur on original inspection:

  a. A lot or batch is rejected.

b. A lot or batch is considered acceptable under reduced inspection but the sampling procedures terminated without either acceptance or rejection criteria having been met. In these circumstances, the lot or batch will be considered acceptable, but normal inspection will be reinstated starting with the new lot or batch.

c. Production becomes irregular or delayed.

d. Other conditions warrant that normal inspection shall be instituted.

- Discontinuation of inspection. If the cumulative number of lots not accepted in a sequence of consecutive lots on tightened inspection reaches five, the acceptance procedures of this standard shall be discontinued. Inspection under the provisions of this standard shall not be resumed until corrective action has been taken. Tightened inspection shall then be used as "normal to tightened" above.

Types of Sampling

ANSI/ASQ Z1.4 allows for single sampling, double sampling, or multiple sampling. The choice of the type of plan depends on many variables. Single sampling is the easiest to administer and perform but usually results in the largest average total inspection (ATI). Double sampling in ANSI/ASQ Z1.4 results in a lower ATI than single sampling, but requires more decisions to be made, such as the following:

- Accept the lot after first sample

- Reject the lot after first sample

- Take a second sample

- Accept the lot after second sample

- Reject the lot after second sample

Multiple sampling plans further reduce the ATI but also increase the number of decisions to be made. As many as seven samples may be required before a decision to accept or reject the lot can be made. This type of plan requires the most administration.

A general procedure for selecting plans from ANSI/ASQ Z1.4 is as follows:

1. Decide on an AQL.

2. Decide on the inspection level.

3. Determine the lot size.

4. Find the appropriate sample size code letter. See Table 1 from ANSI/ASQ Z1.4.

5. Determine the type of sampling plan to be used: single, double, or multiple.

6. Using the selected AQL and sample size code letter, enter the appropriate table to find the desired plan to be used.

7. Determine the normal, tightened, and reduced plans as required from the corresponding tables.

EXAMPLE 4.3

A lot of 1750 parts has been received and is to be checked to an AQL of 1.5%. Determine the appropriate single, double, and multiple sampling plans for general inspection level II.

Steps to define the plans are as follows:

1. ANSI/ASQ Z1.4 stipulates code letter K.
2. Normal inspection is applied. For code letter K, a sample of 125 is specified.
3. For double sampling, two samples of 80 may be required.
4. For multiple sampling, at least two samples of 32 are required and it may take up to seven samples of 32 before an acceptance or rejection decision is made.

A breakdown of all three plans is provided in Table 4.7.

Table 4.7 Acceptance and rejection number for single, double, and multiple sampling plans.

Sampling plan		Sample(s) size	Ac	Re
Single sampling		125	5	6
Double sampling	First	80	2	5
	Second	80	6	7
Multiple sampling	First	32	*	4
	Second	32	1	5
	Third	32	2	6
	Fourth	32	3	7
	Fifth	32	5	8
	Sixth	32	7	9
	Seventh	32	9	10

Ac = Acceptance number
Re = Rejection number
*Acceptance not permitted at this sample size.

Variables Sampling Plans

Variables sampling plans use the actual measurements of sample products for decision making rather than classifying products as conforming or nonconforming, as in attribute sampling plans. Variables sampling plans are more complex in administration than attribute plans; thus, they require more skill. They provide some benefits, however, over attribute plans. Two of these benefits are the following:

1. Equal protection to an attribute sampling plan with a much smaller sample size. There are several types of variables sampling plans in use, three of these being (1) σ known, (2) σ unknown but can be estimated using sample standard deviation s, and (3) σ unknown and the range R is used as an estimator. If an attribute sampling plan sample size is determined, the variables plans previously listed can be compared as a percentage to the attribute plan. The sample size percentages based on these scenarios are shown in Table 4.8, which can be compared to the 100% inspection of items in an attribute sampling plan.

2. Variables sampling plans allow the determination of how close to nominal or a specification limit the process is performing. Attribute plans either accept or reject a lot; variables plans give information on how well or poorly the process is performing.

Variables sampling plans have some di advantages and limitations:

1. Separate characteristics on the same parts will have different averages and dispersions, resulting in a separate sampling plan for each characteristic

2. Variables plans are more complex in administration than attribute plans

3. Variables gauging is generally more expensive than attribute gauging

In addition, for variables sampling plans, it is assumed that the quality characteristic under study is normally distributed.

The most common standard for variables sampling plans is ANSI/ASQ Z1.9, which has plans for (1) variability known, (2) variability unknown (standard deviation method), and (3) variability unknown (range method). Using these methods, this sampling plan can be used to test for a single specification limit, a double (or bilateral) specification limit, estimation of the process average, and estimation of the dispersion of the parent population.

Like ANSI/ASQ Z1.4, ANSI/ASQ Z1.9 uses several AQLs and follows specific switching procedures for normal, reduced, or tightened inspection. ANSI/ASQ Z1.9 allows for the same AQL for each specification limit of double specification limit plans or the use of different AQLs for each specification limit. The AQLs are

Table 4.8 Percentage of acceptance sampling for previously discussed plans.

Plan	Sample size (percent)
σ unknown, range method	60
σ unknown, s estimated from sample	40
σ known	15

designated ML for the lower specification limit and MU for the upper specification limit.

There are two forms used for every specification limit ANSI/ASQ Z1.9 plan. Form 1 provides only acceptance or rejection criteria, whereas form 2 estimates the percentage below the lower specification limit and the percentage above the upper specification limit. These percentages are compared with the AQL for acceptance/rejection criteria. Figure 4.11 summarizes the structure and organization of ANSI/ASQ Z1.9.

An example of the sampling method where the variability is unknown and thus uses the standard deviation is shown in Example 4.4.

There are 14 AQLs used in ANSI/ASQ Z1.9 that are consistent with the AQLs used in ANSI/ASQ Z1.4. Section A of ANSI/ASQ Z1.9 contains both an AQL conversion table and a table for selecting the desired inspection level. Inspection level II should be used unless otherwise specified. See the standard for further information about levels.

Section B contains sampling plans used when the variability is unknown and the standard deviation method is used. Part I is used for a single specification limit, Part II is used for a double specification limit, and Part III is used for estimation of process average and criteria for reduced and tightened inspection.

Section C contains sampling plans used when the variability is unknown and the range method is used. Parts I, II, and III are the same as Parts I, II, and III in Section B.

Section D contains sampling plans used when variability is known. Parts I, II, and III are the same as Parts I, II, and III in Section B.

Following is a detailed description of the standard deviation method when the variability is unknown. This sampling plan is for the situation where the

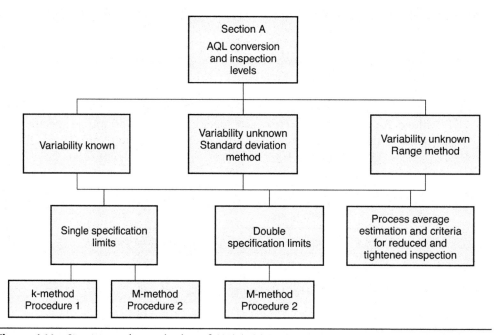

Figure 4.11 Structure and organization of ANSI/ASQ Z1.9.

variability is not known and the standard deviation is estimated from the sample data. The sampling plan will be that for a double specification limit, and it is found in Section B of the standard with one AQL for both upper and lower specification limits combined.

The acceptability criterion is based on comparing an estimated percent non-conforming with a maximum allowable percent nonconforming for the given AQL. The estimated percent nonconforming is found in ANSI/ASQ Z1.9 Table B-5.

The quality indices for this sampling plan are:

$$Q_U = \frac{\text{USL} - \bar{x}}{s} \text{ and } Q_L = \frac{\bar{x} - \text{LSL}}{s} \tag{4.5}$$

where

USL = upper specification limit

LSL = lower specification limit

$\bar{x}$ = sample mean

s = estimate of lot standard deviation

It should be noted that Q_L and Q_U follow a standard normal distribution since the quality characteristic being measured is assumed to be normally distributed.

The quality level of the lot is in terms of the lot percent defective. Three values are calculated: P_U, P_L, and p. P_U is an estimate of conformance with the upper specification limit, P_L is an estimate of conformance with the lower specification limit, and p is the sum of P_U and P_L.

The value of p is then compared with the maximum allowable percent defective. If p is less than or equal to M, or if either Q_U or Q_L is negative, the lot is rejected, since this would be the result of x lying beyond the specification limits. Example 4.4 illustrates the above procedure.

EXAMPLE 4.4

The minimum temperature of operation for a certain device is specified as 180°F. The maximum temperature is 209°F. A lot of 40 items is submitted for inspection. Inspection level II, normal inspection with AQL = 1%, is to be used. ANSI/ASQ Z1.9-2003 (R2018) Table A-2 gives code letter D, which results in a sample size of five from ANSI/ASQ Z1.9-2003 (R2018) Table B-3. The results of the five measurements in degree Fahrenheit are as follows: 197, 188, 184, 205, 201. Determine if the lot meets acceptance criteria.

Given:

- Sample size, $n = 5$

- Upper specification limit, USL = 209

- Lower specification limit, LSL = 180

- From Table B of the ANSI/ASQ Z1.9-2003 (R2018) standard, the maximum allowable percent nonconforming (M) to be M = 3.32%

Let the random variable X represent the temperature of operation.

Continued

The steps for calculating the percent nonconforming are as follows:

1. Calculate the sample mean (see Chapter 6, "Collecting and Summarizing Data," for calculation of the sample mean):

$$\bar{x} = \frac{\sum_{i=1}^{n} x_i}{n} = \frac{\sum_{i=1}^{5} x_i}{5} = \frac{975}{5} = 195$$

2. Calculate the sample standard deviation (see Chapter 6, "Collecting and Summarizing Data," for calculation of the sample standard deviation):

$$s = \sqrt{\frac{\sum_{i=1}^{n}(x_i - \bar{x})^2}{n-1}} = 8.803$$

3. Calculate Q_U:

$$Q_U = \frac{USL - \bar{x}}{s} = \frac{209 - 195}{8.803} = 1.59$$

4. Calculate Q_L:

$$Q_L = \frac{\bar{x} - LSL}{s} = \frac{195 - 180}{8.803} = 1.70$$

From Table B-5 of the ANSI/ASQZ1.9 standard, determine the percent non-conforming:

- The percent above the upper specification limit with $n = 5$ and $Q_U = 1.59$ is 2.19%
- The percent below the lower specification limit with $n = 5$ and $Q_L = 1.70$ is 0.66%

The total percent nonconforming is then 2.19% + 0.66% = 2.85%.

Therefore, since the percent nonconforming (2.85%) is less than the maximum allowable (3.32%), the lot is acceptable.

Sample Integrity

> Identify and apply techniques for establishing and maintaining sample integrity. (Apply)
>
> **Body of Knowledge IV.C.3**

Products are always at risk of contamination and misuse. Sample integrity is vital whenever sampling is done for any purpose, whether to go through a fitness program, for customer evaluation, or for destructive/nondestructive testing. To maintain sample integrity, carefully thought-out controls are necessary. Many people recall the murder trial of O. J. Simpson, where extremely complex and expensive

DNA testing was challenged by the defense because the prosecution could not prove that the DNA sample was completely safe from any contamination at all times. While this is an extreme example, it highlights the importance of maintaining sample integrity. In this section, sample integrity is discussed in terms of batch control, change control, and configuration control.

When products are created in batches (as opposed to discrete item production or continuous processes), it is necessary to keep records on all aspects of the batch. The concept of a batch includes mixing, heating, distilling, and other comparable operations. A recipe is used; documentation that the recipe was followed is vital in all but the most trivial cases. A qualified operator must maintain a log or journal indicating the quantities and products (or identification) of each material that is inserted into the batch. The time that each insertion is made is usually important, as well as the time that different inputs (heat, pressure, and so on) are applied to the batch.

Tests may be required to verify that the batch has developed the needed properties over time. The results of such tests must be tightly linked to the physical batch and to all the other records. In some cases, these details can be automated, but often they must be recorded manually. When the batch is finished, it must be labeled with an identification code that is separate from other batches. The batch (lot) number must be printed or engraved on appropriate cartons, drums, jugs, pallets, and so on. A linkage between batch number and customer name is often necessary when the product is sold, so that it can be tracked through the entire distribution chain.

Change control is a technique for dealing with relatively simple to moderately complex products to which minor changes are made that must be tracked. For example, such products as refrigerators and desktop computers may be changed slightly and new version numbers issued on the same model name/number. For warranty purposes, product repair, and replacement, it is necessary to record each time the product is changed.

Engineers must decide when a change is required and how rapidly it is to be implemented. One priority scheme is to categorize the changes as emergency, priority, or routine. An emergency change is appropriate when a hazardous condition is discovered in the present version. In such cases, no time must be lost in correcting the deficiency. A priority change is called for if there is sound economic reason to make the change promptly, but life and property are not at risk. For example, a product upgrade that reduces power consumption or maintenance could be implemented as a priority change. The final category, routine, is for changes that must be made, but need not be rushed. These are often to accommodate newly designed parts or to allow the product to have slightly more functionality, but not enough to justify an entirely new model.

Configuration control is an extension of change control. The term "configuration" refers to how a complex product is composed of various units and subassemblies. In an evolving product with high research and development content, such as aerospace vehicles, defense weapons, and so on, the field version of the same unit of product gradually changes over time as new engines, new avionics, and new hydraulic systems are installed into existing units of product.

To manage such ongoing field product modifications, a lot of effort must be put into configuration control systems. This is really an adaptation of materials resource planning techniques. Extensive documentation is mandatory for proper control. Usually both computerized database records and hard-copy backup records (often at multiple locations) are required.

Three now-canceled DoD standards addressed the subject of configuration control, DOD-STD-480A, DOD-STD-481, and DOD-STD-973. Standard EIA-649 "National Consensus Standard for Configuration Management," however, can be used as a replacement for these canceled military standards since it is almost a complete duplication of the military standard. Russell (2013) discusses common components in configuration management plans. These elements include a configuration plan, procedures and guidelines, an identification process, the change-control process, a records status process, and an audit process.

A key principle of configuration control is to avoid changes in a given product model unless a clear and compelling benefit can be shown. Management must consider the downsides of change to a product model. Change can result in more complexity in the product line and more chance for confusion. However, some potential benefits are reduced cost, increased performance, better safety, and lower maintenance.

MEASUREMENT AND TEST

A measurement process is a repeated application of a test method using a measuring system. A test method includes requirements for a test apparatus and a well-defined procedure for using it to measure a physical property.

Measurement is the process of evaluating a property or characteristic of an object and describing it with a numerical or nominal value. If the value is numerical, reflecting the extent of the characteristic, the measurement is said to be on a quantitative scale and the actual property is referred to as a variable. Examples of variables inspection are measurements related to weight, length, temperature, and so on.

If the value assigned to each unit is not numerical, the measurement is on a qualitative or classification scale and is referred to as an attribute. In most inspection situations involving nominal or attribute data, there are two possible nominal values: conforming (good) and nonconforming (defective). Each product unit is assigned one of these two labels according to inspection operation results. It is also possible to derive a numerical measure from a qualitative scale. This is achieved by calculating the fraction nonconforming (fraction defective) as the ratio between the number of units labeled as nonconforming and the total number of units inspected.

A measuring system should be able to provide accuracy capabilities that will ensure the attainment of a reliable measurement. In general, the elements of a measuring system include the instrumentation, calibration standards, environmental influences, human operator limitations, and features of the workpiece or object being measured. Each of these elements may involve detailed studies of extended scope and thus fall beyond the purpose of this book. The design of measuring systems also involves proper analysis of cost-to-accuracy considerations (Darmody 1967).

The functional design of measuring systems can include consideration of many approaches and employment of a variety of physical phenomena useful in establishing parametric variables from the measured quantity. In linear measuring systems, the basic function may be mechanical, optical, pneumatic, electronic, radiological, or combinations of these (Darmody 1967).

In contrast to the rather imprecise measurements made in everyday life, measurements and standards applied to manufactured parts must necessarily be extremely precise because they must conform to definite geometric and aesthetic design specifications. The production of quality products in any manufacturing operation requires an efficient and continuous testing program, and such programs have become increasingly important in recent years.

Society has changed its attitude, not only with respect to product safety and cost, but also with respect to product reliability. Variations in product quality that were once accepted as the natural result of industrial systems are no longer tolerated. What is required today is the consistent extraction of the best technological quality available on a routine production basis. In this circumstance, testing serves two functions: (1) to check on the performance of materials or components to obtain design data and (2) to check on the conformity of a product to its design specifications. Testing of the latter type is commonly called inspection.

Because dimensional measurement is very important to every manufacturing operation, much effort has historically been expended toward both improving the techniques and the instrumentation involved and refining the standards employed.

The term "standard" has a dual meaning in the manufacturing environment. It is used to denote universally accepted specifications for devices, components, or processes that ensure conformity and therefore interchangeability throughout a particular industry. Thus, one manufacturer's screw will fit another's nut, all makers of bricks will produce them in the same sizes, and all microscope objectives will fit all microscopes.

As used in metrology, on the other hand, a standard provides a reference for assigning a numerical value to a measured quantity. The term "measurement" implies the comparison of an unknown with a known to determine the qualitative relationship between the two. Each basic, measurable quantity has associated with it an ultimate standard that embodies the definition of a particular unit. Working standards, those used in conjunction with the various measurement-making instruments, are calibrated in terms of the particular unit definitions involved. Obviously, if measurements made at different locations are to be comparable, they must ultimately be traceable to the same standard.

Measurement Tools

> Select and describe appropriate uses
> of inspection tools such as gage blocks,
> calipers, micrometers, optical comparators,
> and coordinate measuring machines (CMM).
> (Analyze)
>
> Body of Knowledge IV.D.1

Selection of a measuring tool or measuring instrument is based on several factors. With advanced technology, measurement tools can be classified into two general categories: contact (e.g., touch probes) and noncontact (e.g., laser scanners). In general, the Rule of Ten serves as a baseline for the selection process of a measurement tool. The Rule of Ten of the Automotive Industry Action Group (AIAG) states that inspection measurements should be better than the tolerance of a dimension by a factor of 10 and calibration standards should be better than the inspection instrument by a factor of 10. Once this rule is implemented, candidate instruments need to be evaluated based on the following criteria:

- Accuracy and precision
- Repeatability
- Sensitivity
- Resolution
- Stability and consistency
- Part or workpiece material
- Shape and dimensions of the part being measured
- Capabilities of the metrology laboratory

The following is a review of the different measurement instruments and technologies employed in common measurement practices such as length and angle measurement, surface texture measurement, and measurement of out-of-roundness.

Current technological advances, including, but not limited to, supercomputers, hybrid manufacturing, semiconductors, and fiber optics, require more sophisticated measurements and/or measurement tools. However, as Whitehouse (2002, 2010) discusses, even with more sophisticated tools, there is still a need to address some of the same, or similar, problems and issues regarding measurements.

Length and Angle Measurements

The standard environmental conditions for length measurements include a temperature of 68°F (20°C) and a barometric pressure of 760 mm Hg (Doiron 2007). Because these conditions are assumed for all precision dimensional measurements, dimensional metrology laboratories are temperature controlled as nearly as is practical to 68°F, and thermal expansion corrections are made for any deviations that may occur. It is seldom necessary to correct for thermal expansion to achieve the accuracy required in industrial movement. Since the majority of precision parts, like the masters against which they are measured, are made of steel, it is generally safe to assume that their thermal expansion coefficients are identical and that no temperature correction need be made. Temperature corrections are also unnecessary when angles alone are measured since a uniform temperature change cannot change the size of an angle. This will definitely change with the introduction of new materials.

Dimensional (or linear) measuring instruments are used to measure length. They are of two types: absolute instrument and comparative instruments, or comparators.

Absolute instruments have their working standards built in and thus require no mastering; they are generally used for long-range measurements. Comparators are short-range devices that measure deviations between a working master and a given part. The yardstick is a crude example of the first type, and the dial indicator is an example of the second.

Table 4.9 details typical units, standards, and instruments for length and angle measurements. Measuring instruments range from very basic tools to more sophisticated measuring machines, such as coordinate measuring machines and laser scanners. The following paragraphs cover the basic measuring tools that are commonly used for many applications:

- Surface plates

- Micrometers

- Verniers

- Comparators

- Dial indicators

- Gage blocks

- Ring, plug, and snap gages

Most of the basic or general-purpose linear measuring instruments are typified by the use of steel rulers, vernier calipers, and micrometer calipers.

Steel rulers are commonly used for linear measurements in which the ends of a dimension being measured are aligned with graduations of the scale from which the length is read directly. A specialized type of steel ruler is the depth ruler, which is used for measuring holes, slots, and so on.

Vernier calipers are used for inside or outside linear measurement. Other types of verniers include digital reading calipers that provide LCD readouts in micrometers (μm) or microinches (μ in) and vernier height gages that can measure external, internal, and distance dimensions, as well as perpendicularity, flatness, straightness, centers, and diameters.

Micrometers come in various types. The measuring element of a micrometer consists of a fixed anvil and a spindle that moves lengthwise as it turns. Vernier

Table 4.9 Typical standards and instrumentation for industrial length and angle measurements.

	Length measurements	**Angle measurements**
Unit of measurement	Meter	Radian
Ultimate standard	Speed of light	Circle
Single-valued working standards	Length gage blocks	Angle gage blocks
Many-valued working standards	Line scales, step bars	Optical polygons, serrated-type index tables
Displacement-measuring	Interferometers	Autocollimator instruments

micrometer calipers use a vernier scale on the sleeve. Digital micrometers use digital readouts to make readings faster and easier. Indicating micrometers have a built-in dial indicator to provide a positive indication of measuring pressure applied.

Angular measurements use the degree as the standard unit. Angular measuring devices range from simple tools such as protractors, bevel protractors, and squares to sine bars and dividing heads. The protractor reads directly in degrees. A bevel protractor utilizes a vernier scale that shows angles as small as five or less minutes.

The sine bar is a more precise device for precision measuring and checking of angles. It consists of an accurately ground flat steel straight edge with precisely affixed round buttons that are a known distance apart and of identical diameters.

Dividing heads are either optical or mechanical devices that often are used for the circular measurement of angular spacing, common in machine tool operations.

Layout and Locating Devices

Surface plates provide a relatively accurate surface plane from which measurements can be made. Surface plates may employ a cast iron or granite surface. Granite surface plates provide better hardness, resistance to corrosion, and non-magnetic characteristics compared with cast iron plates. Granite surface plates also provide less response to temperature changes than cast iron surface plates.

Gages

Gages are used to determine the conformance or nonconformance of a dimension to required specifications without attempting actual measurements. Typical common functional gages are classified according to their use for checking outside dimensions, inside dimensions, or special features. Ring and snap gages are used for checking outside dimensions, plug gages are used for checking inside dimensions, and other gages are used for checking special features like tapers, threads, and splines. They normally provide a decision on part specifications.

A common method of inspection by attributes involves the use of limit gages, also known as fixed limit gages or go/no-go gages. Limit gages are made to sizes essentially identical to the design specification limits of the dimension to be inspected. If a specific gage can properly mate with a part, then the part can be assembled with another part whose physical boundaries do not exceed those of the gage. Consequently, the part is acceptable for assembly. Limit gages designed to identify this condition are called go gages. (See Figure 4.12.)

The "go" end of a go/no-go gage is designed to check the characteristic at the maximum material condition (minimum size for interior features, maximum size

Figure 4.12 Go/no-go gage to check the diameter of a shaft.

for exterior features). The maximum material condition produces the minimum clearance required for assembly. The "no-go" end is designed to detect conditions of excessive clearance. It checks the characteristic at its minimum material condition. A part will not mate with a no-go gage unless the actual condition of the part feature is below the specified minimum. Thus, if the no-go gage mates with the part, then the part dimension is out of specification and the part should be rejected. In practice, go/no-go gages are used together and often appear at opposite ends of an inspection instrument. An acceptable part should mate with the go end but should not mate with the no-go end. Parts that mate with both ends or that do not mate with either end do not meet design specifications and should be rejected.

Other than gauging, most methods of inspection by attributes are largely subjective and depend on the ability of human inspectors to make the right decisions. In many cases, inspection by attributes involves visual characteristics, such as color, shape, or smoothness, and other visual defects.

Dial Indicators, Comparators, and Gage Blocks

Dial indicators magnify the dimension deviation from a standard to which the gage is set. Dial indicators are used for many kinds of checking and gauging operations, checking machines and tools, verifying alignments, and cutter runout. Some indicators employ mechanical mechanisms for their operation and others come with a digital readout.

Comparators normally employ dial indicators for their operation and come in different varieties: mechanical, optical, electronic, and pneumatic. Optical projectors, also known as optical comparators, employ a system in which light rays are directed against the object and then reflected back through a projection lens onto a screen. The projections are large enough to accurately measure small configurations of objects.

Gage blocks are a system for producing precision lengths. They may be used as a reference for the calibration of dial indicators. They are rectangular, square, or round blocks of steel, carbide, or ceramic materials. Each has two faces that are flat, level, and parallel with an accuracy and length grade, depending on the application.

Surface Texture Measurement

Surface metrology is defined as the measurement and characterization of a surface topology (Whitehouse 2002). It is treated separately from length measurement, which is concerned with the relationship of two surfaces on a workpiece. Surface measurement, however, is involved with the relationship between a surface on the workpiece and a reference that is not actually on the workpiece. One aspect of surface metrology is the measurement of surface roughness as an average deviation from a mean center line (Bosch 1984). Townsend et al. (2016) provide a review paper on surface metrology for metal additive manufacturing.

Of all the methods used for the numerical assessment of the surface, the following are the most widely used (Reason 1960):

1. Peak-to-valley measure

2. Mean-line measures (center line average [CLA] and root mean square [RMS])

3. Crest-line measures

4. Envelope method, in which the crest line should be defined as the locus of the center of a circle or defined radius rolling across the surface, the locus being displaced toward the surface until it contacts the crests

The international standard for the assessment of surface texture, ISO/R 468, defines three parameters: R_a (CLA), R_z, and R_{max}, all measured relative to a straight mean line. Note that ISO/R 468 was replaced by ISO 4287:1997. These parameters are shown in Figure 4.13 and can be defined as follows (Spragg 1976):

1. R_a (CLA) value is the arithmetic mean of the departures of a profile from the mean line. It is normally determined as the mean result of several consecutive sample lengths L.

2. R_z (10-point height) is the average distance between the five height peaks and the five deepest valleys within the sampling length and measured perpendicular to it.

3. R_{max} is the maximum peak-to-valley height within the sampling length.

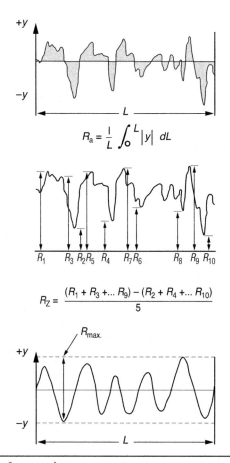

Figure 4.13   ISO/R 468 surface roughness parameters.

Other parameters of surface roughness are shown in Figure 4.14. They are defined as follows (Machinability Data Center 1980):

1. R_{tm} is the average value of $Rmax$'s for five consecutive sampling lengths.

2. R_p is the maximum profile height from the mean line within the sampling length. R_{pm} is the mean value of R_p's determined over five sampling lengths.

3. *Peak count* (PC) is the number of peak/valley pairs per inch projecting through a band of width b centered about the mean line.

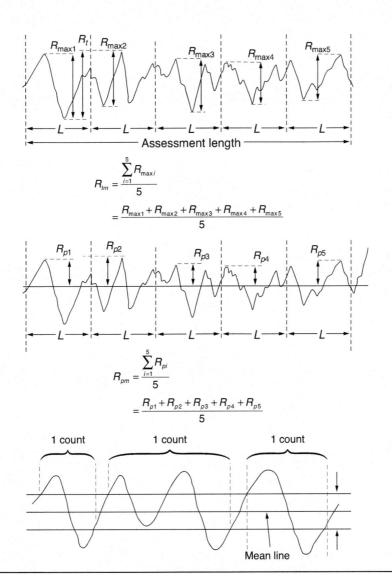

Figure 4.14 Other parameters of surface roughness.

The most common method of surface measurement is to move a stylus over the surface and measure an average electrical signal produced by a transducer attached to the stylus. Other means used less frequently include stylus profiling (where a chart record is produced instead of an average number), reflectance meters, pneumatics, and optical interference. The stylus averaging unit is fast, repeatable, quite easy to interpret, and relatively inexpensive (Bosch 1984).

Measurement of Roundness

Geometrically, a part can be said to be round in a given cross section if there exists within the section a point from which all points on the periphery are equidistant. In practice, however, the radius of nominally round parts tends to vary from point to point. Thus, the problem found by the metrologist is one of displaying and assessing these variations, and correctly interpreting the results (Bosch 1984).

Although many methods have been used for roundness measurement, only those that provide valid radial-deviation data lend themselves to standardization and consistent, accurate measurement of all out-of-roundness conditions. For this reason, current industry, national, and international standards primarily cover measurements taken with precision spindle-type instruments with the data recorded on a polar chart.

Precision spindle instruments include both those in which the spindle supports and rotates the part with the gage tip remaining stationary, and those in which the spindle rotates the gage tip about the part, which remains stationary. Figure 4.15 illustrates these two types of out-of-roundness measurement (Drews 1978).

The center of rotation of the precision spindle and the indicator gage tip provides a master radius to which all the radii of a cross section profile of the part are compared. It is necessary that the center of the part cross section and the spindle axis be adjusted to be concentric within narrow limits. The variations of the cross section radii from the master radius are usually recorded in a highly magnified

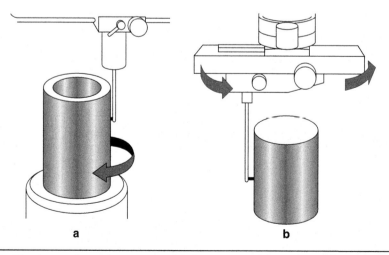

a   b

Figure 4.15   Two types of roundness–measuring instruments: (a) rotating table, (b) rotating workpiece.

form on a polar chart. Because the out-of-roundness value is defined as the difference between the largest and smallest radius that will just contain the measured profile, these radii must be measured from a specified center. The choice of these reference circles is arbitrary but is chosen to fulfill some functional requirements. As shown in Figure 4.16, there are four ways in which a center can be chosen (Drews 1978):

1. Minimum radial separation (MRS) (also known as minimum zone circle [MZC])

2. Least squares circle (LSC)

3. Maximum inscribed circle (MIC)

4. Minimum circumscribed circle (MCC)

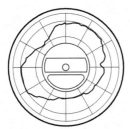

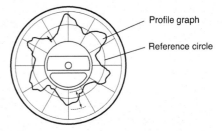

Minimum radial separation (MRS or MZC)

Two concentric circles are chosen so as to have the least radial separation and yet contain between them all of the polar trace. This radial separation is the measure of the out-of-roundness value. The radial difference between concentric circles determined by this method is numerically unique, in that by definition a smaller value cannot exist.

Least squares circle (LSC)

A theoretical circle is located with the polar profile such that the sum of the squares of the radial ordinated between the circle and the profile is a minimum. The out-of-roundness value would be determined by the sum of the maximum inward and maximum outward ordinates divided by the proper chart amplification factor.

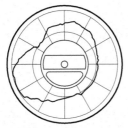

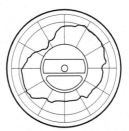

Maximum inscribed circle (MIC)

This procedure determines the center of the polar profile by the center of the largest circle that can be fitted inside the profile. From this circle the maximum outward departure of the profile denotes the out-of-roundness.

Minimum circumscribed circle (MCC)

The profile center is determined by the smallest circle that will just contain the measured profile. From the circle, the maximum inward departure of the profile can be measured; this maximum departure is the out-of-roundness.

Figure 4.16 Four ways by which a center may be chosen.

The magnified profile produced on the polar chart is evaluated by two concentric circles that just contain the profile when centered in accordance with the MRS center criteria. Other center criteria can be specified. For example, the concentric circles could be engraved on a transparent overlay (a more common method). The out-of-roundness value is the separation of the two concentric circles divided by the magnification setting of the instrument. The polar chart clearly shows the number and magnitude of the roundness deviations.

There are many advantages to the precision spindle methods. Accurate measurements of all types of out-of-roundness are possible and a permanent polar chart, which is easily interpreted, is provided. It is also the most accurate method of measurement available. With proper equipment, accuracies of one microinch are attainable. In addition to roundness, the equipment also permits ultraprecise measurement of centricity, squareness, flatness, and other related geometric part feature characteristics.

Coordinate Measuring Machines

Coordinate measuring machines (CMMs) have become a primary means of dimensional quality control for manufactured parts of complex form, where the volume of production does not warrant the development of functional gauging. The advent of increasingly inexpensive computing power and more fully integrated manufacturing systems will continue to expand the use of these machines into an even larger role in the overall quality assurance of manufactured parts.

CMMs can most easily be defined as physical representations of a three-dimensional rectilinear coordinate system. CMMs now represent a significant fraction of the measuring equipment used for defining the geometry of different-shaped workpieces. Most dimensional characteristics of many parts can be measured within minutes with these machines. Similar measurements would take hours using older measuring equipment and procedures. Besides flexibility and speed, CMMs have several additional advantages:

1. Different features of a part can be measured in one setup. This eliminates errors introduced due to setup changes.

2. All CMM measurements are taken from one geometrically fixed measuring system, eliminating the accumulation of errors resulting from using functional gauging and transfer techniques.

3. The use of digital readouts eliminates the necessity for the interpretation of readings, such as with the dial or vernier-type measuring scales.

4. Most CMMs have automatic data recording, which minimizes operator influence.

5. Part alignment and setup procedures are greatly simplified by using software supplied with computer-assisted CMMs. This minimizes the setup time for measurement.

6. Data can be automatically saved for further analysis.

Although CMMs can be thought of as representations of a simple rectilinear coordinate system for measuring the dimensions of different-shaped workpieces, they naturally are constructed in many different configurations, all of which offer different advantages. CMMs provide means for locating and recording the coordinate location of points in their measuring volumes. Traditional CMMs are classified according to their configurations, as follows (ANSI/ASME 1985):

1. Cantilever configuration, in which the probe is attached to a vertical machine ram (z-axis) moving on a mutually perpendicular overhang beam (y-axis) that moves along a mutually perpendicular rail (x-axis). Cantilever configuration is limited to small and medium-sized machines. It provides for easy operator access and the possibility of measuring parts longer than the machine table.

2. Bridge-type configuration, in which a horizontal beam moves along the x-axis, carrying the carriage that provides the y-motion. In other configurations, the horizontal beam (bridge structure) is rigidly attached to the machine base and the machine table moves along the x-axis. This is called fixed bridge configuration. A bridge-type CMM provides more rigid construction, which in turn provides better accuracy. The presence of the bridge on the machine table makes it a little more difficult to load large parts.

3. Column-type configuration, in which a moving table and saddle arrangement provide the x and y motions and the machine ram (z-axis) moves vertically relative to the machine table.

4. Horizontal-arm configuration features a horizontal probe arm (z-axis) moving horizontally relative to a column (y-axis) that moves in a mutually perpendicular motion (x-axis) along the machine base. This configuration provides the possibility of measuring large parts. Other arrangements of horizontal-arm configuration feature a fixed horizontal-arm configuration in which the probe is attached and moving vertically (y-axis) relative to a column that slides along the machine base in the x-direction. The machine table moves in a mutually perpendicular motion (z-axis) relative to the column.

5. Gantry-type configuration comprises a vertical ram (z-axis) moving vertically relative to a horizontal beam (x-axis) that in turn moves along two rails (y-axis) mounted on the floor. This configuration provides easy access and allows the measurement of large components.

6. L-shaped bridge configuration comprises a ram (z-axis) moving vertically relative to a carriage (x-axis) that moves horizontally relative to an L-shaped bridge moving in the y-direction.

Figure 4.17 shows CMM types according to this classification. The most advanced configuration, that of the ring-bridge, is not illustrated.

In addition to classifying CMMs according to their physical configuration, they can also be classified according to their mode of operation: manually oriented, computer-assisted, or direct computer-controlled. With manual machines, the operator moves the probe along the machine's axes to establish and manually record the measurement values that are provided by digital readouts. In some machines, digital printout devices are used.

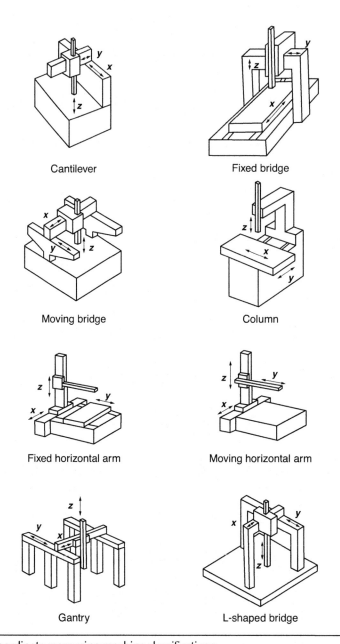

Cantilever

Fixed bridge

Moving bridge

Column

Fixed horizontal arm

Moving horizontal arm

Gantry

L-shaped bridge

Figure 4.17 Coordinate measuring machine classifications.

Computer-assisted CMMs can be either manually positioned (free-floating mode) by moving the probe to measurement locations or manually driven by providing power-operated motions under the control of the operator. In either case, data processing is accomplished by a computer. Some computer-assisted CMMs can perform some or all of the following functions: inch to metric conversion, automatic compensation for misalignment, storing of premeasured parameters and measurement sequences, data recording, means for disengagement of the power drive to allow manual adjustments and manipulations of the machine motions, and geometric and analytical evaluations.

Direct computer-controlled CMMs use a computer to control all machine motions and measuring routines and to perform most of the routinely required data processing. These machines are operated in much the same way as computer numeric control machine tools. Both control and measuring cycles are under program control. Off-line programming capability is also available.

The effective use of computers for CMM applications is a principal feature differentiating available CMM systems. The value of a measurement system depends a great deal on the sophistication and ease of use of the associated software and its functional capabilities. The functional capabilities of a CMM software package depend on the number and types of application programs available.

Destructive and Nondestructive Tests

> Identify when destructive and nondestructive measurement test methods should be used and apply the methods appropriately. (Apply)
>
> **Body of Knowledge IV.D.2**

Testing involves evaluation of product conformance to certain design or production requirements. In addition, the output of testing can be used to evaluate new designs during product development and to define a product's potential failure causes in product reliability evaluation.

Inspection is the evaluation of product quality by comparing the results of measuring one or several product characteristics with applicable standards. From this definition, it is evident that the inspection function involves several tasks:

1. Measurement, which could be on a qualitative or quantitative scale. The objective is to make a judgment about the product's conformance to specifications.

2. Comparison of the measurement results with specific standards that reflect the intended use of the product by the customer and the various production costs. If the product is found to be nonconforming, a decision as to whether nonconforming products are fit for use may be reached.

3. Decision making regarding the disposition of the unit inspected and, under sampling inspection, the lot from which the sample was drawn.

4. Corrective action(s) to improve the quality of the product and/or process based on the aggregate results of inspection over a number of units.

Testing is also carried out to determine the conformity of a product by comparing the results of measuring one or several product characteristics with applicable standards. It involves tasks similar to those of inspection. The difference is that testing can be performed on a part, a product, a subassembly, or an assembly, while inspection is typically performed on a component or a part of a product.

Two terms normally associated with inspection are "gauging" and "testing." *Gauging* determines product conformance with specifications with the aid of measuring instruments such as calipers, micrometers, templates, and other mechanical, optical, and electronic devices. *Testing* refers to the determination of the capability of an item to meet specified requirements by subjecting it to a set of physical, chemical, environmental, or other operating conditions and actions similar to or more severe than those expected under normal use.

Testing may be destructive or nondestructive. In testing, the product is subjected to measuring procedures that render its usefulness to the customer. Gauging, however, is the more common form of inspection and is less costly. This operation has no effect on the product's service capability. Of course, certain product characteristics, mainly those related to failure modes, may only be observed and measured by exposing the product to conditions beyond its designed limits, such as determining the maximum current that an electronic component can carry or the maximum tensile force that a mechanical part can withstand. Most of these procedures normally are destructive testing procedures and may be performed in cases where mandatory requirements are to be met. Nondestructive testing (NDT) of products usually is performed by subjecting the product to tests such as eddy current, ultrasonic resonance, or X-ray testing.

Nondestructive Testing Techniques

Screening or 100% inspection cannot be used when the product is subjected to a destructive testing procedure or the time involved in performing inspection is too long. Another constraint is that the cost of inspection may be too high to justify the economics of inspection. NDT techniques are more common for automated inspection or 100% inspection. The most common NDT techniques include the following:

- Eddy current testing involves the application of an alternating current passing through a coil that is placed near the surface of the part to be inspected. Thus, its application is limited to conducting materials, and the test results are made by comparison.

- Ultrasonic testing is used to check for surface defects that cause deflection of an ultrasonic wave directed on the part surface, thus indicating the presence of a surface defect. For ultrasonic testing, reference standards are required.

- Radiographic or X-ray techniques cause the internal characteristics of the part to be displayed and thus provide information about the presence of defects, cracks, or other impurities.

- Liquid penetration is commonly used for detecting defects on the part surface. It is used for different part configurations, and, unlike magnetic particle testing, it can be used for nonmagnetic materials. However, liquid penetration cannot be used to locate subsurface discontinuities.

- Magnetic particle testing is used when the part material can be magnetized. Part defects, like cracks or discontinuities, can then be detected by the presence of paring magnetic fields. Magnetic particle testing is limited to parts made of iron, steel, or allied materials.

- Other types of NDT include (Hellier 2012):

  - Visual inspection

  - Penetrant testing

  - Thermal infrared testing

  - Acoustic emission testing

  - Digital radiography

  - Phased Array Ultrasonic Testing (PAUT)

  - Ultrasonic phased array testing

  - Ultrasonic guided wave inspection

Other common NDT techniques include the application of some phenomenon, such as thermal, chemical, holographic interferometry (employing interference patterns for checking surface displacements), or optical phenomena. These are used for special testing procedures and often are too expensive to be widely applied.

METROLOGY

> Apply metrology techniques such as calibration, traceability to calibration standards, measurement error and its sources, and control and maintenance of measurement standards and devices. (Apply)
>
> **Body of Knowledge IV.E**

The science of precision measurement, usually referred to as *metrology*, encompasses all scientific disciplines. The word "metrology" is derived from two Greek words: *metro*, meaning "measurement," and *logy*, meaning "science." The term is used in a more restricted sense to mean that portion of measurement science that is often used to provide, maintain, and disseminate a consistent set of units, to provide support for the enforcement of equity in trade by weights and measurement laws, or to provide data for quality control in manufacturing (Simpson 1981).

A measurement is a series of manipulations of physical objects or systems according to a defined protocol that results in a number. The number is purported to uniquely represent the magnitude (or intensity) of a certain property, which depends on the properties of the test object. This number is acquired to form the basis of a decision affecting some goal or fulfilling some need, the satisfaction of which depends on the properties of the test subject.

These needs or goals can be viewed as requiring three general classes of measurements (Simpson 1981):

1. Technical. This class includes those measurements made to ensure dimensional compatibility or conformation to design specifications necessary for proper function, or, in general, all measurements made to ensure fitness for intended use of some object.

2. Legal. This class includes those measurements made to ensure compliance with a law or regulation. This class is the concern of weights and measures bodies, regulators, and those who must comply with regulations. The measurements are identical in kind with those of technical metrology but usually are embedded in a much more formal structure. Legal metrology is more prevalent in Europe than in the United States, although this is changing.

3. Scientific. This class includes those measurements made to validate theories of the nature of the universe or to suggest new theories. These measurements, which can be called scientific metrology (properly the domain of experimental physics), present special problems.

Standards of Measurement

The National Institute of Standards and Technology (NIST) is the American custodian of the standards of measurement. It was established by an act of Congress in 1901, although the need for such a body had been noted by the founders of the Constitution. NIST's two main campuses are in Gaithersburg, Maryland, and Boulder, Colorado, where research into the phenomenon of measurement, the properties of materials, and calibration of the reference standards submitted by laboratories from throughout the United States is carried out. The following is a generalization of the echelons of standards in the national measurement system (Rice 1986):

*   National standards. Include prototype and natural phenomena of SI (Systems International, the worldwide system of weight and measures standards) base units and reference and working standards for derived and other units

*   Metrology standards. Reference standards of industrial or governmental laboratories

*   Calibration standards. Working standards of industrial or governmental laboratories

To maintain accuracy, standards in a vast industrial complex must be traceable to a single source, usually the country's national standards. Since the national laboratories of well-developed countries maintain close connections with the International Bureau of Weights and Measures, there is assurance that items manufactured to identical dimensions in different countries will be compatible (McNish 1967).

Application of precise measurement has increased so much during the past few years that it is no longer practical for a single national laboratory to perform all the calibrations and standardization required by a large country with a high technical development. Malshe et al. (2013) discuss manufacturing and metrology at the micro-scale in their review paper of engineering surface architecture with biological references and inspiration.

Increased precision, tolerance, and technology in measurements have led to the establishment of a considerable number of standardizing laboratories in industry and in various branches of the state and national governments (see Figure 4.18). In order for results of calibrations to be uniform, the standardizing laboratories must maintain close rapport with the national laboratory. This is facilitated by the use of uniform terminology in discussing standards (McNish 1967).

The term "standard" includes three distinct areas, all of which are of importance in metrology (NIST 1981):

- Definitions of base units

- Physical artifacts

- Paper standards

Definitions of Base Units

The definitions of the base units of measurement form a reference from which all other units can be derived. These base units, together with two supplementary

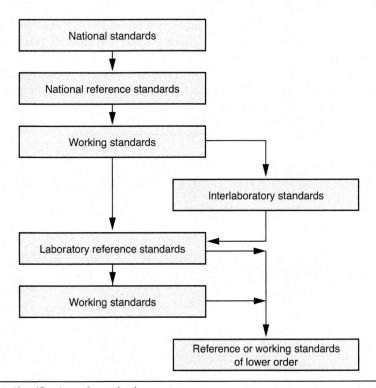

Figure 4.18   Classification of standards.

units related to angle measurement that are necessary to specify a complete system of units, are listed in Table 4.10. Table 4.11 gives the definitions of all the SI units listed in Table 4.10. The definitions can also be found at the NIST website (https://www.nist.gov/pml/nist-guide-si-appendix-definitions-si-base-units). A current chart showing the relationships of all the SI units to which names have been assigned can be found at the NIST website in NIST Special Publication 304A (https://www.nist.gov/publications/si-measurement-system-chart).

All the SI units listed in Tables 4.10 and 4.11 are defined in terms of experiments that can be performed in any suitably equipped laboratory, except for the definition of the unit mass, the kilogram. The kilogram is the only base unit defined in terms of a physical artifact. It must therefore be carefully preserved and protected, and the unit can only be disseminated by direct comparisons with the defining artifact. The kilogram is the mass of the International Prototype of the Kilogram, which is kept at the International Bureau of Weights and Measures near Paris, France.

The standard for angle measurements is present in the form of the circle, and units of angle are defined in terms of this standard. Thus, one degree is the angle that subtends 1/360 of the circumference of a circle, and one radian is the angle that subtends $1/(2\pi)$ times the circumference.

Measurements of length are defined and determined by people. Until 1960, the meter was defined as the distance, under certain specified environmental conditions, between two lines engraved on the neutral axis of the International Prototype Meter, a bar of 90% platinum/10% iridium alloy, which is preserved at the International Bureau of Weights and Measures; Prototype Meter No. 27, whose length was known in terms of the international prototype, served as a standard for the United States. The origins of the meter can be read about at https://www.nist.gov/system/files/documents/pml/div683/museum-timeline.pdf.

This method of defining the meter length was not entirely satisfactory since it required periodic recalibration of the various national standards in terms of the

Table 4.10   Base units of the international system.

Quantity	Name
Length	Meter
Mass	Kilogram
Time	Second
Electric current	Ampere
Thermodynamic temperature	Kelvin
Amount of substance	Mole
Luminous intensity	Candela
Plane angle*	Radian
Solid angle*	Steradian

*Supplementary units

Table 4.11 Definitions of the SI base units.

Unit	Definition
meter–m	The distance traveled by light in a vacuum during a time interval of 1/299,792,458 of a second.
kilogram–kg	A cylinder of platinum-iridium alloy kept by the International Bureau of Weights and Measures at Paris. A duplicate in the custody of the National Institute of Standards and Technology serves as the mass standard for the United States.
second–s	The duration of 9,192,631,770 cycles of the radiation associated with a specified transition of the cesium-133 atom. It is realized by tuning an oscillator to the resonance frequency of cesium-133 atoms as they pass through a system of magnets and a resonant cavity into a detector.
Ampere–A	That current which, if maintained in each of two long parallel wires separated by one meter in free space, would produce a force between the two wires (due to their magnetic fields) of 2×10^{-7} newton for each meter of length.
Kelvin–K	The fraction 1/273.16 of the thermodynamic temperature of the triple point of water. The temperature 0 K is called absolute zero.
mole–mol	The amount of substance of a system that contains as many elementary entities as there are atoms in 0.012 kilogram of carbon-12.
candela–cd	The luminous intensity, in a given direction, of a source that emits monochromatic radiation of frequency 540×1012 (Hz) and that has a radiant intensity in that direction of 1/683 watt per steradian.
radian–rad	The plane angle with its vertex as the center of a circle that is subtended by an arc equal in length to the radius.
steradian–sr	The solid angle with its vertex at the center of a sphere that is subtended by the area of the spherical surface equal to that of a square with sides equal in length to the radius.

Source: NIST Special Publication 304A

international standard. In 1960, the Eleventh General Conference on Weights and Measures redefined the meter as a length equal to 1,650,763.73 wavelengths, in a vacuum, of the orange-red radiation corresponding to the transition between the 2p10 and 5d5 levels of the krypton-86 atom. The meter so defined is identical to that previously defined, within the limits of accuracy of the various measurements involved. The new definition provided a standard for length measurement that was based on an unchanging physical constant that could be reproduced in any properly equipped laboratory in the world. The inch is defined as 0.0254 meters (Taylor and Thompson 2008).

The definition of the meter was again changed in 1983 by the General Conference of Weights and Measures (Taylor and Thompson 2008). The current definition of the meter is the length of a path traveled by light in a vacuum during a time interval of 1/299,792,458 of a second. This definition of the meter thus defines the speed of light to be exactly 299,792,458 meters/second, and with this definition the meter could be realized from the wavelength of any coherent optical source whose frequency is known. The wavelength is the speed of light divided by the frequency.

Physical Artifacts and Paper Standards

Physical artifacts are manufactured with high precision to embody a particular quantity, dimension, or feature. These include such items as gage blocks for length, standard resistors for electrical resistance, standards for cell voltage, and so on. This class of artifacts also includes high-precision analog measurement instruments that can be used as masters for reference, such as mercury in glass thermometers and dead weight testers for pressure.

Paper standards are the many documents published by various technical societies and standards-writing organizations that contain specifications or generally accepted methods for making measurements.

Uncertainty in Metrology

A fundamental role of the metrology and calibration process is to assign accuracy or uncertainty statements to a measurement. This can be achieved by defining characteristics of measuring system elements as well as equipment limitations.

Error in Measurement

Error in measurement is the difference between the indicated value and the true value of a measured quantity. The true value of a quantity to be measured is seldom known. Errors are classified as random errors or systematic errors. Gosavi and Cudney (2012) present an overview of the concepts and techniques used in metrology error. While the paper is generally focused on errors, they also present topics regarding metrology in general.

Random errors are accidental in nature. They fluctuate in a way that cannot be predicted from the detailed employment of the measuring system or from knowledge of its functioning. Sources of errors such as hysteresis, ambient influences, or variations in the workpiece are typical but not all-inclusive in the random category. Systematic errors are those not usually detected by repetition of the measurement operations. An error resulting from either faulty calibration of a local standard or a defect in contact configuration of an internal measuring system is typical, but not completely inclusive in the systematic class of errors (Darmody 1967).

It is important to know all the sources of errors in a measuring system, rather than merely to be aware of the details of their classification. Analysis of the causes of errors is helpful in attaining the necessary knowledge of achieved accuracy.

There are many different sources of errors that influence the precision of a measuring process in a variety of ways according to the individual situation in which such errors arise. The permutation of error sources and their effects, therefore, is quite considerable. In general, these errors can be classified under three main headings:

1. Process environment

2. Equipment limitation

3. Operator fallibility

These factors constitute an interrelated three-element system for the measuring process as shown in Figure 4.19.

The requirement of any precision measuring instrument is that it should be able to represent, as accurately as possible, the dimension it measures. This necessitates that the instrument itself have a high degree of inherent accuracy. Small inaccuracies will exist, however, due to the tolerances permitted in the instrument's manufacture. These inaccuracies will influence the degree of precision attainable in its application.

The identification of measuring situations becomes increasingly complex in modern metrology. As parts become smaller and more precise, greater attention has to be paid to geometric qualities such as roundness, concentricity, straightness, parallelism, and squareness. Deficiencies in these qualities may consume all of the permitted design tolerance, so that a simple dimensional check becomes grossly insufficient.

Operators have to be knowledgeable about what they have to measure and how satisfactorily the requirements of the situation will be met by the measuring instrument. Correct identification of the measuring situation will eliminate those methods unsuitable for the situation. Proper measuring equipment can therefore be selected from a smaller range of measuring process alternatives. Method

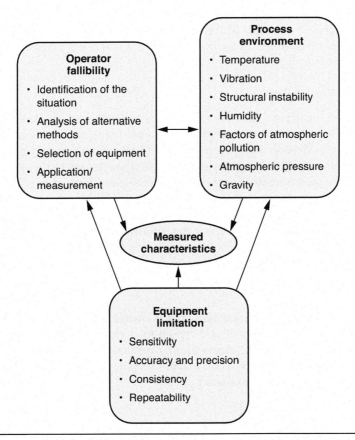

Figure 4.19 Factors affecting the measuring process.

analysis can then be applied to these alternatives to determine which best satisfies the situation. This usually involves examining each method for different characteristics and evaluating the relative accuracies between the different methods.

Accuracy

Accuracy is the degree of agreement of individual or average measurements with an accepted reference value or level (Montgomery 2013). Measurement science encompasses two basic approaches for determining conformity to measurement accuracy objectives: (1) an engineering analysis to determine all causes of error, and (2) a statistical evaluation of data after stripping or eliminating the errors revealed by the engineering analysis (Darmody 1967).

Precision

Precision is the degree of mutual agreement among individual measurements made under prescribed like conditions, or simply, how well identically performed measurements agree with each other (Montgomery 2013). This concept applies to a process or a set of measurements, not to a single measurement, because in any set of measurements the individual results will scatter about the mean. Since the means of the results from groups of measurements tend to scatter less about the overall mean than individual results, reference is commonly made to the precision of a single measurement as contrasted with the precision of groups of measurements, but this is a misuse of the term. What is really meant is the precision of a set of single measurements or the precision of a set of groups of measurements (McNish 1967).

Sensitivity and Readability

The terms "sensitivity" and "readability" often are used in discussing measurement, and sometimes the concepts they involve are confused with accuracy and precision (see McNish 1967). Sensitivity and readability are primarily associated with equipment, while accuracy and precision are associated with the measuring process. The most sensitive or the most readable equipment may not always lead to the most precise or the most accurate results.

Sensitivity can be defined as the least perceptible change in dimension detected by the measuring tip and shown by the indicator. *Readability* is the ease of reading the instrument scale when a dimension is being measured. It is a factor that should remain constant over the full scale range.

Consistency

Consistency is another characteristic of the measuring instrument. Consistency of the reading on the instrument scale when the same dimension is being measured is necessary. This property affects the performance of the measuring instrument, and, therefore, complete confidence in the accuracy of the process cannot be established in the absence of consistency.

Traceability

Traceability is a process intended to quantify a laboratory's measurement uncertainty in relationship to the national standards. It is based on analyses of error contributions present in each of the measurement transfers: the calibration of the laboratory's reference standards by NIST, the measurements made in the calibration transfers within the laboratory, and the measurements made on a product. Evidence of traceability is normally required; it may be as simple as retention of certificates and reports on calibration or as complex as reproduction of the analyses demonstrating the uncertainties claimed for the measurements (Rice 1986).

A laboratory that maintains its own reference standards (i.e., it relies on no laboratory other than NIST for calibration of its standards) must continuously monitor its own performance. Measurements on check standards, intercomparisons of standards, and participation in measurement assurance programs sponsored by NIST are meant to quantify laboratory error sources, as well as to provide indications of the causes (Rice 1986).

Calibration

Calibration refers to measurements where the individual values are reported, rather than to measurements indicating only that an instrument is functioning within prescribed limits. It also refers to the disciplines necessary to control measuring systems to ensure their functioning within prescribed accuracy objectives. The general calibration provisions for a measuring system include the following:

1. Acceptance calibration of a new system

2. Periodic calibration of the system in use or when placed in use after storage

3. Availability of standards traceable to the national standard for the unit of measure under consideration

Normally, a calibration chain or pyramid of echelons is involved in the discipline of metrology control and surveillance. The levels are as follows:

Level 1. The product tolerance or measured quantity Level 2. The calibration of the product measuring system

Level 3. The calibration of the measuring system used to calibrate the product measurement system

Level 4. Local standards, such as gage blocks or standard cells (volts), used for calibration of level 3

Level 5. Referencing local standards of level 4 to the national standard

Each of these levels attempts to achieve an accuracy/tolerance ratio that will satisfy requirements of the preceding level. This achievement is, of course, subject to the limitations of the state of the art, as well as cost–accuracy trade-offs that may come into play.

The aim of all calibration activities is ascertaining that a measuring system will function to ensure attainment of its accuracy objectives.

Periodic calibration of measuring and test equipment is accepted by most as necessary for measurement accuracy. A little more controversial is the question of determining the basis of the period of recalibration. There are several techniques in use to establish calibration intervals initially and to adjust the intervals thereafter. These methods include the following:

1. The same interval for all equipment in the user's inventory

2. The same interval for families of instruments (e.g., oscilloscopes, gage blocks)

3. The same interval for a given manufacturer and model number

Adjustments of these initial intervals are then made for the entire inventory, individual families, or manufacturer and model numbers, respectively, based on analyses or history. A study conducted for NIST in connection with a review of government laboratory practices identifies these and other methods (Vogt 1980).

Calibration Control System

A typical calibration program may involve all or most of the following tasks (Rice 1986):

1. Evaluation of equipment to determine its capability

2. Identification of calibration requirements

3. Selection of standards to perform calibration

4. Selection of methods/procedures to carry out the measurements necessary for the calibration

5. Establishment of the initial interval and the rules for adjusting the interval thereafter

6. Establishment of a recall system to ensure that instruments due for calibration are returned

7. Implementation of a labeling system to visually identify the instrument's due date

8. Use of a quality assurance program to evaluate the calibration system (process, control, audit, corrective action, etc.)

Selection of the standards, methods, and procedures to carry out the calibration includes the decision of where the calibration will be performed. The recall system must be designed to ensure that both the calibration organization and the using organization are aware in advance that an instrument will be due for calibration. Labeling instruments to visually display their calibration due dates is a companion feature to the recall system. Labels indicate (by dates, color codes, or similar symbols) the date the instrument is due for its next calibration. This visual identification may be used by the quality assurance organization to ensure that the instrument is not used beyond its due date. Intervals are established in a variety of ways, as discussed previously. Principal objectives of an interval adjustment program include minimizing the potential for out-of-tolerance instruments in user areas, minimizing the costs of calibration, and ensuring the required accuracy of instrumentation.

Measurement Assurance

Measurement assurance, thought by some to relate only to methods used in the metrology or calibration laboratory to secure calibrations by NIST, is one of the more important concepts in the measurement field.

Traditionally, calibrations by NIST determine the accuracy and precision of the measuring instrument. Measurement assurance protocols (MAPs), on the other hand, are able to include not only the accuracy of the item but also the contribution to error by the metrologist/technician, laboratory environment, and practices/procedures of the laboratory because the experiment involves measurements by participants in their own laboratories (Belanger 1980).

Measurement assurance, in addition to being a concept of importance to metrology and calibration laboratory managers, is something that should interest quality assurance personnel involved in testing and measurement. Most factory testing and measuring involves the use of equipment whose accuracy has been determined through calibration. Little, if any, consideration is given to errors that may be contributed by the test operator, by his or her instructions or procedures, or by the environments in which the equipment is operated. The application of measurement assurance can serve to reduce errors (Rice 1986).

MEASUREMENT SYSTEM ANALYSIS (MSA)

> Calculate, analyze, and interpret repeatability and reproducibility (Gage R&R) studies, measurement correlation, capability, bias, linearity, precision, stability and accuracy, using MSA quantitative and graphical methods. (Evaluate)
>
> **Body of Knowledge IV.F**

Measurement system analysis (MSA) consists of qualifying the measurement process, determining the adequacy of the measurement system for use, and identifying and estimating the process error. A measurement system is the entire process for obtaining measurements on some quality characteristic of interest. This process includes standards, personnel, methods of measurement, and so on.

In this section, definitions as well as the concept of gage repeatability and reproducibility (gage R&R) are introduced.

Terms and Definitions

This section covers types of errors as well as accuracy and precision with respect to measurement systems. Two important and common types of errors in MSA are systematic error and random error. *Systematic errors* can be caused by human interference, poor manufacturing methods, and measuring device imperfections, for example. This error remains fairly constant over repeated measurements collected under identical conditions. The error is systematic, which results in values that are consistently above or consistently below the true or reference value of the quality characteristic.

Random errors vary arbitrarily over all measurements taken under identical conditions. Even when systematic errors have been identified and accounted for, normal random fluctuations will occur. If only random errors are present in the system, then increasing the number of measurements taken will provide a better estimate of the true value of the quality characteristic.

Measurement system error with respect to MSA consists of variability that can be attributed to gage bias, stability, linearity, repeatability, and reproducibility. Accuracy of a measurement system is made up of bias, linearity, and stability. Repeatability and reproducibility are the components that describe precision, or measurement variation.

Accuracy is a qualitative term defined as the difference between the measurement taken and the actual value of the quality characteristic of interest. The three components of accuracy are bias, linearity, and stability.

Bias is defined as the difference between the observed average measurement and a reference value and is a measure of systematic error in terms of the measurement system. Bias is the difference between the observed average and the reference value.

The observed average measurement can be found by measuring a single part multiple times or selecting several parts at random and measuring each part multiple times. The measurements should be taken under identical conditions.

Hypothesis tests can be carried out to test the significance of bias (see AIAG [2010]). If bias is found to be significant, the cause for bias should be identified. Some reasons for significant bias may include (but are not limited to) an incorrect reference value, a worn measuring device, or improper calibration of or incorrect use of the measuring device.

Linearity measures how changes in the size of the part being measured will affect measurement system bias over the expected process range. Consider the previous example (Example 4.6) with three parts of different sizes. Notice that the bias estimates were quite different across the different sizes. There may be evidence of nonlinearity if as the part size increases the bias changes significantly. Tests can be performed to determine whether nonlinearity, if it exists, is significant.

Stability is a measure of how well the measurement system performs over time. It provides a measure of the change in bias over time when the same part is measured. Stability differs from linearity in that only one part, whose reference value is known (or assumed to be known), is measured at different points in time.

This is to determine whether the measurement system has changed over time and after many uses.

In general, accuracy provides information about location, or the relationship between the measurement results and reference value of the quality characteristic.

EXAMPLE 4.5

Suppose three parts of different sizes are selected and the diameter of each part is measured. These parts represent the normal range of part sizes for which the measurement system is used. A reference value is known for each of the parts. Suppose each part is measured five times, with the results displayed in Table 4.12. The observed averages are calculated and the resulting bias estimated for each part.

Table 4.12 Bias and average estimates for parts of different sizes.

	Parts	1	2	3
	Reference value	2.00	3.80	5.60
	1	2.10	3.65	6.21
	2	1.88	4.00	5.40
Trials	3	1.92	3.88	5.26
	4	2.05	3.78	5.98
	5	2.01	4.10	4.93
Average		1.992	3.882	5.556
Bias		–0.008	0.082	–0.044

Precision is defined as the variation encountered when the same part is measured repeatedly using the same measurement system (under the same conditions). The two components of precision are repeatability and reproducibility.

Repeatability represents the variability due to the gage or test instrument when used to measure the same part under identical conditions (i.e., same operator measuring the same part).

Reproducibility, on the other hand, represents the variability due to different operators or setups measuring the same parts using the same measuring device. Reproducibility represents the variability due to the measurement system. Both repeatability and reproducibility will be discussed in more detail in this chapter.

Gage Repeatability and Reproducibility

Gage (or, interchangeably, gauge) repeatability and reproducibility (R&R) studies are used to determine whether a measurement system is capable for its intended purpose. If the measurement system variation is small compared with the process variation, then the measurement system is considered capable. In general, the purposes of a gage R&R study are to:

- Determine the amount of variability in the collected data that can be attributed to the measurement system in place

- Isolate the sources of variability in the measurement system

- Determine whether the measurement system is suitable for use in a broader project

When conducting a gage R&R study, it is often assumed that the "parts" and the "operators" are selected at random from larger populations. The parts are typically selected at random so that they represent the entire operating range of the process. Since the parts and operators are randomly selected, there is a measure of variability associated with each. There are situations where the parts or operators may be fixed. To illustrate, suppose the operators are really automatic gages and there are only three total for a particular process. If all three automatic gages are used, then the factor "operator" is fixed. Assessing the capability of fixed factors is beyond the scope of this handbook, but additional information and references can be found in Burdick, Borror, and Montgomery (2005).

Many issues must be considered when designing a gage R&R experiment, such as the number of parts, the number of operators, and the number of replicates to include. There has been considerable debate about these issues. The "standard" experiment often included 10 parts, three operators, and two replicates. However, research has indicated that these recommendations may not be appropriate for many problems. Burdick and Larsen (1997) demonstrated that the lengths of confidence intervals on the variance components in a gage R&R study are significantly shortened when the number of operators is increased (see Chapter 6 for discussion on confidence intervals). They recommend at least five or six operators in a typical gage R&R study. Increasing the number of parts does not affect the confidence intervals as much as increasing the number of operators. However, it has been shown that if the practitioner has to choose between increasing the number of parts and increasing the number of replicates on each part, a greater benefit is obtained by increasing the number of parts. See the review paper by Burdick, Borror, and Montgomery (2003) and the references within for further discussion of these issues in gage R&R experiments.

Gage variability is a function of variance components. Let $\sigma^2_{\text{Repeatability}}$ represent the inherent variability in the gage and $\sigma^2_{\text{Reproducibility}}$ represent the variability due to the different operators (or setups, different time periods, etc.) using the same gage. Specifically, the measurement error variability can be written as

$$\sigma^2_{\text{Measurement error}} = \sigma^2_{\text{Gage}} = \sigma^2_{\text{Reproducibility}} + \sigma^2_{\text{Repeatability}} \tag{4.6}$$

Furthermore, suppose part-to-part variability is denoted by (σ^2_p), then total variability can be written as a sum of the two variance components.

$$\sigma^2_{\text{Total}} - \sigma^2_{\text{Gage}} + \sigma^2_p \tag{4.7}$$

In a gage R&R study it is important to accurately estimate these variance components for the estimation of repeatability and reproducibility. Two commonly used methods for estimating repeatability and reproducibility are (1) the tabular method (also known as the range method) and (2) the analysis of variance method. Both methods will be presented and discussed in this section.

The Tabular Method (Range Method)

Gage R&R studies were often conducted using a tabular method because the calculations were simple. Software now allows the ANOVA method (discussed in the next subsection) to be used more readily and is more commonly used today. The tabular method is based on information that can be obtained from control charts and from using the sample ranges to estimate variability (see Chapter 6, for discussion of the sample range and control charts).

Estimating Reproducibility

The steps for estimating reproducibility using the tabular method are as follows:

1. Estimate the average measurement for each "operator"

2. Find the range of these averages (largest average – smallest average); this is called R_O (for operator range)

3. Estimate the standard deviation for reproducibility using the relationship

$$\hat{\sigma}_{\text{Reproducibility}} = \frac{R_O}{d_2} \qquad (4.8)$$

4. Estimate the variance component for reproducibility:

$$\hat{\sigma}^2_{\text{Reproducibility}} = \left(\frac{R_O}{d_2}\right)^2 \qquad (4.9)$$

Estimating Repeatability

The steps for estimating repeatability are as follows:

1. Calculate the range for each part (or sample)

2. Calculate the average range across all samples; this is denoted $\overline{R}$

3. Estimate the standard deviation for repeatability:

$$\hat{\sigma}_{\text{Repeatability}} = \hat{\sigma}_e = \frac{\overline{R}}{d_2} \qquad (4.10)$$

4. Estimate the variance component for repeatability:

$$\hat{\sigma}^2_{\text{Repeatability}} = \hat{\sigma}^2_e = \left(\frac{\overline{R}}{d_2}\right)^2 \qquad (4.11)$$

Estimating Part-to-Part Variability

The steps for estimating part-to-part variability are as follows:

1. Calculate the average measurement for each part (or sample)

2. Find the range of these averages (largest average – smallest average); this is denoted R_p (for part range)

3. Estimate the standard deviation for parts:

$$\hat{\sigma}_p = \frac{R_p}{d_2} \tag{4.12}$$

4. Estimate the variance component for parts:

$$\hat{\sigma}_p^2 = \left(\frac{R_p}{d_2}\right)^2 \tag{4.13}$$

Complete details of determining values of d_2 for each of the above quantities can be found in AIAG (2010) or Barrentine (2003). The values of d_2 can also be found in Appendix B and are discussed in more detail in Chapter 6. Additionally, in AIAG (2010) and Barrentine (2003) you will find details of the range method.

The Analysis of Variance Method

One of the reported drawbacks to using the tabular method has been the inability to estimate any possible interaction between operators and parts (or samples).

It is often assumed that the operators are well trained and as a result there should be no significant interaction between these two factors. If, however, there is a significant interaction, this effect should be quantified and taken into consideration when providing estimates of repeatability and reproducibility. Using the tabular or range method, it is not possible to estimate the interaction between operator and part.

The analysis of variance (ANOVA) method has become a common choice for practitioners conducting gage R&R studies since the computations can be easily carried out using modern statistical software. (See Chapter 6 for discussion of interactions, factors, and the general ANOVA method.) Before presenting the ANOVA method, some basic assumptions must be discussed.

Suppose the response of interest in a gage R&R study can easily be expressed by a random two-factor model (see Chapter 6 for more details on modeling a response, factors, two-way interactions, and two-way ANOVA). The factors include "parts," "operators," and possibly the part-by-operator interaction. A gage R&R study is to be carried out involving p parts, m operators, and n replicates. Suppose y represents the response of interest and can be modeled as

$$y_{ijk} = \mu + P_i + O_j + (PO)_{ij} + \varepsilon_{ijk}$$
$$\text{for } i = 1, 2, \ldots, p; \ j = 1, 2, \ldots, m; \ k = 1, 2, \ldots, n \tag{4.14}$$

where

y_{ijk} is the kth measurement of the ith part by the jth operator

μ is the overall process mean

P_i represents the effect of the ith part; we assume that P_i is a random factor that follows a normal distribution with mean zero and variance σ_P^2

O_j represents the effect of the jth operator; we assume that O_j is a random factor that follows a normal distribution with mean zero and variance σ_O^2

$(PO)_{ij}$ represents the part-by-operator interaction effect; we assume that $(PO)_{ij}$ is a random factor that follows a normal distribution with mean zero and variance σ^2_{PO}

ε_{ijk} represents random error; we assume that ε_{ijk} follows a normal distribution with mean zero and variance σ^2_e

The terms σ^2_P, σ^2_O, σ^2_{PO}, and σ^2_e are the variance components. As discussed previously, gage variability is a function of these variance components. Specifically, measurement error (gage) variability was shown in Equation (4.14). Now, the variance components for the random factors are used to determine repeatability, reproducibility, and part variability. Specifically, reproducibility and repeatability variation can be written as

$$\hat{\sigma}^2_{\text{Reproducibility}} = \sigma^2_{PO} + \sigma^2_O \tag{4.15}$$

and

$$\sigma^2_{\text{Repeatability}} = \sigma^2_e \tag{4.16}$$

Part-to-part variability is given by σ^2_P. The variability of the total observed measurement is given by

$$\sigma^2_{\text{Total}} = \sigma^2_{\text{Gage}} + \sigma^2_p \tag{4.17}$$

The variance components will be estimated using the mean squares obtained from an ANOVA table. To begin, a standard ANOVA is conducted assuming that the two-factor standard model given earlier is valid. The reader is encouraged to see Chapter 6 for complete discussion of sum of squares (SS), mean square (MS), ANOVA, p-value, and degrees of freedom (df).

The procedure is as follows:

- Treat the problem as a designed experiment (see Chapter 6 for details on designed experiments)

- Conduct an ANOVA (set up an ANOVA table—see Chapter 6)

- Use the mean square values from the ANOVA table to estimate the variance components (see Chapter 6 for discussion of mean square)

Some of the quantities from the ANOVA table are given in Table 4.13. Standard statistical software packages will provide these values, so it is not necessary to carry out the calculations by hand.

The estimates of the variance components given earlier are

$$\text{Operators: } \hat{\sigma}^2_O = \frac{\text{MS}_O - \text{MS}_{PO}}{pn} \tag{4.18}$$

$$\text{Part} \times \text{operator: } \hat{\sigma}^2_{PO} = \frac{\text{MS}_{PO} - \text{MS}_E}{n} \tag{4.19}$$

$$\text{Parts: } \hat{\sigma}^2_P = \frac{\text{MS}_P - \text{MS}_{PO}}{mn} \tag{4.20}$$

Table 4.13 Necessary quantities for an analysis of variance.

Source	DF	SS	MS
Part	$p-1$	SS_P	MS_P
Operator	$m-1$	SS_O	MS_O
Part × operator	$(p-1)(m-1)$	SS_{PO}	MS_{PO}
Error (repeatability)	$mp(m-1)$	SS_E	MS_E
Total	$mpn-1$	SS_T	

$$\text{Error: } \hat{\sigma}_e^2 = MS_E \tag{4.21}$$

It is possible that one or more of the variance components could result in a negative value. Some researchers have maintained that if any variance component estimate is negative, it is set equal to zero. Other researchers recommend using different approaches for estimating these quantities so that the estimates are nonnegative (see Montgomery [2013] for more details). The variance component estimates are then used to estimate reproducibility, repeatability, and part-to-part variation, as well as the total variability, using the equations given previously.

Example of Gage R&R

An experiment was conducted on the thermal performance of a power module for an induction motor starter. The response was thermal performance measured in degrees C per watt. Table 4.14 displays a partial list of data collected for 20 motors by six operators. Each operator measured all parts twice. The original data have been multiplied by 100 for convenience. (The original problem statement for this example is from Houf and Berman [1988].) The specification limits are LSL = 18 and USL = 58. It is assumed that each motor and the operators have been selected

Table 4.14 Typical data for the gage R&R experiment.

	Operator 1		Operator 2			Operator 6	
Part	1	2	1	2	...	1	2
1	44	34	43	44	...	46	46
2	21	23	20	22	...	21	21
⋮	⋮	⋮	⋮	⋮	...	⋮	⋮
20	29	31	31	30	...	31	29

at random from larger populations. The model of interest involves operators, parts, and the operator-by-part interaction.

In this problem, $p = 20$, $m = 6$, and $n = 2$. The results of the gage R&R study using both the tabular method and the ANOVA method will be examined. The calculations for the variance components were carried out using Minitab statistical software for both methods.

Tabular Method Results

The results of the tabular method are given in Table 4.15. The second column in Table 4.15 provides the estimates for the variance components:

$$\hat{\sigma}^2_{Repeatability} = \hat{\sigma}^2_e = 0.5678$$

$$\hat{\sigma}^2_{Reproducibility} = \hat{\sigma}^2_O = 0.2607$$

$$\hat{\sigma}^2_P = 54.8697$$

$$\hat{\sigma}^2_{Measurement\ error} = \hat{\sigma}^2_{Gage} = \hat{\sigma}^2_{Reproducibility} + \hat{\sigma}^2_{Repeatability}$$
$$= 0.2607 + 0.5678$$
$$= 0.8285$$

$$\hat{\sigma}^2_{Total} = \hat{\sigma}^2_{Gage} + \hat{\sigma}^2_P$$
$$= 0.8285 + 54.8697$$
$$= 55.6982$$

The last column in Table 4.15 provides the percentage of the total variability contributed by each source. For example, the percent contribution for "Repeatability" was found by

$$\%\ contribution = \frac{\hat{\sigma}^2_{Repeatability}}{\hat{\sigma}^2_{Total}}(100\%) = \frac{0.5678}{55.6982}(100\%) = 1.02\%$$

From Table 4.15, it can be concluded that the largest source of variability is differences between parts.

Table 4.15 Gage R&R estimates using the tabular method.

Source	Variance component	% contribution
Total gage R&R	0.8285	1.49
Repeatability	0.5678	1.02
Reproducibility	0.2607	0.47
Part-to-part	54.8697	98.51
Total variation	55.6982	100.00

ANOVA Method Results

Before estimating the variance components using the ANOVA method, one can determine if there is a statistically significant difference between parts or between operators, and if there exists a statistically significant interaction between parts and operators. An ANOVA was carried out, with the results provided in Table 4.16.

The variance components can be estimated as follows (although generally it is not necessary to calculate these by hand) using Equations (4.26) through (4.29), respectively:

$$\text{Operators: } \hat{\sigma}_O^2 = \frac{MS_O - MS_{PO}}{pn} = \frac{13.580 - 2.060}{20(2)} = 0.288$$

$$\text{Part} \times \text{operator: } \hat{\sigma}_{PO}^2 = \frac{MS_{PO} - MS_E}{n} = \frac{2.060 - 0.733}{2} = 0.6635$$

$$\text{Parts: } \hat{\sigma}_P^2 = \frac{MS_P - MS_{PO}}{mn} = \frac{591.479 - 2.060}{6(2)} = 49.118$$

$$\text{Error: } \hat{\sigma}_e^2 = MS_E = 0.733$$

The gage R&R estimates are then:

$$\hat{\sigma}_{\text{Reproducibility}}^2 = \hat{\sigma}_{PO}^2 + \hat{\sigma}_O^2 = 0.6635 + 0.288 = 0.9515$$

$$\hat{\sigma}_{\text{Repeatability}}^2 = \hat{\sigma}_e^2 = 0.733$$

$$\hat{\sigma}_{\text{Measurement error}}^2 = \hat{\sigma}_{\text{Gage}}^2 = \hat{\sigma}_{\text{Reproducibility}}^2 + \hat{\sigma}_{\text{Repeatability}}^2$$
$$= 0.9515 + 0.733$$
$$= 1.6845$$

$$\hat{\sigma}_P^2 = 49.118$$

$$\hat{\sigma}_{\text{Total}}^2 = \hat{\sigma}_{\text{Gage}}^2 + \hat{\sigma}_P^2$$
$$= 1.6845 + 49.118$$
$$= 50.803$$

Table 4.16 ANOVA for the gage R&R example.

Source	DF	SS	MS	F	P
Part	19	11,238.1	591.479	287.126	0.000
Operator	5	67.9	13.580	6.592	0.000
Part × operator	95	195.7	2.060	2.810	0.000
Error (repeatability)	120	88.0	0.733		
Total	239	11,589.7			

Table 4.17   Gage R&R results using the ANOVA method.

Source	Variance component	% contribution
Total gage R&R	1.6850	3.32
Repeatability	0.7333	1.44
Reproducibility	0.9515	1.87
Operator	0.288	0.57
Part × operator	0.6635	1.31
Part-to-part	49.1181	96.86
Total variation	50.8031	100.00

As with the tabular method, the variance components for the gage R&R study and the percent contribution can be found using a statistical software package such as Minitab. The results are given in Table 4.17.

The slight differences between the estimates computed by hand and those provided by the software package for the ANOVA method are strictly due to rounding error. From the results in Table 4.17, it can be concluded that most of the total variability is due to differences in the parts. However, the ANOVA results in Table 4.16 show that there appears to be a significant difference between operators as well as a significant interaction between operators and parts (p-values are zero for all practical purposes; see Chapter 6 for discussion of p-values). Since there is a significant interaction between parts and operators, this may be evidence that more operator training is necessary.

Comparison of the Results

It is important to more fully examine and compare the results that were obtained with these two methods. The variance component estimates for both methods are repeated in Table 4.18.

The differences between the two methods are striking. The tabular method uses sample ranges to estimate the variance components, while the ANOVA method uses arguably more efficient estimates based on functions of sample variances (see Chapter 6). In addition, when using the tabular method, the variance component for the operator-by-part interaction could not be estimated. As a result, very different estimates for reproducibility and therefore total gage R&R are obtained. From the tabular method, total gage R&R is found to be 0.8286, while for the ANOVA method it is 1.6850.

The Role of the Control Chart in Gage R&R Studies

Control charts (presented in Chapter 6) play an integral role in gage R&R studies. Control charts display information about gage capability. Consider the $\bar{x}$ and R charts for the thermal performance example (displayed in Figure 4.20). The x chart shows the gage's ability to distinguish between parts. In a gage R&R study, it is

Table 4.18 Variance component estimates for both methods.

Source	Tabular method	ANOVA method
Total gage R&R	0.8286	1.6850
Repeatability	0.5678	0.7333
Reproducibility	0.2607	0.9515
Operator	0.2607	0.2882
Part × operator	–	0.6635
Part-to-part	54.8697	49.1181
Total variation	55.6983	50.8031

desirable for the $\bar{x}$ chart to have many out-of-control points. Each point on the x chart represents the average of the two measurements taken by an operator on a part. Each point on the R chart represents the range between the two measurements taken by an operator on a part. There are a total of 120 samples on each chart.

The upper and lower control limits on the $\bar{x}$ control chart were determined using the average range (see Chapter 6). As a result, the $\bar{x}$ control chart reflects the within-sample variability, which is related only to gage repeatability. Notice that many of the points on the $\bar{x}$ control chart plot beyond the control limits (what would usually be considered evidence that the process is out of control). In a gage R&R study, this is desirable since it indicates that the gage is capable of discriminating between different parts. If most of the samples on this control chart plotted within the control limits, it would signify that it is difficult for the gage to clearly identify different parts. In this example, there are several points that lie within the control limits. It may be necessary to determine if these are chance occurrences or if they indicate that the gage is having difficulty discriminating between the different parts. It is not clear in this example, so further investigation is most likely needed.

The R chart can provide information about special causes of variation. For example, if many of the ranges plot beyond the control limits, this could indicate problems with operator experience, training, or fatigue, which would also result in differences among operators. It is desirable for the points on the R chart to plot within the control limits. This condition signifies that the operators exhibit consistency in their use of the gage. The R chart for the example has several points outside the control limits. This is not surprising since the ANOVA indicated that there was a significant interaction between operators and parts. Further investigation is needed.

Interpretation of Gage R&R Estimates

Since many of the variance component estimates are also used in the calculation of measures such as signal-to-noise ratios (SNR), precision-to-tolerance ratios (PTR),

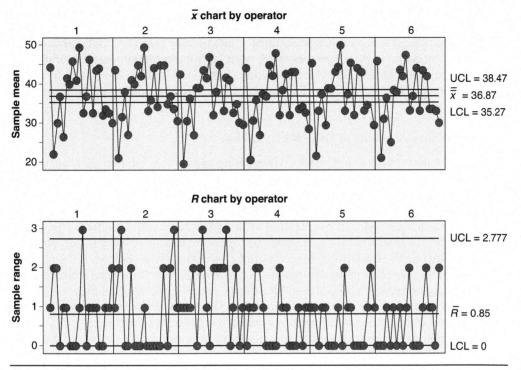

Figure 4.20 $\bar{x}$ and R control charts for the thermal performance example.

discrimination ratios (DR), and process capability ratios, it is imperative that these estimates be as reliable as possible. The example described in the "Example of Gage R&R" section of this chapter illustrates that the two methods could lead to different estimates. In turn, it is possible that the two methods could lead to very different conclusions about the adequacy of the measurement system. As a simple illustration, one formula for the PTR is

$$PTR = \frac{6\hat{\sigma}_{Gage}}{USL - LSL} \tag{4.22}$$

Note that another form uses 5.15 in place of 6. Since $\hat{\sigma}_{Gage}$ is simply the square root of the variance component for total gage variability $\hat{\sigma}^2_{Gage}$, the PTR for this example can be calculated using results from both the tabular method and the ANOVA method. For the tabular method, PTR is

$$PTR = \frac{6\hat{\sigma}_{Gage}}{USL - LSL} = \frac{6\left(\sqrt{0.8286}\right)}{58 - 18} = 0.137$$

For the ANOVA method, PTR is

$$PTR = \frac{6\hat{\sigma}_{Gage}}{USL - LSL} = \frac{6\left(\sqrt{1.6850}\right)}{58 - 18} = 0.195$$

Measurement systems with PTRs less than 0.10 (10%) are generally considered to be acceptable measurement systems. PTRs between 0.10 and 0.30 (10% to 30%) may be adequate for some applications. PTRs greater than 0.30 (30%) are considered unacceptable (Montgomery 2013; AIAG 2010). For details on PTR, SNR, and DR, see AIAG (2010), Wheeler and Lyday (1989), or Montgomery (2013). Woodall and Borror (2008) provide a discussion of the relationships between these measures as well.

Issues and Considerations in Gage R&R Studies

Several assumptions are made when using either the tabular method or the ANOVA method to carry out a gage R&R study. One such assumption involves replication (replication is defined and discussed in Chapter 6). In particular, it is assumed that each measurement (replicate) is made independently of one another, where a unique setup or preparation of the measuring device is made before the next measurement is taken. Suppose an operator measures a part four times. If the setup of the measuring device is not changed or reset before the next measurement, then the measurements are not true replicates. If the measurements are taken consecutively without resetting the measuring device, then they are a type of repeated measure. The analysis to obtain the estimates of the variance components would have to be different from what has been presented here.

Another assumption related to replication is randomization (randomization is discussed more fully in Chapter 6). Randomization in a gage R&R study is understood to mean that the operator measures each part in random order. A part is selected at random and measured, and then the next part is randomly selected and measured. The operator does not randomly select a part, take four measurements, put the part back, and then select the next part. In that case, the actual randomization is a form of restricted randomization and requires estimation of repeatability and reproducibility using methods other than what has been presented. There are numerous applications where complete randomization or true replication is not practical or possible. In those situations, other methods would have to be employed to provide reliable estimates of the necessary variance components.

There are advantages and disadvantages to using either the tabular method or the ANOVA method. The tabular method is easy to carry out using ranges to estimate variance components. In addition, interpretation of the results is often intuitive for the practitioner. However, the tabular method is restricted to investigating a measurement system that involves only parts (with one operator) or parts and several operators. It does not lend itself to more complex measurement systems that may involve more than two factors (parts and operators). Furthermore, it does not adequately lend itself to dealing with systems where randomization is restricted or true replication is not possible. In general, as long as you are interested only in parts and possible operators (and not even the interaction between them), then the tabular or range method can be used—again, only if complete randomization can be guaranteed.

The ANOVA method can be more computationally intensive than the tabular method, but with modern computer software this is less of an issue. The ANOVA method is more flexible than the tabular method in that it can handle unusual experimental conditions. For example, the ANOVA method can be used if there are more factors than just parts or operators. Suppose that in addition to parts and operators, location on the part is also a factor to consider. In this case, a nested design may be appropriate. The necessary variance components can be easily estimated using ANOVA for a nested design (see Burdick, Borror, and Montgomery [2005] for details on gage R&R studies for nested designs). Note that the tabular method cannot be used for this more complex experimental situation. It should also be noted that just including a third factor (not necessarily nested) and estimating variance components for the factors, all two-factor interactions, and the three-factor interaction is not possible using the tabular approach. A simple extension of the standard two-factor design cannot be handled using the tabular approach.

In summary, the ANOVA method for estimating repeatability and reproducibility is more flexible than the tabular method. It also uses more efficient estimates than sample ranges to obtain the necessary variance components' estimates. With modern computational capabilities, the ANOVA method is no more difficult to carry out than the range method.

For further details on gage R&R studies or measurement systems in general, please see AIAG (2010); Barrentine (2003); Borror, Montgomery, and Runger (1997); Burdick, Allen, and Larsen (2002); Burdick, Borror, and Montgomery (2003, 2005); Dolezal, Burdick, and Birch (1998); Engel and deVries (1997); Jensen (2002); Larsen (2002); Mader, Prins, and Lampe (1999); Majeske and Andrews (2002); Montgo ery (2013); Montgomery and Runger (1993a, 1993b); Vardeman and VanValkenburg (1999); and Weaver et al. (2012).

For an example of an application of a gage R&R, see, for example, Erdmann, Does, and Bisgaard (2009), which presents a case study of gage R&R in a hospital. The authors describe a study to measure temperature with an ear thermometer.

Additional Considerations for Measurement Systems

In this chapter, MSA has been presented for typical manufacturing situations. There are, of course, numerous applications of agreement analysis in nonmanufacturing settings. As more quality engineers become involved in the service sector, it will be imperative that they understand the use of appropriate statistical methods for assessing the capability of a measurement system.

Methods for assessing the capability of a quantitative measurement system as discussed in this chapter are well documented in the literature. Sometimes, the measurement system involves attribute data. This is more common in the service and nonmanufacturing industries than in the manufacturing industry. In the case of attribute data, the standard quantitative methods are no longer appropriate. An attribute gage measurement system is appropriate when the parts or objects of interest are placed into one of two or more possible categories (Windsor 2003). The measurement of interest is the classification of the item. For example, consider tax documents, insurance appraisals, or electronic medical records. These documents are read by many people and correctness of the documents or items in the document may be assessed.

Several assessment statistics and approaches that deal with categorical measurements include the following:

1. Appraiser agreement statistics such as κ statistics and intraclass correlation

2. The analytic method

3. Latent-class models

These three approaches can provide some measure of reproducibility or repeatability, and in some cases bias. For more details on appraiser agreement statistics, the reader is encouraged to see AIAG (2010); Banerjee et al. (1999); Bloch and Kraemer (1989); Cicchetti and Feinstein (1990); Cohen (1960); Conger (1980); de Mast and van Wieringen (2007); Feinstein and Cicchetti (1990); and Fleiss (1971). For more discussion of the analytic method or latent-class models, see AIAG (2010); Agresti (1988, 1992); Agresti and Lang (1993); Banerjee et al. (1999); Boyles (2001); de Mast and van Wieringen (2004); McCaslin and Gruska (1976); Sweet, Tjokrodjojo, and Wijaya (2005); Uebersax and Grove (1990); and van Wieringen and van Heuvel (2005).

Chapter 5
Continuous Improvement

Some of the most successful organizations are those in which all members of the organization believe that a part of each person's daily job is the improvement of the processes they work with. This chapter describes tools and techniques for accomplishing this vital task and helping with continuous improvement efforts. The chapter is divided into five sections: "Quality Control Tools," which describes the seven original problem-solving tools; "Quality Management and Planning Tools," which discusses what have become known as the seven new tools; "Continuous Improvement Techniques," which introduces several of the broader, more systematic approaches to quality; "Corrective Action"; and "Preventive Action." The novice practitioner may feel overwhelmed by the array of tool options. The best advice is to identify a problem and try to use one or more of the tools in its solution, rather than study the tools and memorize their individual traits. Experience with these tools provides a depth of understanding not attainable from the written word alone.

QUALITY CONTROL TOOLS

> Select, construct, apply, and interpret the following quality control tools:
>
> 1. Flowcharts
> 2. Pareto charts
> 3. Cause and effect diagrams
> 4. Control charts
> 5. Check sheets
> 6. Scatter diagrams
> 7. Histograms (Analyze)
>
> Body of Knowledge V.A

Quality control tools as defined by ASQ and as accepted throughout the quality engineering community include the following:

- Flowcharts

- Pareto charts

- Cause and effect diagrams

- Control charts

- Check sheets

- Scatter diagrams

- Histograms

Collectively, these tools are commonly referred to as the seven basic tools. Kaoru Ishikawa (1985) is credited with making the following statement with respect to these tools: "As much as 95 percent of all quality-related problems in the factory can be solved with seven fundamental quantitative tools."

Ishikawa's statement provides three key insights into these tools—namely, that these seven tools are:

1. Applicable in problem-solving situations most encountered by certified quality engineers (CQEs)

2. Quantitative in nature and rely, with possibly the exception of flowcharts and cause and effect diagrams, on numerical data

3. Most used in quality control—that is, as aids in tracking, monitoring, and analyzing data—as opposed to the planning functions associated with quality assurance

This section discusses six of the seven basic tools (control charts are discussed in considerable detail in Chapter 6). The following subsections describe the purpose of each tool, provide information about the tool's applications and mechanics, and give at least one illustration of the tool's use.

Flowcharts

The purpose of a flowchart is to provide a graphical representation of the elements, components, or tasks associated with a process. Flowcharts are helpful for documentation purposes and, through standardized symbols, promote a common understanding of process steps and the relationships or dependencies among those process steps.

Flowcharts can be prepared for and used at a high level where users may not be familiar with process-specific jargon or terminology. In the high-level application, flowcharts are intended to help users understand what may be a complex process without providing unnecessary, and potentially confusing, details.

Likewise, flowcharts can be prepared for and used at a detail level where users have familiarity and expertise with a given process. In the detail-level application, flowcharts are intended to help users perform analyses most related to optimization or process improvement.

A flowchart can be created through the following steps.

1. Select start and stop points. A flowchart, by definition, must specify start and end points. Since it is possible to have many flowcharts describing various sections, elements, or components of a process, particularly when the process is large and complex, start and end points for flowcharts are defined in terms of boundaries. Boundaries are naturally occurring breaks or division points that separate processes or systems at the macro level, or sections, elements, or components of a process at the micro level.

2. List major steps/tasks and decision points. List, in sequential order, each of the major steps or tasks and decision points that occur as part of the process between the start and stop points.

3. Use standardized graphical symbols to document the process. Using standardized symbols, document each of the steps/tasks identified above (Gilbreth and Gilbreth 1921). Placement of appropriately labeled symbols and the use of arrows define the sequence of events. Four primary flowcharting symbols are depicted in Figure 5.1. While there are many symbols for flowcharting, these primary flowcharting symbols are capable of and adequate for documenting any process.

4. Review results. Compare the flowchart with the process to verify that the flowchart is complete and accurately describes the process. Having more than one person independently verify the flowchart is generally considered standard protocol.

Hallock, Alper, and Karsh (2006) present a process improvement study on diagnostic testing in an outpatient healthcare facility. The purpose of the study was to determine what factors contributed to the delay of notification of test results to

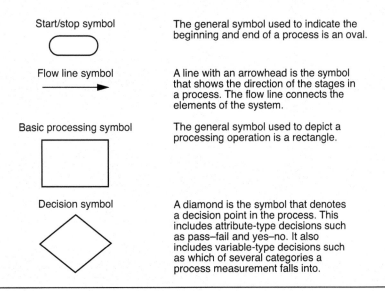

Figure 5.1   Four primary flowcharting symbols.

patients. A general flowchart for the overall diagnostic testing process, similar to the one in Figure 5.2, was presented.

Pareto Charts

The purpose of a Pareto chart is to identify those "vital few" areas that account for the largest frequency or relative frequency in a data set and separate them from the "trivial many."

A Pareto chart graphically depicts the "80/20 rule" originally postulated by the Italian economist Vilfredo Pareto to explain economic phenomena and later adapted by Juran and Gryna (1980) for quality applications. The 80/20 rule allows users to identify and focus on the approximately 20% of factors (i.e., columns or categories) that account for approximately 80% of potential problems.

To create a Pareto chart, follow the steps detailed below:

1. Rank order the columns or categories of data. Columns or categories of data displayed previously as check sheets or histograms are rank ordered from the highest frequency or relative frequency on the left to the lowest frequency or relative frequency on the right.

2. Prepare the graphic. As the data from a check sheet or histogram are rearranged for display in a Pareto chart, the title of the chart is changed,

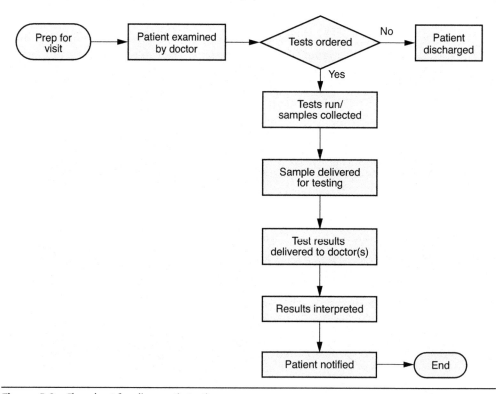

Figure 5.2 Flowchart for diagnostic testing process.

as are the column or category titles when the corresponding data are placed into different column or category locations.

3. Calculate and place a relative frequency line above the data columns or categories. A relative frequency line can be calculated and placed above the data in a Pareto chart for quick assessment of the relative contribution made by each column or category.

Figure 5.3 depicts a notional Pareto chart of problems found in the inspection of school buses based on the scenario presented in Stevenson (2000). Each column for the tally data corresponds to an occurrence of a problem, and the columns or categories have been rank ordered.

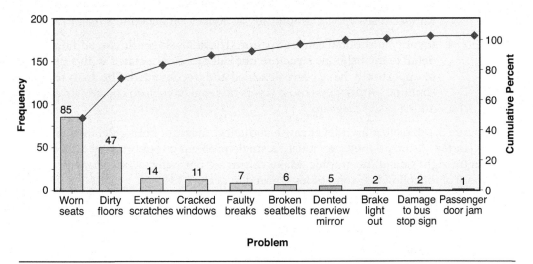

Figure 5.3 Typical Pareto chart.

Cause and Effect Diagrams

The purpose of a cause and effect diagram, also known as a fishbone diagram or Ishikawa diagram, is to graphically document the analysis of factors (causes) that relate to a single problem or opportunity (effect). Cause and effect diagrams are used in problem-solving situations and in general analysis to help the problem-solving or analysis team both understand how those factors may cause the given effect and focus on "next steps" in process improvement.

A cause and effect diagram is most successful when created by a multidisciplinary team of people. The team creates the cause and effect diagram using the following steps:

1. Select a single problem or opportunity (the effect). A cause and effect diagram is useful for analyzing only one problem or opportunity at a time. The problem or opportunity that is selected for analysis is documented by a keyword or short narrative description placed in a rectangle or box, generally on the right side of the diagram. When analyzing more than one problem or opportunity, a separate cause and effect diagram is used for each problem or opportunity.

2. Identify the major causes of the problem or opportunity. Cause and effect diagrams have been described as fishbone diagrams, where major causes are documented as the major bones of a fish skeleton. Major causes are generally described as they relate to people, hardware/equipment, the intended operating environment, methods, and materials. Teams should be formed to brainstorm possible causes or opportunities.

3. Identify the minor causes associated with each major cause. For each major cause (i.e., people, hardware/equipment, environment, methods, measurements, and materials) associated with a problem or opportunity, minor causes are identified. Identification of minor causes may be graphically described as adding more structure to the fishbone skeleton. Minor causes appear graphically as "bones" attached to a major cause.

4. Identify additional cause structure. The analysis continues, adding detail to the fishbone structure until all causes associated with a problem or opportunity have been identified and documented. The analysis may continue until several more layers of detail have been considered and added to the diagram.

Figure 5.4 depicts a high-level cause and effect diagram before detailed analysis is started. As mentioned previously, a single problem or opportunity is identified on the right side of the graphic. Major causes are normally associated with one or more of the following, sometimes referred to as the 6 Ms:

- Man (people or personnel)
- Machines (hardware/equipment)
- Materials
- Methods

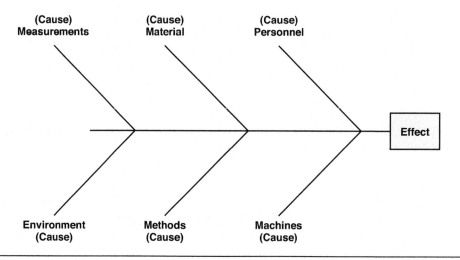

Figure 5.4   Cause and effect diagram/template.

- Measurements

- Mother Nature (environment)

Major causes graphically represent the major bones of a fish, while minor causes represent additional structure in the diagram. Figure 5.4 generally is the starting point for a cause and effect analysis and, therefore, may be used as a template to help quality engineers begin.

Figure 5.5 illustrates a continuation of the example shown in Figure 5.4 for a case where products of a company are damaged after shipping. In Figure 5.5, the effect of interest is "damaged product after shipping." Also, the performance improvement team identified major causes of personnel, materials, measurements, methods, and environment but no causes related to machines. In the major cause "Methods," for example, "wrong packing material" is a causal factor associated with damaged products after shipping. The analysis continues until each major cause has been investigated and enough supporting structure has been added to the diagram to identify all the causes associated with the problem or opportunity.

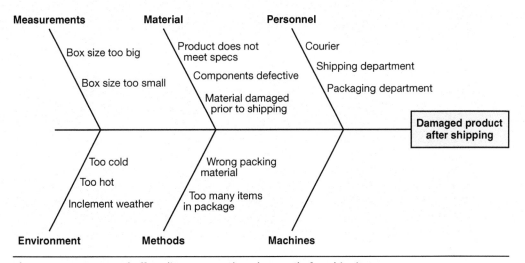

Figure 5.5   Cause and effect diagram: product damaged after shipping.

Control Charts

Control charts are discussed in detail in Chapter 6. This section will focus on a related tool, run charts. While run charts are not specifically identified in the CQE BoK, they are an important tool for quality engineers. The purpose of a run chart is to track and monitor the number of event occurrences over time.

Quality engineers use run charts to understand how a parameter or metric is behaving or performing over time. The run chart tracks and monitors a metric or parameter without regard to control limits or tolerances. In fact, it is the exclusion of control limits or tolerances that differentiates the run chart from various types of control charts.

A run chart is constructed using the following steps:

1. Select a parameter or metric of interest. The run chart focuses on only one parameter or metric.

2. Set a scale for the *y*-axis. Once the parameter or metric has been selected, it will be graphed on the *y*-axis or vertical axis. A scale must be set for the *y*-axis that distributes the data throughout the scale.

3. Identify the time intervals for the graphic. Since the run chart displays data over time, the time frame must be meaningful for the application. Time frames such as hourly, each shift, daily, weekly, and monthly are commonly used.

4. Collect and chart the data. Having set up the graphic, collect and chart or plot the parameter or metric over the time intervals specified.

5. Calculate the average. The parameter or metric average is normally calculated for a run chart once sufficient data have been collected. A line indicating the average is plotted directly on the run chart.

Figure 5.6 is a run chart of the data collected via check sheet in the next section, considering the case of defects associated with school buses as originally conceived by Stevenson (2000).

Stevenson originally discussed a set of data identifying 27 defects or deficiencies associated with a school bus safety inspection. It is reasonable to extend Stevenson's analysis by concluding that the inspection occurred at a specific time, say, in September at the start of the school year.

Figure 5.6 shows that 27 defects or deficiencies were recorded in September during a regular inspection of the school bus fleet. Since safety inspections are a regularly occurring event, it would be reasonable, interesting, and important to track and monitor the results of similar inspections as they occur monthly during the course of a school year. The results of such safety inspections, completed each calendar month, are summarized in Figure 5.6. As would be expected, the number of defects or discrepancies is higher in the beginning of the school year when the

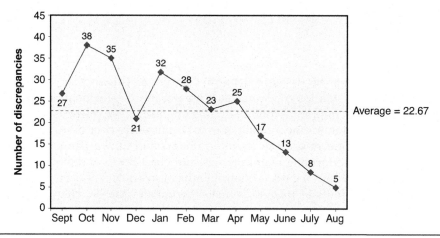

Figure 5.6 Run chart example.

buses are used very frequently and decreases substantially later in the year when the buses are not used as frequently. The parameter metric average in this case is defects or discrepancies per month.

Check Sheets

The purpose of a check sheet is to summarize, and in some cases graphically depict, a tally count of event occurrences. For example, a check sheet can be used to count the number of defects. In many instances, a check sheet will summarize count data related to certain types of defects and will provide a rough graphical representation of where in a part or process defects occur.

Check sheets can be created using the following steps:

1. Design the check sheet for a given application. A check sheet is a tool designed for a specific application and must, therefore, include any and all information pertinent to the application. In general, the design of a check sheet should include enough administrative data to facilitate referencing and analysis. Administrative data frequently include identification of the product or process, duration of the data collection period, individuals responsible for the product or process, and individuals responsible for the data collection. A check sheet should also include space to record tally data for event occurrences, a rough graphical representation of where in the part, product, or process events occur, and a space to record notes.

2. Record the data. Using the space provided to record tally data, indicate each occurrence of an event with a symbol such as an "x," check mark, or circle/dot. Each event occurrence receives one mark or symbol. Check sheets also frequently identify, through a rough graphical representation, where in the part or process events occur by highlighting that portion of the rough graphical representation provided.

3. Use the data for analysis or as input to additional graphical tools. Count data summarized on a check sheet frequently are analyzed to identify, track, or monitor defects associated with a particular area on a part or location in a process. The analysis performed on check sheet data is frequently used to trigger process improvement efforts. The data may also be used as input to other graphical tools, such as histograms and Pareto charts, discussed in the next two sections.

Figure 5.7 depicts tally data related to specific types of problems found during the inspection of school buses (see Stevenson 2000). Each column for the tally data corresponds to an occurrence of a problem, as follows:

- Column A: Dirty floors
- Column B: Cracked windows
- Column C: Exterior scratches
- Column D: Worn seats
- Column E: Faulty brakes

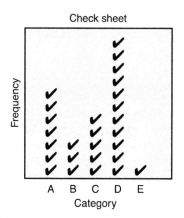

Figure 5.7 A simple check sheet.

Source: W. Stevenson, "Supercharging Your Pareto Analysis," ASQ *Quality Progress* (October 2000): 51–55. Used with permission.

Many different types of check sheets can be created. The user should customize the check sheet by including such information as dates, shifts, and so on to allow for ease of interpretation. See Bothe (2001) or Montgomery (2013) for more details.

Scatter Diagrams

The purpose of a scatter diagram is to graphically display indications of a relationship between two quantitative variables. A quality engineer interested in how a variable may perform or behave relative to another variable may use a scatter diagram to analyze quantitative data. The relationship being investigated is called a correlation, and Figure 5.8 identifies three possible relationships as positive correlation, no correlation, and negative correlation. Correlation is discussed in detail in Chapter 6, "Relationships Between Variables."

To create a scatter diagram, use the following steps:

1. Select two variables of interest. The scatter diagram focuses on possible correlations between two variables. The two variables of interest should have the potential for a cause-and-effect relationship.

2. Set a scale for the axes. Since one variable will be plotted on the *x*-axis while the other variable is plotted on the *y*-axis, a scale must be selected for each axis such that the data use all, or nearly all, of the scale.

3. Collect and chart the data. Having set up the graphic, collect and chart or plot the data in accordance with the scale specified.

4. Evaluate the results. Using Figure 5.8, evaluate the results to identify any relationships.

Table 5.1 provides the data for Figure 5.9. The data provided are derived from a training analysis in which the number of defects produced by employees is compared with the number of hours of employee training. The *x*-axis (representing training hours) documents how many hours employees spent in training.

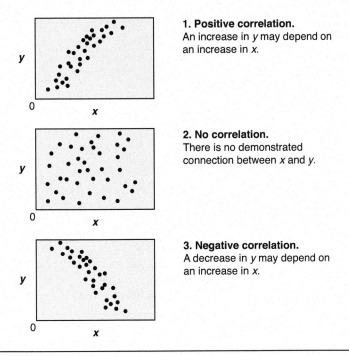

1. **Positive correlation.**
An increase in *y* may depend on an increase in *x*.

2. **No correlation.**
There is no demonstrated connection between *x* and *y*.

3. **Negative correlation.**
A decrease in *y* may depend on an increase in *x*.

Figure 5.8   Three possible relationships identified by scatter diagrams.

Table 5.1   Training data.

Training Hours versus Number of Defects						
Observation	Training hours	Defects		Observation	Training hours	Defects
1	1.00	33		10	3.25	23
2	1.25	33		11	3.50	20
3	1.50	32		12	3.75	17
4	1.75	31		13	4.00	14
5	2.00	30		14	4.25	12
6	2.25	28		15	4.50	9
7	2.50	27		16	4.75	8
8	2.75	27		17	5.00	8
9	3.00	25		18	5.25	7

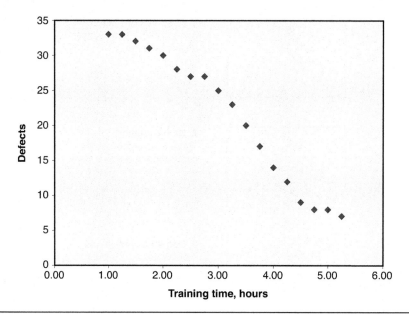

Figure 5.9 Training time versus defects.

The *y*-axis (representing defects) documents tally or count data of the number of defects produced by employees who received the training.

Histograms

The purpose of a histogram is to graphically depict the frequency of occurrence of events, where event occurrences are sorted into categories of a defined range along a continuous scale. Histograms are helpful for displaying the distribution of event occurrences among the various columns or categories of event types. Histograms are used when it is important to see and understand how a particular set of data are distributed relative to each other, and possibly to a target or tolerance. The data are recorded in each column or category as they occur, and columns are not sorted by frequency.

To create a histogram, use the following steps:

1. Determine the amount of data to be collected. As a starting point for a histogram, it is necessary to identify approximately how much data will be collected. One data point will be collected for each event occurrence.

2. Determine the number of columns or bins to be used. Numerous guidelines are available for determining the number of bins. For example, one recommendation is that the number of bins be approximately equal to $\sqrt{n}$, where *n* is the number of data points. Computer software packages use several different algorithms for determining the number of bins, including those based on Scott (1979), Freedman and Diaconis (1981), and variations of Sturges's rule (Sturges 1926). The width of the bins should be of equal size to avoid graphing misleading results.

3. Collect and record data. As data for a histogram are collected, they are recorded in tabular or tally form.

4. Prepare the graphic. To prepare the histogram for plotting data, it is necessary to provide a descriptive title for the graphic, label each axis, provide a measurement scale for each axis, label the columns, and provide a data summary.

5. Graph the data. Using the data summary, plot the frequency or relative frequency in each column.

Note that the histogram is often considered a large-sample graphical technique and can be unreliable for small sample sizes. Some researchers argue that the histogram should not be used for samples with fewer than 75–100 observations (Montgomery 2013). For small samples, the histogram can be quite sensitive regarding the number and width of the bins chosen.

As an example, consider the use of high-strength concrete mixtures in roadway and bridge construction. With increased use of these mixtures, quality improvement and quality assurance procedures have become an important aspect of production monitoring. Reducing the use of costly, but necessary, materials while maintaining a high level of quality and meeting required specifications has become increasingly important due in part to the growing demand for materials worldwide. Quality improvement tools will aid suppliers in improving the manufacturing process and reducing product variation and unnecessary waste. One important quality characteristic is the compressive strength of concrete, which is directly related to the amount of Portland cement used (in addition to many other variables influencing compressive strength).

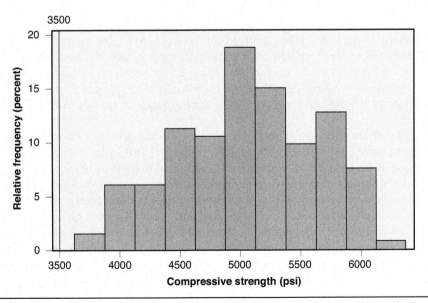

Figure 5.10   Histogram of compressive strength of concrete samples, where 3500 psi is the minimum allowed strength.

Figure 5.10 displays a histogram of compressive strengths for 133 samples collected for a particular product from one company. The minimum acceptable compressive strength in this case is 3500 psi, which is indicated on the histogram in Figure 5.10. The histogram clearly shows that quite often the strength of concrete delivered can be as much as 1500 psi to 2500 psi higher than the specified minimum. The amount of cement that could be saved by reducing the total cement content in the mixture is significant.

QUALITY MANAGEMENT AND PLANNING TOOLS

Select, construct, apply, and interpret the following quality management and planning tools:

1. Affinity diagrams and force field analysis
2. Tree diagrams
3. Process decision program charts (PDPC)
4. Matrix diagrams
5. Interrelationship digraphs
6. Prioritization matrices
7. Activity network diagrams (Analyze)

Body of Knowledge V.B

The concept of quality has existed for as long as people have existed. *Qualities*, defined as physical or nonphysical characteristics that constitute the basic nature of things, are readily accepted as part of the package that encompasses a good or a service. Shewhart (1980) captured the concept in the first part of the twentieth century: There are two common aspects of quality, one of these has to do with the consideration of the quality of a thing as an objective reality independent of the existence of man. The other has to do with what people think, feel, or sense because of the objective reality. This subjective side of quality is closely linked to value.

Shewhart and others such as Deming (1986), Juran (1989), Crosby (1979), Feigenbaum (2004), Ishikawa (1985), Shingo (1986), and Taguchi (1986) have helped us understand the essence of quality and helped us bring it to the point of actionable issues. There have been, and continue to be, several approaches and initiatives that advocate quality as a scientific discipline. But, on the other hand, there are also many anecdotal approaches and initiatives that treat quality as an art.

Interest in tactical, in-process approaches that stress the importance of meeting substitute quality characteristics (as opposed to strategic approaches that stress true quality characteristics) helped to move the quality concept upstream from final product inspection. This evolutionary branch was eventually called kaizen or incremental improvement (a management-by-fact related approach) and was applied primarily in production-related processes (Imai 1986). Here, evolving practices were observed and eventually tools were identified, described, and adopted. Tools such as the seven basic tools—cause and effect diagram, flowchart, check sheet, histogram, scatter diagram, Pareto analysis, and control chart—were recognized as useful.

The Japanese further expanded the quality concept in a formal sense in the late 1970s and early 1980s with what they termed the seven "new" quality tools (Mizuno 1988). This new era was based on two fundamental requirements: (1) the creation of added value over and above consumer needs, and (2) the prevention, rather than the rectification, of failure in meeting customer needs. Hence, these tools were positioned to address strategic (as opposed to tactical) quality issues. Seven tools—relations diagram, affinity diagram, systematic diagram, matrix diagram, matrix data analysis, process decision program chart (PDPC), and arrow diagram—were the result of this initiative.

In the 1990s, based on Shewhart's definition of quality, field experience/ observation, and Ishikawa's (1985) concepts of true and substitute quality characteristics, Kolarik (1995) postulated a scientific framework. This framework has two major components: the experience of quality and the creation of quality. The experience of quality is a function of the fulfillment of human needs and expectations. Quality is created through processes that are developed and maintained (Kolarik 1995).

The following sections describe the CQE BoK management and planning tools plus several other useful tools that help us create quality. These sections describe, position, and illustrate a selected cross section of 11 quality-related tools. The eight BoK tools are marked with an asterisk (*). The four remaining tools—process maps, process value chain diagrams, SIPOC diagrams, and benchmarking—are included to provide extended quality management/planning capabilities.

1. Affinity diagrams and force field analysis*

2. Tree diagrams

3. Process decision program charts*

4. Matrix diagrams*

5. Interrelationship digraphs*

6. Prioritization matrices*

7. Activity network diagrams*

8. Process maps and SIPOC diagrams

9. Process value chain diagrams

10. Benchmarking

These tools help to formulate and organize thoughts and ideas so that they can be leveraged directly toward quality/business improvement. More elaborate discussions of quality strategies, initiatives, and tools appear in Kolarik (1999).

Affinity Diagrams and Force Field Analysis

Affinity Diagrams

The purpose of an affinity diagram is to help people collect, organize, summarize, and communicate facts, opinions, and ideas. The affinity diagram is useful when faced with describing, organizing, and communicating the general nature of a relatively complicated situation that can be described in terms of many facts, opinions, and/or ideas. It allows grouping or clustering of facts, opinions, and/or ideas into categories with some common feature to be able to locate, classify, describe, or summarize the basic issues. The affinity principle (of association and clustering) is useful in the initial stages of constructing a relationship diagram or in any situation where it is desired to discover, summarize, and organize a variety of facts, opinions, and/or ideas.

To create an affinity diagram:

1. Identify a general theme. The theme may be associated with a problem situation or an opportunity situation, or simply a situation in our physical and/or social environments.

2. Collect facts, opinions, and ideas. Data/information may be generated by a group of people in any number of formats; for example, use work teams, focus groups, or groups of experts. Also consider data/information existing in files or archives.

3. Express and enter the data/information in a common format. Possibly use sticky notes on a wall, cards on a table, or computer software capable of expressing each piece of data/information in a medium that can be "moved around."

4. Identify the groups/clusters. Here, identify, label, and describe the groups or clusters regarding the common attributes or summary characteristics that apply.

5. Cluster the data/information pieces. At this point, cluster or organize our data/information into cohesive groups.

6. Repeat steps 4 and 5 to form supergroups/superclusters. It may be possible to relate two or more of the initial groups/clusters and develop a supergroup or supercluster. Supergrouping can be repeated until the facts, opinions, or ideas are suitably classified/organized.

7. Present the results. The final product is an organized set of facts, opinions, and ideas that make sense in terms of providing help in understanding the nature of the situation or theme from step 1.

Figure 5.11 depicts the results of a student focus group session. The goal of the focus group was to communicate issues that are important to undergraduate students in their college program. Here it is clear that many concerns were voiced, in no particular order, and that the affinity principle was used to sort, organize, and isolate/label relevant issues for further action. For more information on affinity diagrams see Mizuno (1988), Brassard (1989), and Kolarik (1995, 1999).

Theme: Undergraduate program improvement issues
Source of comments: Undergraduate focus group

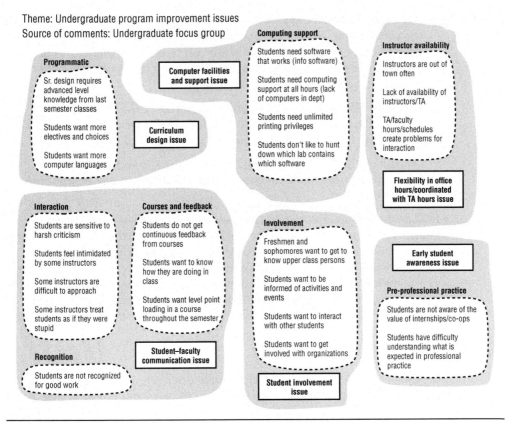

Figure 5.11 Student focus group affinity diagram.

Force Field Analysis

While affinity diagrams are useful for organizing ideas into relationships, the purpose of force field analysis is to take these ideas a step further by identifying driving and opposing forces associated with a desired change in an organization. A force field analysis is created by a group environment and is done by completing the following steps:

1. Identify a desired change. Ideally, if this change is accomplished, the results would provide positive outcomes within an organization. The driving force should be written at the top of a document, and a vertical line should be drawn under it.

2. Brainstorm forces for the change.

   a. Driving forces should be identified and written below the desired change on the left side of the vertical line.

   b. Opposing forces should be identified and written below the desired change on the right side of the vertical line.

3. Estimate the strength of the forces identified. For all driving and opposing forces, the team should decide on the strength of the

associated force. Arrows can be drawn next to the force pointing toward the vertical line. The strength of the force can be represented by the length or size of the arrow. While this can be quite subjective, it will provide a quick visual reference for identifying the strongest forces discouraging and encouraging the change.

4. Discuss methods for reducing opposing forces. The opposing forces hinder a desired change. If there are methods for reducing the impact or eliminating the forces, they should be identified and targeted.

5. Discuss methods for enhancing/encouraging supporting forces. Supporting forces that help create positive change should be identified and encouraged.

Force field analysis highlights weaknesses and strengths and is useful in determining whether a change is feasible. Force field analysis is sometimes used after the construction of a fishbone diagram, because each cause identified can be related to a desired change (Tague 2005). In the affinity diagram in Figure 5.11, computing support is identified as a computer facilities and support issue. Improved computing support is a desired change of the undergraduate program. Figure 5.12 illustrates a simplified example result of a force field analysis for this change.

Tree Diagrams

The purpose of a tree diagram is to help people discover, visualize, and communicate logical hierarchical relationships between critical events or goals/objectives and means. Tree diagrams are useful in situations where it is desired to define a hierarchical relationship between events, both desirable and undesirable. A fault tree can be constructed to relate an undesirable "top event" or failure to a sequence of events that led to the top event. In other words, the fault tree depicts logical pathways from sets of basic causal events to a single undesirable result or top event. Logical operators, such as AND or OR gates, are typically used to connect lower-level events with higher events. Hence, once the logic has been described, quantification can take place and risk level can be assessed.

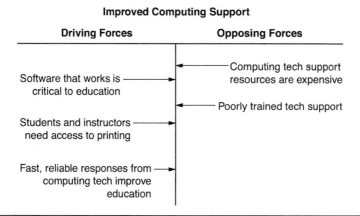

Figure 5.12 Force field analysis for computer support.

Several steps are involved in the development of the fault tree:

1. Identify the top event. The top event is an undesirable event that it is desired to prevent.

2. Identify the next-level events. The second-level events represent events that could lead to the top event.

3. Develop logical relationships between the top and next-level events. Here use logical operators, for example, AND or OR gates, to connect the second-level events to the top event.

4. Identify and link lower-level events. Develop the logic tree down to the lowest level desired by repeating steps 2 and 3, moving down through event sequences one level at a time.

5. Quantify the fault tree (optional). Develop probability of occurrence estimates for the events in the fault tree and then develop a probability statement and estimate for the top event.

Figure 5.13 presents a fault tree focused on unintended line shutdowns. This illustration contains OR gates that connect lower-level events with higher-level events.

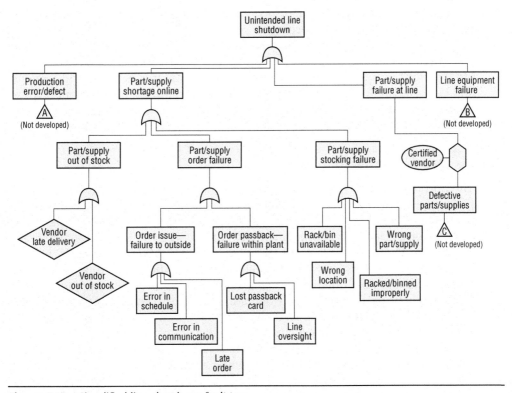

Figure 5.13   Simplified line shutdown fault tree.

Source: Reproduced by permission from W. J. Kolarik, *Creating Quality: Process Design for Results* (New York: McGraw-Hill, 1999), 469.

A fault tree does not contain all possible failure modes or all possible fault events that could cause system failure. However, a fault tree can consider or modeling human error, hardware and software failures, and acts of nature. It finds widespread use in the fields of reliability, safety, and risk analysis. The fault tree is a more focused tool than the FMEA. FMEA is sometimes used to help determine the top event in a fault tree. Fault trees work well for independent events; common cause is difficult to model, especially in terms of quantification.

Other tree diagram formats include event trees, systematic diagrams, and goal trees, as well as concept fans. Event trees are simply tree diagrams that start with an event and work backward from the event by defining binomial response (yes or no) branches. The response branches form a hierarchy of responses that eventually lead to an outcome. A systematic diagram depicts a sequence of goals or objectives and their respective means chained together so that one can visualize our possible alternatives with respect to the accomplishment of the high-level goal/objective. The goal tree is very similar to the systematic diagram in that it is built around a high-level goal that needs to be accomplished. It is also similar to the fault tree in that it links lower-level subgoals, functions, and success trees together with logic symbols or gates that lead up to the top goal.

A concept fan is built in a tree format but differs from the other formats significantly. The concept fan is a creativity-based tool, beginning with a purpose or functional requirement in a generic sense and expanding backward to provide alternative concepts that can accomplish the purpose or functional requirement. It is simple to construct and allows us to visualize possibilities for accomplishing our purpose early in the creative process.

A partial goal tree is illustrated in Figure 5.14. This tree structure uses AND gates to connect goals, subgoals, and functions. Success trees are then hooked into the functions using OR gates. The essence of the goal tree is to support strategic and tactical planning by depicting paths of goal accomplishment. For more information on treelike diagrams, see Mizuno (1988), Brassard (1989), Kolarik (1995, 1999), and Tague (2005).

Process Decision Program Charts

The purpose of a process decision program chart (PDPC) is to help people organize and evaluate process-related events and contingencies with respect to implementation and/or early operations. The PDPC is useful in helping us proactively evaluate or assess process implementation at a high level, early in the planning stage, or in the initial start-up phases of process operations. The PDPC may be used to argue or work our way through implementation, including events that might occur and possibly disrupt our process and/or its implementation. Or the PDPC might be used to guide early operations in case of deviations from plan. The key use of the PDPC is to help us both anticipate deviations from expected events and provide effective contingencies for these deviations.

The PDPC can take several general formats. One format resembles an annotated tree diagram. Another format resembles an annotated process flowchart. In either case, the distinguishing mark of a PDPC is its ability to offer the user an overview of possible contingencies regarding process implementation and/or operations.

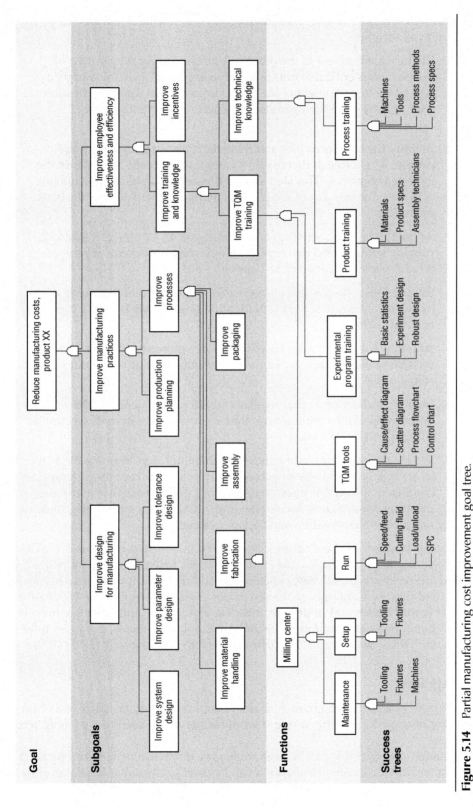

Figure 5.14 Partial manufacturing cost improvement goal tree.

Source: Reproduced by permission from W. J. Kolarik, *Creating Quality: Process Design for Results* (New York: McGraw–Hill, 1999), 269.

Although the PDPC can take several general formats, several steps are common to all formats:

1. Identify the purpose of the process. Understanding the purpose of the process is critical to building and using the PDPC. This purpose will guide development of the PDPC from the standpoint of possible contingencies and their resulting impacts relative to the desired outcome.

2. Identify the basic activities and related events associated with the process. Use a tree or process flow format to place the activities in the expected sequence. This step should present a graphical depiction of activities that are part of the plan to be implemented and/or the basic operation.

3. Annotate the basic activities and related events. Working from step 2, provide summarized descriptions of activities and events relative to what is normally expected to happen.

4. Superimpose the possible (conceivable) deviations. At this point, add branches/events that represent identified deviations from the expected activities/events.

5. Annotate the possible deviations. Provide summarized descriptions relative to the deviations that have been mapped onto our chart in step 4.

6. Identify and annotate contingency activities. This step provides a description of the contingencies that are identified to avoid or counter the mapped deviations.

7. Weight the possible contingencies. At this final step, examine the PDPC as a whole, consider the purpose, and select/mark the most appropriate contingencies. At this point a contingency plan is completed with our priorities for avoiding and/or dealing with possible deviations from our original implementation and/or operational plan.

A receiving/storage/stocking subprocesses PDPC is depicted in Figure 5.15. This depiction provides a basic look at the existing process, with several deviations indicated: damage, shortage, salvage, expedition, and line delay. It provides a number of facts and figures. Contingency-related issues are discussed in Table 5.2 relative to possible root causes and impact. In this case, general contingencies are process improvement, process redefinition, or the status quo subprocess. For more information on PDPCs, see Mizuno (1988), Brassard (1989), and Kolarik (1995, 1999).

Matrix Diagrams

The purpose of a matrix diagram is to help people discover, visualize, and communicate relationships within a single set of factors or between two or more sets of factors.

A matrix diagram is typically used to display relationships between two sets of characteristics or factors. However, it can be used to display interrelationships

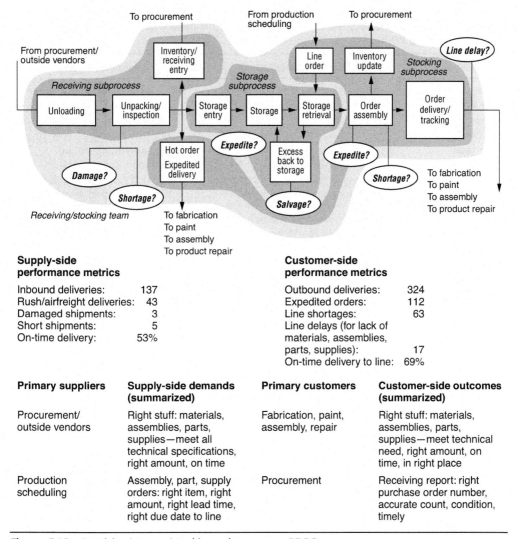

Supply-side performance metrics

Inbound deliveries:	137
Rush/airfreight deliveries:	43
Damaged shipments:	3
Short shipments:	5
On-time delivery:	53%

Customer-side performance metrics

Outbound deliveries:	324
Expedited orders:	112
Line shortages:	63
Line delays (for lack of materials, assemblies, parts, supplies):	17
On-time delivery to line:	69%

Primary suppliers	Supply-side demands (summarized)	Primary customers	Customer-side outcomes (summarized)
Procurement/ outside vendors	Right stuff: materials, assemblies, parts, supplies—meet all technical specifications, right amount, on time	Fabrication, paint, assembly, repair	Right stuff: materials, assemblies, parts, supplies—meet technical need, right amount, on time, in right place
Production scheduling	Assembly, part, supply orders: right item, right amount, right lead time, right due date to line	Procurement	Receiving report: right purchase order number, accurate count, condition, timely

Figure 5.15 Receiving/storage/stocking subprocesses PDPC.

Source: Reproduced by permission from W. J. Kolarik, *Creating Quality: Process Design for Results* (New York: McGraw-Hill, 1999), 446.

within one set of characteristics or factors. The typical layout is a two-dimensional matrix with the vertical dimension used to lay out one set of factors and the horizontal dimension used to lay out the other set. In the case of displaying interrelationships within one set of factors, the same factors are laid out in both the horizontal and vertical dimensions. Relationships are typically identified and documented within each set and between the two sets at intersection points in the graphic.

The concept of a matrix diagram is relatively simple; essentially, it is developed it help relate sets of factors or characteristics, usually in a qualitative fashion. The actual development of a matrix diagram, however, is rather involved in terms

Table 5.2 Issues, possible root causes, and general impact summary for receiving/storage/stocking PDPC.

Issue	Possible root causes	General impact
1. Our vendors are not aware of, or responsive to, our line shortage problems—why?	We do not communicate as well as we should with our vendors. Our vendors do not see High Lift as a large account. Our vendors are not capable of providing better service to us under current conditions.	More prompt deliveries from our vendors could decrease our airfreight costs and reduce our line shortages, speeding up/smoothing out our assembly subprocess. Estimated savings potential: $1.1 million per year.
2. Line flow is faster than the master schedule algorithm reflects in order issuance—why?	Our manufacturing time estimates that drive several parts of our master scheduling system were made using time estimates from our former/pre-redefinition product/production processes. Our redefined product/ production processes flow better than we anticipated/ estimated—provided materials, assemblies, parts, and supplies are readily available.	A lack of current reality of our present redefined processes within our scheduling algorithm is holding our production process back from realizing its full potential. Present mismatches are putting brakes on potential assembly improvement on the lines. Estimated savings potential: $1 million to $10 million per year.
3. Everything that enters receiving goes through the storage area, with the exception of "hot" items that are needed to resolve a line shortage—why?	High Lift supplies centralized storage/inventory system solutions to its customers. This concept is a part of High Lift culture and reflected in current operations. Centralized storage for all items is questionable.	Centralized storage capital as well as operational costs are running about $1.2 million per year. Material, assembly, part, and supply obsolescence costs are running at about 5% of purchased part costs or about $2 million dollars per year. Potential customers are brought in to observe the technical operations of the High Lift storage system. This demonstration is viewed as a decisive element in customers choosing High Lift. Such observation is involved with about 45% of system sales.

Source: Reproduced by permission from W. J. Kolarik, *Creating Quality: Process Design for Results* (New York: McGraw-Hill, 1999), 451.

of defining the level of detail, completeness, and association. Quantification and prioritization are addressed in the "Prioritization Matrices" section of this chapter.

In quality-related work, a primary application of the matrix diagram is to relate customer needs, demands, and expectations in the customer's language to technical characteristics of the product/process expressed in the producer's language. Figure 5.16 illustrates this application of a matrix diagram. This illustration contains interrelationships in the triangular appendages at the left side and the top of the matrix. Here, the "+" and "−" symbols to represent positive and negative relationships, respectively. The bull's-eye, open circle, and triangle symbols represent, respectively, very strong, strong, and weak relationships between characteristics of the two sets. In this matrix diagram, included are customer needs, demands, and expectations; technical definition characteristics; and competitor characteristics together.

Matrix diagrams differ in scope and detail, as well as in layout format. See Mizuno (1988), Akao (1990), Day (1993), and Kolarik (1995, 1999) for details regarding the matrix diagram in general and specific QFD applications in particular.

Figure 5.16 provides a simplified matrix diagram regarding a laundry service. Ignoring the quantification numbers in the matrix for now, customer demands are on the left and technical quality characteristics are on the top. Two interrelationship matrices appear at the left and top. Customer degrees of importance and laundry sales points appear in vertical columns. Here, critical laundry sales points include clean clothes, good-looking clothes, friendly service, and return of pocket contents. This type of matrix diagram is commonly found in QFD work.

Interrelationship Digraphs

The purpose of an interrelationship digraph is to help people discover, visualize, and communicate high-level sequential and/or cause and effect relationships. Constructing an interrelationship digraph is best addressed in a team environment, to capture a diversity of perspectives regarding sequences, effects, and causes. Typical starting points include effects or symptoms, both undesirable and desirable. Logical development from these effects back to potential causes is common to most relations diagramming efforts. Clustering and sequencing of causes are common to all interrelationship digraphs. Boxes, circles, ovals, loops, and directional arrows are used to depict cause-to-effect flows.

In general, the interrelationship digraph helps us to identify and isolate relevant causal factors concerning a situation, a problem, or an opportunity. Ultimately, it helps us understand and communicate the essence of causal or sequential relationships regarding a situation in our physical and/or social environments. It is a graphical aid in cause-and-effect discovery as well as relationship determination and expression. Interrelationship digraphs express basic causal sequences, introduce assertions, assess or project resulting effects, and communicate critical relationships. The interrelationship digraph is one form of relationship diagram (see Brassard [1989] for details).

The mechanics of constructing an interrelationship digraph generally follow the same lines as in the affinity diagram but extend the affinity diagramming process into cause–effect and/or sequential ordering, generally indicated by arrows that connect the "boxes" or statements.

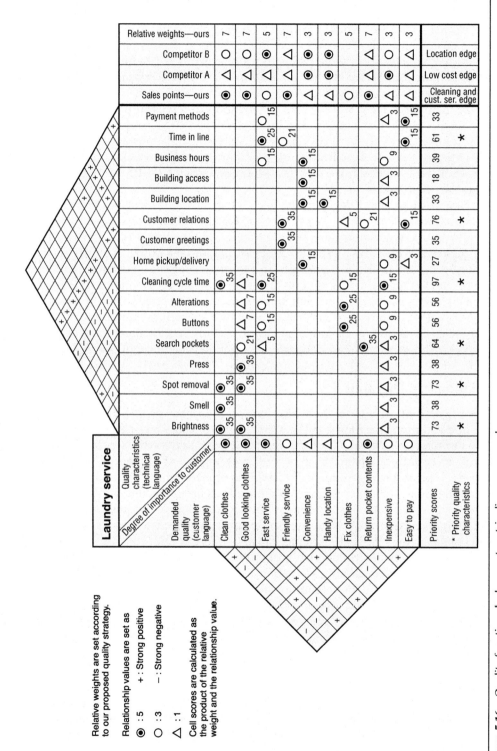

Figure 5.16 Quality function deployment matrix diagram example.

Source: Reproduced by permission from W. J. Kolarik, *Creating Quality: Process Design for Results* (New York: McGraw-Hill, 1999), 150.

Steps in constructing an interrelationship digraph are as follows:

1. Identify a general situation. The situation may be associated with a problem or an opportunity in our physical, economic, and/or social environments.

2. Collect facts, opinions, and ideas. Data/information may be generated from a group of people in any number of formats; for example, use work teams, focus groups, or groups of experts.

3. Express and enter the data/information in a common format. Use sticky notes on a wall, cards on a table, or computer software capable of expressing each piece of data/information in a medium that can be "moved around."

4. Identify the groups/clusters. Identify, label, and describe the groups or clusters regarding the common attribute(s) or summary characteristics that apply and describe their relationship (as a group) to the situation at hand.

5. Cluster the data/information pieces. Cluster or organize our data/information into cohesive groups.

6. Identify relations/sequences. Once basic descriptions and clusters/groups are identified, express the relationships between these entities with arrows.

7. Repeat steps 4, 5, and 6 to form supergroups/superclusters. It may be possible to relate two or more of the initial groups/clusters and develop a supergroup or supercluster. Supergrouping can be repeated until the facts, opinions, and ideas are suitably classified/organized. The result here is a supergroup and its description/relationship to the situation.

8. Present the results. The final product is an organized set of facts, opinions, and ideas that make sense in terms of providing help in understanding the nature of the situation from step 1, and summarizing the situation in a problem or opportunity format that flows logically from the facts and figures.

The illustration in Figure 5.17 provides a relatively simple interrelationship digraph where the situational descriptions are grouped and labeled using the affinity principle. Arrows are then used to indicate convergence toward a logical, actionable conclusion. For more information on interrelationship digraphs, see Mizuno (1988), Brassard (1989), Kolarik (1995, 1999), and Tague (2005).

Prioritization Matrices

Once one develops or identifies relationships and options or alternatives through a relationship matrix, a relations diagram, a tree diagram, or some other means, decision mode is entered. The purpose of a prioritization matrix is to help people measure/evaluate relationships from a matrix or tree analysis relative to a weighting scheme and decision criteria to set implementation priorities for the decisions at hand. The prioritization matrix allows us to make relative comparisons

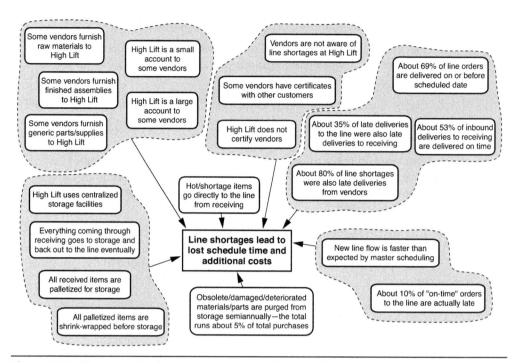

Figure 5.17 Line support subprocess interrelationship digraph.

Source: Reproduced by permission from W. J. Kolarik, *Creating Quality: Process Design for Results* (New York: McGraw-Hill, 1999), 450.

and present our information in an organized manner so that decisions can be supported with consistent, objective, quantitative evaluation.

Prioritization typically requires two things: (1) decision criteria and (2) a means of structuring relative comparisons. Decision criteria stem from our perception of what is important. For example, economics, timeliness, physical performance, and customer service form basic categories from which to develop decision criteria. Once developed, these criteria must be assessed as to their importance within the judgment of each decision maker and collectively between decision makers. This assessment may be carried out subjectively or objectively.

In the subjective case, individuals draw on our past experiences and perceptions of the future and collectively use some sort of consensus/voting/ranking-based process. Various types of rating/voting schemes include the Delphi method and the nominal group technique. The matrix diagram illustration in Figure 5.13 contains two sets of rankings, one for the strength of the relationships in the body and one for the relative importance of our sales points. Together, these two sets allow us to quantify the body of the matrix and develop quality characteristic scores. Hence, thinking/action can be prioritized in terms of the more critical quality characteristics. In this case, criticality is indicated by the asterisk symbol (*), and a total score of 60 (selected subjectively) was used as the criterion for selection.

In the objective case, relative weighting values are assigned and values quantitatively manipulated to converge on a relative priority number. Several techniques exist for objectively establishing prioritization criteria. The analytical hierarchy process (AHP) is widely described as a quantitative technique (Saaty

1982). The AHP allows several decision makers to integrate their priorities into a priority matrix where the decision criteria are compared as to relative importance in a pairwise fashion. The results include a decision criteria priority matrix and a corresponding alternative priority-weighted matrix. Hence, a quantitative group consensus analysis matrix emerges. From this analysis, the alternatives can be selected with the confidence that all criteria—economic, technological, and intangible factors—are integrated into the decision process. For more information on prioritization matrices, see Brassard (1989).

Activity Network Diagrams

The purpose of activity network diagramming is to help people sequentially define, organize, and manage a complex set of activities and events with respect to time schedule planning and implementation.

The Japanese scheduling/planning tool known as an arrow diagram is a hybrid derived from Gantt chart technology and a simplified extraction from the PERT and CPM technologies (see Kolarik [1995] and Mizuno [1988]). An arrow diagram is a network planning method that displays activities on the "arrows" as opposed to on the "nodes." An activity network diagram is a derivation of PERT, CPM, and the arrow diagram (Brassard 1989). A useful simplified version of CPM with activities on the nodes is described.

Complex processes are typically made up of several activities that must be carried out in a defined sequence to accomplish the desired result. An activity/ sequence list is used to identify and organize a set of activities as to sequence and estimated duration.

In general, each activity involved with an endeavor will be sequential, parallel, or coupled with other activities. Sequential activities require that a predecessor activity be completed before its successor can begin. Parallel activities can be undertaken and executed simultaneously. Coupled activities are executed together and hence their progression is linked together in some manner. The activity/sequence list addresses these relationships. First, each activity on the list is uniquely identified. Then, the sequence as to predecessor and successor activities is established. Finally, duration is estimated for each activity. An example activity/ sequence list appears in Table 5.3.

From the activity/sequence list, CPM-like networks of planned activities are constructed, to organize and display a schedule of project activities/events regarding starting and finishing time estimates, both as a whole project and as individual activities.

To develop a CPM network for a project, first identify activities and events. An *activity* is something that requires action of some type, such as shingling a roof. An *event* happens at a specific time, for example, the beginning or ending point of an activity. Our critical events represent milestones, points at which progress is reassessed. The activity/sequence list is a helpful tool to summarize activities, sequences, and time estimates.

A CPM-like network diagram is depicted in Figure 5.18. Here, the symbol, sequence, and duration information are taken from the activity/sequence list in Table 5.3. The network flows from left to right in a time sequence. Each activity is represented by a node, that is, a circle. Within each circle are the activity's

Table 5.3 Line support improvement process activities, sequences, and durations.

Activity description	Activity symbol	Predecessor	Duration, days
Explain change/plan to affected areas	A		2
Identify rackable/binnable items	B	A	7
Design racks/bins/storage facility modifications	C	B	21
Build/test racks/bins*	D*	C	14
Identify/inform affected vendors	E	A	4
Prepare High Lift and vendor training/certification materials	F	A	15
Gain vendors' cooperation	G	E	8
Certify/train vendors*	H*	G, F	10
Review/modify High Lift team needs	I	F	2
Train High Lift people*	J*	I	5
Modify staging facilities	K	C	12
Modify in/out facilities	L	C	14
Develop procurement scheduling/card system*	M*	F	25
Rack/bin existing bulk inventory*	N*	D, K, L	14
Stage racks/bins to line	O	N	5
Remove/salvage old storage area	P	O	20
Limited-scale operation, test/tune/mistakeproof*	Q*	H, J, M, O	30
Full-scale operations	R	Q	–

Source: Reproduced by permission from W. J. Kolarik, *Creating Quality: Process Design for Results* (New York: McGraw-Hill, 1999), 474.
*Indicates milestone activities; milestone occurs at the end of the marked activity.

symbol and its estimated time duration. Other information developed includes earliest start time (ES), earliest completion time (EC), latest start time (LS), and latest completion time (LC). These estimates are provided for each node/activity on the network.

The *critical path* is defined as the path that determines the minimum completion time for the entire project. Boldface arrows usually depict the critical path. If a delay occurs on any activity on the critical path, then the project duration will be increased. Hence, people watch the activities on the critical path very carefully with respect to time duration violations.

The ES and EC estimates are developed on a forward pass through the network of activities and durations. The network is developed using a start event and a finish event. Start at time zero and finish at the shortest time possible, considering our time/duration estimates. On the forward pass, begin at the start node and develop ES_j estimates for each node. Usually, assume the ES_{Start} node is equal to zero. However, some positive value could also be assumed. Then, develop ES_j estimates for each activity moving from left to right (across time) through the network. Each ES_j is equal to the maximum of the EC_i estimates taken from the set of all immediate predecessor activities. Each ES_j is estimated by summing its ES_j and its duration, t_j. The EC_{Finish} node is equal to the maximum of the EC_i estimates taken from the set of all immediate predecessor activities.

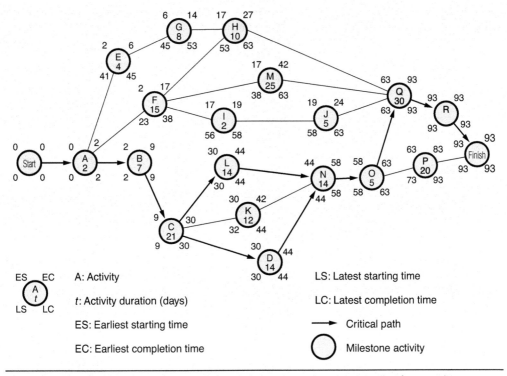

Figure 5.18 Simplified CPM schedule network–line support improvement implementation.

Source: Reproduced by permission from W. J. Kolarik, *Creating Quality: Process Design for Results* (New York: McGraw-Hill, 1999), 475.

The LC and LS estimates are developed on a backward pass through the network of activities. Starting at the finish node, set the LC_{Finish} node equal to the EC_{Finish} node. Set the LS_{Finish} node equal to the LC_{Finish} node. Estimate LC_j as the minimum of the LS_i estimates taken from the set of all immediate successor activities. Each LS_j is equal to its LC_j minus its activity duration, t_j.

Tables such as Table 5.4 are constructed to both facilitate network development and summarize results. Activity descriptions, symbols, and durations are usually repeated. Listed are the ES, EC, LS, and LC estimates, which match those in our CPM network. Additionally, included are estimates of total slack (TS) and free slack (FS). In the CPM network method, *TS* is the amount of time activity *j* may be delayed from its earliest starting time without delaying the latest completion time of the project.

$$TS_j = LC_j - EC_j = LS_j - ES_j \qquad (5.1)$$

Whenever the TS_j equals zero, the activity is a critical path activity.

FS is defined as the amount of time activity *j* may be delayed from its earliest starting time without delaying the starting time of any of its immediate successor activities.

$$FS_j = Min\ \{(ES_i = 1 - EC_j),\ (ES_i = 2 - EC_j),\ \ldots, \qquad (5.2)$$
$$(ES_i = Last\ successor\ activity - EC_j)\}$$

Table 5.4 Line support improvement scheduling details.

Activity description	Activity symbol	Duration, days	ES	EC	LS	LC	TS	FS	Critical?
Explain change/plan to affected areas	A	2	0	2	0	2	0	0	Yes
Identify rackable/binnable items	B	7	2	9	2	9	0	0	Yes
Design racks/bins/storage facility modifications	C	21	9	30	9	30	0	0	Yes
Build/test racks/bins*	D*	14	30	44	30	44	0	0	Yes
Identify/inform affected vendors	E	4	2	6	41	45	39	0	No
Prepare High Lift and vendor training/certification materials	F	15	2	17	21	36	19	0	No
Gain vendors' cooperation	G	8	6	14	45	53	39	3	No
Certify/train vendors*	H*	10	17	27	53	63	36	36	No
Review/modify High Lift team needs	I	2	17	19	56	58	39	0	No
Train High Lift people*	J*	5	19	24	58	63	39	39	No
Modify staging facilities	K	12	30	42	32	44	2	2	No
Modify in/out facilities	L	14	30	44	30	44	0	0	Yes
Develop procurement scheduling/card system*	M*	25	17	42	38	63	21	21	No
Rack/bin existing bulk inventory*	N*	14	44	58	44	58	0	0	Yes
Stage racks/bins to line	O	5	58	63	58	63	0	0	Yes
Remove/salvage old storage area	P	20	63	83	73	93	10	10	No
Limited-scale operation, test/tune/mistake-proof*	Q*	30	63	93	63	93	0	0	Yes
Full-scale operations	R		93	93	93	93	0	0	Yes

Source: Reproduced by permission from W. J. Kolarik, *Creating Quality: Process Design for Results* (New York: McGraw-Hill, 1999), 476.
*Indicates milestone activities; milestone occurs at the end of the marked activity.

where i corresponds to the index for all successor activities, $i = 1, 2, \ldots$, last successor for activity j.

CPM graphics and tables can be used to update the plan as activities are completed. Additionally, changes in subsequent activity estimates can be projected. The same basic rules are used that were used to develop the initial CPM network but beginning at the end of the completed event. Hence, updated ES, EC, LS, and LC estimates for the remaining activities can be generated, as well as redeveloped slack estimates. It can also be determined whether the critical path has changed because of the changes. Additional details pertaining to project planning and implementation are available in project management texts, such as Badiru and Pulat (1995).

Process Maps and SIPOC Diagrams

The purpose of a process map is to help people discover, understand, and communicate the input-to-transformation-to-output characteristics of a process. Process flowcharts are used to map processes at any level of detail. Gross-level maps are useful in high-level planning work, while minute-level maps are useful in process control work. A flowchart depicts process flow by using a sequence of symbols and words to represent process flow components, all connected with directional lines/arrows to indicate flow paths. A wide variety of processes are charted, and hence a wide variety of symbols are used. In some cases, simple box or rectangular symbols are used that are self-descriptive or annotated near the symbol. In other cases, the symbols are iconic in the sense that the symbol shape is indicative of the process element. Usually, a legend is provided to define specialized symbols. Typically, the more focused the flowchart, the more specialized the symbols. Process mapping is performed by teams and individuals such as operators, technicians, engineers, specialists, and/or managers. Diverse perspectives are gained through process mapping when an interdisciplinary team is involved with the mapping. See Kolarik (1995) for general details, Barnes (1980) for specialized charting techniques relative to classical industrial engineering, and Hughes (1995) for automatic process control–related flowcharting basics.

Processes are mapped to help people understand how processes work or how they are expected to work. Process flow mapping usually involves several steps:

1. Establish flowchart/map purpose. Clearly state the purpose for our charting efforts. This purpose will dictate the level of detail needed in the map.

2. Define map boundaries. Determine the starting and ending points for the mapping effort, relative to purpose and necessary observations.

3. Observe process. Provided the process is in operation, direct process observation/experience is necessary to develop the process map. Possibly observe/map processes in other organizations through benchmarking activities.

4. Establish gross process flow. Develop/chart a process overview depicting the production system or process in terms of major components, for example, processes or subprocesses, respectively.

5. Develop map details. Once the general essence of the process flow is captured, focus on details, cascading the level of detail down to the point where it is compatible with our purpose. Details are sequenced to represent the order/position that they occupy in the actual process.

6. Check for validity/completeness. Move from level to level in our maps, examining them for validity and completeness. Validity checks typically involve map review as to accuracy of inputs, transformation, output, and sequence. Completeness extends to the level of detail within the target process as well as interactions with other processes.

Figure 5.19 provides an illustration of a macro-level process map, broken out by the seven fundamental processes: market/definition, design/development, production, distribution/marketing/sales/service, use/support, disposal/recycle, and business integration. Here, a global depiction of the essential processes involved in an enterprise is seen. These fundamental processes can be drilled down to build more detailed process maps, sometimes resembling a PDPC in nature. Figure 5.20 provides an illustration of such a map for a visual manufacturing alternative subprocess plan. Process maps may be layered to depict a process hierarchy; see Kolarik (1999) for details.

The SIPOC diagram is a high-level process map used to identify the important aspects of the current process, such as the process outputs and customers,

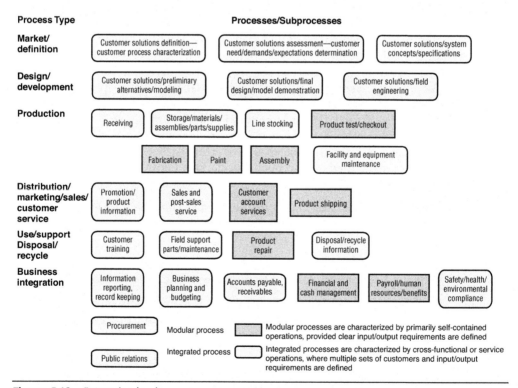

Figure 5.19 Enterprise-level process map.

Source: Reproduced by permission from W. J. Kolarik, *Creating Quality: Process Design for Results* (New York: McGraw-Hill, 1999), 441.

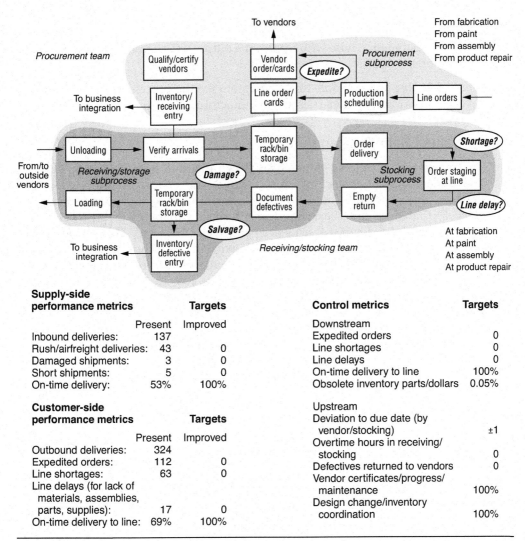

Figure 5.20 Visual alternative-improved subprocess map/PDPC.

Source: Reproduced by permission from W. J. Kolarik, *Creating Quality: Process Design for Results* (New York: McGraw-Hill, 1999), 468.

to capture the voice of the customer. It is a useful tool in the early stages of the DMAIC process to determine the critical-to-quality factors (see the "Total Quality Management" section of this chapter for a discussion of the DMAIC methodology). SIPOC is an acronym for suppliers, inputs, process, outputs, and customers—which are defined as follows:

- **Suppliers.** Those who provide inputs to the process, including materials, resources, services, information, and so on.

- **Inputs.** Materials, services, resources, information, and so on.

- **Process.** Process description and listing of all key process steps.

- **Outputs.** Products, information, services, and so on.

- **Customers.** Those who receive the outputs. Customers may be internal or external.

Figure 5.21 displays a simple SIPOC diagram for the process used to report and investigate work-related injuries at a manufacturing firm.

Process Value Chain Diagrams

The purpose of a process value chain (PVC) diagram is to help people depict and understand a sequence of cause-to-effect and effect-to-cause relationships between business results/outcomes and basic physical, economic, and social variables. PVC analysis links basic physical and social variables with business results so that value-added process sequences are clearly depicted. This linkage is not precise, because each basic variable has its own natural/technical units of measure (e.g., length, pressure, volume, or composition), while process/business results are expressed in their own units or unitless ratios (e.g., production units, percent conformance, scrap rate, efficiency, cost, revenue, profit, and return on investment [ROI]). Hence, PVCs have discontinuities where unitary incompatibility presents gaps and challenges. The point is to link variables related to specific process decisions and process control points to business results and vice versa as well as possible. Hence, understanding as to cause–effect and time lags in moving from cause to effect become more obvious for all concerned (e.g., operators, engineers, and managers).

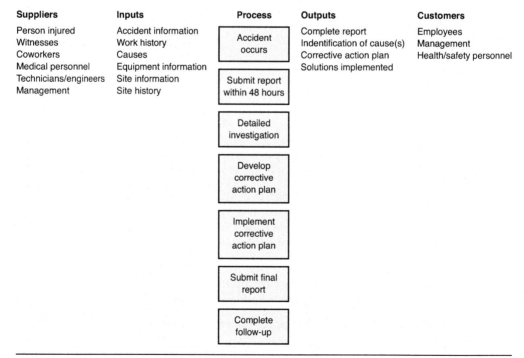

Suppliers	Inputs	Process	Outputs	Customers
Person injured	Accident information	Accident occurs	Complete report	Employees
Witnesses	Work history		Indentification of cause(s)	Management
Coworkers	Causes		Corrective action plan	Health/safety personnel
Medical personnel	Equipment information	Submit report within 48 hours	Solutions implemented	
Technicians/engineers	Site information			
Management	Site history	Detailed investigation		
		Develop corrective action plan		
		Implement corrective action plan		
		Submit final report		
		Complete follow-up		

Figure 5.21   SIPOC diagram for work–related injuries.

The PVC diagram connects the business world to the technical world through a logical, sequential linkage that cascades up and down all processes and their respective subprocesses. PVC diagrams are useful for operators to see how operational decisions in the technical world ultimately impact business results. They are useful for managers/leaders to clearly see that business targets are met through a sequence of operational decisions. An efficient and effective PVC adds value to products throughout the chain.

A generic PVC is depicted in Figure 5.22. Across the top are basic business outputs on the right-hand side and basic inputs in the form of controlled and uncontrolled variables on the left-hand side. Transformations in the form of processes and subprocesses are depicted in the middle. The oval cycle on the bottom half of the figure shows that a PVC is developed by working from one of several starting points. One may start somewhere in our outputs (the business results) and work toward inputs (the basic variables). Or, one may start somewhere in our input variables and work toward our business outputs. The focus is to understand how the

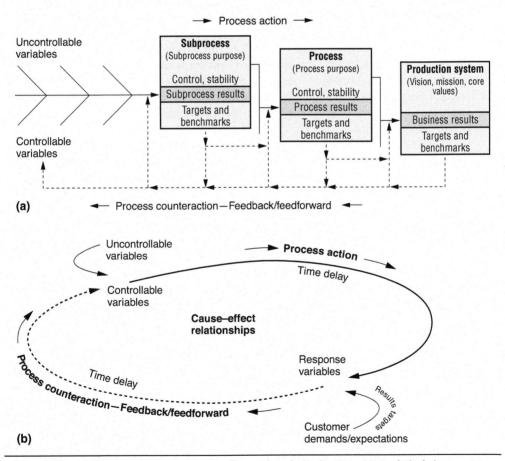

Figure 5.22 Generic production system process value chain diagram. (a) Analytical view. (b) General systems view.

Source: Reproduced by permission from W. J. Kolarik, *Creating Quality: Process Design for Results* (New York: McGraw-Hill, 1999), 54.

processes work and how they impact the business objectives. See Kolarik (1999) for more details regarding PVC.

Benchmarking

The purpose of benchmarking is to help people learn from the work of others—seek out, study, and emulate the best practices associated with high performance/results—to enhance or better their own performance.

People tend to perceive an organization as the "best" through rather subjective arguments, for example, exhortations of various types. In reality, perceptions may not be accurate. One may lack insight as to what is happening around us: what others are doing and the results they obtain. In essence, there is a need for outside standards/benchmarks from which to judge our own performance. Benchmarking helps us to both gain an awareness of shortfalls in our own performance and plan and implement countermeasures to enhance our performance.

Informal benchmarking is a matter of natural curiosity and has always been practiced; however, formal benchmarking was positioned as an organizational initiative at Xerox. Kerns and Nadler (1992) define benchmarking as "the continuous process of measuring products, services, and practices against the toughest competitor or those companies recognized as industry leaders." Camp (1989, 1995) defines benchmarking as "the search for and implementation of best practices." Benchmarking encompasses four aspects: (1) analyze the operation, (2) know the competition and industry leaders, (3) incorporate the best of the best, and (4) gain superiority. The formal scope of benchmarking includes products, processes, and performance metrics.

Camp (1989, 1995) cites four types of benchmarking: internal, competitive, functional, and generic. Internal benchmarking focuses on best practices within our own organization. Competitive benchmarking provides a comparison between direct competitors. Functional benchmarking refers to comparisons of methods across organizations executing the same basic functions outside our industry. Generic process benchmarking focuses on innovative work processes in general, wherever they occur.

Benchmarking, which was also discussed in Chapter 1, is a broad initiative. Watson (1993) describes the evolution of benchmarking in terms of generations. He cites reverse engineering as the first generation. This is essentially a rote copying strategy. The second generation is termed competitive benchmarking, which focuses on direct competitors. As the third generation, he cites process benchmarking, where processes common to different industries are assessed for best practices. The fourth generation is termed strategic benchmarking. Here, the focus is on the strategies that a competitor or noncompetitor uses to guide their organization. The fourth generation is used to feed process reengineering initiatives. A futuristic fifth generation is cited as global benchmarking. Here, the focus is international in scope and deals with trade, cultural, and business process distinctions among companies. In all cases, the driving force is "profit oriented," as addressed through three parameters: (1) quality beyond that of competitors, (2) technology before that of competitors, and (3) costs below those of competitors.

The benchmarking initiative focuses on two basic issues: (1) best practices and (2) metrics or measurement. Performance gaps are recognized and addressed with improvement plans. Management commitment, communication, and employee participation are all critical elements in a benchmarking initiative. For more information on benchmarking, see Camp (1989, 1995), Kolarik (1995, 1999), and Watson (1993).

Steps in the benchmarking process are as follows:

1. Preplan the benchmarking initiative. Assess and understand customer needs and the business results/outcomes desired.

2. Plan and execute the initiative. Identify comparative organizations and what is to be benchmarked. Determine data collection methods and collect data.

3. Analyze the data and information collected. Determine the current performance gap. Project future performance levels/goals.

4. Integrate the information into actionable issues. Communicate the findings and gain acceptance within your organization. Establish functional goals that are actionable.

5. Prepare for action and act. Develop action plans, implement specific actions, monitor progress, and recalibrate the benchmarks.

6. Gain maturity in benchmarking. Attain a leadership position and integrate benchmarking practices into processes.

Benchmarking clearly is an invaluable asset in quality improvement work. It provides a perspective of how things are done in other organizations, leads to the identification of best practices, and encourages adoption of the same. However, a best practice today will undoubtedly be eclipsed by a better practice in the near future.

In many cases, creative elements are injected within/beyond current practices. These extensions require creative thinking or breakthrough thinking. Breakthrough thinking typically is approached very differently from benchmarking. Here, "out of the box" thinking is encouraged as opposed to thinking "in the box" (e.g., finding an existing best practice). Creative thinking is the only tool available that allows us to move beyond best practices.

Creativity has received considerable attention in quality improvement work (Kolarik 1995, 1999). Nadler and Hibino (1994) proposed seven principles of breakthrough thinking: (1) the uniqueness principle, (2) the purposes principle, (3) the solution-after-next principle, (4) the systems principle, (5) the limited information collection principle, (6) the people design principle, and (7) the betterment time line principle. DeBono (1992) encourages the use of hats in creative thinking: the white hat (data and information), the red hat (feelings, intuition, hunches, and emotions), the black hat (pessimistic perspective), the yellow hat (optimistic pespective), the green hat (creative effort), and the blue hat (thinking process control). Figure 5.23 depicts an overview of the integration of breakthrough thinking into a benchmarking model. From this depiction, it is clear that breaking through focuses on the essence of the product, technologies (relative to both products and process), and services. The long-term focus of breakthrough thinking tends to complement the shorter-term focus of benchmarking, yielding a broad view of improvement efforts.

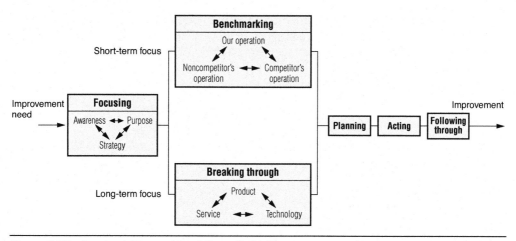

Figure 5.23 Benchmarking and breakthrough thinking.

Source: Reproduced by permission from W. J. Kolarik, *Creating Quality: Process Design for Results* (New York: McGraw–Hill, 1999), 164.

CONTINUOUS IMPROVEMENT METHODOLOGIES

> Define, describe, and apply the following continuous improvement methodologies:
>
> 1. Total quality management (TQM)
> 2. Kaizen
> 3. Plan-do-check-act (PDCA)
> 4. Six sigma (Analyze)
>
> **Body of Knowledge V.C**

Quality improvement is achieved by continuously improving the production and business processes of an organization (Besterfield 1999). It is optimized by:

- Viewing all work as a process, whether it is associated with production or business activities

- Making all processes effective, efficient, and adaptable

- Anticipating changing customer needs

- Controlling in-process performance using metrics such as scrap and cycle time, and monitoring tools such as control charts

- Maintaining constructive dissatisfaction with the present level of performance

- Eliminating waste and rework wherever they occur

- Investigating activities that do not add value to the product or service, with the aim of eliminating those activities

- Eliminating nonconformities in all phases of everyone's work, even if the increment of improvement is small

- Using benchmarking to improve competitive advantage

- Innovating to achieve breakthroughs

- Holding gains so there is no regression

- Incorporating lessons learned into future activities

- Using technical tools such as SPC, experimental design, benchmarking, QFD, etc.

Continuous process improvement is designed to utilize the resources of the organization to achieve a quality-driven culture. Individuals must think, act, and speak quality. An organization attempts to reach a single-minded link between quality and work execution by educating its constituents to continuously analyze and improve their own work, the processes, and their work group (Langdon 1994).

Process improvement achieves the greatest results when it operates within the framework of the problem-solving method. In the initial stages of a program, quick results are frequently obtained because the solution is obvious or an individual has a brilliant idea. There are many models for quality improvement. See total quality management (TQM), kaizen, PDCA (sometimes known as PDSA), and Six Sigma in the following sections.

Total Quality Management

TQM is based on the principles of Feigenbaum, Deming, and Juran. The exact origin of TQM has been debated, but TQM as a process improvement methodology received the most use and attention in the mid-1980s and early 1990s before being mostly replaced by lean and Six Sigma efforts, which focus on more rigorous statistical methods. The goal of TQM is to manage quality improvement methods across the entire organization. Some sources claim that the TQM name was developed by the United States Navy and originally used at the Naval Air Systems Command (A. Houston and S. L. Dockstader, *Total Quality Leadership: A Primer*, (https://citeseerx.ist.psu.edu/viewdoc/download?doi=10.1.1.601.6121&rep=rep 1&type=pdf). TQM encompasses the following ideas:

- Customer focus. The customer determines whether a product or service is good enough.

- Employee empowerment. All employees must understand that continuous improvement is a part of everyone's job.

- Leadership. Upper management must provide the impetus and motivation for the quality programs. Many TQM organizations have quality councils that lead strategic quality initiatives.

This model, when properly implemented, often results in an enterprise that is more productive and more competitive. Customer loyalty will improve and stakeholder value will increase. As Montgomery (2013) argues, many organizations focused on training their workforce in quality and basic methods but did not emphasize tools used to reduce variability or how to implement these methods in practice.

Kaizen

Kaizen is a Japanese word for the philosophy that defines management's role in continuously encouraging and implementing small improvements involving everyone in an organization. It is a method of continuous improvement in small increments that makes processes more efficient, effective, under control, and adaptable. Improvements are usually accomplished at little or no expense and without sophisticated techniques or expensive equipment.

Kaizen focuses on simplification by breaking down complex processes into their subprocesses and then improving them. Its application is not limited to quality, but quality professionals have effectively applied it. When done correctly, it humanizes the workplace, eliminates hard work (both mental and physical), and teaches people how to use the scientific method and to detect waste. Some companies have created a spin-off called kaizen blitz. This is a carefully orchestrated intensive activity designed to produce a significant improvement quickly.

The kaizen improvement involves the following activities and assessment:

1. Value-added and non-value-added work activities (see the "Lean Tools" section of this chapter for details).

2. *Muda*, which refers to the seven classes of waste: overproduction, delay, transportation, processing, inventory, wasted motion, and defective parts (see the "Lean Tools" section of this chapter for details).

3. Principles of motion study.

4. Principles of materials handling.

5. Documentation of standard operating procedures.

6. The five S's for workplace organization, which are five Japanese words that mean proper arrangement (*seiri*), orderliness (*seiton*), personal cleanliness (*seiso*), cleanup (*seiketsu*), and discipline (*shitsuke*). Various authors have translated them slightly differently. NIST, through the Manufacturing Extension Partnership, uses sort, set in order, shine, standardize, and sustain (refer to the "Lean Tools" section of this chapter for more information).

7. Visual management by means of visual displays that everyone in the plant can use for better communications.

8. Just-in-time principles to produce only the right units in the right quantities, at the right time, and with the right resources.

9. Poka-yoke to prevent or detect errors.

10. Team dynamics, which include problem solving, communication skills, and conflict resolution (Gee, McGrath, and Izadi 1996).

Kaizen relies heavily on a culture that encourages suggestions by operators who continually try to incrementally improve their job or process. An example of a kaizen-type improvement would be changing the color of a welding booth from black to white to improve operator visibility. This change would result in a small improvement in weld quality and a substantial improvement in operator satisfaction. The PDSA cycle, described next, may be used to help implement kaizen concepts.

Plan-Do-Check-Act (PDCA)

The basic plan-do-check-act (PDCA) cycle was originally developed by Shewhart as the plan-do-study-act (PDSA) cycle and is an effective improvement technique. It is sometimes called the Shewhart cycle or the Deming cycle (see Figure 5.24).

The four steps in the cycle are exactly as stated. First, plan carefully what is to be done. Next, carry out the plan (do it). Third, study the results: Did the plan work as intended or were the results unexpected? Finally, act on the results by identifying what worked as planned and what did not. Using the knowledge learned, develop an improved plan and repeat the cycle. The PDSA cycle is a simple adaptation of the more elaborate Six Sigma process, discussed in the "Lean Tools" section of this chapter.

PDSA is still widely used as an effective tool in industry. For example, two PDSA cycles were used in a quality improvement project for the Cancer Genetics Service clinic at the National Cancer Centre in Singapore. The PDSA cycles identified the need for a genetic counselor. The results of the quality improvement project were improved patient access and reduced costs (Tan et al. 2016).

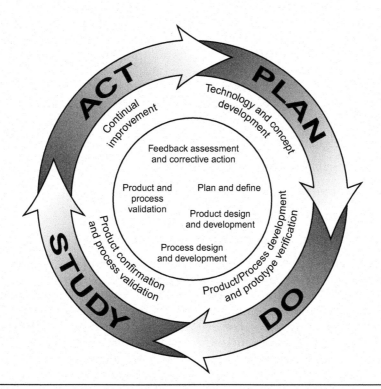

Figure 5.24 Basic plan-do-study-act cycle.

Six Sigma

The average half-life of companies is about 10 years, regardless of past performance or the type of product produced (Daepp et al. 2015). Companies are embracing Six Sigma not only as a method to reduce defects but also as a catalyst to change their culture and impact how employees engage in their everyday work.

Utilizing a Six Sigma business strategy, organizations can understand threats and recognize new opportunities for growth, not only to survive but also to thrive within competitive environments.

Quality practitioners often note that the tools of Six Sigma are not unique. It is true that most Six Sigma techniques are familiar; however, the power of properly integrating them as a total system is new. Six Sigma creates a road map for changing data into knowledge, resulting in process-focused change and bottom-line benefits for organizations. Not all organizations have achieved success with Six Sigma, which depends on the successful integration of two components: strategy and metrics.

The strategy of Six Sigma relates to how the methodology (tools and techniques) is integrated into an organization through key projects, yielding substantial benefits to the organization's bottom line. Companies experiencing success with Six Sigma have created an effective infrastructure for selecting, supporting, and executing projects. These projects are focused on achieving strategic business goals, as well as addressing the voice of the customer.

The success of Six Sigma also depends on the wise application of metrics. Unfortunately, much confusion exists relative to the metrics of Six Sigma. There is no "one size fits all" metric applicable to every project. Effective metrics are cross-functional, providing a holistic view of the process and contributing insight to the project team. A lot of resources will be wasted if Six Sigma metrics are not applied wisely and subsequently used to orchestrate improvement activities. "Fire prevention" is preferred to "firefighting."

This section details the two components previously mentioned, as well as other important aspects of a successful Six Sigma implementation, including the following:

- Six Sigma needs assessment

- Six Sigma as a business strategy

- Implementing Six Sigma

- The metrics of Six Sigma

- Sustaining and communicating change

Organizations often become overwhelmed with day-to-day activities and lose sight of what needs to be done to make process-focused improvements or changes to survive the "long haul." Individuals within organizations might be aware of Six Sigma and think that the techniques could be useful to reduce the number of firefighting activities that occur; however, they may have trouble determining where it applies and where the benefits are achievable. This type of organization requires a simple and quick approach to make a Six Sigma needs assessment.

For this situation, people within the organization should respond to the Six Sigma needs checklist shown in Table 5.5. Upon completion of this survey, the

Table 5.5 Six Sigma needs checklist.

Six Sigma needs checklist	Answer yes or no
Do you have multiple "fix-it" projects in a critical process area that seem to have limited or lasting impact?	
Are you aware of a problem that management or employees are encountering?	
Are you aware of any problem that a customer is having with the products/ services your organization offers?	
Do you believe that primary customers might take their business elsewhere?	
Is the quality from competitive products/services better?	
Are your cycle times too long in certain process areas?	
Are your costs too high in certain process areas?	
Do you have concerns that you might be "downsized" from your organization?	
Do you have a persistent problem that you have attempted to fix in the past with limited success?	
Do you have regulatory/compliance problems?	

Source: F. W. Breyfogle III, J. M. Cupello, and B. Meadows, *Managing Six Sigma* (New York: John Wiley & Sons, 2000). Adapted by permission of John Wiley & Sons, Inc.

additional question can then be asked, "How much money are the affirmative responses costing the business annually?" An improvement opportunity often can be accurately quantified if the amount is initially determined as a percentage of the gross revenue of the organization.

Monetary estimates from this survey could be considered the perceived "cost of doing nothing" within the organization—that is, the cost to the business of not "doing Six Sigma." When this survey is conducted during a meeting of informed individuals, an even more accurate estimate of this cost can be obtained. During this meeting, individuals describe the logic used for their vote. Consensus might then be achieved for an overall monetary estimate for the group. When consensus does not seem possible, an average of the responses can give a very good estimate.

Estimated projected benefits from Six Sigma could then be determined as the projected monetary "cost of doing nothing." Full-time Six Sigma Black Belts (i.e., Six Sigma practitioners) can save an organization large amounts of money (direct impact on company finances) annually, depending on the following:

- Executive-level support
- Process focus area (i.e., some areas have more room for improvement than others)
- Team motivation
- Six Sigma Black Belt proficiency

A question frequently heard from executives is, "How does Six Sigma fit with other corporate initiatives?" Six Sigma should not be considered just another initiative but should be integrated with other programs (e.g., lean manufacturing and kaizen) at a higher level as part of an overall business strategy. Six Sigma should not replace other initiatives but instead create an infrastructure that offers a tactical approach to determine the best solution for a given process/situation.

Successful implementation should be viewed as an ongoing process of infusing the Six Sigma methodology into the way your employees approach their everyday work. It requires a proactive view and the commitment to evolve into a more process-oriented culture and reduce the amount of daily firefighting on strategic processes. The implementation process requires up-front work to develop awareness and generate buy-in before projects are selected. This process often displays unique characteristics in each organization; however, two elements are essential for success: executive leadership and customer focus.

To date, companies achieving significant results with Six Sigma have the commitment of their executive management. Executive leadership is the foundation of any successful Six Sigma business strategy. Upper-level managers need to develop an infrastructure to support the changes that implementing Six Sigma will create, not only to strategic business processes but also, as previously discussed, to the culture of the organization. Past quality programs resulted in varying success because they typically did not have an infrastructure that supported change.

The results received from a Six Sigma business strategy are highly dependent on how well leaders understand the value of wise implementation of the methodology and sincerely promote it within their organization. An executive retreat can help identify true champions who will promote change and can also prioritize the actions necessary to establish a road map to successful implementation. Through discussion and the careful planning of the process of successfully implementing Six Sigma, employees will have an easier journey to success in applying the methodology to their projects.

Establishing a customer focus mind-set within an organization goes hand in hand with creating a successful Six Sigma business strategy. The factors that are critical to your customers' success are necessary to a process improvement team's success. Therefore, evaluating customers' perception of quality should be at the forefront of the implementation process.

Every complaint from a customer should be viewed as an opportunity for growth and increased market share, a spotlight on areas needing process improvement focus. The key to success in this initial step is to make it easy for your customers' comments to be heard. Various methods exist to obtain this valuable input, including walking the customer process, performing customer surveys, conducting personal interviews with key customers, establishing feedback complaint systems, and developing customer panels.

Depending on the size of your organization and its core values, the word "customer" can take on many different definitions. When collecting feedback, care should be taken to maintain a comprehensive view of your customers. By combining external feedback with such things as internal business strategies, employee needs, and government regulations, your organization will obtain a balanced list of customer needs.

Through customer feedback, learning about what works and what does not will help to establish a mind-set of continual process improvement within your organization. Jack Welch, former CEO of GE and advocate of Six Sigma, has been quoted as saying that a business strategy alone will not generate higher quality throughout an organization.

Implementing Six Sigma

Six Sigma can be either a great success or a failure, depending on how it is implemented. Implementation strategies can vary significantly between organizations, depending on their distinct culture and strategic business goals. After completing a needs assessment and deciding to implement Six Sigma, an organization has two basic options:

1. Implement a Six Sigma program or initiative

2. Create a Six Sigma infrastructure

Option 1: Implement a Six Sigma Program or Initiative

The traditional approach to deploying statistical tools within an organization has not been very effective. With this approach, certain employees (practitioners) are taught the statistical tools from time to time and asked to apply a tool on the job when needed. The practitioners might then consult a statistician if they need help. Successes within an organization might occur; however, these successes do not build on each other to encourage additional and better use of the tools and overall methodology.

When organizations implement Six Sigma as a program or initiative, it often appears that they have only added, in an unstructured fashion, a few new tools to their toolbox through training classes. A possible extension of this approach is to apply the tools as needed to assigned projects. However, the selection, management, and execution of projects are not typically an integral part of the organization. These projects, which often are created at a low level within the organization, do not have the blessing of upper management; hence, resistance is often encountered when the best solution directly affects another group that does not have buy-in to the project. In addition, there typically is no one assigned to champion projects across organizational boundaries and facilitate change.

A program or initiative does not usually create an infrastructure that leads to bottom-line benefits through projects tied to the strategic goals of the organization. As a program or initiative, Six Sigma risks becoming the "flavor of the month" and will not capture the buy-in necessary to reap a large return on the investment in training. With this approach, employees may end up viewing Six Sigma as a program similar to TQM and other quality programs that may have experienced only limited success within their organization.

Even if great accomplishments occur through the individual use of statistical tools within organizations, there is often a lack of visibility of the benefits to upper management. A typical missing element for success with this approach is management buy-in. Because of this lack of visibility, practitioners often have to fight for funds, and these funds may be eliminated whenever the organization becomes financially strained. Effective use of statistical tools often does not get recognized and the overall company culture is not affected. For true success, executive-level support is needed that asks the right questions and leads to the wise application of statistical tools and other Six Sigma methodologies across organizational boundaries.

Option 2: Create a Six Sigma Infrastructure

Instead of focusing on the individual tools, it is best when Six Sigma training provides a process-oriented approach that teaches practitioners a methodology to select the right tool, at the right time, for a predefined project. Training of Six Sigma practitioners (Black Belts) utilizing this approach typically consists of four weeks of training over four months, where students work on their projects during the three weeks between training sessions.

Deploying Six Sigma as a business strategy through projects instead of tools is the more effective way to benefit from the time and money invested in Six Sigma training. Consider the following benefits of Six Sigma deployment via projects that have executive management support:

- Offers bigger impact through projects tied to bottom-line results
- Utilizes the tools in a more focused and productive way
- Provides a process/strategy for project management that can be studied and improved
- Increases communications between management and practitioners via project presentations
- Facilitates the detailed understanding of critical business processes
- Gives employees and management views of how statistical tools can be of significant value to organizations
- Allows Black Belts to receive feedback on their project approach during training
- Deploys Six Sigma with a closed-loop approach, creating time for auditing and incorporating lessons learned into an overall business strategy

A project-based approach relies heavily on a sound project selection process. Projects should be selected that meet the goals of an organization's business strategy. Six Sigma can then be utilized as a road map to effectively meet those goals. Once a strategic project has been selected, many practitioners (Black Belts) find a "21-step integration of tools" road map helpful in developing a plan for the specific project.

Initially, companies might choose projects that are too large, or may not choose certain projects because of their lack of strategic impact to the bottom line. Frustration with the first set of projects can be vital experience that motivates improvement in project selection in the next phase of implementing Six Sigma. Six Sigma is a long-term commitment. Treating deployment as a process allows objective analysis of all aspects of the process, including project selection and scoping. Utilizing lessons learned and incorporating them into subsequent waves of an implementation plan creates a closed feedback loop and real opportunities for improvement. Deploying Six Sigma through projects can lead to dramatic bottom-line benefits if the organization invests the time and executive energy necessary to implement Six Sigma as a business strategy.

The Metrics of Six Sigma

Much confusion exists relative to the metrics of Six Sigma. The sigma level (i.e., sigma-quality level) sometimes used as a measurement within a Six Sigma program includes a ±1.5σ value to account for "typical" shifts and drifts of the mean, where σ is the standard deviation of the process. This sigma-quality-level relationship is not linear. In other words, a percentage unit improvement in parts per million (ppm) defect rate (or defects per million opportunities [DPMO] rate) does not equate to the same percentage improvement in the sigma-quality level.

Figure 5.25 shows the sigma-quality level associated with various services (considering the 1.5σ shift of the mean). From this figure, note that the sigma-quality level of most services is about four sigma, while "world class" is considered six.

Figures 5.26, 5.27, and 5.28 illustrate various aspects of a normal distribution as it applies to Six Sigma program measures and the implication of the 1.5σ shift. Figure 5.26 illustrates the basic measurement concept of Six Sigma, where parts are to be manufactured consistently and well within their specification range. Figure 5.27 shows the number of ppm that would be outside the specification limits if the data were centered within these limits and had various standard deviations. Figure 5.28 extends Figure 5.26 to noncentral data relative to specification limits, where the mean of the data is shifted by 1.5σ. Figure 5.29 shows the relationship of ppm defect rates versus sigma-quality level for a centered and 1.5σ shifted

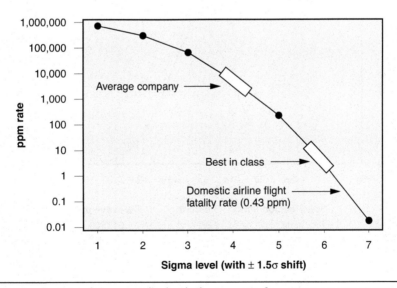

Figure 5.25 Implication of sigma-quality level. The ppm rate for part or process step considers a 1.5σ shift of the mean where only 3.4 ppm fail to meet specifications at a six sigma quality level.

Source: F. W. Breyfogle III, *Implementing Six Sigma* (New York: John Wiley & Sons, 1999). Adapted by permission of John Wiley & Sons, Inc.

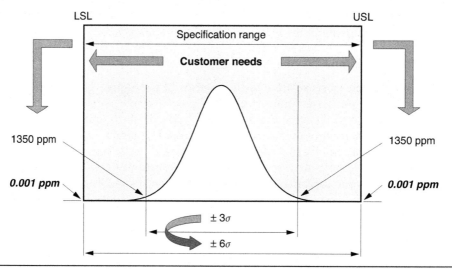

Figure 5.26 Normal distribution curve illustrates three sigma and six sigma parametric conformance.

Source: Copyright of Motorola, used with permission.

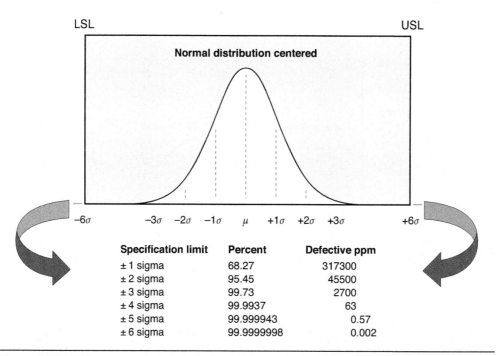

Specification limit	Percent	Defective ppm
± 1 sigma	68.27	317300
± 2 sigma	95.45	45500
± 3 sigma	99.73	2700
± 4 sigma	99.9937	63
± 5 sigma	99.999943	0.57
± 6 sigma	99.9999998	0.002

Figure 5.27 With a centered normal distribution between six sigma limits, only two devices per billion fail to meet the specification target.

Source: Copyright of Motorola, used with permission.

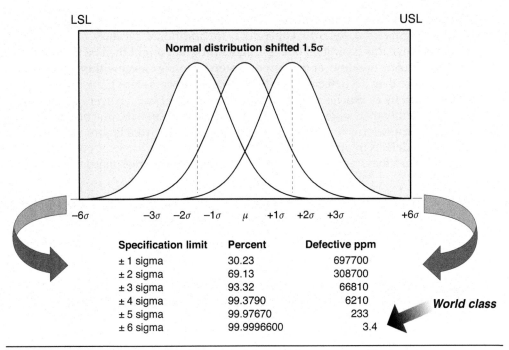

Figure 5.28 Effects of a 1.5σ shift where only 3.4 ppm fail to meet specifications.
Source: Copyright of Motorola, used with permission.

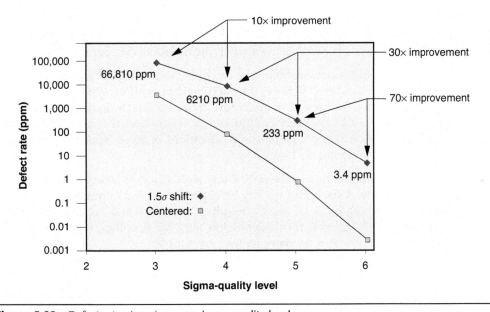

Figure 5.29 Defect rates (ppm) versus sigma-quality level.
Source: F. W. Breyfogle III, *Implementing Six Sigma* (New York: John Wiley & Sons, 1999). Adapted by permission of John Wiley & Sons, Inc.

process, along with a quantification for the amount of improvement needed to change a sigma level. Refer to Appendix D for additional Z-values.

To achieve this basic goal of a Six Sigma program might then be to produce at least 99.99966% "quality" at the "process step" and part level within an assembly (i.e., no more than 3.4 defects per million parts or process steps if the process mean were to shift by as much as 1.5σ). If, for example, there was on average one defect for an assembly that contained 40 parts and four process steps, practitioners might consider the assembly to be at a four sigma quality level from Figure 5.29, since the number of defects in ppm is $(1 \div 160)(106) = 6250$.

Problems that can occur using the sigma-quality-level metric include the following:

- The improvement from 4.1 to 4.2 sigma-quality level is not the same as improvement from 5.1 to 5.2 sigma-quality level.

- Determining the number of opportunities for any given process can be dramatically different between individuals.

- A sigma-quality-level metric can be deceiving. For example, one process might have a 50% defective unit rate and a sigma-quality level much greater than six, while another process might have a 0.01% defective unit rate and a sigma-quality level much worse than six. To illustrate this, first consider the counting of opportunities for failure within a computer chip as junctions and "components." The sigma-quality-level metric for this situation typically leads to a very large number of opportunities for failure for a given computer chip; hence, a very high sigma-quality level is possible even when the defective rate per unit is high. Compare this situation with another situation in which only a very small number of components or steps are required for a process. The sigma-quality-level metric for this situation typically leads to a very low number of opportunities for failure; hence, a very low sigma-quality-level metric is possible even when the defective rate per unit is low.

- The sigma-quality-level metric can only be determined when there are specifications. Service/transactional applications typically do not have specifications as manufacturing does. When a sigma-quality level is forced on a service/transactional situation, this can lead to the fabrication of specifications and alterations of these "specifications" to "make the numbers look good."

Another Six Sigma metric that describes how well a process meets requirements is process capability. A six sigma–quality level process is said to translate to process capability index values for C_p and C_{pk} requirements of 2.0 and 1.5, respectively.

Unfortunately, there is much confusion with these values, even though the following basic equations for these metrics are simple:

$$C_p = \frac{\text{USL} - \text{LSL}}{6\sigma} \tag{5.3}$$

$$C_{pk} = \min\left(\frac{\text{USL} - \mu}{3\sigma}, \frac{\mu - \text{LSL}}{3\sigma}\right) \tag{5.4}$$

where USL is the upper specification limit, LSL is the lower specification limit, and σ is the standard deviation. Computer programs often will not even give the same answer for a given set of data. Some programs consider the standard deviation to be short term, while others consider standard deviation to be long term. There are many ways to estimate standard deviation. Breyfogle (1999) describes eight different approaches. Process capability indices are discussed in detail in Chapter 6.

Another metric is rolled throughput yield (RTY). Reworks within an operation make up what is termed the hidden factory. RTY measurements can give visibility to process steps that have high defect rates and/or rework needs. One way to find RTY is to first determine the yield for all process operations. Then, multiply these process operation yields together. A cumulative throughput yield up through a process step can be determined by multiplying the yield of the current step by the yields of previous steps.

RTY can be calculated from the number of defects per unit (DPU) using the relationship:

$$RTY = e^{-DPU} \tag{5.5}$$

To understand this relationship, consider that the probability of observing exactly x events in the Poisson situation is given by the Poisson probability density function (pdf):

$$P(X = x) = \frac{e^{-\lambda}\lambda^x}{x!} = \frac{e^{-np}(np)^x}{x!} \qquad x = 0, 1, 2, 3 \ldots \tag{5.6}$$

where e is a constant approximately equal to 2.71828, x is the number of occurrences, and λ can be equated to a sample size multiplied by the probability of occurrence (i.e., np). It then follows that

$$RTY = P(X = 0) = e^{-\lambda} = e^{-DPU} \tag{5.7}$$

It is best not to force a sigma-quality metric on the various groups and/or projects within an organization. It is most important to use the right metric for any given situation. However, the sigma-quality-level metric should be included, along with the other Six Sigma metrics, in all Six Sigma training. The positive, negative, and controversial aspects of each Six Sigma metric should be covered within the training so that organizations can more effectively communicate with their customers and suppliers. Often, customers and suppliers ask the wrong questions relative to Six Sigma and other metrics. When people understand the pluses and minuses of each metric, they can work with their customers and/or suppliers to direct their efforts toward the best metric for a given situation, rather than react to issues that result from mandated metrics that make no sense.

The training people receive in Six Sigma should lead them to the right metric for a given situation. As depicted in Figure 5.30, in addition to devising a business strategy, organizations wanting success with Six Sigma must be able to understand, select, and communicate Six Sigma metrics, including sigma-quality levels; C_p, C_{pk}, P_p, and P_{pk}; RTY; DPMO; cost of poor quality (COPQ); and "30,000-foot level" control charts (Breyfogle 2003).

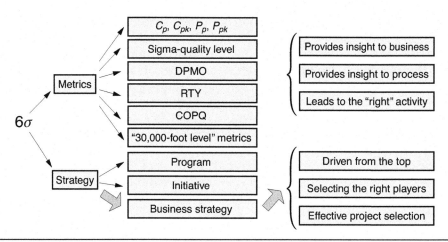

Figure 5.30   Six Sigma metrics and implementation strategy.

Care must be taken that the training an organization receives in Six Sigma metrics is not sugarcoated or avoided altogether. In addition to the careful selection of metrics, Six Sigma training should also address the effective use of statistical methodologies, providing insight into how one can best determine what truly is causing a problem.

The DMAIC Process

DMAIC is a data-driven quality strategy used to improve processes. It is an integral part of a Six Sigma initiative, but in general it can be implemented as a stand-alone quality improvement procedure or as part of other process improvement initiatives such as lean (which is discussed in the next section). DMAIC is an acronym for the five phases that make up the process:

1. Define the problem, improvement activity, opportunity for improvement, project goals, and customer (internal and external) requirements

2. Measure process performance

3. Analyze the process to determine root causes of variation, poor performance (defects)

4. Improve process performance by addressing and eliminating the root causes

5. Control the improved process and future process performance

The DMAIC process easily lends itself to the project approach to quality improvement encouraged and promoted by Juran. There are many tools used at each step of the process, most of which are described in this handbook. The reader is encouraged to consult additional resources for detailed discussion of the DMAIC process, Six Sigma quality initiatives, and the numerous tools used. See, for example, the ASQ website (http://www.asq.org); Britz and Emerling (2000); Hahn, Doganaksoy, and Stanard (2001); Hoerl (2001); Hoerl and Snee (2012); Snee and

Hoerl (2003, 2004); Montgomery (2013); and the numerous references within these sources.

Additional data-driven process improvement methods have been proposed since the inception of DMAIC. Anderson-Cook and Lu (2015) introduced a process called DMRCS (define, measure, reduce, combine, select), which is similar to the DMAIC process in that DMRCS is a structured approach for identifying and comparing alternative solutions for multi-objective problems. DMRCS is especially helpful as a decision-making tool. See additional details in Anderson-Cook (2017) and Anderson-Cook and Lu (2015).

Sustaining and Communicating Change

Many companies attempt to improve products with numerous small changes or tweaks to their current processes; however, changes frequently are not documented and the associated results not reported. Substantial results are rarely obtained with this half-hearted method of change. When employees in this type of corporate culture hear of a new initiative such as Six Sigma, they wonder what will be different.

In today's constantly changing marketplace, companies that are able to embrace change in a focused and proactive manner are leaders in their field. Companies that not only master the technical side of Six Sigma but also overcome the cultural challenges associated with change can realize significant bottom-line benefits.

Launching a Six Sigma business strategy is an excellent opportunity to assess current culture in an organization. Consider the following questions:

- How has your company historically dealt with change initiatives?

- Does your company often make changes that do not last?

- How effective are your project teams?

- Are you frequently focusing on the same problem?

- How do your employees attack problems and conduct their daily work?

- What is required within your company culture to make continual process improvement a lasting change?

- What will prevent your company from achieving success with Six Sigma?

By evaluating the key cultural drivers and restraints to embracing Six Sigma, organizations can develop plans that enhance the key drivers and mitigate the critical restraints.

A common key driver of sustaining Six Sigma change that is often overlooked is a communication plan. Company leaders usually implement Six Sigma because they possess a clear vision of what their company can achieve. Frequently, however, they do not realize the power behind effectively communicating this vision throughout the corporation. Executives need to get everyone engaged in and speaking the language of Six Sigma. A shared vision of how Six Sigma fits the strategic needs of the business should be created. A communication plan should be carefully considered and executed with enthusiasm. If successful, it will be your biggest ally in key stakeholder buy-in.

Implementing Six Sigma does not guarantee tangible benefits within an organization. However, when Six Sigma is implemented wisely as a business strategy accompanied by effective metrics, as illustrated in Figure 5.30, organizations can yield significant bottom-line benefits. Through the wise implementation of Six Sigma, the successes of individual projects can build on each other, gaining the sustained attention of executive management and resulting in a corporate culture change from a reactive or firefighting environment to a learning organization.

LEAN TOOLS

Define, describe, and apply the following lean tools:

1. 5S
2. Value-stream mapping
3. Kanban
4. Visual control
5. 8 Wastes
6. Standardized work
7. Takt time
8. Single minute exchange of die (SMED)
9. Overall equipment effectiveness (OEE)
(Evaluate)

Body of Knowledge V.D

Achieving what is known as a lean enterprise requires a change in attitudes, procedures, processes, and systems. It is necessary to "zoom out" and look at the flow of information, knowledge, and material throughout the organization. In any organization there are multiple paths through which products, documents, and ideas flow.

The traditional manufacturing strategy is to study the marketplace to obtain a forecast of sales of various products. This forecast is used as a basis for orders that are issued to suppliers and to departments responsible for fabrication and assembly. This is referred to as a push system. One major problem with this strategy is that if the forecast is imperfect, products are produced that are not wanted by customers and/or products that customers want are not available. A second major problem with the forecast-based strategy is the increasing expectation of customers for exactly the product they want and exactly when they want it. These two problems have led to a response by manufacturers that is sometimes called mass customization. As illustrated by the automotive industry, a customer order of a vehicle with choices among dozens of options with perhaps hundreds of possible combinations cannot be accurately forecasted. Instead, the customer order initiates the authorization to build the product. This is referred to as a pull system because the pull of the customer instead of the push of the forecast activates the system.

Rather than producing batches of identical products, a pull-oriented organization produces a mix of products with the mix of features that customers order. In the ideal pull system, the receipt of the customer order initiates orders for the component parts to be delivered to the assembly line at scheduled times. The mixture of features of the components as they continuously flow to and through the line results in exactly the product the customer needs. Making this happen in a reasonable amount of time would have been unthinkable only a few years ago.

When a pull system is in a state of perfection, each activity moves a component through the value stream so that it arrives at the next activity at the time it is needed. Achieving and maintaining this may require a great deal of flexibility in allocating resources to various activities. Cross-training of personnel is essential. The resulting flexibility and system nimbleness permits reduction of WIP.

Kaizen, which was discussed in the "Kaizen" section of this chapter, is a term often associated with, but not limited to, lean and quality principles. Its focus is on continuous improvement of functions within an organization, and it places a heavy emphasis on employee involvement. The goals of kaizen include the elimination of waste (defined as activities that add cost but do not add value), just-in-time delivery, production load leveling of amount and types, standardized work, paced moving lines, right-sized equipment, and others. Some of these goals are accomplished with lean tools such as muda (a Japanese word meaning wastefulness and a process associated with the removal of waste). Muda is discussed in the "8 Wastes" section of this chapter. Takt time is included in the "Takt Time" section, which is focused on two methods of evaluation: cycle time and takt time.

5S

5S is viewed as both an element of visual control and a methodology to help develop a better work environment, both physically and mentally. 5S is based on five Japanese words all starting with the letter *s*: *seiri, seiton, seiso, seiketsu,* and *shitsuke*. In English, these words can be translated to sort, straighten, shine, standardize, and sustain. The 5S methodology helps improve the layout of a space based on efficiency and effectiveness. Each of these elements helps improve the work area. The purpose of sorting is to eliminate all unnecessary items and keep only what is required. Straightening is done to arrange the necessary items and to have a designated place for everything; this makes the work area more efficient because less time is required to search for tools, documents, equipment, and so on. Shine means to keep the work area clean. Standardizing enforces work to be done in a consistent manner and may include implementing regular cleaning and maintenance schedules. This element makes it easy to determine when problems occur. Finally, similar to many improvement methodologies, the goal of sustain is to maintain all of these elements and make 5S a way of life in the work area. As new equipment, new products, or new employees join the work area, 5S must adapt to remain effective (ReVelle 2004).

ReVelle (2004) lists several benefits gained by implementing 5S:

- Improved safety

- Higher equipment availability

- Lower defect rates

- Reduced costs

- Increased production agility and flexibility

- Improved employee morale

- Better asset utilization

- Enhanced enterprise image to customers, suppliers, employees, and management

Van Patten (2006) emphasizes that 5S is not simply "cleaning up a shop floor." 5S can provide many benefits, one of which includes cleaning. 5S should change the way the workforce thinks about their work area and can therefore provide a foundation for all future improvement. "Within a culture of 5S, employees are expected to be organized, neat, clean, standardized, and disciplined in everything they do" (Van Patten 2006).

Value Stream Mapping

A *value stream map* (VSM) is similar to a flowchart but includes additional information about various activities that occur at each step of the process. Value stream mapping is a powerful tool based on the principles of lean and is used to identify opportunities for improvement of a process and track performance. Current-state VSMs provide information about the process as it is currently defined. Future-state

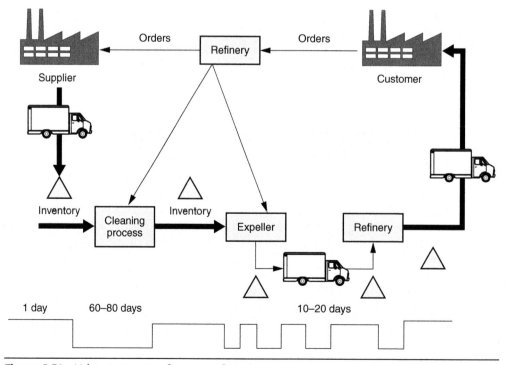

Figure 5.31 Value stream map for a manufacturing process.

VSMs provide information about the process as it could look once it has been redefined. Figure 5.31 displays a generic VSM for a manufacturing process. Detailed examples can be found in Manos (2006) and Montgomery (2013).

The process of applying lean thinking to such a path can be divided into the following steps:

1. Produce a VSM (also referred to as a value chain diagram). Rother and Shook (1999) describe this diagram in detail. It has boxes labeled with each step in the process. Information about timing and inventory is provided near each process box. Figure 5.32 shows an example of a VSM. Some symbols used on VSMs include the following:

△ = inventory—originally a tombstone shape indicating dead material.

目 = supermarket where employees can pick needed parts. Supermarkets are usually replenished by stockroom staff.

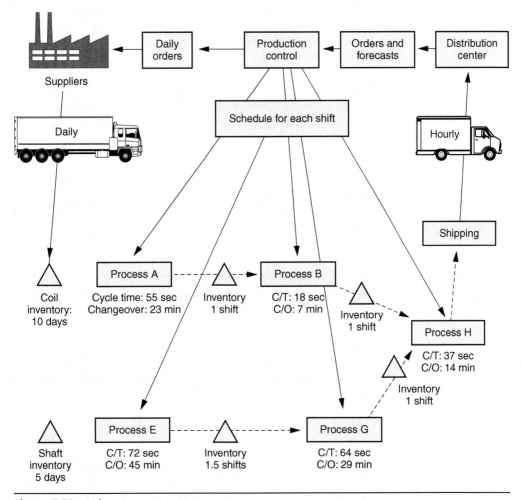

Figure 5.32 Value stream map.

$\curlyvee$ = kanban post where cards or other visual signals are displayed.

$\infty\frown$ = visual signal used to make stocking decisions.

$\underset{\text{275 sec.}}{\rule{0pt}{0pt}}\sqcap\underset{\text{315 sec.}}{\rule{0pt}{0pt}}\sqcap$ = graph of value-added versus non-value-added times.

2. Analyze all inventory notations with an eye toward reduction or elimination. Inventory tends to increase costs because:

   a. Storage space may be expensive (rubber awaiting use in a tire factory is stored at 120°F; wood inventory may need to have humidity control).

   b. Quality may deteriorate (rust, spoilage, etc.).

   c. Design changes may be delayed as they work their way through the inventory.

   d. Money invested in inventory could be used more productively elsewhere.

   e. Quality problems that are not detected until a later stage in the process will be more expensive to correct if an inventory of defective products has accumulated.

   One company refers to its racks of safety stock as the "wall of shame."

3. Analyze the entire value stream for unneeded steps. These steps are called non-value-added activities, as discussed in the "Value Stream Mapping" section of this chapter.

4. Determine how the flow is driven. Strive to move toward value streams in which production decisions are based on the pull of customer demand. In a process where pull-based flow has reached perfection, a customer order for an item would trigger the production of all the component parts for that item. These components would arrive, be assembled, and be delivered in a time interval that would satisfy the customer. In many situations, this ideal has not been reached and the customer order will be filled from finished goods inventory. The order will, however, trigger activities back through the value chain that produce a replacement part in finished goods inventory before it is needed by a customer.

5. Extend the VSM upstream into suppliers' plants. New challenges occur regarding compatibility of communication systems. The flows of information, material, knowledge, and money are all potential targets for lean improvements.

When beginning the process, pick a narrow focus—do not try to boil the ocean, as the saying goes.

Kanban

Kanban is a pull-based inventory control system that is used in lean manufacturing and just-in-time initiatives. A kanban system can be used to simplify and improve resupply procedures for inventory. The idea of the kanban system is to incorporate organization by setting visual and sometimes online queues that provide a more efficient and cost-effective method for keeping track of and restocking inventory.

While kanban systems can be arranged in different ways, most kanban systems use a two-bin arrangement. In a typical two-bin kanban arrangement, when the first bin is emptied, the user uses the second bin to restock the first bin. Then the user signals resupply personnel to restock the second bin and continues to periodically check the bins. The indication that inventory is needed is the "pull" part of the system: inventory is restocked only when needed. The signal for needed inventory is usually visual and may be placement of a card that came with the bin, turning on a light, or just displaying the empty bin. The resupply employee gathers the information on supplies needed and replenishes the bins. Sometimes the bins are resupplied from a stockroom, although it is often from a closer supply point, sometimes referred to as the supermarket. In some cases, bins are replenished directly by an outside vendor. The entire string of events occurs routinely, often with no paperwork. The result is smoother flow and less inventory.

An example of a kanban system from a manufacturing laboratory is shown in Figure 5.33. As seen in the top shelf of Figure 5.33, the angled bins are the first bin in the two-bin kanban system, and the second bins are located behind them.

In some of the newer kanban systems, the process is integrated into the Enterprise Resource Planning (ERP) system so that the replenishment of supplies can be done online and in a more seamless manner. Automated material

Figure 5.33   Example of a kanban system.

Source: Photo taken in the Toyota Production Systems Laboratory in the Industrial and Systems Engineering Department, Rochester Institute of Technology.

handling systems or conveyors can also be used to deliver materials throughout an organization.

Visual Control

In a *visual factory*, locations for tools, inventory, safety equipment, and so on, are clearly marked and identified. Signs and floor paint designate traffic patterns and storage locations. Information needed by personnel to perform their functions is readily available. Monitors display current information about the activity. An example of visual control in a manufacturing laboratory is shown in Figure 5.34. In this system, a red light can be turned on to signify that a restock is required. In addition, the digital displays (not in the photo) indicate the quantity of the items. For example, in bin 74, the display would read that there are three cereal boxes remaining.

8 Wastes

Some functions perform activities that do not change the form or function of the product or service. The customer is not willing to pay for these activities. These

Figure 5.34 Example of visual control.

Source: Photo taken in the Toyota Production Systems Laboratory in the Industrial and Systems Engineering Department, Rochester Institute of Technology.

activities are labeled non-value-added. A classic example is rework. The customer expects to pay for the printing of a document, for instance, but does not want to pay for corrections that are needed because of supplier error. A key step in making an organization leaner is the detection and elimination of non-value-added activities.

In searching for non-value-added activities, the operative guideline should be "question everything." Steps that are assumed to be necessary are often rife with opportunities for improvement. Team members not associated with a process will often provide a fresh eye and ask the impertinent questions.

Some authors list seven or eight categories of waste, or *muda* as it is referred to in some sources. These lists usually include overproduction, excess motion, waiting, inventory, excess movement of material, defect correction, excess processing, and lost creativity. The following paragraphs examine the causes and results of each of these wastes.

Overproduction is defined as making more than is needed or making it earlier or faster than is needed by the next process. The principal symptom of overproduction is excess WIP. Companies adopt overproduction for various reasons, including long setup times, unbalanced workload, and a just-in-case philosophy. One company maintains a six-month supply of a particular small part because the machine that produces it is unreliable. In some cases, accounting methods have dictated that machines overproduce to amortize their capital costs. All WIP should be continuously scrutinized for possible reduction or elimination.

Excess motion can be caused by poor workplace layout, including awkward positioning of supplies and equipment. This often results in ergonomic problems, time wasted searching for or moving supplies or equipment, and reduced quality levels. Kaizen events, discussed in the "Kaizen" section of this chapter, have been effectively used to focus a small, short-term team on improvements in a particular work area. The team must include personnel with experience at the positions involved as well as those with similar functions elsewhere. In addition, it is essential to include people with the authority to make decisions. Such teams have made startling changes in two to five days of intense activity.

Waiting typically is caused by such events as delayed shipments, long setup time, or missing people. This results in a waste of resources and, perhaps more importantly, demoralization of personnel. Setup time reduction efforts and TPM are partial answers to this problem. Cross-training of personnel so that they can be effectively moved to other positions is also helpful in some cases. Most important, of course, is carefully laid and executed scheduling.

Inventory is wasteful when inventories of raw materials, finished goods, or WIP are maintained; costs are incurred for environmental control, record keeping, storage and retrieval, and so on. These functions add no value for the customer. Of course, some inventory may be necessary; however, if a competitor finds ways to reduce costs by reducing inventory, business may be lost. One of the most tempting times to let inventory levels rise is when a business cycle is in the economic recovery phase. Instead of increasing inventories based on forecasts, the proper strategy is to synchronize production to increase with actual demand. Similarly, production or administrative functions that use more space or other resources than necessary increase costs without adding value. The overused analogy of the sea of inventory shown in Figure 5.35 illustrates how excess inventory makes it

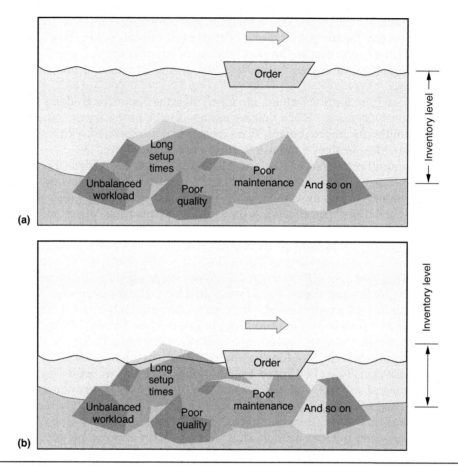

Figure 5.35   A sea of inventory often hides unresolved problems.

possible to avoid solving other problems. As the level of inventory is lowered, some problems will rear their ugly heads and need to be solved before further progress is possible.

There are various methods for sorting inventory. Toyota created the *heijunka box* tool, which is a visual scheduling tool used to improve the flow of production. Figure 5.36 provides an example of a typical heijunka box. The rows in the box represent product or part numbers (in this case, part number), and the columns (slots) represent the material and information flow timing (Lean Enterprise Institute, "Heijunka Box," https://www.lean.org/lexicon/heijunka-box). The vertical columns should be organized into equally spaced time intervals and include cards that describe the material location and quantity to obtain from a kanban system.

Excess movement of material, as indicated by large conveyor systems, huge fleets of forklifts, and so on, makes production more costly and complex, often reducing quality through handling and storing. Poor plant layout is usually to blame. Plants with function-oriented departments (such as all lathes together and all presses together) require excessive material movement. A better plan is to gather together equipment that is used for one product or product family. This may mean having a manufacturing cell contain several types of equipment requiring personnel with

Figure 5.36 Example of a heijunka box.

Source: Photo taken in the Toyota Production Systems Laboratory in the Industrial and Systems Engineering Department, Rochester Institute of Technology.

multiple skills. Many companies have had success with cells that form a C shape (as shown in Figure 5.37) because they can be staffed in several ways. If demand for the cell's output is high, six people could be assigned there, one per machine. If demand is very low, one person could move from machine to machine producing parts one at a time.

Defect correction is non-value-added because the effort required to fix the defective part is wasted. Typical causes of defects are poor equipment maintenance,

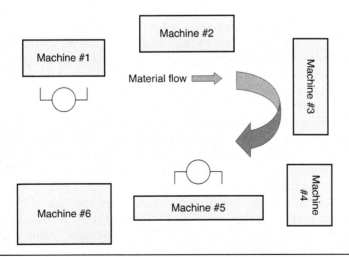

Figure 5.37 C-shaped manufacturing cell.

poor quality system, poor training and/or work instructions, and poor product design. Lean thinking demands a vigorous look at these and other causes to continually reduce defect levels.

Excess processing is often difficult to recognize. Sometimes entire steps in the value chain are non-value-added. A steel stamping operation produces a large volume of parts before they are scheduled for painting, which necessitates the practice of dipping parts in an oil solution to prevent rust as they wait to be painted. As the paint schedule permits, the parts are degreased and painted. The customer is unwilling to pay for the dip/degrease activities because they do not enhance the product. The best solution in this case is to schedule the pre-paint activities so that the parts are painted immediately upon production. This solution may require smaller batch sizes and improved communication procedures, among other things. The purpose of the grinding step that often follows a welding operation is to remove some of the weld imperfections. Improving the welding process may reduce or eliminate the need for grinding. In this case, the unnecessary grinding would be classified as excessive processing. Excessive processing can occur in the office as well as on the plant floor. Information from customer purchase orders is sometimes entered into a database and the order itself is filed as a backup hard copy to resolve any later disagreements. One company revealed that the hard copies, although they are occasionally pulled from files and initialed, stamped, stapled, and so on, really serve no useful purpose. The company now discards the purchase order once the information has been entered. The processes of filing, storing, and maintaining these records required one person performing non-value-added activity for half the time.

Lost creativity is perhaps the most unfortunate waste. Most manufacturing employees have ideas that would improve processes if implemented. Standard organizational structures sometimes seem designed to suppress such ideas. Union/management divides seem almost impossible to bridge. Lean thinking recognizes the need to involve employees in teams that welcome and reward their input. These teams must be empowered to make changes in an atmosphere that accepts mistakes as learning experiences. The resulting improved morale and reduced personnel turnover impact the bottom line in ways that no accountant has calculated.

There are, of course, gray areas where the line between valued-added and non-value-added may not be obvious. One such area is inspection and testing. A process may be so incapable that its output needs to be inspected to prevent defective parts from entering downstream processes. It could be argued that this inspection is a value-added activity because the customer does not want defective products. The obvious solution is to work on the process, making it capable and rendering the inspection activity unnecessary. Most authorities would agree that this inspection is non-value-added. On the other hand, a gas furnace manufacturer must fire test every furnace to comply with Canadian Standards Association (CSA) requirements. Customers are willing to pay for the CSA listing, so this test step is a value-added activity.

Studies have shown that an overwhelming percentage of lead time is non-value-added, much of it spent waiting for the next step. Yet over the years, efforts to decrease lead time often have focused on accelerating value-added functions rather than reducing or eliminating non-value-added functions.

Standardized Work

The lean tool called *standard work* states that each activity should be performed the same way every time. The application of this principle can help reduce variation in cycle time, can produce a better, more consistent product or service, and can also simplify downstream activities. The best procedure is to have the people involved with the activity reach a consensus regarding the standard method and agree to use it. The agreed-upon method should be documented and readily available to all involved. Charts and posters in the work area are often used to reinforce the method. These documents must be updated as continuous improvements are made.

An example of a standard work chart is shown in Figure 5.38. This standard work chart is a printed document that is hung above workstation 5 in a skateboard production line. Workstation 5 is the station in the production line where the wheels are added to the skateboard. The standard work chart provides a sequence of steps for the operator at the station to follow. The pictures provide additional clarity for the operator.

Takt Time

Cycle time and takt time are metrics associated with the evaluation of a process. *Cycle time*, displayed below each process in Figure 5.32, is defined as the amount of time required to complete the named activity for one product or service. If the cycle time is variable, it is useful to show a range and average on the VSM.

Reducing variation in cycle time makes a system more predictable. Sometimes the cycle time variation can be reduced by using the cycle times of sub-activities instead. For example, suppose the activity consists of using a word processor to modify a standard bid form. Sub-activities might include inserting client information, listing proposed budget, detailing alternatives, and so on. The total time to

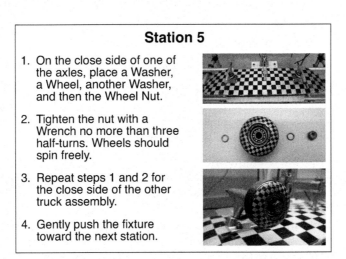

Figure 5.38 An example of a standard work chart for a skateboard assembly production line.

Source: Photo taken in the Toyota Production Systems Laboratory in the Industrial and Systems Engineering Department, Rochester Institute of Technology.

prepare the bid might vary a great deal, while the time required to accomplish each sub-activity should show less variation. The activities performed should be continually studied to eliminate non-value-added components and find better and faster ways to complete the value-added components.

Some techniques that have been successfully applied to accomplish these goals are kaizen methods, kaizen blitz, and rapid continuous improvement (RCI). The usual procedure is to form a small team that is given a process to improve and a limited time frame, often only a few days. The team should include the people who perform the targeted activity, outsiders who can provide a fresh perspective, and people who are authorized to approve changes.

The team observes the process and raises questions about its various parts. Typical questions might include:

- Why is that stored there? Is there a better place to put it?

- Why do things in that order?

- Would a different table height work better?

- Could your supplier (internal or external) provide a better service? Does your supplier know what you need?

- Are you providing your customer, whether internal or external, with the best possible services?

- Do you know what your customer needs?

- Should parts of this activity be performed by the customer or the supplier?

- Are there steps that can be eliminated?

- Is there enough light, fresh air, and so on, to do the job efficiently?

- Would another tool, software package, or other material be more helpful?

- Are tools conveniently and consistently stored?

- Can the distance the person and/or product moves be reduced?

- Should this activity be moved closer to the supplier or customer?

- How many of these items should be kept on hand?

- Would it help to do this activity in less space?

In other words, the team questions everything about the process and its environment. Kaizen activity usually results in making several small improvements. In many situations, the team actually implements a change and studies the result before making a recommendation.

Cycle time must not be confused with takt time. *Takt time* is determined by customer demand. Its formula is time available divided by units required. For example, if 284 units are to be produced in a shift consisting of 27,000 seconds, then takt time = $27{,}000 \div 284 \cong 95$ seconds. That is, the system must average one unit every 95 seconds. To meet this demand rate, the cycle time for each process must be less than 95 seconds. The basic relationship between cycle time and takt time is that cycle time is less than or equal to takt time. If cycle time exceeds takt time, more than one person is needed. To approximate the number of people required, use the following formula: cycle time divided by takt time.

Takt time is recalculated whenever the production schedule is changed. In the previous example, if 312 units are scheduled, the takt time is reduced to 87 seconds. Adjustments to cycle times, possible by adding people or equipment, may be necessary.

Single Minute Exchange of Die (SMED)

Lean thinking is built on timely satisfaction of customer demand, which means there must be a system for quickly responding to changes in customer requirements. In metal-forming industries, it was common practice to produce thousands of parts of a particular type before changing the machine's dies and producing thousands of another part. This often produced vast inventories of WIP and the associated waste. These procedures were justified because changing machine dies took several hours. In a process value chain map of a given process, the time required to change over from one part to another is displayed below. The system used to reduce changeover time and improve timely response to demand is called *single minute exchange of dies* (SMED). Shigeo Shingo is given credit for developing the SMED concept and using it in the Toyota Production System. The goal is to reduce the time from the last good part of one type to the first good part of the successive run. The initial application of SMED often requires considerable resources in special staging tables and die storage areas, among others. Activities done while the machine is down are referred to as internal activities versus the external activities performed in preparation for or follow-up to the die change. Shingo's method is to move as many activities from internal to external as possible. A useful technique is to make a video recording of a typical changeover and have involved personnel use it to identify internal activities that can be converted to external activities. Positioning correct tooling, equipment, and manpower should all be done in external time. Activities that don't involve die changes also need to be nimble in their response to changing customer requirements. This can be achieved through analysis of the changeover process.

As an example, consider the application of SMED to a photography operation. The current procedure for changing cameras requires several steps:

1. Shoot last good picture with camera A.
2. Remove camera A and its power supply and place in storage cupboard.
3. Remove type A tripod.
4. Remove type A lighting and reflectors.
5. Install type B lighting and reflectors.
6. Install type B tripod. Measure distance to subject with tape measure.
7. Locate camera B in cupboard and install it and its power supply.
8. Shoot first good picture with camera B.

A team working to reduce changeover time designed a fitting so both cameras could use the same tripod. Purchasing extra cables made it possible to avoid moving power supplies. More flexible lighting reflectors were designed so one set would work with both cameras. Taped marks on the floor now show where to locate tripod feet to avoid the necessity of using a tape measure. Another alternative would be to obtain a more versatile camera that would not need to be changed.

Another potential application of SMED is in an assembly line of a factory. An assembly department that produced three different models spent considerable time converting the assembly line from one model to another. They found that three different assembly lines worked best for them. They now switch models by walking across the room. Opportunities to apply SMED concepts abound in many businesses and industries. Recognizing and developing these opportunities depend on the creativity and perseverance of the people involved.

Overall Equipment Effectiveness (OEE)

OEE is a rate metric that is calculated to determine how well a manufacturing unit, for example a machine, is operating when compared against its full potential in terms of operating time, performance, and quality performance. It covers three questions:

1. Is the equipment running?

2. If the equipment is running, is it running at its ideal speed?

3. How many of the parts produced are good?

The term OEE stands for "Overall Equipment Effectiveness." Seiichi Nakajima of the Japan Institute of Plant Maintenance (JIPM) is attributed to have coined the term. He was also the pioneer behind TPM (Total Productive Maintenance) (Nakajima 1988, 1989). OEE is calculated as a product of Availability, Performance and Quality, each of which is calculated as a rate.

$$\text{OEE} = \text{Availability} \times \text{Performance} \times \text{Quality} \qquad (5.8)$$

Nakajima noted that there are "six big losses" in any manufacturing environment that can impact the equipment effectiveness. The six losses and their relationship to OEE are shown in Table 5.6.

Availability: How long is the equipment available for running?

Availability is measured as the ratio of operation time to loading time. The operation time is the actual time the equipment is available for running, and loading time is the scheduled/planned production time for the equipment. Therefore, Availability is the ratio of actual versus potential run time for the equipment. The operation time is loading time minus all the unplanned downtimes. The loading time does not include the planned downtime such as breaks or scheduled maintenance, etc. For example, for an 8-hour day (without including lunch), there are 480 minutes. Subtracting the scheduled downtime for two breaks of 10 minutes each, the loading time can be calculated as 460 minutes. If there were down time events such as a machine breakdown of 20 minutes, setup time of 20 minutes, and adjustment time of 20 minutes, the operation time can be calculated as 400 minutes.

Table 5.6 The six big losses

#	Loss	Description	Goal	OEE Category
1	Breakdown losses	Sporadic breakdowns due to equipment failure including tool failure and machine failure. Preventive and predictive maintenance activities are very useful in tackling breakdown losses.	Zero breakdown losses	Down time losses (impacting **Availability**)
2	Setup and adjustment	Loss of time from changing over to a new job or from shortage of material/labor or from the warm-up time needed for the machine. The set-up times can be minimized through SMED (Single Minute Exchange of Die) activities.	Minimize setup and adjustment	
3	Idling and minor stoppages	Minor stoppages can occur when production is interrupted by a simple malfunction such as part blockage or jam in the chute. It may also be due to sensor failures that stops the machine. Since these are minor stoppages, these are often ignored.	Zero idling and minor stoppages	Speed losses (impacting **Performance)**
4	Reduced speed	Every machine is designed to run at an ideal speed. Due to various conditions such as wear and tear or mechanical problems or fear of "abusing" the equipment or inefficient manpower, the equipment is run at a lower speed. The goal is to eliminate the gap between the ideal speed and actual speed.	Zero losses from reduced speed	
5	Process defects	This includes all quality defects and reworks. These losses are due to malfunctioning equipment or material or operator issues.	Zero process defects	Defect Losses (impacting **Quality**)
6	Reduced yield	This is also referred to as startup losses. This loss is specifically during machine startup until stable product is achieved. This includes scrap and reworks incurred during the startup time.	Minimize losses from reduced yield	

$$\text{Availability} = (\text{Operation Time} / \text{Loading Time}) \times 100$$
$$= ((\text{Loading Time} - \text{Unplanned Downtime})/\text{Loading Time}) \times 100$$
$$= ((460 - (20 + 20 + 20))/460) \times 100$$
$$= 87\%$$

Performance: How fast is the equipment running?

Performance is measured as the product of the operating speed rate and the net operating rate. Operating speed rate is the ratio of the ideal cycle time to the actual cycle time. This takes into account the ideal speed of the equipment. The net operating rate is measured as the ratio of actual processing time to the operation time. Here the actual processing time includes the time taken to produce both good parts and bad parts. For example, let's assume that the ideal cycle time is 0.5 minutes per part, and the actual cycle time was 0.8 minutes per part. Additionally, let's assume that 350 good parts and 50 bad parts were produced. The Performance can be calculated as follows:

Operating Speed Rate = Ideal Cycle Time / Actual Cycle Time
Net Operating Rate = Actual Processing Time / Operation Time
            = (Processed Parts x Actual Cycle Time) / Operation Time

Performance = (Operating Speed Rate x Net Operating Rate) x 100
      = ((Total Processed Parts x Actual Cycle Time) / Operation Time x Ideal Cycle Time / Actual Cycle Time) x 100
      = ((Total Processed Parts x Ideal Cycle Time) / Operation Time) x 100
      = ((400 parts x 0.5 minutes) / 400 minutes) x 100
      = 50%

Quality: Are the parts produced good?

Quality is measured as the ratio of good parts produced to the total parts produced. In the example above, if 400 total parts were produced and 350 of them were good, then the quality rate can be calculated as follows:

Quality = (Good Parts produced / Total Processed Parts) x 100
    = (350/400) x 100
    = 87.5%

OEE: Overall Equipment Effectiveness

The various aspects of OEE are depicted in Figure 5.39. It can be seen that OEE is a measure of the actual value-added time spent in making good parts.
Putting it all together, the OEE is calculated as follows:

OEE = Availability x Performance x Quality
  = 87% x 50% x 87.5%
  = 38.1%

It can be seen from the example that even though the production team may assume that the machine is running 87% of the time with 87.5% quality rate, the overall equipment effectiveness is quite low. A lower OEE means that there is a lot of untapped potential still remaining. In a utopian world, if a machine is working 100% at 100% efficiency with 0 rejects, it will have an OEE of 100%. Nakajima

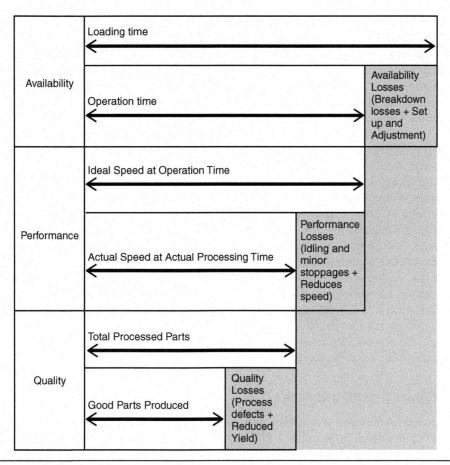

Figure 5.39 Elements of OEE

proposed that the ideal OEE is ≥ 85%. He noted that based on experience, the ideal conditions are:

Availability → greater than 90%
Performance efficiency → greater than 95%
Rate of quality products → greater than 99%

Therefore, the ideal OEE is:

0.90 x 0.95 x 0.99 x 100 → ≥ 85%

Although OEE presents one single metric, the production team must be aware of how the three factors are contributing for the calculation of the metric. OEE provides an impetus for continuous learning and continuous improvement.

Poka-Yoke

A *poka-yoke* device is designed to prevent errors. Suppose several people placed documents in four separate trays, depending on the type of document. A kaizen team discovered that a person sorts the trays at the end of the day because about 5% of the documents are in the wrong tray, even though signs clearly state document type. The team recommended printing the documents on different colored paper and printing the signs on the corresponding paper color. This reduced the percentage of misplaced documents to 0.7% and made the sorting job much easier. Figure 5.40 illustrates a poka-yoke device used to ensure that round and square tubing items are placed in the correct containers.

The technique ensures that the round and square parts are placed in the correct containers. Neither part will fit through the hole in the top of the incorrect container.

Poka-yoke methods are helpful in both reducing the occurrence of rare events and serving as a preventive action tool. In one example, a manufacturer found that about 1 in 2000 of its assemblies shipped was missing 1 of its 165 components. A poka-yoke technique was used to eliminate this defect. The manufacturer now barcodes each component and scans serial number and component bar codes as each component is added to the assembly. The software is written so that the printer at the shipping department will not print a shipping label if any component is missing. Another example of poka-yoke involves the selection of the correct part from several bins with similar contents. As the product reaches the workstation, its barcode is read. Light beams crisscross the front of the bins. If the operator reaches into the wrong bin, as determined from the bar code, the conveyor stops until appropriate corrections have been made.

Total Productive Maintenance

For lean systems to work, all equipment must be ready to quickly respond to customer needs. This requires a system that foresees maintenance needs and takes appropriate action. A *total productive maintenance* (TPM) system uses historical data, manufacturer's recommendations, reports by alert operators, diagnostic tests, and other techniques to schedule maintenance activity so that machine downtime can be minimized. TPM goes beyond keeping everything running, however. A TPM system includes continuous improvement initiatives as it seeks more effective and more efficient ways to predict and diagnose problems.

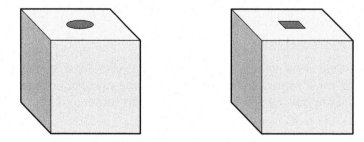

The technique ensures that the round and square parts are placed in the correct containers. Neither part will fit through the hole in the top of the incorrect container.

Figure 5.40 A poka-yoke technique example.

CORRECTIVE ACTION

> Identify, describe, and apply elements of
> the corrective action process, including
> problem identification, failure analysis, root
> cause analysis, 5 Whys, problem correction,
> recurrence control, and verification of
> effectiveness. (Evaluate)
>
> **Body of Knowledge V.E**

Corrective and preventive actions often are best taken using a problem-solving method. Problem-solving methods (also called the scientific method) have many variations, depending, to some extent, on the use; however, they are all similar. The seven phases of corrective action are shown in Figure 5.41, which also shows the relationship to the PDSA cycle. The phases are integrated in that they are all dependent on the previous phase. Continuous improvement is the objective, and these phases are the framework to achieving that objective.

Another method, described by Duffy (2014), is called the eight disciplines (8D) model. The 8D model is a problem-solving approach typically employed by quality engineers for establishing permanent corrective action. The disciplines as stated in Duffy (2014) are as follows:

- D0: Plan

  - Plan for solving the problem

  - Determine the prerequisites

  - Identify and prioritize opportunities for improvement

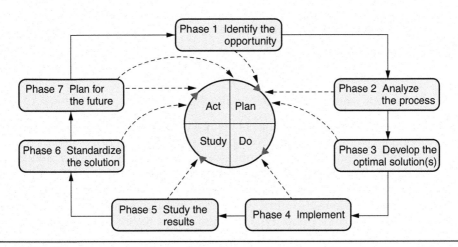

Figure 5.41 The seven phases of corrective action.

- D1: Use a team
  - Establish a team of people
  - Team members should have product and process knowledge
- D2: Define and describe the problem
  - Specify the problem by identifying it in quantifiable terms
  - Answer the questions of who, what, where, when, why, how, and how many (5W2H) for the problem
- D3: Develop interim containment plan
  - Implement and verify interim actions
  - Define and implement containment actions to isolate the problem from any customer
- D4: Determine, identify, and verify root causes and escape points
  - Identify all applicable causes that could explain why the problem occurred
  - Identify why the problem was not noticed at the time it occurred
  - Cause and effect diagrams can be used to map causes against the problem identified
- D5: Choose and verify permanent corrections (PCs) for problem/nonconformity
  - Through pre-production programs, quantitatively confirm that the selected correction will resolve the problem for the customer
- D6: Implement and validate corrective actions
  - Define and implement the best corrective actions
- D7: Take preventive measures
  - Modify the management systems, operation systems, practices, and procedures to prevent recurrence of this and all similar problems
- D8: Congratulate your team
  - Recognize the collective efforts of the team
  - The team needs to be formally thanked by the organization

Continuous improvement means not being satisfied with merely doing a good job or having a good process but striving to improve that job or process. It is accomplished by incorporating process measurement and team problem solving into all work activities. TQM tools and techniques are used to improve quality, delivery, and cost. All must continuously strive for excellence by reducing complexity, variation, and out-of-control processes. Lessons learned in problem solving, communications, and group dynamics, as well as technical know-how, must be transferred to appropriate activities within the organization.

The most common elements of the corrective action process are problem identification, failure and root cause analysis, problem correction, recurrence control, and verification of effectiveness. Each of these items is described in the subsequent subsections.

Problem Identification

The objective of the planning phase is to identify and prioritize opportunities for improvement, which is done by the team. If the team is a natural work group or one where members already work together, then this part is complete. If the problem is of a multifunctional nature, then the team should be selected and directed by the quality council to address the improvement of a specific process. The team leader is then selected and becomes the owner of the process improvement. Goals and milestones are established. If the improvement strategy is the repair or refinement of an existing process, an individual, rather than a team, may be assigned.

Defining the problem involves identification and scope. Problem identification answers the questions of who, what, where, when, and why, but specifically drives at the question, "What are the problems?" The answer leads to those problems that have the greatest potential for improvement and have the greatest need for solution. Problems can be identified from a variety of inputs, such as:

- Pareto analysis of repetitive external alarm signals, such as field failures, complaints, returns, and others

- Pareto analysis of repetitive internal alarm signals (e.g., scrap, rework, sorting, and the 100% test)

- Proposals from key insiders (managers, supervisors, professionals, and union stewards)

- Proposals from suggestion schemes

- Field study of users' needs

- Data on performance of competitors (from users and from laboratory tests)

- Comments of key people outside the organization (customers, suppliers, journalists, and critics)

- Findings and comments of government regulators and independent laboratories

- Customer surveys

- Employee surveys

- Brainstorming by work groups, for example, through fishbone diagrams

Problems identified provide opportunities for improvement. For a condition to qualify as a problem, it must meet the following three criteria:

1. Variable performance from an established standard

2. Deviation from the perception and the facts

3. The cause is unknown; if the cause is known, there is no problem

Identifying problems for improvement is not difficult, as there often are many more than can be analyzed. The quality council or work group must prioritize them using the following selection criteria:

1. Is the problem important and not superficial? Why?

2. Will problem solution contribute to the attainment of goals?

3. Can the problem be defined clearly using objective measures?

In selecting its initial improvement opportunity, a work group should find one that gives the maximum benefit for the minimum amount of effort. Problem identification should include scope. Failure in problem solving is frequently caused by poor definition of the problem. A problem well stated is half solved. Criteria for a good problem statement are as follows:

- It clearly describes the problem as it currently exists and is easily understood

- It states the effect: what is wrong, when it happens, and where it is occurring, not why it is wrong or who is responsible

- It focuses on what is known, what is unknown, and what needs to be done

- It uses facts and is free of judgment

- It emphasizes the impact on the customer

An example of a well-written problem statement is the following:

As a result of a customer satisfaction survey, a sample of 150 billing invoices showed that 18 had errors that required one hour to correct.

This example statement describes the current state. Alternately, the desired state may be described, such as "Reduce billing errors by 75%."

In addition to the problem statement, this phase requires a comprehensive charter for the team. The charter specifies the following:

1. Authority. Who authorized the team?

2. Objective and scope. What are the expected outputs and specific areas to be improved?

3. Composition. Who are the team members and process and subprocess owners?

4. Direction and control. What are the guidelines for the internal operation of the team?

5. General. What are the methods to be used, the resources, and the specific milestones?

Failure and Root Cause Analysis

After problem identification, if possible, the team should implement and verify interim actions. Containment actions can be used to isolate the problem from any customer. After containment is established, it is critical to understand the process and how it is currently performed. Key activities are to define process boundaries, outputs and customers, inputs and suppliers, and process flow; determine levels of customer satisfaction and measurements needed; gather data; and identify root causes. Identification of why the problem was not noticed at the time it occurred can be helpful. All causes shall be verified or proved, not determined by fuzzy brainstorming. Flow diagrams, cause and effect diagrams, and 5-Why Analysis are useful tools for root cause investigation.

A flow diagram translates complex work into an easily understood graphic description. This activity often is an eye-opening experience for the team because it is rare that all members of the team understand the entire process.

Next, the target performance measures are defined. Measurement is fundamental to meaningful process improvements. If something cannot be measured, it cannot be improved. There is an old saying that what gets measured gets done. The team will determine whether the measurements needed to understand and improve the process are presently being used; if new ones are needed, the team will:

- Establish performance measures with respect to customer requirements
- Determine data needed to manage the process
- Establish regular feedback with customers and suppliers
- Establish measures for quality/cost/timelines of inputs and outputs

Once the target performance measures are established, the team can collect all available data and information. If these data are not enough, then additional new information is obtained. Gathering data (1) helps confirm that a problem exists, (2) enables the team to work with facts, (3) makes it possible to establish measurement criteria for a baseline, and (4) enables the team to measure the effectiveness of an implemented solution. It is important to collect only needed data and to get the right data for the problem. The team should develop a plan that includes input from internal and external customers and answers the following questions:

1. What problem or operation does the team wish to learn about?
2. What are the data used for?
3. How much data is needed?
4. What conclusions can be drawn from the collected data?
5. What action should be taken as a result of the conclusion?

Data can be collected by several methods, such as check sheets, computers with application software, data-collection devices like hand-held gages, or an online system.

The team will identify the customers and their requirements and expectations as well as the inputs, outputs, and interfaces of the process. Also, the team will systematically review the procedures currently being used. Common items of data and information are as follows:

- Customer information, such as complaints and surveys
- Design information, such as specifications, drawings, function, bills of materials, costs, design reviews, field data, service, and maintainability

- Process information, such as routing, equipment, operators, raw material, and component parts and supplies

- Statistical information, such as average, median, range, standard deviation, skewness, kurtosis, and frequency distribution

- Quality information, such as Pareto diagrams, cause and effect diagrams, check sheets, scatter diagrams, control charts, histograms, process capability, acceptance sampling, run charts, life testing, inspection steps, and operator and equipment matrix analysis

- Supplier information, such as process variation, on-time delivery, and technical competency

The cause-and-effect diagram is particularly effective in this phase. Determining all the causes requires experience, brainstorming, and a thorough knowledge of the process. It is an excellent starting point for the project team. One word of caution: the objective is to seek causes, not solutions. Therefore, only possible causes, no matter how trivial, should be listed.

It is important to identify the root cause. This activity can sometimes be determined by voting. It is a good idea to verify the most likely cause because a mistake here can lead to the unnecessary waste of time and money by investigating possible solutions to the wrong cause.

Some verification techniques are the following:

1. Examine the most likely cause in regard to the problem statement

2. Recheck all data that support the most likely cause

3. Check the process when it is performing satisfactorily versus when it is not by using the who, where, when, how, what, and why approach

4. Utilize an outside authority who plays devil's advocate with the data, information, and reasoning

5. Use experimental design and other advanced techniques to determine the critical factors and their levels

6. Save a portion of the data used in the analysis to confirm during verification

5-Why Analysis

A 5-Why analysis is an effective tool wherein asking the question "why" multiple times will lead you to the root cause. See below for specific instructions on how to complete a 5-Why analysis:

1. Write down the specific problem. Writing the issue helps you formalize the problem and describe it completely. It also helps a team focus on the same problem.

2. Ask Why the problem happens and write the answer down below the problem.

3. If the answer you just provided doesn't identify the root cause of the problem that you wrote down in step 1, ask Why again and write that answer down.

4. Loop back to step 3 until the team agrees that the problem's root cause is identified. Again, this may take fewer or more times than five Why's.

Poor examples of a root cause:

- The supplier is responsible.

- The operator used the wrong part.

- The operator wasn't trained.

- The inspector reported the wrong results.

Better examples of a root cause:

- P/N XYZ failed because the incorrect Laser Mark Program was used. This failure occurred because the Manufacturing Instructions for P/N XYZ was not clear. There is no review with the operator prior to marking the part.

- P/N XYZ failed due to laser marking issues (wrong P/N and UDI). There is a lack of control of our labels during the manufacturing process. There is no documented process or procedure for laser marking/line clearances. There is no requirement.

This methodology is closely related to the cause-and-effect diagram and can be used to complement the analysis necessary to complete a cause-and-effect diagram.

Once the root cause is determined, the next phase of problem solving can begin.

Problem Correction

The objectives of corrective action are establishing potential and feasible solutions and recommending the best solution to improve the process. Once all the information is available, the project team begins its search for possible solutions. Frequently, more than one solution is required to remedy a situation. Sometimes the solutions are quite evident from a cursory analysis of the data.

In this phase, creativity plays a major role and brainstorming is the principal technique. Brainstorming on possible solutions requires not only a knowledge of the problem but also innovation and creativity.

There are three types of creativity: (1) create new processes, (2) combine different processes, or (3) modify the existing process. The first type is innovation in its highest form, such as the invention of the transistor. Combining two or more processes is a synthesis activity to create a better process. It is a unique combination of what already exists. This type of creativity relies heavily on benchmarking. Modification involves altering a process that already exists so that it does a better job. It succeeds when managers utilize the experience, education, and energy of empowered work groups or project teams. There is not a distinct line between the three types; they overlap (Rother and Shook 1999).

Creativity is a unique quality that separates mankind from the rest of the animal kingdom. Most of the problems that cause inefficiency and ineffectiveness in organizations are simple problems. There is a vast pool of creative potential available to solve these problems. Quality is greatly improved because of the finding and fixing of a large number of problems, and morale is greatly increased because it is enormously satisfying to be allowed to create (Mallette 1993).

Areas for possible change include the number and length of delays, bottlenecks, equipment, timing and number of inspections, rework, cycle time, and materials handling. Consideration should be given to simultaneously combining, eliminating, rearranging, and executing the process steps.

Once possible solutions have been determined, evaluation or testing of the solutions comes next. As mentioned, more than one solution can contribute to the situation. Evaluation or testing determines which of the possible solutions has the greatest potential for success and the advantages and disadvantages of these solutions. Criteria for judging the possible solutions include such things as cost, feasibility, resistance to change, consequences, and training. Solutions also may be categorized as short range and long range. At a minimum, the solution must prevent reoccurrence.

Control charts give us the ability to evaluate possible solutions. Whether the idea is good, poor, or has no effect is evident from the chart.

Once the best solution is selected, it can be implemented. Although the project team usually has some authority to institute remedial action, more often than not the approval of the quality council or other appropriate authority is required. If such is the case, a written and/or oral report is given. The contents of the implementation plan report must fully describe:

- Why it will be done

- How it will be done

- When it will be done

- Who will do it

- Where it will be done

The report will designate required actions, assign responsibility, and establish implementation milestones. The length of the report is determined by the complexity of the change. Simple changes may require only an oral report, whereas others may require a detailed written report. After approval by the quality council, it is desirable to obtain the advice and consent of departments, functional areas, teams, and individuals that may be affected by the change. A presentation to these groups will help gain support from those involved in the process and provide an opportunity for feedback with improvement suggestions.

The final element of the implementation plan is the monitoring activity, which answers the following:

- What information will be monitored or observed, and what resources are required?

- Who will be responsible for taking the measurements?

- Where will the measurements be taken?

- How will the measurements be taken?

- When will the measurements be taken?

Another step of problem correction is monitoring and evaluating the change by tracking and studying the effectiveness of the improvement efforts through data collection and review of progress. It is vital to institutionalize meaningful change and ensure ongoing measurement and evaluation efforts to achieve continuous improvement. Measurement tools such as run charts, control charts, Pareto diagrams, histograms, check sheets, and questionnaires are used to monitor and evaluate the process change.

The team should meet periodically during this phase to evaluate the results to see if the problem has been solved or if fine-tuning is required. In addition, they will want to see if any unforeseen problems have developed as a result of the changes. If the team is not satisfied, some of the phases will need to be repeated.

Recurrence Control

Once the team is satisfied with the change, it must be institutionalized by positive control (positrol) of the process, process certification, and operator certification. Positrol ensures that important variables are kept under control. It specifies the what, who, how, where, and when of the process and is an updating of the monitoring activity. Standardizing the solution prevents backsliding. Table 5.7 illustrates a few variables of a wave soldering process.

In addition, the quality peripherals (the system, environment, and supervision) must be certified. The partial checklist in Table 5.8 provides the means to initially evaluate the peripherals and periodically audit them to ensure that the process will meet or exceed customer requirements for the product or service.

Finally, operators must be certified to know what to do and how to do it for a particular process. Also needed is cross-training in other jobs within the process to ensure next-customer knowledge and job rotation. Total product knowledge is also desirable. Operator certification is an ongoing process that must occur periodically.

Table 5.7 Positrol of a wave soldering process.

What	Specs	Who	How	Where	When
An 880 flux	0.864 g ± 0.0008	Lab technician	Specific gravity meter	Lab	Daily
Belt speed	ft/min ± 10%	Process technician	Counter	Board feed	Each change
Preheat temperature	220° ± 5°	Automatic	Thermocouple	Chamber entrance	Continuous

Source: Reprinted from *World Class Quality* by Kiki Bhote. ©1991 AMACOM, a division of the American Management Association International. Reprinted by permission of AMACOM, a division of American Management Association International, New York, NY. All rights reserved. http://www.amanet.org.

Table 5.8 Checklist for process certification.

Quality system	Environment	Supervision
Authority to shut down line	Water/air purity	Coach, not boss
Preventive maintenance	Dust/chemical control	Clear instructions
Visible, audible alarm signals	Temperature/humidity control	Combining tasks
Foolproof inspection	Electrostatic discharge	Encourage suggestions
Neighbor and self-inspection	Storage/inventory control	Feedback of results

Source: Reprinted from *World Class Quality* by Kiki Bhote. ©1991 AMACOM, a division of the American Management Association International. Reprinted by permission of AMACOM, a division of American Management Association International, New York, NY. All rights reserved. http://www.amanet.org.

Verification of Effectiveness

This final stage of corrective action has the objective of achieving improved levels of process performance. Regardless of how successful initial improvement efforts are, the improvement process must continue. Everyone in the organization is involved in a systematic long-term endeavor to constantly improve quality by developing processes that are customer oriented, flexible, and responsive.

A key activity is to conduct regularly scheduled reviews of progress by the quality council and/or work group. Management must establish the systems to identify areas for future improvement and to track performance with respect to internal and external customers. They also must track changing customer requirements. Durivage (2017) notes that good verification of effectiveness is specific, measurable, achievable, relevant, and time bound. Corrective action is only useful if it is effective. Incorporating the five questions that the verification of effectiveness is specific, measurable, achievable, relevant, and time bound can help ensure that the corrective action plan is effective and has not caused unintended consequences.

PREVENTIVE ACTION

> Identify, describe, and apply various preventive action tools such as error-proofing/poka-yoke and robust design, and analyze their effectiveness. (Evaluate)
>
> **Body of Knowledge V.F**

The problem-solving method discussed in the previous section often may be useful for preventive actions. The function of quality engineers has moved from that of detection of defects to prevention of defects. The concept of preventive action has been around for many years and has been practiced extensively in Japan, where it has the name "poka-yoke," which was discussed in the "Poka-Yoke" section of this chapter.

Error Proofing

There are five error-proofing principles: elimination, replacement, facilitation, detection, and mitigation. Elimination of the possible error occurs when the process or product is redesigned so that the error can no longer occur. Replacement is a change to a more reliable process. Facilitation occurs when the process is made easier to perform and, therefore, more reliable. Detection occurs when the error is found before the next operation. Mitigation minimizes the effect of the error. Each of the error-proofing principles can be applied with the following methods of preventive action: fail-safe devices, magnification of senses, redundancy, countdown, and special checking and control devices. Each of these methods is discussed in turn below. Prevention can also be considered an error-proofing principle. One method for prevention is robust design, which was discussed at the end of this section.

Fail-safe devices are used to ensure that problems or abnormalities in processes will be discovered in a manner that will maintain a safe working environment and ensure that quality is not compromised. See Table 5.9.

Magnification of senses is used to increase the power of human seeing, hearing, smelling, feeling, tasting, and muscle power. Some examples are optical magnification, multiple visual and audio signals, remote-controlled viewing of a hazardous process, robotic placement of parts or tools, and use of pictures rather than words.

Redundancy is the use of additional activities as a quality safeguard. Multiple-identity codes, such as bar and color codes, are used to prevent product mix-ups. Redundant actions and approvals require two individuals working independently. Audit review and checking procedures ensure that plans are being followed. Design for verification utilizes special designs, such as holes for viewing, to determine whether the product or process is performing satisfactorily. Multiple

Table 5.9 Types of fail-safe devices.

Type of fail-safe device	Device function
Interlocking sequences	Ensure that the next operation cannot start until the previous operation is successfully completed
Alarms and cutoffs	Activate if there are any abnormalities in the process
All-clear signals	Activate when all remedial steps have been taken
Foolproof work-holding devices	Ensure that a part can be located in only one position
Limiting mechanisms	Ensure that a tool cannot exceed a certain position or amount

test stations may check various attributes, such as those that occur on a high-speed production line.

Countdown, which structures sensing and information procedures to parallel the operating procedures to check each step, is another category of fail-safe devices. The most familiar example of this category of error-proofing is the launching of a space vehicle. It also has been effectively used in surgical operations and in welding.

Special checking and control devices are another method of preventive action. A familiar example is the computer checking of credit card numbers whereby invalid numbers are rejected and instant feedback provided.

Robust Design

Creating a robust process or product is another method of preventive action. A product or process is called robust if its function is relatively unaffected by variation in the environment in which it operates, as shown in the following examples:

- A laundry appliance must operate correctly with a variety of water chemistry and cleaning products as well as variations in temperature, humidity, and other factors.

- An automobile must function correctly under various weather conditions as well as variation in operator techniques.

- The process of assembling a bid must be performed in an area where frequent interruptions, phone calls, and so on, occur. To make certain that all 23 required elements of the bid document are included, 23 color-coded trays are set out with the appropriate form in each tray before the document is assembled.

- The raw material for a punching process has a wide variation in thickness; in other words, the process operates in an environment of thickness variation. This results in unacceptable burrs on some parts. One solution is to impose a tighter thickness specification on the raw material supplier. The robust design solution might be a new die that would prevent burrs regardless of the thickness.

It is not enough to merely plan and execute preventive actions. In accordance with the PDSA and PDCA models, the effectiveness of preventive actions must be verified. Such verification can be difficult, however, since preventive actions that are effective eliminate problems before they occur. In this respect, verification of preventive actions is completed by ensuring that problems for which preventive actions have been planned and executed have not, in fact, recurred.

Chapter 6
Quantitative Methods and Tools

This chapter covers eight topics in data analysis that CQEs must understand and routinely employ: collecting and summarizing data, quantitative concepts, probability distributions, statistical decision making, relationships between variables, statistical process control, process and performance capability, and the design and analysis of experiments.

The methods and tools presented in this chapter, although complex in their details, provide a basis for what is sometimes referred to as management by fact. The proper use of this content will permit the user to determine how best to collect and analyze data so that sound decisions are possible.

COLLECTING AND SUMMARIZING DATA

This section covers six aspects related to collecting and summarizing data: types of data, measurement scales, data collection methods, data accuracy and integrity, graphical methods for depicting relationships, and descriptive statistics.

Types of Data

> Define, classify, and compare discrete (attributes) and continuous (variables) data.
> (Apply)
>
> Body of Knowledge VI.A.1

Two types of data are encountered in practice: discrete data and continuous data. *Discrete* (count) data are obtained when the characteristic being studied can only take on certain values and is countable—for example, number of nonconforming units in a lot, pass/fail data, or number of successes per trial. Another example would be the number of scratches on an object. In this case, the possible values are 0, 1, 2, . . . , a so-called countably infinite set. In quality control, discrete data are referred to as attribute data.

Continuous (variables) data are obtained when the characteristic being studied can take on any value over an interval of numbers. For example, the length of a part can be any value above zero. Between each two values on a continuous scale there are infinitely many other values. For example, between 2.350 inches and 2.351 inches are the values 2.3502 inches, 2.35078 inches, and so on.

Measurement Scales

> Define and describe nominal, ordinal, interval, and ratio scales. (Understand)
>
> **Body of Knowledge VI.A.2**

There are four types of measurement scales: nominal, ordinal, interval, and ratio.

Nominal scales classify data into categories with no order implied, such as an equipment list of presses, drills, and so on. Sometimes zero and one are assigned to represent, say, a conforming item and a nonconforming item; however, the numbers have no meaning in terms of order.

Ordinal scales refer to positions in a series where order is important, but precise differences between values are not defined. For example, on the Mohs hardness scale of 10 minerals, talc has a hardness of one, fluorite has a hardness of four, and topaz has a hardness of eight. However, topaz is harder than fluorite, but not twice as hard. Another example of an ordinal scale is survey responses, such as strongly dissatisfied, dissatisfied, neutral, satisfied, and strongly satisfied, which can be scaled as 1, 2, 3, 4, and 5.

Interval scales have meaningful differences but no absolute zero. In this case, ratios are not meaningful. An example is temperature measured in degrees Fahrenheit (°F). In this case, 20°F is not twice as warm as 10°F. Although the Fahrenheit scale has a zero, it is not an absolute zero. That is, the zero value does not signify that there is an absence of temperature. Data on an interval scale can be added and subtracted but cannot be multiplied or divided.

Ratio scales have meaningful differences and an absolute zero exists. One example of a ratio scale is length in inches because zero length is defined as having no length, and 20 inches is twice as long as 10 inches. Heat in degrees kelvin (K) is another example of a ratio scale because zero degrees K is defined as having no heat and 10 degrees K has twice as much heat as 5 degrees K.

Data Collection Methods

> Describe various methods for collecting data, including tally or check sheets, data coding, automatic gaging, data automation, database integration, and identify the strengths and weaknesses of the methods. (Apply)
>
> **Body of Knowledge VI.A.3**

In this section check sheets, automatic gauging, and data coding as ways of tallying are discussed.

A tally or check sheet consists of a column of potential values usually shown from smallest to largest. As measurements are read, a tally mark is placed next to the appropriate value. Although no sophisticated analysis is provided, the tally sheet is very simple to use and understand. An illustration of such a sheet is shown in Figure 6.1. The data represent a sample of diameters from a drilling operation.

Data also may be collected by automatic gauging equipment. Potential advantages of this approach include improved precision as well as reduction of labor, time, error rates, and costs. When considering automated inspection, CQEs must pay attention to the possibility of high initial costs, including the possibility of part redesign to adapt the part to the constraints of the measurement system. If the measured values are fed directly into a database, care must be taken to make certain that the communication link is reliable and free of noise.

EXAMPLE 6.1

A dimension has values that range from 1.031 to 1.039. For convenience, these numbers may be coded using digits from 1 to 9 so that:

$$1 \rightarrow 1.031$$

$$2 \rightarrow 1.032 \text{ and so on}$$

Coding data can simplify recording and analysis. Sometimes it is useful to code data using an algebraic transformation. Suppose a set of data has mean μ and standard deviation σ (see the "Descriptive Statistics" section of this chapter for more details on μ and σ). A new set of data may be formed using the formula $y = ax + b$. That is, each element of the new set is formed by multiplying an element of the original set by a, then adding b. The mean μ_y, standard deviation σ_y, and variance σ_y^2 of the new set are

$$\mu_y = a\mu + b \tag{6.1}$$

Raw data: 0.127 0.125 0.123 0.123 0.120 0.124 0.126 0.122 0.123 0.125 0.121
0.123 0.122 0.125 0.124 0.122 0.123 0.123 0.126 0.121 0.124 0.121
0.124 0.122 0.126 0.125 0.123

Value	Tally
0.120	I
0.121	III
0.122	IIII
0.123	IIIIIII
0.124	IIII
0.125	IIII
0.126	III
0.127	I

Figure 6.1   Example of tally or check sheet.

$$\sigma_y = |a|\sigma \qquad (6.2)$$

$$\sigma_y^2 = a^2\sigma^2 \qquad (6.3)$$

For further information on the effect of algebraic transformations, see Hogg, Tanis, and Zimmerman (2014).

Data collection is the initial point of an organizations' capability to use information stored in data, uncover innovative insights, and achieve superior business decisions. Data collection can be accomplished using several methods from simple pen and pencil to advanced Internet of Things (IoT). It is common to have the so-called "Hybrid" approach of data collection, consisting of low to high-end data collection methods.

Internet of Things is a novel paradigm that allows billions of intelligent devices to be connected to the Internet. Such devices can be sensors/actuators which can operate and transmit data to other systems with or without minimal human intervention (Biru et al. 2015). There is a wide array of IoT definitions. In general, IoT refers to a self-configuring, adaptive, complex network that allows a variety of things or objects, e.g., Radio Frequency Identification (RFID) tags, sensors, actuators, and mobile phones, through unique addressing schemes, to interact and cooperate to reach common goals (Atzori et al. 2010).

The first step in the high volume, variety, and velocity of data that any organization faces today is developing an architecture, scope, and framework for a data collection program that identifies the data required for their current and future business needs. That step is followed with the use of the extract, transform, load (ETL) or extract, load, transform (ELT) process (see Figure 6.2). The selection of the ETL or ELT methodology is determined based on various factors. Some of the vital elements that should be taken into consideration are:

- need for real-time decision making based on collected data,
- data transformation speed,
- amount of data,
- type of data: structured or unstructured,
- need to access to all raw data to use it in machine learning projects,
- need to ensure compliance with established standards for protecting the sensitive data,
- data warehouse/data lake support, and
- use of a legacy system or with on-premises relational databases.

The Data Transform phase's main goal is preparing data to fit the parameters of another system. Transformations may include:

- data sorting and filtering to get rid of irrelevant items,
- de-duplicating and cleansing,
- translating and converting,
- removing or encrypting to protect sensitive information, and
- splitting or joining tables, etc.

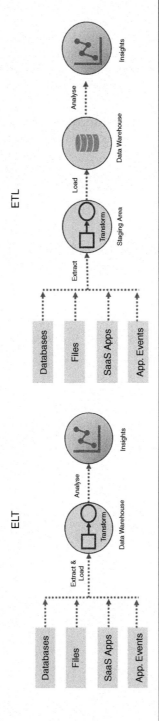

Figure 6.2 ELT and ETL framework.

During data analysis, data that are collected automatically and/or manually need to be cleaned, including addressing unusual observations and missing data. Data analysts need to be aware that some missing data may be coded as zero values. In addition, before analysis is performed, additional tests such as data normality are required. If non-normal data are identified, it is recommended to "clean" and/or transform the data. Several approaches are available in this situation, such as the Outlier Test, autocorrelation, and distribution identification tests. These tests can be done quickly using statistical software (see Figures 6.3, 6.4, and 6.5).

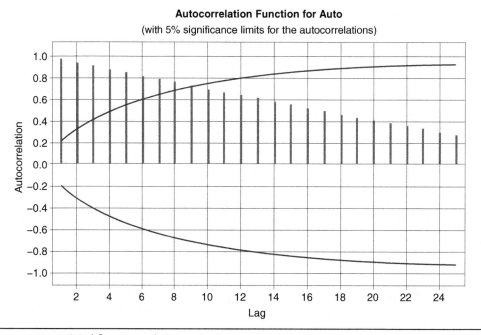

Figure 6.3 Minitab© autocorrelation output.

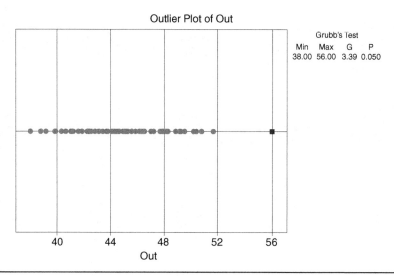

Figure 6.4 Minitab© outlier plot test.

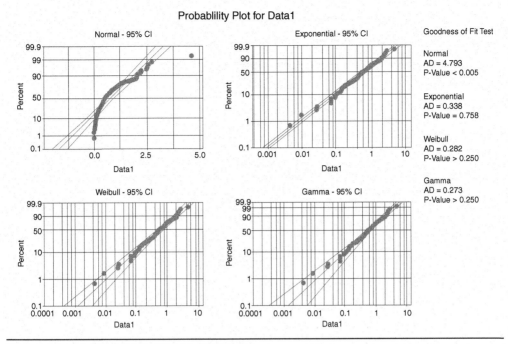

Figure 6.5 Minitab© distribution identification.

Finally, if there is a need to do a data coding transformation, several approaches may be taken. One of the common, if appropriate, is to use Box-Cox or Johnson transformation in the case of non-normal data which do not fit any distribution.

Data Accuracy and Integrity

> Identify factors that can influence data accuracy such as source/resource issues, flexibility, versatility, inconsistency, inappropriate interpretation of data values, and redundancy to ensure data accuracy and integrity. (Apply)
>
> **Body of Knowledge VI.A.4**

In this section data collection errors and sampling methods are discussed.

Data Collection

The best data collection and analysis techniques can be defeated if the data have errors. Common causes of errors include the following:

- Units of measure that are not defined (e.g., feet or meters?).
- Similarity of handwritten characters (e.g., 2 or Z?).

- Inadequate measurement system.
- Rounding (generally should only be done at last stage of computation).
- Batching input versus real-time input.
- Inadequate use of validation techniques.
- Multiple points of data entry.
- Poor instructions or training.
- Ambiguous terminology (e.g., calendar or fiscal year? day ends at 3 pm or midnight?). For example, the NASA team working with the Mars rovers uses the term "sol" to designate a Martian day to avoid confusion with earth days (thus,"yestersol" refers to the previous Martian day).

Use strategies like these to minimize error:

- Have a carefully constructed data collection plan
- Maintain a calibration schedule for data collection equipment
- Conduct gage R&R studies on data collection equipment
- Record appropriate auxiliary information regarding units, time of collection, conditions, measurement equipment used, name of the data recorder, and so on
- Use appropriate statistical tests to identify potential outliers
- If data are transmitted or stored digitally, use an appropriate redundant error-correction system
- Provide clear and complete instruction and training

If data are obtained through sampling, the sampling procedure must be appropriately designed. Some of the techniques that can be used to establish a well-designed sampling strategy are discussed in the following section.

Sampling Methods

Simple random sampling is a procedure by which each item has an equal probability of being selected as part of the sample. One way to do this is to assign each item a number and create a set of numbered tags so that each tag number corresponds to exactly one item. The tags are thoroughly mixed in a container and one is drawn out. The number on the tag identifies which item is selected as part of the sample. If the population size is quite large, the use of tags may not be feasible. In this situation, random numbers generated by calculators or computer software such as Microsoft Excel can be used to select the elements of the sample.

If the population of parts to be sampled is naturally divided into groups, it may be desirable to use *stratified sampling*. For example, suppose 300 parts came from Cleveland, 600 came from Chicago, and 100 came from Green Mountain. A stratified sample of size 50 could be formed by randomly selecting 15 items from the Cleveland batch, 30 from the Chicago batch, and 5 from Green Mountain. In other words, each group makes up a proportional part of the stratified sample.

Sample homogeneity refers to the need to select a sample so that it represents just one population. Sample homogeneity is desirable regardless of the type of sampling. In the case of the stratified sampling procedure, the population consists of the original 1000 parts, and stratification is used to help ensure that the sample represents the various strata.

When selecting the data collection scheme for time-related data, the entire sample should be collected at the same time in the process so that it comes from the population being produced at 9:00 am, not that produced at 9:15 am, which may be a different population. In fact, the purpose of a control chart is to use sampling to determine whether the population produced at one time is different from the other populations sampled.

For additional information on data collection methods see Vining (2013) and Doganaksoy and Hahn (2012). Doganaksoy and Hahn provide a structured process to gather data.

Data Visualization Techniques

> Apply and interpret data visualization techniques using dashboards, and select the appropriate metrics for dashboards. (Apply)
>
> **Body of Knowledge VI.A.5**

A dashboard provides a visual, at-a-glance display of key business indicators (see Figure 6.6). Dashboards provide a compact view of the current organizational state. Dashboards may include trend charts and bar charts, and green/yellow/red lights to indicate performance relative to a target. Some dashboards include "drill down" features so that managers can dig into lower-level data. Digital dashboards must be customized for various activities throughout the organization. High-level dashboards are appropriate for executives, but frontline employees need to access low-level data appropriate for their sphere of influence.

The elements in a dashboard should be linked to the strategic objectives. Sales for the example company shown in Figure 6.6 are targeted to grow at 3.75% per year. To avoid revealing confidential information, the dashboard shows only differences from target. Sales below target are negative. In Figure 6.6, although sales in the recent past have fallen short of the goal, the trend is favorable. Inventory turns (annual sales divided by current inventory) have met or exceeded the target in two of the past three quarters. The milestone review for new product development shows two tasks behind schedule. The year-to-date (YTD) performance to target chart includes several elements that were selected in the balanced scorecard process. Calculating the ratio between actual performance and the target allows us to combine various metrics on a single chart with a common scale. In this example, management should be concerned that employee suggestions are not being closed promptly and that customer calls are still not being processed fast enough through the call center.

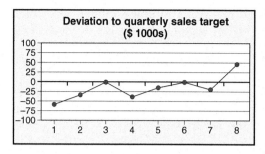

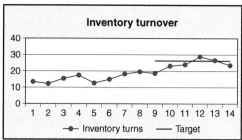

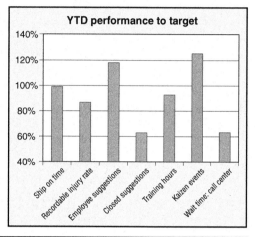

Figure 6.6   XYZ corporation dashboard.

Remember that what you measure will determine to a great extent the activities of your organization. Therefore, carefully select the metrics for your dashboards, scorecards, and other performance measurement tools. More information on performance measures such as process capability indices is presented in the "Process and Performance Capability" section of this chapter.

Descriptive Statistics

Describe, calculate, and interpret measures of central tendency and dispersion, apply the central limit theorem, and construct and interpret frequency distributions, including simple, categorical, grouped, ungrouped, and cumulative. (Evaluate)

Body of Knowledge VI.A.6

The two principal types of statistical studies are *descriptive* and *inferential*. The purpose of descriptive statistics is to present data in a way that will facilitate understanding. Some important statistics that can be used to describe a set of data include:

- A measure of the center of the population or a sample
- A measure of the variability (measure of the spread of the data) for the population or a sample
- A graphical display (displaying overall shape) of the data

Center, spread, and shape are key to understanding data and the process that generated them. The next few paragraphs discuss these attributes. (Complete definitions and discussion of population, sample, parameters, and statistics are provided in the "Terminology" section of this chapter.)

Measures of Central Tendency

Three ways to quantify the center of a data set are the mean (or average), median, and mode.

The *mean* is the arithmetic average of a set of data or observations. The mean is also referred to as a "balancing point" for the set of observations. Suppose the data in a sample of size n are denoted by $x_1, x_2, x_3, \ldots, x_n$. The *sample mean*, denoted $\bar{x}$ (read "x-bar"), is given by

$$\bar{x} = \frac{x_1 + x_2 + x_3 + \ldots + x_n}{n} = \frac{\sum_{i=1}^{n} x_i}{n} \tag{6.4}$$

EXAMPLE 6.2

Emergency room waiting times are continually increasing. One factor that was identified as affecting wait time was turnaround time for basic blood analysis. Turnaround times (in minutes) for 10 such tests on one particular day are:

| 62 | 68 | 72 | 60 | 50 | 58 | 58 | 49 | 66 | 70 |

The average turnaround time is

$$\bar{x} = \frac{62 + 68 + 72 + 60 + 50 + 58 + 58 + 49 + 66 + 70}{10}$$

$$= 61.3 \text{ min}$$

If the data represent the entire population of interest, then the average is the *population mean* and commonly denoted by μ. Suppose there are N observations in the population. The *population mean* is

$$\mu = \frac{x_1 + x_2 + x_3 + \ldots + x_N}{N}$$

$$= \frac{\sum_{i=1}^{N} x_i}{N} \tag{6.5}$$

EXAMPLE 6.3

An accident investigator has been contracted by a large tire company to investigate accidents where the company's tire may have been at fault. The investigator was contracted by this company for a total of six months before the company determined that his work was unacceptable. At the time his contract was terminated, the investigator had submitted a total of eight invoices for time spent at accident scenes. The amounts for each invoice are:

$4390 $3285 $1582 $725 $3001 $2971 $463 $8923

Since these invoice amounts are the *only* amounts for this investigator's work for the tire company, they represent the *entire population of amounts*. Therefore, the average invoice amount will be the population mean:

$$\mu = \frac{x_1 + x_2 + x_3 + \ldots + x_N}{N}$$

$$= \frac{4390 + 3285 + 1582 + 725 + 3001 + 2971 + 463 + 8923}{8} = \$3167.50$$

EXAMPLE 6.4

Consider the turnaround times for blood analysis given in Example 6.2, now written in increasing order:

49   50   58   58   60   62   66   68   70   72

Since there are $n = 10$ observations in the data set, the location of the median is $(10 + 1)/2 = 5.5$. Therefore, the median is the average of the fifth and sixth observations from the smallest in the data set:

$$M = \frac{60 + 62}{2}$$

$$= 61 \text{ min}$$

The *median* is the value that divides ordered data into two equal parts—half of the data lie at or below that value and half of the data lie above that value. Suppose the sample of size is n. If the sample contains an odd number of observations, the sample median is the central value. If there is an even number of observations, the median is the average of the two central values. The *location* of the median for n observations is $(n + 1)/2$. The sample median is often denoted by M.

The *sample mode* is the observation that occurs most often in the sample. There can be more than one mode for a set of data. For example, the mode for the blood analysis turnaround times is 58 minutes, since it occurs more often than any other observation.

As with the mean, the population median and population mode can be determined if the entire population is known. The mean and median are the most used measures of the center of a data set.

One final note on measures of the center: the median is known as a *resistant* measure of the center, while the mean is not a resistant measure. A resistant measure is one that is not highly influenced by extreme observations. For example, the median is often used as the measure of the center for data that involve prices or salaries, or for any data that may naturally contain extreme observations.

EXAMPLE 6.5

Housing prices in Glendale, Arizona, vary over a wide range. Suppose five houses on the market in May 2008 were listed at the following prices:

$54,900 $75,000 $79,000 $101,500 $386,000

The average house price for this set of data is $139,280. Does the average appear to represent the sample of data itself? The price of $139,280 lies above all but one house price. The median house price for this set of data is $79,000. The average was pulled toward the extreme value of $386,000 while the median was not influenced by this particular value.

Now suppose that the house priced $386,000 was reduced to $345,000. All other housing prices remained constant at the time of the data collection. With this reduction, the sample mean house price is now $131,080; the sample median house price remains at $79,000. Therefore, the median was resistant to the change in price while the mean was not resistant.

Measures of Variability (Spread)

Measures of variability describe the spread of the data around the center or central point of the distribution of the data. Three common measures of variation are the range, variance, and standard deviation.

The *sample range* is the difference between the maximum value (x_{max}) and the minimum value (x_{min}) in the sample. The sample range is often denoted by R and given by

$$R = x_{max} - x_{min} \tag{6.6}$$

For example, the sample range for the blood analysis turnaround times given previously is $R = 72 - 49 = 23$ minutes.

The *sample variance* is a measure of the variability based on the deviations of the actual observations from the mean. Suppose the sample size is n with observations $x_1, x_2, \ldots, x_n$. The sample variance is

$$s^2 = \frac{\sum_{i=1}^{n}\left(x_i - \bar{x}\right)^2}{n-1} \tag{6.7}$$

EXAMPLE 6.6

Consider the blood analysis turnaround times (in minutes) given in Example 6.2:

49   50   58   58   60   62   66   68   70   72

Continued

The sample average was found to be $\bar{x} = 61.3$ minutes. The sample variance is

$$s^2 = \frac{\sum_{i=1}^{n}(x_i - \bar{x})^2}{n-1}$$

$$= \frac{(49-61.3)^2 + (50-61.3)^2 + \ldots + (72-61.3)^2}{10-1}$$

$$= 62.23 \, \text{min}^2$$

The *population variance*, denoted by σ^2, can be determined if the data from the entire population are given. Suppose the population consists of N observations and the population mean is given by μ. The population variance is

$$\sigma^2 = \frac{\sum_{i=1}^{N}(x_i - \mu)^2}{N} \tag{6.8}$$

Notice that the unit of measure of the variance is the square of the unit of measure of the original data and the mean. It is more convenient to have summary statistics (such as the measure of the center and measure of variability) in the same unit of measure as the original data. The measure of variability that is in the same unit of measure as the original data and mean is the *standard deviation*. The standard deviation is simply the positive square root of the variance. The sample standard deviation is

$$s = \sqrt{\frac{\sum_{i=1}^{n}(x_i - \bar{x})^2}{n-1}} \tag{6.9}$$

and the population standard deviation is

$$\sigma = \sqrt{\frac{\sum_{i=1}^{N}(x_i - \mu)^2}{N}} \tag{6.10}$$

For example, the sample standard deviation for the blood analysis turnaround times is $s = \sqrt{62.23 \, \text{min}^2} = 7.89$ minutes.

Shape of the Data

Graphical displays, discussed earlier, include dot plots, box pots, stem-and-leaf plots, and histograms. These displays can be used to interpret the shape of the sample or population (i.e., the form the data take on). For example, a dot plot (also known as a dot diagram) for the blood analysis turnaround times is shown in Figure 6.7. The display reveals the spread of the data as well as possible outliers.

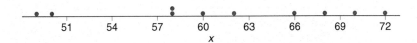

Figure 6.7   Dot plot of blood analysis turnaround times.

Data can assume numerous possible shapes. Consider Figure 6.8. Figure 6.8a represents a histogram of the diameters from the drilling operation in Table 6.1. The distribution is symmetric and bell shaped, and there do not appear to be any potential outliers or unusual observations. Figure 6.8b displays lifetime data of a manufactured part. The lifetime data follow a skewed distribution, specifically a *right-skewed distribution*. Figure 6.8c displays data representing time to show symptoms in rats that have been subjected to a particular treatment. This is a left-skewed distribution. Finally, Figure 6.8d represents a *bimodal distribution*. This type of distribution has many applications, but sometimes this shape can indicate a mixed distribution of data (data may be coming from two different distributions).

A *frequency distribution* is a compact summary of data collected. The frequency distribution can be displayed in table form, graphical form, or some functional form. An *ungrouped frequency distribution* in table form displays the individual observations and the number of times that each value appears in the data set. A frequency distribution of the diameters from the drilling operation is given in Table 6.1.

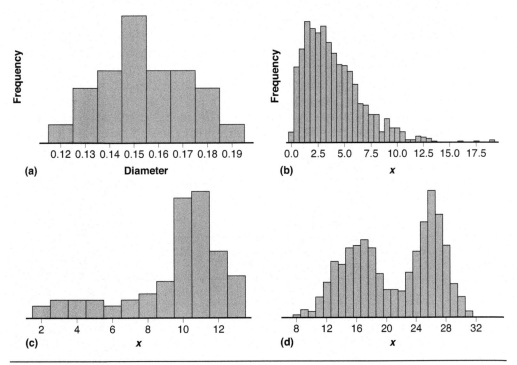

Figure 6.8   Histograms of variously shaped distributions.

Table 6.1 Frequency and cumulative frequency distributions for the ungrouped diameter data.

Measurement	Frequency	Cumulative frequency
0.120	1	1
0.121	3	4
0.122	4	8
0.123	7	15
0.124	4	19
0.125	4	23
0.126	3	26
0.127	1	27

The *cumulative frequency distribution* contains the observations themselves as well as the frequency of the occurrence of the current and preceding observations. The cumulative frequency distribution of the diameters from the drilling operation is given in the last column in Table 6.1.

Another way to present the diameter data from the previous example would be to group the measurements together as shown in Table 6.2.

If the data represent numbers of items in nonnumerical groups or categories, a *categorical frequency distribution* is used. An example of a categorical frequency distribution is displayed in Table 6.3 for several important types of defects in a manufacturing process.

Cumulative frequency distributions should not be used when the groups are categories where order does not matter.

Frequency distributions and cumulative frequency distributions provide a simple way to quickly examine the variability of data around the center. These distributions also aid in the calculation of statistics from the data, such as the sample mean and sample standard deviation. In addition, data from the frequency and cumulative frequency distributions can easily be displayed graphically, such as in a histogram.

Table 6.2 Frequency and cumulative frequency distributions for the grouped diameter data.

Group	Frequency	Cumulative frequency
0.120–0.121	4	4
0.122–0.123	11	15
0.124–0.125	8	23
0.126–0.127	4	27

Table 6.3 Categorical frequency distribution of manufacturing defects.

Defect type	Frequency	Relative frequency
Chip	3	0.143
Scratch	5	0.238
Ink smear	4	0.190
Fold mark	7	0.333
Tear	2	0.095

Graphical Methods for Depicting Distributions

> Apply and interpret diagrams such as probability plots for normal and other distributions. (Analyze)
>
> **Body of Knowledge VI.A.7**

Graphical displays of data are important tools that can help determine important properties of the data. Using graphical displays, the overall shape, location of the center, and measure of variability can be approximately estimated. These displays can also be used to possibly determine the type of distribution that the data may follow. One graphical display that can be used for determining the type of distribution the data may follow is the *probability plot*.

The probability plot displays the actual data on the x-axis, plotted against *percentiles* based on the hypothesized or assumed distribution of interest on the y-axis. For example, the normal probability plot displays the actual data against percentiles from a normal distribution. If the data fall—at least approximately—along a straight line, then they are said to be approximately normally distributed. Probability plots can be constructed for many distributions, including the normal, lognormal, Weibull, and exponential. Two of the most used are the normal and Weibull probability plots.

The assumption of at least approximate normality is often necessary to satisfactorily apply many statistical tests. The normal probability plot can be used to determine whether a given set of data come from a population that is normally distributed. In general, the data are plotted on a probability plot where the vertical axis has been scaled according to a normal distribution. It is unnecessary to create these plots manually. Most statistical software packages will generate these plots for any set of data. If the data fall at least approximately along a straight line, then the distribution of interest (in this case the normal distribution) is assumed to be a reasonable form for the data.

The Weibull probability plot is used to determine whether a particular set of data follows a Weibull distribution. The Weibull distribution is often used in reliability problems. Similar to the normal probability plot, the actual data are plotted against a percentile that is based on the Weibull distribution. The Weibull probability plot is more difficult to construct by hand than the normal probability plot and so will not be outlined here. Many statistical packages have the capability to construct Weibull probability plots.

Interpretation of probability plots can be subjective. One person may interpret the data as normally distributed, for example, while someone else examining the same plot could say that they are not normally distributed. The closer the data fall along a straight line, the more evidence there is that the distribution of interest is reasonable for that particular set of data. If the plot exhibits curvature or an "S" shape, then other distributions should possibly be investigated. Goodness-of-fit tests are often more reliable approaches to determining the appropriateness of a particular distribution (see Devore 2016).

EXAMPLE 6.7

Sumithra and Bhattacharya (2008) present a study on the toasting of corn flakes. Appropriately toasted flakes possess the desired moisture content, texture, and color. In their study, the authors investigated the effect of three independent variables—moisture content, toasting temperature, and toasting time—on several responses of interest. One response was the force needed to puncture the toasted flake. The puncture force data (measured in Newton) for this experiment are:

5.34, 6.62, 2.90, 2.07, 5.87, 4.02, 3.45, 2.24, 3.80, 3.80,

2.27, 6.62, 3.95, 4.12, 2.95, 2.80, 2.81, 2.80, 2.90, 2.95

A normal probability plot of the puncture force data is given in Figure 6.9. The data do not appear to fall along a straight line, so the normal distribution may not be the best to model puncture force.

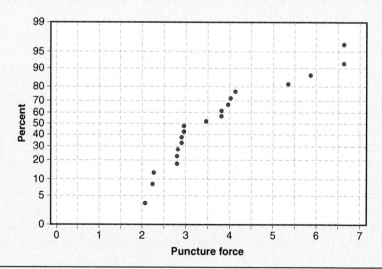

Figure 6.9 Normal probability plot of puncture force for toasted corn flakes.

EXAMPLE 6.8

The following data represent the life of a particular part used in the semiconductor manufacturing industry. Fifteen parts are selected at random and their life (in hours) recorded when the parts are in use. The data are:

479.23, 43.17, 3219.41, 558.46, 56.00, 705.37, 12.02, 280.42,

3867.95, 6672.37, 8494.07, 1220.94, 66.92, 2078.13, 6431.02

It is important to determine the distribution that the data may follow. The Weibull distribution could be investigated. The Weibull probability plot for this set of data is shown in Figure 6.10.

The data mostly fall along a straight line. Therefore, the data appear to follow a Weibull distribution. The Weibull distribution appears to be valid for this set of data.

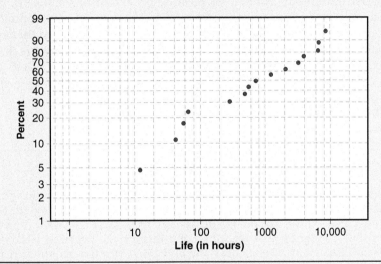

Figure 6.10 Weibull probability plot for life of a part.

QUANTITATIVE CONCEPTS

Define and apply quantitative terms, including population, parameter, sample, statistic, random sampling, and expected value. (Analyze)

Body of Knowledge VI.B.1

This section lays the foundation for understanding how to draw statistical conclusions and how to apply probability terms and concepts.

Terminology

A *population* is the entirety of all items or units being studied. A *sample* is a subset of items or measurements selected from the larger population. Since it is often impractical to obtain information on all the items or units in the population, Information is acquired on a subset of them to draw conclusions about the rest. A *parameter* is a quantity that describes characteristics of a population, for example, mean (μ), standard deviation (σ), correlation coefficient (ρ), or fraction nonconforming (p). The value of the population parameter is often unknown and must be estimated. A *statistic* is a characteristic of a sample and is an estimator of a population parameter. A representative sample is taken from the population and summary statistics calculated, such as the average or mean ($\bar{x}$), standard deviation (s), correlation coefficient (r), or fraction nonconforming ($\hat{p}$). In this case, $\bar{x}$ is an estimator for μ.

Probability is a numerical measure representing the likelihood that a particular outcome will occur. The probability that a particular event occurs is a number between zero and one inclusive. For example, if a lot consisting of 100 parts has 4 nonconforming parts, the probability that a randomly selected part will be nonconforming is 0.04, or 4%.

These concepts are summarized in the following example.

EXAMPLE 6.9

The thickness of a printed circuit board (PCB) is an important characteristic. If the thickness does not meet specification, the circuit board is reworked or scrapped. The average thickness of the PCB is assumed to be 0.0630 inches (i.e., $\mu = 0.0630$). The thickness of 25 randomly chosen PCBs is measured and the average thickness is found to be 0.06314 inches (i.e., $\bar{x} = 0.06314$ inches). The probability that the sample average diameter is larger than 0.06314 (for a sample size of 25) is 0.0105.

In this problem:

- The *population* is all printed circuit boards manufactured by this company with this process

- The *sample* is the 25 randomly chosen printed circuit boards

- The *parameter* is the population average or mean μ and is assumed to be $\mu = 0.0630$ inches

- The *statistic* is the sample average or sample mean $\bar{x}$, calculated using the sample of 25 printed circuit boards, which was found to be $\bar{x} = 0.06314$ inches

- A *probability* associated with this sample is 0.0105

Drawing Statistical Conclusions

> Distinguish between numeric and analytical studies. Assess the validity of statistical conclusions by analyzing the assumptions used and the robustness of the technique used. (Evaluate)
>
> **Body of Knowledge VI.B.2**

The purpose of inferential statistics is to infer (arrive at a conclusion by reasoning from evidence) properties of a population through analysis of a sample. This type of study is sometimes referred to as a numeric study. These studies are valid only if the sample is from a stable underlying population. For example, if a control chart is used on a stable process, the data from the chart can be used to conduct a capability study for the material produced while the chart was in use. This *capability study* infers information about the process population based on the sample used for the control chart and would therefore be a numeric study.

Sample data may also be used to study either stable or non-stable processes with the goal of process improvement, which may involve the use of knowledge, experience, creativity, and basic science. Such a study is not numeric, because rather than infer properties of the population, the study seeks to determine the causes that impact the process. Inferential methods are inappropriate because the underlying population is often not stable and the goal is to change it rather than determine its characteristics. W. Edwards Deming called these analytical studies. A control chart, when used to take action on the process to maintain statistical control, is an example of a tool for analytical study.

In the "Statistical Decision-Making" section of this chapter several statistical tests are described. Each has assumptions or conditions that must be met for the test to be valid. It is critical that a test's assumptions or conditions be satisfied before applying the test. In some cases the discussion accompanying the statistical test may state that the test is *robust* to minor deviations from the assumptions or conditions. For example, if one of the conditions of a test is that the population be normal, the test may be robust to minor deviations in this condition. This means that even if the population is almost normal, the test could be applied, with caution about the precision of the conclusion. Decisions in situations like this require judgment and experience.

Probability Terms and Concepts

> Describe concepts such as independence, mutual exclusivity, multiplication rules, complementary probability, and joint occurrence of events. (Apply)
>
> **Body of Knowledge VI.B.3**

Before discussing probability and probability rules, it is important to define terms that describe the experiment under study. In this context, *experiment* refers to a *random* experiment where different outcomes could be obtained even if the experiment is repeated under identical conditions.

Sample Spaces and Events

The *sample space* is the set of all possible outcomes of an experiment or a set of conditions (this is also referred to as the *universal set* in set theory). The sample space is usually denoted by the capital letter S. If the outcomes are finite or countably infinite, then the sample space is considered discrete. If the outcomes are values over an interval of real numbers, then the sample space is considered continuous. (Further discussion of continuous and discrete random variables and distributions is given in the "Probability Distributions" section of this chapter.) An *event* is a subset of the sample space and is often denoted by a capital letter such as A, B, C, and so on. If an outcome x is an element or outcome in A, for example, it is written as $x \in$ A. To illustrate these concepts, consider an experiment where a single piston ring for an automobile motor is randomly selected from a lot and classified as conforming (C) or nonconforming (N). The sample space for this experiment is S = {C, N}. If there is only interest in the event where the piston ring is nonconforming (call this event E), this event would be E = {N}. As a second illustration, suppose the experiment was to determine how long it takes a worker to complete a task (in minutes). Let x represent the time to complete the task. The sample space consists of all positive real numbers. This can be written as S = $\{x \mid x > 0\}$. If the event or sample space has no outcomes in it, then it is the empty set, denoted Ø.

It is often of interest to combine events to form other events. There are three basic set operations used to create new events of interest:

- The *union* of two events A and B is that event consisting of all outcomes that are contained in A, in B, or in both. The union is denoted as A ∪ B (read "A or B").

- The *intersection* of two events A and B is that event consisting of all outcomes that are contained in both A and B. The intersection is denoted as A ∩ B (read "A and B").

- The *complement* of any event in a sample space is an event that contains all the outcomes in the sample space that are *not* in the event itself. The complement of event A is denoted as A' (read "A complement" or "not A"). Other notation used to represent the complement of an event includes Ã, AC, and sometimes *A*. Here, the prime notation, A', is used.

It should be noted that if the intersection of any two events results in the empty set (i.e., A ∩ B = Ø), then those two events are called *mutually exclusive*.

EXAMPLE 6.10

A simple illustration involves the rolling of a single, fair six-sided die. In this random experiment, the sample space is S = {1, 2, 3, 4, 5, 6}. Suppose A is the event where the outcome on a single roll is an even number; so A = {2, 4, 6}. Suppose B is the event where the outcome on a single roll is greater than 3; so B = {4, 5, 6}. In this situation:

- $A \cup B = \{2, 4, 5, 6\}$

- $A \cap B = \{4, 6\}$

- $A' = \{1, 3, 5\}$, $B' = \{1, 2, 3\}$

- $A \cap A' = \varnothing$ (and $B \cap B' = \varnothing$); the intersection of an event and its complement is *always* the empty set

- $A \cup A' = S$ (and $B \cup B' = S$); the union of any event and its complement *always* equals the sample space

As stated previously, *probability* is a numerical measure that represents the likelihood that a particular outcome will occur. The probability that a particular event occurs is a number between zero and one inclusive. The probability of an event, say E, is written as P(E).

If the elements of E are mutually exclusive, then P(E) is equal to the sum of the probabilities of the outcomes that make up that event. To illustrate, suppose an event E contains elements a, b, c, d, and e, that is, E = {a, b, c, d, e}. Then the probability of event E with these five mutually exclusive events would be

$$P(E) = P(a) + P(b) + P(c) + P(d) + P(e) \tag{6.11}$$

Suppose there are N possible mutually exclusive outcomes in an experiment, all equally likely to occur (such as in the rolling of a fair six-sided die). The probability of any one outcome is $1/N$. Another way to look at probability is as a relative frequency. That is, the probability of an outcome would be the number of times that outcome occurs divided by the total number of possible outcomes.

Probability Properties

Consider a sample space S and two events A and B from that sample space. Then

1. $P(S) = 1$

2. $0 \leq P(A) \leq 1$

3. $P(A') = 1 - P(A)$

4. If two events A and B are mutually exclusive, then $P(A \cap B) = 0$

An important result of rule 4 is sometimes referred to as the *special addition rule* for mutually exclusive events and is given as

$$P(A \cup B) = P(A) + P(B) \tag{6.12}$$

In other words, when two events are mutually exclusive, the probability that an outcome in event A will occur, an outcome in event B will occur, or an outcome in both A and B will occur can be found by adding the individual probabilities of each event.

EXAMPLE 6.11

Suppose the number of medication errors that occur for a patient at a particular hospital have the following probabilities:

Table 6.4 Probabilities associated with medication errors.

Number of medication errors	0	1	2	3
Probability	0.90	0.07	0.02	0.01

Let A be the event of at most one medication error occurring, that is, A = {0, 1}. Let B be the event where exactly two medication errors occur, that is, B = {2}. We note that these events are mutually exclusive. For this situation:

- $P(A) = P(0) + P(1) = 0.90 + 0.07 = 0.97$
- $P(B) = P(2) = 0.02$
- $P(A') = 1 - P(A) = 1 - 0.97 = 0.03$
- $P(A \cap B) = 0$
- $P(A \cup B) = P(A) + P(B) = 0.97 + 0.02 = 0.99$

The special addition rule applies only to experiments where the two events of interest have no outcomes in common (mutually exclusive). When the events are *not* mutually exclusive, a more general addition rule applies:

$$P(A \cup B) = P(A) + P(B) - P(A \cap B) \qquad (6.13)$$

EXAMPLE 6.12

Cellular phones are put through several inspections before being shipped to the customer. Two defect types are important: critical (C) and major (M) defects. Phones with either critical or major defects are completely reworked. Using recent inspection data, it was determined that 2% of the cell phones have critical defects only, 5% have major defects only, and 1% have both critical *and* major defects. The manufacturer wants to know what percentage of all phones would require complete rework.

In this situation, the information given is:

- $P(C) = 0.02$
- $P(M) = 0.05$
- $P(C \text{ and } M) = P(C \cap M) = 0.01$

Complete rework is necessary if the phone has critical *or* major defects or both. This is the event $C \cup M$. The percentage of all phones needing rework is then given by $P(C \cup M)$. Using the addition rule, the percentage of phones needing rework would be

$$P(C \cup M) = P(C) + P(M) - P(C \cap M)$$
$$= 0.02 + 0.05 - 0.01$$
$$= 0.06$$

Based on this information, roughly 6% of the cell phones will need rework.

Contingency Tables

Suppose each part in a lot is one of four colors (red [R], yellow [Y], green [G], or blue [B]) and one of three sizes (small [S], medium [M], or large [L]). These attributes can be displayed in a contingency table like the one in Table 6.5. (Contingency tables are also used to determine statistical independence of characteristics. This application is discussed in the "Goodness-of-fit Tests" section of this chapter.)

It is often useful to include the row and column totals for calculating quantities of interest, such as probabilities. The total number of parts ($N = 192$) is written in the bottom right-hand corner of the table. The row and column totals provide a great deal of information about the categories of interest. For example, the column total for red is 46. This indicates that the total number of red parts (regardless of size) in the lot is 46. In addition, the row total for medium parts is 57, which means that the total number of medium parts (regardless of color) is 57. The entries in each cell of the table itself (not including the row and column totals) represent the number of parts that have both characteristics. For example, 16 parts are both small *and* red.

Table 6.5 Contingency table of part color and part size.

	Red	Yellow	Green	Blue	Totals
Small	16	21	14	19	70
Medium	12	11	19	15	57
Large	18	12	21	14	65
Totals	46	44	54	48	192

EXAMPLE 6.13

It is desired to determine several probabilities using the contingency table given in Table 6.5. Assume that one of the parts is selected at random.

The probability that the part is small would be

$$P(S) = \frac{70}{192} = 0.365$$

Continued

The probability that the part is red would be

$$P(R) = \frac{46}{192} = 0.240$$

The probability that the part is small *and* red would be

$$P(S \cap R) = \frac{16}{192} = 0.083$$

The probability that the part is small *or* red is

$$P(S \cup R) = P(S) + P(R) - P(S \cap R)$$
$$= 0.365 + 0.240 - 0.083$$
$$= 0.522$$

Using the same formulas, the probability that a randomly selected part is yellow would be $P(Y) = 0.229$. The probability that the part is red or yellow would be

$$P(R \cup Y) = P(R) + P(Y) - P(R \cap Y)$$
$$= 0.240 + 0.229 - 0$$
$$= 0.469$$

Notice that the events "red" and "yellow" are mutually exclusive (a part cannot be both red and yellow). The special addition rule could have been used to find this probability:

$$P(R \cup Y) = P(R) + P(Y)$$
$$= 0.240 + 0.229$$
$$= 0.469$$

Conditional Probability

Following is an example of conditional probability.

EXAMPLE 6.14

Continuing with the previous example, suppose the selected part is *known* to be green. With this knowledge, what is the probability that the part is large?

Solution:

It is a given that the part is one of the 54 green parts. Now, the number of the 54 green parts that are large is 21. Therefore, the probability that a part will be large, given that it is green is 21/54 = 0.389.

The previous example involves conditional probability. It is referred to as conditional probability because it is conditioned on the fact that the part is green. In the example, the "probability that the part is large given that it is green" is denoted $P(L \mid G)$. It is useful to remember that the category to the right of the $\mid$ sign represents the *given* condition.

Suppose there are two events A and B. The probability that event A occurs given that event B has already occurred is

$$P(A \mid B) = \frac{P(A \cap B)}{P(B)} \qquad (6.14)$$

EXAMPLE 6.15

Using the information given in Table 6.5, find:

a. The probability that a part is small given that it is blue

b. The probability that a small part is blue

c. The probability that a green part is red

Solution:

a. $P(S \mid B) = \dfrac{P(S \cap B)}{P(B)} = \dfrac{\left(\dfrac{19}{192}\right)}{\left(\dfrac{48}{192}\right)} = \dfrac{19}{48} = 0.396$

b. The given condition is that the part is small. Given that the part is small, the probability that it is blue is

$P(B \mid S) = \dfrac{P(B \cap S)}{P(S)} = \dfrac{\left(\dfrac{19}{192}\right)}{\left(\dfrac{70}{192}\right)} = \dfrac{19}{70} = 0.271$

Note that $P(B \cap S) = P(S \cap B)$.

c. $P(R \mid G) = \dfrac{P(R \cap G)}{P(G)} = \dfrac{\left(\dfrac{0}{192}\right)}{\left(\dfrac{54}{192}\right)} = \dfrac{0}{54} = 0$

Note that red and green are mutually exclusive, so $P(R \cap G) = 0$.

If the practitioner has any two of the three probabilities needed to calculate the conditional probability given earlier, the third unknown probability can be found. The conditional probability can be rewritten as

$$P(A \cap B) = P(A \mid B)P(B) \qquad (6.15)$$

This is sometimes referred to as the *general multiplication rule.* Verifying that this formula is valid will aid in understanding this concept.

EXAMPLE 6.16

Using the contingency table given in Table 6.5, it is known that the probability a part is red and medium is

$$P(R \cap M) = \frac{12}{192} = 0.0625$$

Using the general multiplication rule, the same result would be obtained:

$$P(R \cap M) = P(R \mid M)P(M) = \left(\frac{12}{57}\right)\left(\frac{57}{192}\right) = \frac{12}{192} = 0.0625$$

Independence and the Probability of Independent Events

Events are said to be *independent* if the occurrence of one event does not depend on the occurrence or lack of occurrence of another (or preceding) event. The probability of two independent events occurring can be found by multiplying the individual probabilities of each event. If two events A and B are independent of one another, then the probability of both event A and event B occurring is

$$P(A \cap B) = P(A)P(B) \qquad (6.16)$$

For more than two independent events, the independence rule can be extended as

$$P(A \cap B \cap C \cap \ldots) = P(A)P(B)P(C) \ldots \qquad (6.17)$$

EXAMPLE 6.17

Assume that the probability that a blood specimen contains high levels of lead contamination is 0.05. Levels of contamination from one person to the next (thus, one sample to the next) are assumed to be independent. If two such samples are analyzed, then the probability that both will contain high levels of contamination is

P(both contaminated) = P(1st contaminated ∩ 2nd contaminated)
$$= P(\text{1st contaminated})P(\text{2nd contaminated})$$
$$= (0.05)(0.05)$$
$$= 0.0025$$

Recall the definition of conditional probability. If two events A and B are known to be independent, then $P(A \cap B) = P(A)P(B)$. Therefore, if two events are independent, the probability that event A occurs given that event B has already occurred is

$$P(A \mid B) = \frac{P(A \cap B)}{P(B)} = \frac{P(A)P(B)}{P(B)} = P(A)$$

In other words, knowing that event B has occurred does not affect the probability that event A will occur. In situations where objects or items are selected at random, one after the other, the items are said to be independent if the first item chosen is placed back into the group before the second item is chosen (with replacement).

EXAMPLE 6.18

A box holds 129 parts, of which 6 are defective. A part is randomly drawn from the box and placed in a fixture. A second part is then drawn from the box. This is referred to as drawing without replacement. What is the probability that the *second* part is defective (note that there is no condition on the first part chosen)? Let D_i represent the event where the *i*th part chosen is defective, and let G_i represent the event where the *i*th part is good.

Solution:

Of interest in this example is $P(D_2)$. There are two mutually exclusive events that can result in a defective part on the second draw: good on first draw and defective on second or else defective on first and defective on second. Symbolically these two events are $(G_1 \cap D_2)$ or else $(D_1 \cap D_2)$. The first step is to find the probability for each of these events. By the general multiplication rule:

$$P(G_1 \cap D_2) = P(G_1)P(D_2 \mid G_1) = \left(\frac{123}{129}\right)\left(\frac{6}{128}\right) = 0.045$$

and

$$P(D_1 \cap D_2) = P(D_1)P(D_2 \mid D_1) = \left(\frac{6}{129}\right)\left(\frac{5}{128}\right) = 0.002$$

Since the two events $(G_1 \cap D_2)$ and $(D_1 \cap D_2)$ are mutually exclusive, the special addition rule can be used to find the probability that the second part is defective:

$$P(D_2) = 0.045 + 0.002 = 0.047$$

When drawing two parts at random without replacement, what is the probability that one will be good (G) and one defective (D)?

Solution:

Drawing one good and one defective can occur in two mutually exclusive ways (using Equation (6.12)):

$$P(G \cap D) = P(G_1 \cap D_2) + P(G_2 \cap D_1)$$

From the previous example $P(G_1 \cap D_2) = 0.045$. Use the general multiplication rule to find $P(G_2 \cap D_1)$:

$$P(G_2 \cap D_1) = P(D_1)P(G_2 \mid D_1) = \left(\frac{6}{129}\right)\left(\frac{123}{128}\right) = 0.045$$

Therefore, the probability that one randomly selected part will be good and one will be defective is

$$P(G \cap D) = 0.045 + 0.045 = 0.090$$

Summary of Key Probability Rules

For events A and B:

Special addition rule: $P(A \cup B) = P(A) + P(B)$ (Use only if A and B are mutually exclusive)

General addition rule: $P(A \cup B) = P(A) + P(B) - P(A \cap B)$ (Always true)

Special multiplication rule: $P(A \cap B) = P(A)P(B)$ (Use only if A and B are independent)

General multiplication rule: $P(A \cap B) = P(A)P(B \mid A)$ (Always true)

Conditional probability: $P(B \mid A) = P(A \cap B)/P(A)$

Mutually exclusive (or disjoint):

1. A and B are mutually exclusive if they cannot occur simultaneously

2. If A and B are mutually exclusive, then $P(A \cap B) = 0$

3. If A and B are mutually exclusive, then $P(A \cup B) = P(A) + P(B)$

Independence:

1. A and B are independent events if the occurrence of one does not change the probability that the other occurs

2. If A and B are independent events, then $P(B \mid A) = P(B)$ (and $P(A \mid B) = P(A)$)

3. If A and B are independent events, then $P(A \cap B) = P(A)P(B)$

PROBABILITY DISTRIBUTIONS

This section focuses on the two kinds of probability distributions: continuous distributions and discrete distributions:

- *Continuous distributions* are used when the parameter being measured can be expressed on a continuous scale. Examples include the diameter of piston rings, tensile strength, output voltage, and so on.

- *Discrete distributions* are used when the parameter being measured takes on only certain values, such as integers 0, 1, 2, ... Examples include the number of defects or the number of nonconformities.

Theoretical Probability Functions

Before commencing discussion of the continuous and discrete distributions, important theoretical probability concepts must be introduced. For continuous distributions, the probability density function and the cumulative density function will be discussed. These are also referred to as, respectively, probability distribution functions and cumulative distribution functions. For discrete distributions, the probability mass function and the cumulative distribution functions will be discussed.

Probability Density Functions and Cumulative Density Functions

Probability density functions (pdfs) are mathematical expressions that describe the probability distribution of a continuous random variable. The pdf is denoted by $f(x)$. In most cases, the probabilities associated with some random variable can be described by a pdf. Figure 6.11 represents a pdf for a random variable X. The x-axis represents all possible values of the random variable; the y-axis represents the pdf $f(x)$. Suppose it is desired to find the probability that the random variable X lies between two real numbers a and b (i.e., $P(a < X < b)$). Graphically, this probability is the shaded area under the curve $f(x)$ and between the X values of a and b (see Figure 6.11).

For any continuous random variable X, the pdf $f(x)$ is a function with the following properties:

$$f(x) \geq 0 \text{ for all } x \tag{6.18}$$

$$\int_{-\infty}^{\infty} f(x)dx = 1 \tag{6.19}$$

$$P(a \leq X \leq b) = \int_{a}^{b} f(x)dx \tag{6.20}$$

Equation (6.20) is the area under the curve $f(x)$ and between the values a and b.

The first property (Equation (6.18)) guarantees that all probability values are nonnegative. The second property (Equation (6.19)) can be compared to the concept of sample space given in the "Collecting and Summarizing Data" section of this chapter. That is, the total area under the curve must equal one (or 100%) and can be verified by integrating $f(x)$ over all real numbers. Equation (6.20) simply describes how the probability that X will lie between two real numbers a and b can be determined by integrating $f(x)$ over the range $[a, b]$. Although these calculations may seem complicated, calculus is not necessary to find most of the probabilities

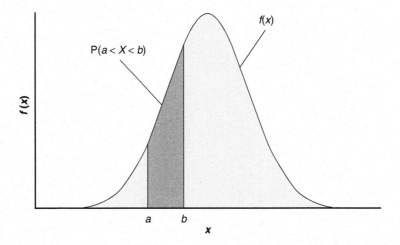

Figure 6.11 A probability density function for a random variable X.

that are needed in quality engineering. Tables with probabilities for specific distributions are available as well as software that routinely calculates these probabilities. It should be noted that for continuous distributions, the probability that the random variable equals some specific value is always zero, that is, P($X = a$) = 0. As a result

$$P(a \leq X \leq b) = P(a < X \leq b) = P(a \leq X < b) = P(a < X < b)$$

A *cumulative distribution function* (cdf) is denoted by $F(x)$ and describes the cumulative probability for a random variable X:

$$F(x) = P(X \leq x) = \int_{-\infty}^{x} f(v)dv \tag{6.21}$$

The cdf can be used to find probabilities of interest for the random variable X. Suppose a and b are any real numbers where $a < b$. Then,

$$P(X \leq a) = F(a) \tag{6.22}$$

$$P(a < X < b) = P(X \leq b) - P(X \leq a) = F(b) - F(a) \tag{6.23}$$

$$P(X > a) = 1 - P(X \leq a) = 1 - F(a) \tag{6.24}$$

Probability Mass Functions and CDFs

Probability mass functions (pmfs) are expressions that describe the probability outcomes of a discrete random variable X. The pmf is denoted by $p(x)$ and defined for every number the random variable can take on, x, by

$$p(x) = P(X = x) \tag{6.25}$$

The pmf for the medication errors in Example 6.11 is shown graphically in Figure 6.12. The probability is plotted on the y-axis and the values for the random

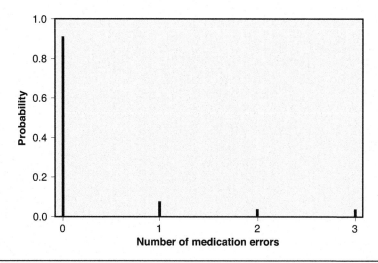

Figure 6.12   A line graph of the pmf for random variable X.

variable on the x-axis. In Figure 6.12, the probability associated with 0 medication errors is 0.9 and represented by the height of the line in the graph.

For any discrete random variable X, the pmf $p(x)$ is a function with the following properties:

$$p(x) \geq 0 \text{ for all } x \tag{6.26}$$

$$\sum_{all\ x} p(x) = 1 \tag{6.27}$$

The condition specified in Equation (6.26) ensures that all probabilities are non-negative, and the condition specified in Equation (6.27) ensures that the sum of all probabilities is equal to 1.

The cdf for discrete random variables is also denoted $F(x)$ and is defined by

$$F(x) = P(X \leq x) = \sum_{y:y \leq x} p(y) \tag{6.28}$$

For any number x, $F(x)$ is the probability that the observed value of X will be at most x. See Devore (2016) for further details.

General Form of Expected Value and Variance

In this section, formulas for expected value and variance for continuous and discrete distributions are presented.

The expected value of a continuous random variable X with pdf $f(x)$ is

$$E(X) = \mu_X = \int_{-\infty}^{\infty} x f(x) dx \tag{6.29}$$

The variance of a continuous random variable X with pdf $f(x)$ is

$$V(X) = \sigma_X^2 = \int_{-\infty}^{\infty} (x - \mu_X)^2 f(x) dx \tag{6.30}$$

The expected value of a discrete random variable X with pmf $p(x)$ is

$$E(X) = \mu_X = \sum_{all\ x} x p(x) \tag{6.31}$$

for all outcomes x from the distribution. Remember, $f(x)$ describes the probability that x will occur.

The variance of a discrete random variable X with pmf $p(x)$ is

$$V(X) = \sigma_X^2 = \sum_{all\ x} (x - \mu)^2 p(x) \tag{6.32}$$

As shown previously, the standard deviation for a random variable X, discrete or continuous, is the positive square root of the variance.

Continuous Distributions

> Define and distinguish between these
> distributions such as normal, uniform,
> exponential, lognormal, Weibull, Student's t,
> and F. (Analyze)
>
> **Body of Knowledge VI.C.1**

In this section several common continuous distributions are presented.

Normal Distribution

An important family of continuous distributions is the *normal distribution*. Example applications of the normal distribution include modeling height, weight, sample averages, and many other quality characteristics. The normal distribution is a symmetric, bell-shaped distribution. The parameters of the normal distribution are the population mean μ and the population variance σ^2. The normal distribution is depicted in Figure 6.13. The center line represents the mean of the distribution. The area under the curve represents *probability* (or percentage or proportion). The probability can be determined using the standard normal curve table in Appendix E, "Areas under Standard Normal Distribution to the Left of Z-Values." In a normal distribution, a Z-score for a random variable X is defined as the number of standard deviations between X and the mean of the distribution. Specifically,

---

EXAMPLE 6.19

Recall the number of medication errors provided in Table 6.4. The probability of 0, 1, 2, and 3 errors is 0.9, 0.07, 0.02, and 0.01, respectively. The expected number of medication errors is:

$$E(X) = \mu_X = \sum xp(x) = 0(0.90) + 1(0.07) + 2(0.02) + 3(0.01) = 0.14$$

The variance of the number of medication errors is:

$$V(X) = \sum (x - \mu)^2 p(x)$$

$$= (0 - 0.14)^2(0.90) + (1 - 0.14)^2(0.07) + (2 - 0.14)^2(0.02) + (3 - 0.14)^2(0.01)$$

$$= 0.2204$$

$$Z = \frac{X - \mu}{\sigma} \tag{6.33}$$

To illustrate, suppose X follows a normal distribution with mean $\mu = 20$ and standard deviation $\sigma = 4$. The Z-score using Equation (6.33) for an X value of 14 is

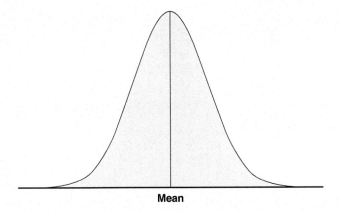

Mean

Figure 6.13   Probability density function for the normal distribution.

$$Z = \frac{X - \mu}{\sigma} = \frac{14 - 20}{4} = -1.5$$

That is, the value of 14 is 1.5 standard deviations *below* the population mean of 20.

By transforming the original random variable into a Z-score, one can find probabilities without having to use calculus, as demonstrated in Example 6.20.

Standard Normal Distribution

If a random variable is normally distributed with mean $\mu = 0$ and variance $\sigma^2 = 1$, it is called a *standard normal random variable* and often denoted as Z. Probabilities for the standard normal distribution are given in Appendix E. The values in this table are the cumulative probabilities $P(Z \leq z)$, where capital Z represents a random variable and lowercase z is a real number. The cumulative probabilities in Appendix E can be used to find any probability of interest involving a random variable that is normally distributed. Some examples illustrating the use of Appendix E follow.

EXAMPLE 6.20

Let *Z* be a random variable that follows a standard normal distribution. Find the probability that *Z* will be less than 2.5.

Solution:

The probability of interest is $P(Z < 2.5)$. This probability is shown graphically in Figure 6.14. It shows that the probability of interest is the area to the left of 2.5.

In Appendix E, the values of Z are written down the left-hand column and across the top of the table. The entries in the body of the table are the cumulative probabilities, $P(Z \leq z)$. In this example the z value is 2.5. In the table, read down the left-hand column to find the value 2.5, then across until you reach the column heading of 0 (since the value in the second decimal place of the z value is 0). The entry in the body of the table for the row of 2.5 and the column of 0 is 0.9938. Therefore, the probability that the random variable Z is less than 2.5 is 0.9938.

Continued

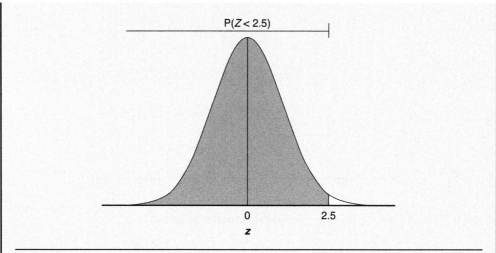

Figure 6.14 Probability density function for a standard normal distribution.

EXAMPLE 6.21

Find the probability that the random variable Z is greater than -2.5.

Solution:

The probability of interest is $P(Z > -2.5)$. In Appendix E, the probability given in the body of the table for -2.5 is 0.0062. But the probabilities in this table are the probabilities that Z is at most that value. That is, $P(Z < -2.5) = 0.0062$, but the objective is $P(Z > -2.5)$. To find this probability, use the result that the total area under the curve (total probability) must equal 1. Therefore, if $P(Z < -2.5) = 0.0062$, then $P(Z > -2.5) = 0.9938$. More generally, this probability is as follows:

$$P(Z > -2.5) = 1 - P(Z < -2.5) = 1 - 0.0062 = 0.9938$$

EXAMPLE 6.22

Find the probability that Z lies between 1.42 and 2.33.

Solution:

The probability of interest is $P(1.42 < Z < 2.33)$. The probability is displayed graphically in Figure 6.15.

The area (thus the probability) of interest lies under the curve and between 1.42 and 2.33, as illustrated in Figure 6.15. The probability of interest can be found using the cumulative probabilities from Appendix E and subtraction:

$$P(1.42 < Z < 2.33) = P(Z < 2.33) - P(Z < 1.42) = 0.9901 - 0.9222 = 0.0679$$

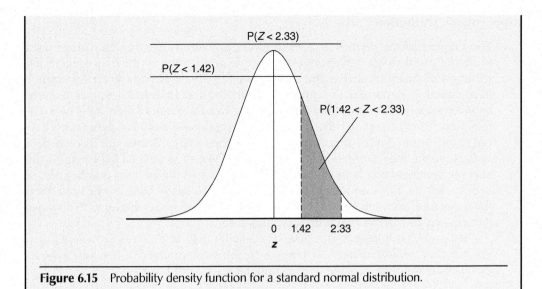

Figure 6.15 Probability density function for a standard normal distribution.

One can now find the probability for any normal random variable by using a simple transformation.

If X is a random variable that follows a normal distribution with mean μ and variance σ^2, then the random variable Z is also normally distributed with mean $\mu = 0$ and variance $\sigma^2 = 1$. That is, Z is a random variable that follows a standard normal distribution.

EXAMPLE 6.23

A product-fill operation produces net weights that are normally distributed with mean $\mu = 8.06$ ounces and standard deviation $\sigma = 0.37$ ounces. Estimate the percentage of containers that have a net weight less than 7.08 ounces.

Solution:

Let X represent the weight of the containers. The probability of interest is $P(X < 7.08)$. Transform X into the random variable Z using the relationship

$$Z = \frac{X - \mu}{\sigma}$$

then from Appendix E, "Areas under Standard Normal Distribution to the Left of Z-Values," find the appropriate probability.

$$P(X < 7.08) = P\left[\frac{X - \mu}{\sigma} < \frac{7.08 - 8.06}{0.37}\right] = P(Z < -2.65) = 0.0040$$

This indicates that approximately 0.40% of the containers have a net weight less than 7.08 ounces. This can also be stated as the probability that a randomly selected container will have a net weight less than 7.08 is approximately 0.0040.

Exponential Distribution

The *exponential distribution* is a continuous probability distribution often used to model problems in reliability. An example application of the exponential distribution includes modeling the time between patient arrivals to an emergency department. In particular, the exponential distribution models the time or distance between successive events (such as failures) when the events follow a Poisson distribution. The Poisson distribution is often a reasonable model of defects in material or the number of failures in systems. (The Poisson distribution for discrete data is discussed in the next section of this chapter.) When it is desired to determine the average time between failures, calculate the inverse of the average number of failures or defects. For example, if there is an average of 0.69 failures per hour, then the mean time between failures (MTBF) is $1/0.69 = 1.45$ hours. Figure 6.16 displays an exponential distribution with a mean of 1.45.

Suppose X represents the time or distance between successive events of a Poisson process with mean λ (where $\lambda > 0$). The random variable X is said to be an exponential random variable with parameter λ. The pdf for X is

$$f(x) = \lambda e^{-\lambda x}, \text{ for } x \geq 0 \tag{6.34}$$

The cdf for an exponentially distributed random variable X is given by

$$F(x) = P(X \leq x) = 1 - e^{-\lambda x}, \text{ for } x \geq 0 \tag{6.35}$$

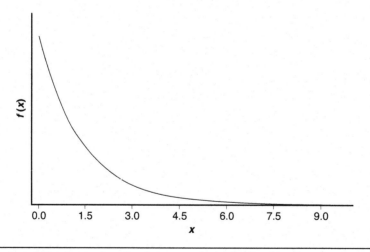

Figure 6.16   Probability density function for an exponentially distributed random variable.

EXAMPLE 6.24

The time between calls to a customer service center is an exponentially distributed random variable with a mean time between calls of two minutes. What is the probability that the next phone call will be received in the next one minute?

Solution:

Let X represent the time between phone calls received at the customer service center. X follows an exponential distribution with parameter $\lambda = 0.5$ (recall that the mean of an exponential distribution is $1/\lambda$ and the mean in this case is two minutes; thus $\lambda = 1/2 = 0.5$). The probability of interest is $P(X < 1)$ and can be found using the cdf for the exponential:

$$P(X < 1) = F(1) = 1 - e^{-0.5(1)} = 1 - 0.6065 = 0.3935$$

Therefore, the probability that the next phone call will be received within the next minute is 0.3935.

Weibull Distribution

The *Weibull distribution* is a commonly used distribution in areas such as reliability. The Weibull is extremely flexible in modeling failure distributions, for example, the fatigue time of a component or product, that can take on many different shapes. Let X represent a random variable that follows a Weibull distribution. The pdf for the Weibull distribution is

$$f(x) = \left(\frac{\beta}{\theta}\right)\left(\frac{x-\gamma}{\theta}\right)^{\beta-1} e^{-\left(\frac{x-\gamma}{\theta}\right)^{\beta}}, \text{ for } x \geq 0 \tag{6.36}$$

where

β is the shape parameter ($\beta > 0$)

θ is the scale parameter ($\theta > 0$)

γ is a threshold parameter ($\gamma \geq 0$)

This pdf is referred to as a three-parameter Weibull distribution. The threshold parameter allows the user to model a distribution that cannot practically begin at zero. It simply shifts the beginning point away from zero. The pdf for the Weibull distribution with $\beta = 1.2$ and $\theta = 20$ is displayed in Figure 6.17.

The cdf for a random variable that follows a three-parameter Weibull distribution with parameters β, θ, and γ is

$$P(X \leq x) = F(x) = 1 - e^{-\left(\frac{x-\gamma}{\theta}\right)^{\beta}} \tag{6.37}$$

The cdf can be used to easily find probabilities associated with the Weibull distribution.

The beauty of the Weibull function is that it takes on many shapes depending on the value of β. For example, when $\beta = 1$, the function is exponential, and when $\beta = 3.5$, the function is approximately the normal distribution. If the threshold parameter is set equal to zero (i.e., $\gamma = 0$), then the three-parameter Weibull reduces to the two-parameter Weibull distribution—another commonly used distribution in reliability. The Weibull function is sometimes used for reliability data when the underlying distribution is unknown. This is discussed in more detail in Chapter 3.

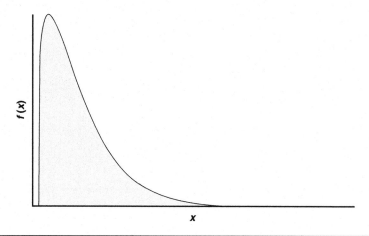

Figure 6.17   Probability density function for the Weibull distribution.

Continuous Uniform Distribution

The *continuous uniform distribution* is one that has a flat probability distribution between two points a and b. That is, if each value of the random variable has the same probability of occurring, the distribution is called the uniform distribution. The plot of a uniform distribution has a horizontal line as its upper boundary. An example is given in Figure 6.18.

The pdf for the continuous uniform distribution on the interval $[a, b]$ is

$$f(x) = \begin{cases} \dfrac{1}{b-a}, & a \leq x \leq b \\ 0, & \text{otherwise} \end{cases} \tag{6.38}$$

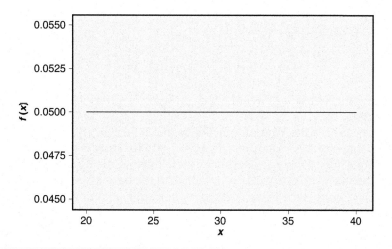

Figure 6.18   Continuous uniform probability distribution.

The cdf is

$$P(X \le x) = F(x) = \begin{cases} 0, & x < a \\ \dfrac{(x-a)}{(b-a)} & a \le x < b \\ 1 & b \le x \end{cases} \tag{6.39}$$

The cdf can easily be used to find probabilities associated with the uniform distribution, using the relationships shown previously in this section.

EXAMPLE 6.25

The thickness of a manufactured airplane part is uniformly distributed between 2.2 and 2.8 millimeters. What is the probability that the thickness is less than 2.6 millimeters?

Solution:

Let X represent the thickness of the airplane part. The objective is to find $P(X < 2.6)$.

Since what is needed is X less than some value, $P(X < 2.6) = F(2.6)$. Since the number of interest (2.6) lies between the endpoints 2.2 and 2.8, the equation to use is $F(X) = (x - a)/(b - a)$. The probability that the thickness is less than 2.6 millimeters is

$$P(X < 2.6) = F(2.6) = (2.6 - 2.2)/(2.8 - 2.2) = 0.667$$

Lognormal Distribution

If a variable X follows a normal distribution, then the variable $Y = e^X$ follows a *lognormal distribution*. This distribution has applications in modeling life spans for products, response time, and time-to-failure data, as well as certain economic variables. An example application of the lognormal distribution is modeling systolic blood pressure in adults or modeling fatigue time of a product. Some important properties of the lognormal distribution are the following:

- It assumes only positive values

- It is a right-skewed distribution

- It is the distribution of the random variable whose logarithm follows the normal distribution

Suppose X follows a normal distribution with mean μ_X and variance σ_X^2, and $Y = e^X$. Then, Y follows a lognormal distribution with the following mean and variance:

$$\mu_Y = E(Y) = e^{\mu_X + (1/2)\sigma_X^2} \tag{6.40}$$

$$V(Y) = \sigma_Y^2 = e^{2\mu_X + \sigma_X^2}(e^{\sigma_X^2} - 1) \tag{6.41}$$

When the data follow a lognormal distribution, a transformation of data can be done to make the data follow a normal distribution to find probabilities, construct confidence intervals, and conduct tests of hypotheses (all of which depend on the assumption that the log-transformed data follow a normal distribution).

Summary of Continuous Distributions

Table 6.6 summarizes the pdf, mean (expected value), and variance for certain continuous distributions.

Discrete Distributions

> Define and distinguish between these distributions such as binomial, Poisson, hypergeometric, and multinomial. (Analyze)
>
> **Body of Knowledge VI.C.2**

Typical applications for discrete distributions in quality engineering include situations where the variable of interest is either the number of nonconformities or the number of nonconforming units in a sample. The variable represents a count and takes on values of zero or a positive whole number.

Binomial Distribution

The *binomial distribution* can be applied in situations where the experiment can result in only one of two possible outcomes, for example, good/bad, go/no-go, with/without, conforming/nonconforming, success/failure. In addition, the outcome of one run of the experiment (often referred to as a *trial*) does not affect the outcomes of subsequent trials; that is, the trials are said to be independent. The outcomes are often referred to as a success or failure. Examples include the number of heads on 50 flips of a fair coin and the number of manufactured parts that are out of specification. In one type of problem that is frequently encountered, the

Table 6.6 pdf, mean, and variance for certain continuous distributions.

Distribution	pdf ($f(x)$)	Mean	Variance
Normal	$\frac{1}{\sqrt{2\pi}\sigma}e^{-\frac{(x-\mu)^2}{2\sigma^2}}$	μ	σ^2
Exponential	$\lambda e^{-\lambda x}$	$\frac{1}{\lambda}$	$\frac{1}{\lambda^2}$
Weibull (three-parameter)	$\left(\frac{\beta}{\theta}\right)\left(\frac{x-\gamma}{\theta}\right)^{\beta-1}e^{-\left(\frac{x-\gamma}{\theta}\right)^{\beta}}$	$\gamma+\theta\Gamma\left(\frac{1}{\beta}+1\right)$	$\theta^2\left[\Gamma\left(\frac{2}{\beta}+1\right)-\Gamma^2\left(\frac{1}{\beta}+1\right)\right]$
Uniform	$\frac{1}{b-a}$	$\frac{a+b}{2}$	$\frac{(b-a)^2}{12}$

Note: $\gamma(n) = (n-1)!$ for integer value n and $\Gamma(z) = \int_0^{\infty} x^{z-1}e^{-x}dx$ for non-integer value z.

engineer needs to determine the probability of obtaining a certain number of non-conforming units in a sample. Example applications of the binomial distribution include modeling the number of defective units in a lot of n items, the number of successful tests of n components, and the number of positive outcomes in a clinical trial with 100 participants.

The necessary conditions for a random variable to follow the binomial distribution are as follows:

- There are a fixed number of observations or trials n.

- The n trials are independent.

- Each trial results in one of two possible outcomes (success or failure).

- The probability of a success is denoted by p; the probability of a failure is then $1 - p$. The probability of a success is assumed constant trial to trial.

Suppose an experiment consists of n independent trials. Let X represent the number of successes in n trials. Furthermore, let p be the probability of success in one trial. Then, the probability of getting x successes in n trials is described by the pmf

$$p(x) = P(X = x) = {}_nC_x p^x (1-p)^{n-x} \tag{6.42}$$

where

x is the number of successes, with a probability of each success given by p

The number of failures is then $n - x$, where $1 - p$ is the probability of a failure

The combination nCx represents the number of ways x successes can occur in n trials, where

$$_nC_x = \binom{n}{x} = \frac{n!}{x!(n-x)!} \text{ and } n! = n(n-1)(n-2)...(1) \tag{6.43}$$

EXAMPLE 6.26

Ten manufactured parts are randomly selected from a batch where it is believed that the percent nonconforming is 15%. It is important to determine the probability that exactly 2 out of the 10 manufactured parts will be nonconforming. Success is defined as a nonconforming part. Let X represent the number of nonconforming parts. In this scenario, $n = 10$, $x = 2$, and $p = 0.15$. Then,

$$_nC_x = {}_{10}C_2 = \binom{10}{2} = \frac{10!}{2!(10-2)!} = 45$$

and, using Equation (6.42),

$$P(X = 2) = {}_{10}C_2 (0.15)^2 (1-0.15)^{10-2}$$
$$= 45(0.0225)(0.85)^8$$
$$= 0.2759$$

The probability that a sample of size 10 will have exactly 2 nonconforming parts is approximately 0.2759.

EXAMPLE 6.27

Consider the previous example. Suppose now there is interest in the probability of finding fewer than 2 nonconforming parts. If X represents the number of nonconforming parts, the probability that fewer than 2 nonconforming parts will be found in the sample is $P(X < 2)$.

Solution:

The value 2 is not included in this event of interest. So the probability can be written equivalently as

$$P(X < 2) = P(X \leq 1) = P(X = 0) + P(X = 1)$$

In this case, the binomial formula must be applied twice:

$$P(X < 2) = P(X \leq 1) = P(X = 0) + P(X = 1)$$

$$= {}_{10}C_0 (0.15)^0 (1 - 0.15)^{10-0} + {}_{10}C_1 (0.15)^1 (1 - 0.15)^{10-1}$$

$$= 1(1)(0.85)^{10} + 10(0.15)(0.85)^9$$

$$= 0.1969 + 0.3474$$

$$= 0.5443$$

The probability that fewer than 2 parts out of 10 will be nonconforming is approximately 0.5443.

Poisson Distribution

When observations take place over a continuum, such as time or space, there is not a finite series of discrete trials and the Poisson distribution may be used to model these events. Example applications of the Poisson distribution include modeling the number of medication errors for patients in a hospital, the number of nonconformities in a lot of manufactured products, the number of dents on a table, and the number of cases of the flu in a city.

The necessary conditions for a random variable to follow a Poisson distribution are as follows:

- The counts or occurrences are independent of each other

- The probability that a count occurs in an interval is the same for *all* intervals of that size or length

Let λ be a parameter representing the mean number of counts over an interval. Let X represent the number of counts in the interval. Then, the probability that x counts occur in an interval is described by the pmf

$$p(x) = P(X = x) = \frac{e^{-\lambda} \lambda^x}{x!}, \text{ for } x = 0, 1, 2, \ldots \tag{6.44}$$

EXAMPLE 6.28

A company has a rate of serious accidents of three per year. The probability that at most one serious accident will occur during the next year is as follows. The probability of interest is P($X \leq 1$) = P($X = 0$) + P($X = 1$).

$$P(X \leq 1) = P(X = 0) + P(X = 1)$$

$$= \frac{e^{-3}3^0}{0!} + \frac{e^{-3}3^1}{1!}$$

$$= 0.05 + 0.149$$

$$= 0.199$$

Therefore, the probability that at most one serious accident will occur during the next year is approximately 0.2.

Hypergeometric Distribution

When sampling from a finite population where independence is not assumed—for example, drawing cards without replacement from a deck of 52 cards, or selecting a sample of items from an isolated lot—the probability changes with each observation.

The *hypergeometric distribution* is used when items are drawn without replacement from a population of interest; specifically, the items are not returned to the population before the next items are drawn. It is often used for samples taken from small populations. The items must fall into one of two categories, such as conforming or nonconforming. Recall that the binomial distribution assumes either an infinite population or sampling with replacement (independent events). There can be a considerable difference when the population is small (results will be similar when the total population is large).

Suppose there is a finite population of size N from which a sample of size n is drawn (without replacement). Furthermore, let A represent the number of nonconforming units in the population, and let x represent the number of nonconforming units in the sample. The probability of obtaining x nonconforming items in a sample of size n for this situation is given by

$$f(x) = \frac{\binom{A}{x}\binom{N-A}{n-x}}{\binom{N}{n}}, \text{ for } x = 0, 1, 2, \ldots n \qquad (6.45)$$

where the combinations are as follows:

$\binom{A}{x}$ is the number of ways of choosing x nonconforming units from A total possible nonconforming units

$\binom{N-A}{n-x}$ is the number of ways of choosing $(n-x)$ conforming units from a total of $(N-A)$ conforming units in the population

$\binom{N}{n}$ is the number of ways of choosing a sample of size n from a population of size N

EXAMPLE 6.29

The risk of implanting a biomedical device that may be nonconforming is important to quantify. Several assumptions must be made to obtain an accurate estimate of the risk, such as whether the devices have the same failure rate, how long the devices are stored before implantation, and so on. In addition, the number of nonconforming medical devices in a population of devices often has to be estimated using prior knowledge and/or previous data. For one of these biomedical devices manufactured by a local company, there has been one known failure after implantation within the last month. Based on prior information, it is assumed that out of 200 devices there are 3 that are nonconforming. If 30 medical devices are randomly selected out of the 200 devices, what is the probability that exactly one device will be nonconforming?

Solution:

For this situation, $N = 200$, $n = 30$, $A = 3$, and $x = 1$, and the probability of interest is $P(X = 1)$, which can be calculated with Equation (6.45) as:

$$P(X = 1) = \frac{\binom{3}{1}\binom{200-3}{30-1}}{\binom{200}{30}} = 0.3281$$

The probability of selecting a sample of 30 devices and one is nonconforming is 0.3281.

Other Discrete Distributions

The *multinomial distribution* is used when an experiment consisting of n trials could result in *more* than two possible outcomes; the outcome is placed into one of several categories. For example, a randomly selected part could be classified as good, fair, or poor. As another example, a nonconforming part from a manufacturing process could be due to machine wear, temperature, or a problem with raw material.

The *geometric distribution* involves independent trials that can result in one of only two possible outcomes, similar to the binomial distribution. However, for the geometric distribution the number of trials is not fixed. The random variable X represents the number of trials until the first success is obtained. An example would be determining the probability that x acceptable parts are produced before the first nonconforming part is generated, or the number of darts necessary until the bull's-eye is hit.

The geometric distribution is a special case of a more general distribution known as the *Pascal distribution* (also known as the *negative binomial distribution*). For the geometric distribution, sampling is terminated once the first success is obtained. For the Pascal distribution, sampling is terminated only after a fixed number of successes r have been obtained. Obviously, when $r = 1$ there is the special case of the geometric distribution. An example of the negative binomial distribution is modeling the number of trials necessary until r components fail.

Summary of Discrete Distributions

The following rules can be applied for the binomial, Poisson, and hypergeometric distributions:

- Use with binary information (yes/no, conforming/nonconforming) and for nonconformities

- Use the hypergeometric distribution when $n > 5\%N$ and when the sample is taken without replacement

- Use the binomial distribution when the sample is taken with replacement or when $n < 5\%N$ and the sample is taken without replacement

- Use the Poisson distribution when there can be more than one nonconformity per item or as an approximation for the binomial distribution when $n > 100$ and $np < 10$

Figure 6.19 is an illustration of common rules of thumb for approximations. In this figure, H, B, P, and N represent the hypergeometric, binomial, Poisson, and normal distributions, respectively. Table 6.7 summarizes the pmf, mean, and variance for certain discrete distributions.

Central Limit Theorem

An important statistical principle is the *central limit theorem*, which states that

The distribution of sample averages will tend toward a normal distribution as the sample size n approaches infinity.

The central limit theorem guarantees at least approximate normality for the distribution of sample averages, even if the population from which the sample is drawn is not normally distributed. A frequent question in the minds of quality engineers is the validity of $\bar{x}$ control charts (discussed in the "Statistical Process Control" section of this chapter) when the population is not normally distributed.

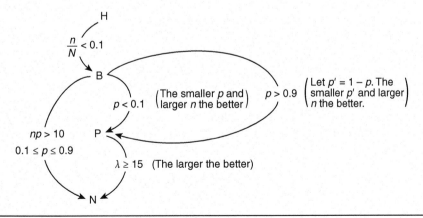

Figure 6.19   Approximations to probability distributions.

Source: D. C. Montgomery, *Introduction to Statistical Quality Control*, 7th ed. (Hoboken, NJ: John Wiley & Sons, 2013).

Table 6.7 pmf, mean, and variance for certain discrete distributions.

Distribution	pmf ($p(x)$)	Mean	Variance
Binomial	$_nC_x p^x (1-p)^{n-x}$	np	$np(1-p)$
Poisson	$\dfrac{e^{-\lambda}\lambda^x}{x!}$	λ	λ
Hypergeometric	$\dfrac{\dbinom{A}{x}\dbinom{N-A}{n-x}}{\dbinom{N}{n}}$	$\dfrac{nA}{N}$	$\dfrac{nA}{N}\dfrac{(N-A)(N-n)}{N(N-1)}$

Because the $\bar{x}$ control chart involves plotting averages, the central limit theorem implies that normality is approximately guaranteed. The approximation improves as the sample size n increases. In some cases, the approximation will be applicable for sample sizes as small as 10. In other situations, the required sample size for the approximation to be valid can be quite large (say, $n > 100$). Finally, if the underlying distribution of the data does not depart significantly from the normal distribution, sample sizes as small as $n = 3$ can be appropriate. For details on the normality assumption in statistical process control, see Montgomery (2013).

Suppose $X_1, X_2, \ldots, X_n$ is a random sample taken from a distribution with mean μ and variance σ^2. If n is sufficiently large, then the sample mean $\bar{X}$ follows approximately a normal distribution with $\mu_{\bar{x}} = \mu$ and variance $\sigma_{\bar{x}}^2 = \sigma^2/n$.

Notice that the definition does not state that the underlying distribution from which the sample is drawn must be normally distributed. The true form of the distribution does not have to be normally distributed as long as the sample size is sufficiently large. There have been several recommended cutoffs for large n, including $n > 40$ (Devore 2016).

However, if the underlying distribution is normal, then the large n requirement is not necessary. In this case, the sampling distribution of X will also follow a normal distribution with $\mu_x = \mu$ mean and variance $\sigma_x^2 = \sigma^2/n$.

An important application of the central limit theorem described here has been in calculating probabilities associated with the sample mean. In addition, it is important in statistical inference, statistical process control, process capability analysis, and so on, as will be seen in the remaining sections of this chapter.

Recall that if a random variable X follows a normally distributed random variable with mean μ and variance σ^2, then the random variable Z will follow a standard normal distribution with $\mu = 0$ and $\sigma^2 = 1$. By the central limit theorem stated above,

$$Z = \frac{\bar{X} - \mu_{\bar{x}}}{\sigma_{\bar{x}}} = \frac{\bar{X} - \mu}{\sigma/\sqrt{n}} \tag{6.46}$$

also follows a standard normal distribution with $\mu = 0$ and $\sigma^2 = 1$. Using this result, probabilities associated with the sample mean can be found.

EXAMPLE 6.30

Recall the product-fill operation, where the product-fill operation produces net weights that are normally distributed with mean $\mu = 8.06$ ounces and standard deviation $\sigma = 0.37$ ounces

a. What is the probability that a randomly selected container will weigh less than 7.08 ounces?

b. What is the probability that a sample of nine randomly selected containers will have an average net weight less than 7.08 ounces?

Solution:

Let X represent the weight of the containers.

a. The probability of interest is $P(X < 7.08)$. Transform X into the random variable Z using the relationship

$$Z = \frac{X - \mu}{\sigma}$$

then from Appendix E find the appropriate probability.

$$P(X < 7.08) = P\left(\frac{X - \mu}{\sigma} < \frac{7.08 - 8.06}{0.37}\right) = P(Z < -2.65) = 0.0040$$

Therefore, the probability that a randomly selected container will have a net weight less than 7.08 is approximately 0.0040. (Note that this is the same answer found previously.)

b. The probability of interest here is $P(\bar{X} < 7.08)$. Transform $\bar{X}$ into the random variable Z using the relationship

$$Z = \frac{\bar{X} - \mu}{\sigma / \sqrt{n}}:$$

$$P(\bar{X} < 7.08) = P\left(\frac{\bar{X} - \mu}{\sigma / \sqrt{n}} < \frac{7.08 - 8.06}{0.37 / \sqrt{9}}\right) = P(Z < -7.95) \cong 0$$

Therefore, it would be very unlikely that a random sample of nine such containers would have an average net weight less than 7.08 ounces.

Note: In the above example, the value $z = -7.95$ is not given in the standard normal table in Appendix E. The table values extend only from -3.59 to 3.59. If the z value is not in the table, this does not mean that it is not a possible value. When the value of z is not in the table, the probability of interest will be practically zero or one, depending on the area of interest under the curve and the sign on the z-value. For example, $P(Z < -7.95) \cong 0$, $P(Z > -7.95) \cong 1$, $P(Z < 7.95) \cong 1$, $P(Z > 7.95) \cong 0$.

Sampling Distributions

A *sampling distribution* is the probability distribution of a sample statistic. Several sampling distributions are used in the "Statistical Decision-Making" section of this chapter. Each sampling distributions can be defined in terms of normally distributed random variables. Their theoretical bases are introduced here.

Student's *t* Distribution

Let Z be a standard normal random variable, and let W be a χ^2 random variable with k degrees of freedom, where Z and W are statistically independent. Then the random variable T, defined as

$$T = \frac{Z}{\sqrt{\dfrac{W}{k}}} \qquad (6.47)$$

has a pdf given by

$$f(x) = \left(\frac{\Gamma\left(\dfrac{k+1}{2}\right)}{\sqrt{\pi k}\,\Gamma\left(\dfrac{k}{2}\right)} \right) \frac{1}{\left(\dfrac{x^2}{k}+1\right)^{(k+1)/2}}, \text{ for } -\infty < x < \infty, k = 1, 2, \ldots \qquad (6.48)$$

which follows a *t* distribution with k degrees of freedom. For $k > 1$, the mean and variance for the *t* distribution are $\mu = 0$ and $\sigma^2 > 1$. For $k = 1$, the *t* distribution is a *Cauchy* distribution, which has no mean or variance. Figure 6.20 displays *t* distributions for various degrees of freedom. The *t* distribution is very similar to the standard normal distribution since both are symmetric, are bell-shaped, and have $\mu = 0$. However, the tails of the *t* distribution are heavier than the standard normal; in other words, there is more probability in the tails (extreme values) of the *t* distribution than in the standard normal distribution. Notice that as the degrees of freedom go to infinity, the form of the Student's *t* distribution becomes the standard normal distribution.

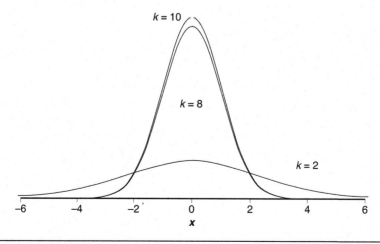

Figure 6.20 Probability density functions for three *t* distributions.

F Distribution

Suppose Y and W are independent chi-square random variables with k_1 and k_2 degrees of freedom, respectively. Then the random variable

$$F = \frac{Y / k_1}{W / k_2} \qquad (6.49)$$

is said to follow an F distribution with k_1 and k_2 degrees of freedom.

Sampling Distribution of the Sample Mean

Another important statistical principle refers to the distribution of sample means. The *sample mean* is a statistic calculated from a sample of data. Since the sample mean can take on different values for different samples taken from the same population, the sample mean is a random variable. As such, the sample mean has its own distribution. The distribution of the sample mean is referred to as the *sampling distribution of the sample mean*. An important statistical principle states:

If samples of size n are randomly drawn from a population with mean μ and standard deviation σ, then the distribution of sample means has the following properties:

- Its mean, denoted $\mu_{\bar{x}}$ is equal to the population $\mu_{\bar{x}} = \mu$ mean:

- Its variance, denoted $\sigma_{\bar{x}}^2$ is equal to the population variance divided by the sample size n:

$$\sigma_{\bar{x}}^2 = \frac{\sigma^2}{n} \qquad (6.50)$$

- Its standard deviation is equal to the positive square root of the variance:

$$\sigma_{\bar{x}} = \frac{\sigma}{\sqrt{n}} \qquad (6.51)$$

The standard deviation of the sampling distribution of $\bar{x}$ is referred to as the standard error.

EXAMPLE 6.31

Consider the time it takes to repair a robotic arm in a manufacturing facility. The mean repair time is $\mu = 1.27$ hours and standard deviation $\sigma = 0.17$ hours. Assume that the underlying distribution is normally distributed. Compute the mean and standard deviation of the mean repair times for a sample of 10 robotic arm repairs.

Solution:

The goal is to determine the sampling distribution for the mean repair time for robotic arms. The mean is $\mu_{\bar{x}} = \mu = 1.27$ hours. The standard error is $\sigma_{\bar{x}} = \sigma/\sqrt{n} = 0.17/\sqrt{10} = 0.054$.

The mean repair time for sample of size 10 has a normal distribution with mean 1.27 hours and standard deviation 0.054 hours.

In theory, the expected value of any single observation x_i taken from a random sample is equal to the mean of the population μ from which the observation has come. The notation is given as $E(x_i) = \mu$. In essence, this states that an unknown value x_i from some population of interest would be expected to be equal to the true population mean.

EXAMPLE 6.32

A part is selected at random from a population. The true diameter of this population of parts is believed to be 12 mm (i.e., $\mu = 12$). Therefore, without actually measuring the part selected at random, one would *expect* the diameter to be 12 mm (i.e., $E(x_i) = 12$).

Now, the expected value of the *sample mean* is also μ, the mean of the population. The notation for expected value of the sample mean is $E(\bar{x})$ such that

$$E(\bar{x}) = \mu$$

for a sample of size n.

Example 6.33 summarizes the use of expected value and standard error of the mean.

EXAMPLE 6.33

A sample of 100 parts is selected at random from a population. The true diameter of the population of parts is believed to be 12 mm ($\mu = 12$) with a standard deviation of 0.05 mm (i.e., $\sigma = 0.05$). Therefore, one would in theory *expect* the sample of 100 parts to have an average diameter of 12 mm or

$$E(\bar{x}) = \mu = 12$$

The standard error of the sample mean is found as

$$\sigma_{\bar{x}} = \frac{\sigma}{\sqrt{n}} = \frac{0.05}{\sqrt{100}} = 0.005$$

The value 0.005 represents the variability associated with the mean of the 100 parts chosen at random.

STATISTICAL DECISION-MAKING

Point Estimates

Define, describe, and assess the bias of estimators. Calculate and interpret standard error, tolerance intervals, and confidence intervals. (Evaluate)

Body of Knowledge VI.D.1

Suppose an estimate is needed for the average coating thickness of a population of 1000 circuit boards received from a supplier. Rather than measure all 1000 boards, randomly select a sample of 40 for measurement. Suppose that the average coating thickness of these 40 boards is 0.003 and the standard deviation of the 40 coating measurements is 0.005. The estimate for the average coating thickness on the entire lot of 1000 is then around 0.003. This value is called the *point estimate*. In this case, the sample mean is a *point estimator* of the population mean (recall the definitions of population mean, sample mean, parameter, and statistic given in the "Terminology" section of this chapter).

To find information about a population of interest, it is important to obtain information about the parameters that describe the population. Recall that parameters include the population mean μ and population variance σ^2, for example. It is important to be able to estimate the parameters using information acquired from a sample taken from the population. A statistic, such as the sample mean, is used as a point estimator for a parameter, in this case the population mean (keep in mind that "statistic" refers to a value obtained from a sample and "parameter" is a characteristic of a population).

The point estimator is said to be *unbiased* if its expected value is equal to the parameter that it is estimating. Consider the sample and population means. If a sample consists of n observations, $X_1, X_2, \ldots, X_n$, taken from a normal population, then the sample mean $\overline{X}$ is known to be an unbiased estimator of the population mean μ, that is, $E(\overline{X}) = \mu$. It can also be shown that the sample variance s^2 for the same situation (n observations taken from a normal distribution) is an unbiased estimator for the population variance σ^2, that is, $E(s^2) = \sigma^2$. However, the sample standard deviation s is *not* an unbiased estimator for σ, yet the bias is often negligible for all but very small sample sizes.

Sometimes there is more than one possible unbiased point estimator for a parameter. One point estimator for a parameter is said to be more efficient than another if the variance of the point estimator is smaller than the variance of its competitor. As a simple example, consider a random sample of observations, $X_1, X_2, \ldots, Xn$, taken from a population with mean μ and variance σ^2. The sample mean $\overline{X}$ is one point estimator for the population mean μ. However, any one observation X_i is also a possible point estimator for μ. Recall from the "Probability Distributions" section of this chapter that the variance of the sampling distribution of $\overline{X}$ is is σ^2/n (i.e., $V(\overline{X}) = \sigma_{\overline{x}}^2 = \sigma^2/n$) and the variance of a single observation from a population with variance σ^2 is simply σ^2 (i.e., $V(X_i) = \sigma^2$). Since $V(\overline{X}) < V(X_i)$, $\overline{X}$ is said to be a more efficient point estimator than X_i for μ.

The standard error of a statistic was briefly introduced in the "Probability Distributions" section of this chapter. In general, the *standard error* (s.e.) of a point estimator provides a measure of precision of the estimate and is simply the square root of the variance of the point estimator. For example, the variance of the sampling distribution of the point estimator $\overline{X}$ is σ^2/n. The standard error is then $\sigma/\sqrt{n}$. You sometimes see this written as s.e. $(\overline{X}) = \sigma/\sqrt{n}$.

To calculate a statistic of interest, such as the sample mean, from real populations of interest, this estimate is not exactly equal to the true population mean. One could select 15 different samples of the same size n from the same population and calculate 15 sample means, and most if not all of them would be different. So which of the 15 would be the best estimate? Well, any one of the sample means would be an appropriate estimate of the population mean. As the sample size n

increases, estimates become more precise. If the entire population were used, the estimate would be perfect, but that is rarely found in practice. In nearly all cases, the sample means will be different even though they are drawn from the same population. The variability in the estimates needs to be quantified somehow.

Confidence Intervals

In this section confidence intervals for the following are presented:

- A single population mean μ
- A single population variance σ^2
- A single population standard deviation σ
- A single population proportion p

In the example given in previous section, is the population mean exactly 0.003? Almost surely not, due to sampling error. To capture information about a parameter, one needs to quantify the variability in this estimate and then report it in a meaningful way. One type of estimation that can be used is called interval estimation. One of the most useful interval estimation approaches is constructing confidence intervals on the parameter of interest.

In general, a confidence interval on a population parameter depends on the following:

- A point estimate for the parameter of interest
- An estimate of the standard error of the point estimate
- A stated level of confidence, denoted by $1 - \alpha$
- In some cases, an idea of the approximate distribution of the underlying population

For example, suppose the objective is to construct a 95% confidence interval on a population mean μ (complete details and discussion of confidence intervals are presented later in this section). A random sample should be taken from the population, followed by calculating the necessary statistics (e.g., sample mean and sample variance—if population variance is not known), and constructing an interval on μ using the sample information (and some other information). Suppose the 95% confidence interval on μ is found to be $16 \leq \mu \leq 22$. This is much more informative than just reporting that the sample mean was found to be $\bar{x} = 19$.

The general form of a $100(1 - \alpha)\%$ two-sided confidence interval for any population parameter (denoted as θ) is

$$L \leq \theta \leq U$$

where

L = lower endpoint of the confidence interval

U = upper endpoint of the confidence interval

θ = parameter of interest, such as μ or σ

α = significance level

There are two general interpretations of the results from a confidence interval: the probabilistic interpretation and the practical interpretation.

The *probabilistic interpretation* of the confidence level is the proportion of all confidence intervals constructed on that parameter (under repeated sampling and identical conditions) that would contain the true parameter. For example, a 95% confidence interval on μ would be interpreted as the percentage of all confidence intervals constructed (under repeated sampling and identical conditions) that would contain the population mean μ. Consider a normal population with known mean $\mu = 25$ from which 20 samples of size $n = 100$ are selected. Twenty 95% confidence intervals on μ are constructed, with the following results:

(24.4713, 25.6473)	(24.0548, 25.2308)
(24.5202, 25.6962)	(23.9702, 25.1461)
(24.3994, 25.5754)	(24.8004, 25.9763)
(24.1861, 25.3620)	(24.4020, 25.5780)
(24.7750, 25.9510)	(23.8412, 25.0172)
(24.0617, 25.2377)	(24.4872, 25.6632)
(24.2578, 25.4337)	(24.4695, 25.6455)
(24.0038, 25.1798)	(25.0248, 26.2008)
(24.1231, 25.2991)	(24.4982, 25.6742)
(24.2900, 25.4659)	(24.1859, 25.3619)

What percentage of these confidence intervals contain the true population mean $\mu = 25$? In this scenario, 19 out of 20 (or 95%) confidence intervals constructed contain the true population mean $\mu = 25$. That also means that 5% of all intervals constructed do not contain the true population mean.

Since the true parameter value, such as the population mean μ, is usually unknown in practice, the probabilistic interpretation may not be very useful. Additionally, there is often only one sample of data, not 20. The *practical interpretation* of a confidence interval constructed in this situation would be a statement of degree of belief that the confidence interval contains the true μ. For example, there is 95% confidence that the 95% confidence interval will contain the true population mean μ.

It should be noted that the practical interpretation should never be misconstrued as saying that the "probability that the confidence interval contains the true value μ is 0.95." Remember, the true value of the population mean μ exists but is unknown. Therefore, when a confidence interval is constructed on μ, either the interval contains the true value of μ (probability of 1) or it does not (probability of 0).

Next, confidence intervals involving single samples are covered. Confidence intervals involving two samples are presented in the "Paired-comparison Tests" section of this chapter as part of the discussion on hypothesis testing.

Confidence Intervals for a Single Population Mean μ

In this section, the presentation of confidence intervals on a population mean is divided into two cases:

1. Confidence intervals on μ when the population variance σ^2 is assumed known

2. Confidence intervals on μ when the population variance σ^2 is assumed unknown

Case 1: Population Variance σ^2 Is Assumed Known

Let X_1, X_2, . . . , X_n represent a random sample taken from a normal distribution with known variance σ^2 but unknown– population mean μ. From the "Probability Distributions" section of this chapter, the sampling distribution of $\overline{X}$ is normally distributed with mean μ and variance σ^2/n. And

$$Z = \frac{\overline{X} - \mu_{\overline{x}}}{\sigma_{\overline{x}}} = \frac{\overline{X} - \mu}{\sigma/\sqrt{n}}$$

follows a standard normal distribution. It can be shown that a general $100(1 - \alpha)\%$ confidence interval on μ is given by

$$\overline{x} - z_{\alpha/2}\frac{\sigma}{\sqrt{n}} \leq \mu \leq \overline{x} + z_{\alpha/2}\frac{\sigma}{\sqrt{n}} \tag{6.52}$$

where

$\overline{x}$ = sample mean.

n = sample size.

$\dfrac{\sigma}{\sqrt{n}}$ = standard error of the mean.

$z_{\alpha/2}$ = multiple of the standard error of the mean, which determines the width of the interval. It is a direct result of the level of confidence $1 - \alpha$ and is found using the standard normal distribution. The subscript $\alpha/2$ is the area to the right of the number $z_{\alpha/2}$ under the standard normal curve.

EXAMPLE 6.34

A manufacturing process has been running in control for some length of time. The quality characteristic of interest is the diameter of the manufactured part (measured in mm). It is believed there may have been a shift in the process mean due to the change of a raw material. A sample of 25 items is randomly selected from the process and measured, and the sample average is found to be 103 mm. The in-control process average has been 102 mm, which is nominal. The standard deviation during the time the process was believed to be in control was 3 mm. The customer wants to construct a 95% confidence interval on the true process mean to determine whether the process has shifted away from nominal.

Solution:

The necessary information is:

- $\bar{x} = 103$.

- $\sigma = 3$.

- $n = 25$.

- $1 - \alpha = 0.95$, and solving for α, the result is $\alpha = 0.05$. This value is necessary to find the multiple $z_{\alpha/2}$ from the standard normal table.

From the standard normal table in Appendix E with $\alpha = 0.05$, $z_{\alpha/2} = z_{0.05/2} = z_{0.025} = 1.96$. The resulting 95% confidence interval (using is then

$$103 - 1.96 \frac{3}{\sqrt{25}} \leq \mu \leq 103 + 1.96 \frac{3}{\sqrt{25}}$$

$$103 - 1.176 \leq \mu \leq 103 + 1.176$$

$$101.824 \leq \mu \leq 104.176$$

With a 95% level of confidence, one can say 101.824 mm $\leq \mu \leq$ 104.176 mm. Since the nominal value of 102 mm is contained in this interval, there is insufficient evidence to conclude at the 95% level of confidence that the process mean has shifted.

Examine the 95% and 90% confidence intervals. Decreasing the confidence level from 95% to 90% decreased the width of the confidence interval. Decreasing (increasing) the level of confidence—while all other quantities remain constant—will always result in a decrease (increase) in the width of the confidence interval.

There are many situations where the practitioner would like to know how large a sample is needed to estimate a population mean with some level of precision. This information can be obtained using the $100(1 - \alpha)\%$ confidence interval and making some reasonable assumptions.

The length of the confidence interval provides a measure of *precision* of estimation. The *margin of error* in the confidence interval formula is

$$z_{\alpha/2} \frac{\sigma}{\sqrt{n}} \tag{6.53}$$

This quantity provides information about the *accuracy* of the confidence interval. That is, when $\bar{x}$ is used as the estimate for μ, the error

$$E = |\bar{x} - \mu| \tag{6.54}$$

will be at most

$$z_{\alpha/2} \frac{\sigma}{\sqrt{n}}$$

So, if

$$E = z_{\alpha/2} \frac{\sigma}{\sqrt{n}}$$

is an upper bound on the amount of error the practitioner is willing to live with, an appropriate sample size can be determined. That is, for a given level of confidence, an assumed value of σ, and a margin of error E one is willing to live with, a minimum sample size can be found using the relationship

$$E = z_{\alpha/2} \frac{\sigma}{\sqrt{n}} \tag{6.55}$$

and solving for n:

$$n \geq \left(\frac{\sigma z_{\alpha/2}}{E} \right)^2 \tag{6.56}$$

If the value of n is not an integer, round up to the nearest integer.

EXAMPLE 6.35

Suppose the turnaround time for basic blood analysis for the emergency room at a local hospital is of interest. A goal is to be able to estimate the true average turnaround time μ. Specifically, it is of interest to obtain an estimate that is within three minutes of the true average turnaround time with 95% confidence. Based on prior information it is assumed that $\sigma = 8$ min. How many turnaround times should be obtained to estimate the true average turnaround time and meet the requirements stated? That is, what is n?

Solution:

First, note that the problem states that the estimate is "within three minutes of the true average." This implies that estimate is allowed to be at most three minutes less than the true average or at most three minutes greater than the true average. In this case, the acceptable margin of error is $E = 3$ min. The level of confidence is 95%, so $1 - \alpha = 0.95$, $\alpha = 0.05$, and $z_{\alpha/2} = z_{0.025} = 1.96$. With $\sigma = 8$ min, the minimum sample size needed is

$$n \geq \left(\frac{\sigma z_{\alpha/2}}{E} \right)^2 = \left(\frac{8(1.96)}{3} \right)^2 = (5.227)^2 = 27.32$$

Therefore, to meet the requirements of 95% confidence, a margin of error of no more than three minutes, and $\sigma = 8$ min, the minimum number of times to obtain would be $n = 28$.

Case 2: Population Variance σ^2 Is Assumed Unknown

Suppose the population of interest is normally distributed with unknown mean μ and unknown variance σ^2. Let $X_1, X_2, \ldots, X_n$ be a random sample taken from the population, and let the sample mean and variance be denoted by $\bar{x}$ and s^2, respectively. When σ is unknown, it can be estimated by s. Furthermore, if the sample size n is small, the standard normal distribution is no longer an appropriate distribution for the sample mean. In its place the Student's t distribution will be used (recall the t distribution from the "Hypothesis Testing" section of this chapter).

Let $X_1, X_2, \ldots, X_n$ be a random sample taken from a normal population, and let the sample mean and variance be denoted by $\bar{x}$ and s^2, respectively. The random variable

$$T = \frac{Z}{\sqrt{\dfrac{W}{k}}}$$

follows a t distribution with $k = n - 1$ degrees of freedom as shown in Equation (6.47). It should be noted that the t distribution is defined by its degrees of freedom, which are directly related to the sample size n. As the degrees of freedom go to infinity, the t distribution approaches the standard normal distribution. The degrees of freedom are of particular interest. The degrees of freedom for T is $n - 1$. This is a direct result of using s^2 as an estimate for σ^2. Recall that the sample variance is based on the deviations $x_1 - \bar{x}, x_2 - \bar{x}, \ldots, x_n - \bar{x}$, and that

$$\sum_{i=1}^{n}\left(x_i - \bar{x}\right) = 0 \tag{6.57}$$

Since Equation (6.57) holds, this implies that for $n - 1$ of these deviations, the nth deviation is automatically determined (and cannot vary freely). That is, only $n - 1$ of these deviations can vary freely. The degrees of freedom for the t distribution represent the number of deviations that can vary freely.

It can be shown that the $100(1 - \alpha)\%$ confidence interval on the population mean μ is given by

$$\bar{x} - t_{\alpha/2,k}\frac{s}{\sqrt{n}} \le \mu \le \bar{x} + t_{\alpha/2,k}\frac{s}{\sqrt{n}} \tag{6.58}$$

where $t_{\alpha/2,k}$ is the multiple of the standard error of the mean $(s/\sqrt{n})$ and determines the width of the interval. It is a direct result of the level of confidence $1 - \alpha$ and is found using Student's t distribution. The subscript $\alpha/2$ is the area to the right of the number $t_{\alpha/2,k}$ that is needed, and $k = n - 1$ is the degrees of freedom for a particular problem. Probabilities and values for the t distribution are given in Appendix O, "Values of t Distribution."

EXAMPLE 6.36

A study on the effect the type of joystick has on powered wheelchair driving performance was conducted. In the study, one type of joystick used was a position-sensing joystick. Suppose eight subjects are asked to use a position-sensing joystick, and the time to complete a predetermined task is recorded (in minutes). The results are:

30.7, 31.2, 26.1, 29.4, 34.6, 26.8, 33.1, 25.5

Assume that time to complete the task is well approximated by a normal distribution. The investigators would like to construct a 95% confidence interval on the true time to complete the task using the position-sensing joystick.

Continued

Solution:

First, calculate the values $\bar{x}$ and s:

$$\bar{x} = \frac{\sum_{i=1}^{n} x_i}{n} = 29.675$$

$$s = \sqrt{\frac{\sum_{i=1}^{n}(x_i - \bar{x})^2}{n-1}} = 3.3363$$

For a level of confidence of 95%, $1 - \alpha = 0.95$, and solving for α, $\alpha = 0.05$. The degrees of freedom for this problem is $k = n - 1 = 7$. These values are necessary to find the multiple $t_{\alpha/2,k}$ from the t distribution. From the t distribution table in Appendix O, with $\alpha = 0.05$, $t_{\alpha/2,k} = t_{0.025,7} = 2.365$. The resulting 95% two-sided confidence interval (using Equation (6.60)) is then

$$29.675 - 2.365\frac{3.3363}{\sqrt{8}} \le \mu \le 29.675 + 2.365\frac{3.3363}{\sqrt{8}}$$

$$= 29.675 - 2.790 \le \mu \le 29.675 + 2.790$$

$$= 26.89 \le \mu \le 32.47$$

With a 95% level of confidence, the true time to perform the task using the position-sensing joystick lies between 26.89 minutes and 32.47 minutes.

In the previous example, the sample size was small, $n = 8$. In cases where the sample size is small (Devore [2016] suggests $n < 40$), the population is known to be normally distributed, and the population variance is unknown, the t distribution is an appropriate distribution. In cases where the sample size is sufficiently large, the population is known to be normally distributed, and the population variance is unknown, the standard normal distribution or the t distribution could be used. Again, the t distribution and standard normal distribution are approximately of the same form, as the sample size n goes to infinity.

Now in addition to the population mean and population variance being unknown, assume that the underlying distribution is not necessarily normally distributed. In this situation, if the sample size is large, then the central limit theorem applies and the $100(1 - \alpha)\%$ confidence interval

$$\bar{x} - z_{\alpha/2}\frac{s}{\sqrt{n}} \le \mu \le \bar{x} + z_{\alpha/2}\frac{s}{\sqrt{n}} \tag{6.59}$$

can be used. However, if the sample size is small and the underlying distribution is decidedly non-normally distributed, then nonparametric methods should be used to construct the confidence interval (see Devore 2016).

Confidence Intervals on a Population Variance and Standard Deviation

As stated previously, the sample variance s^2 can be used as the point estimate for the population variance σ^2. The sample standard deviation s can be used as the point estimate for σ. Suppose instead of relying on a point estimate of σ^2, one can construct a confidence interval. Assume a normally distributed population from which a random sample $X_1, X_2, \ldots, X_n$ is selected.

The $100(1 - \alpha)\%$ two-sided confidence interval on the population variance σ^2 is given by

$$\frac{(n-1)s^2}{\chi^2_{\alpha/2,k}} < \sigma^2 < \frac{(n-1)s^2}{\chi^2_{1-\alpha/2,k}} \tag{6.60}$$

where $\chi^2_{\alpha/2,k}$ and $\chi^2_{1-\alpha/2,k}$ are valuesare values obtained from the chi-square distribution with $\alpha/2$ and $(1 - \alpha/2)$ being the areas under the chi-square curve and to the right of the value of interest to be put into the confidence interval. Again, $k = n - 1$ is the degrees of freedom. Table values of the chi-square distribution are given in Appendix J, "Chi-Square Distribution."

EXAMPLE 6.37

A heart rate stress test was administered to 10 men. The heart rates (in beats per minute [bpm]) were recorded. The average heart rate was found to be $\bar{x} = 100$ bpm with a standard deviation of $s = 16.2$ bpm. A confidence interval was constructed on the mean heart rate, and it is now desired to construct a 95% confidence interval on the variance in heart rate.

Solution:

The necessary information is:

$s^2 = (16.2 \text{ bpm})^2 = 262.44 \text{ bpm}^2$

$k = n - 1 = 9$

$1 - \alpha = 0.95$, therefore $\alpha = 0.05$ and the corresponding chi-square values obtained from a chi-square table are

$$\chi^2_{\alpha/2,k} = \chi^2_{0.05/2,9} = \chi^2_{0.025,9} = 19.023$$

$$\chi^2_{1-\alpha/2,k} = \chi^2_{1-0.05/2,9} = \chi^2_{0.975,9} = 2.700$$

The resulting 95% two-sided confidence interval on the popula tion variance is

$$\frac{(10-1)262.44}{19.023} < \sigma^2 < \frac{(10-1)262.44}{2.700}$$

$$= 124.16 < \sigma^2 < 874.80$$

With a 95% level of confidence, the true population variance in heart rate lies within 124.16 bpm^2 and 874.80 bpm^2.

An approximate confidence interval on the population standard deviation σ can easily be found by taking the square of the bounds on the population variance. An approximate $100(1 - \alpha)\%$ confidence interval on σ is given by

$$\sqrt{\frac{(n-1)s^2}{\chi^2_{\alpha/2,k}}} < \sigma < \sqrt{\frac{(n-1)s^2}{\chi^2_{1-\alpha/2,k}}} \tag{6.61}$$

EXAMPLE 6.38

Reconsider the previous example. A 95% confidence interval on the standard deviation of heart rate is

$$\sqrt{124.16} < \sqrt{\sigma^2} < \sqrt{874.80}$$
$$11.14 < \sigma < 29.58$$

With a 95% level of confidence, the true population standard deviation will lie between 11.14 bpm and 29.58 bpm.

Confidence Intervals on a Population Proportion p

The population proportion p often represents the fraction nonconforming or the fraction of defective items in a population of items. Since it is often impossible or impractical to find the exact value of p, a point estimate is used to estimate the true proportion. A sample proportion denoted $\hat{p}$ will be used as a point estimate for p. The sample proportion is calculated using

$$\hat{p} = \frac{x}{n} \tag{6.62}$$

where x is the number of successes out of n trials. If n is sufficiently large, then it can be shown that the random variable

$$Z = \frac{\hat{p} - p}{\sqrt{\dfrac{p(1-p)}{n}}} \tag{6.63}$$

follows a standard normal distribution. This relationship allows for the development of a confidence interval on the true population proportion of interest.

A $100(1 - \alpha)\%$ confidence interval on a population proportion p is given by

$$\hat{p} - z_{\alpha/2}\sqrt{\frac{\hat{p}(1-\hat{p})}{n}} \leq p \leq \hat{p} + z_{\alpha/2}\sqrt{\frac{\hat{p}(1-\hat{p})}{n}} \tag{6.64}$$

EXAMPLE 6.39

Billing statements for 1000 patients discharged from a particular hospital were randomly selected for errors. Out of the 1000 billing statements, 102 were found to contain errors. Using this information, it is desired to construct a 99% confidence interval on the true proportion of billing statements with errors.

Solution:

In this problem, a "success" is a billing statement with errors. Therefore, $X = 102$ and $n = 1000$. The sample proportion is then

$$\hat{p} = \frac{102}{1000} = 0.102$$

and provides the best estimate for the true proportion of billing statements with errors. The corresponding 99% confidence interval is

$$\hat{p} - z_{\alpha/2}\sqrt{\frac{\hat{p}(1-\hat{p})}{n}} \leq p \leq \hat{p} + z_{\alpha/2}\sqrt{\frac{\hat{p}(1-\hat{p})}{n}}$$

$$0.102 - 2.576\sqrt{\frac{0.102(1-0.102)}{1000}} \leq p \leq 0.102 + 2.576\sqrt{\frac{0.102(1-0.102)}{1000}}$$

$$0.077 \leq p \leq 0.127$$

With a 99% level of confidence, the true proportion of billing statements that contain errors would be between 7.7% and 12.7%.

Note: The procedure outlined here for the population proportion assumes that the normal distribution is a good approximation to the binomial. That is, the parameter of interest is a proportion that is well modeled by the binomial distribution, but if the sample size is large enough, the normal distribution is a good approximation to the binomial.

Recommendations have been that $np \geq 5$ and $np(1 - p) \geq 5$. However, if the sample size is small, the confidence interval given previously may not be a good approximation, and the binomial distribution rather than the standard normal distribution should be used to find the multiple of the standard error in the confidence interval. Agresti and Coull (1998) present an alternative form of a confidence interval for small n (in addition, see Devore [2016]).

Statistical Tolerance Intervals

Consider a population of manufactured steel rods. Suppose the diameters of these steel rods follow a normal distribution with mean $\mu = 25$ mm and standard deviation $\sigma = 4$ mm. Then the interval $(\mu - 1.96\sigma, \mu + 1.96\sigma) = (17.16, 32.84)$ would capture the diameters of 95% of the steel rods. This is a result of the fact that 95% of the area under the normal curve lies between -1.96 and 1.96.

In many situations, μ and σ are unknown and are estimated using $\bar{x}$ and s. The interval $(\bar{x} - 1.96s, \bar{x} + 1.96s)$ may not actually contain 95% of the values in the population (since there is variability in the estimates in this case, there is no guarantee that the tolerance interval will contain 95% of the values). The solution to the problem is to replace 1.96 with some value that will make the resulting interval contain 95% of the values with a high level of confidence. This interval is referred to as a *tolerance interval.*

Suppose it is desired to capture at least τ% of the values in a normal distribution with a $100(1 - \alpha)$% level of confidence. The appropriate two-sided tolerance interval is

$$\bar{x} - Ks, \bar{x} + Ks \tag{6.65}$$

where K is a tolerance interval factor found in Appendix C, "Statistical Tolerance Factors for at Least 99% of the Population." Only selected values of K are given in the table, in particular for 99% of the population for 90%, 95%, and 99% levels of confidence.

EXAMPLE 6.40

Suppose the time to complete a task is of interest. A sample of $n = 10$ times is collected and it is found that $\bar{x} = 31.50$ and $s = 2.764$. Time to complete the task is assumed to be normally distributed. Suppose the objective is to find a tolerance interval for time that includes 99% of the values in the population with 95% confidence.

From Appendix C with $n = 10$ and confidence level of 0.95 $K = 4.433$. The resulting tolerance interval is

$$(\bar{x} - Ks, \bar{x} + Ks) = (31.50 - 4.433(2.764), 31.50 + 4.433(2.764)) = (19.25, 43.75)$$

It can be concluded with 95% confidence that at least 99% of all times to complete the task are between 19.25 minutes and 43.75 minutes.

Hypothesis Testing

Define, interpret, and apply hypothesis tests for means, variances, and proportions. Apply and interpret the concepts of significance level, power, type I, and type II errors. Define and distinguish between statistical and practical significance. (Evaluate)

Body of Knowledge VI.D.2

The hypothesis test, another tool used in inferential statistics, is closely related to confidence intervals, a relationship that is illustrated in this section. Textbooks tend to treat hypothesis tests as somewhat more formal procedures. Many list seven or eight steps to be followed for each type of test. Although not all books agree on the steps themselves, they share some generic steps:

1. State the null hypothesis (H_0) and alternative hypothesis (H_a)

2. Choose the level of significance α

3. Determine the rejection region for the statistic of interest

4. Calculate the test statistic

5. Decide whether the null hypothesis should be rejected

6. State the conclusion in terms of the original problem

General descriptions of each step are provided.

1. Write the assumption that is claimed to be true in a null hypothesis. The *null hypothesis* is denoted by H_0. This is the statement that is assumed to be true and that you are trying to find evidence against. For example, from past experience the average time to complete a task is five minutes, and the objective is to test this claim. The null hypothesis would be $H_0: \mu = 5$.

State the alternative hypothesis. The notation for the alternative hypothesis is usually H_a. If the null hypothesis is rejected, then an alternative must be provided. The *alternative hypothesis* contains the statement that you would eventually like to support (the alternative can be supported only if the null hypothesis is rejected). For example, suppose the goal is to show that the average time to complete a task is actually longer than five minutes. The alternative hypothesis would be $H_a: \mu > 5$.

2. Choose the level of significance for the test. The *significance level* (denoted α) is the probability of making the mistake of rejecting the null hypothesis when it is in fact true. This type of mistake is called a *type I error* (as opposed to a *type II error*, which is the mistake of not rejecting the null hypothesis when it is in fact false). The probability of committing a type I error should be small (i.e., $\alpha \leq 0.10$) and should be set before performing the test. The significance level α is the same α used in the level of confidence in constructing confidence intervals (recall that $1 - \alpha$ is the level of confidence, so α is the level of significance). Choosing the level of significance is sometimes an economic decision. It is established based on how expensive a particular mistake may be (this expense is not necessarily monetary and could include personal injury or loss of life).

3. Determine the rejection region. The *rejection region* consists of all those values of the test statistic for which the null hypothesis would be rejected. The rejection region is determined by the stated level of significance and the alternative hypothesis. *Critical values* are those values that determine the rejection region (they are cutoff values for the test statistic—discussed in the next step).

4. Calculate the test statistic. The *test statistic* is simply a statistic (such as the sample mean or sample variance) that has been transformed to compare this value with some standard (critical values). An example of a test statistic is a sample mean $\overline{X}$ transformed into a Z-score. The Z-score is used to determine whether the null hypothesis should be rejected.

5. Compare the test statistic with the critical value. If the test statistic falls within the rejection region, then the null hypothesis would be rejected. Large test statistic values (in absolute value) will provide evidence against the null hypothesis. It is important to note that rejecting the null hypothesis is a strong claim. It takes significant evidence to reject the claim associated with H_0. As a result of using a small level of significance, rejecting the null hypothesis is a *strong claim*. Failing to reject the null hypothesis is a *weak claim*. That is, by failing to reject the null hypothesis, it cannot be said that the claim is true, just that there is not sufficient evidence to reject the claim.

6. Once it has been determined whether the null hypothesis can be rejected, the results are written in terms of the problem statement.

Hypothesis Tests for a Single Population

In this section hypothesis tests are presented for the following:

- A single population mean μ
- A single population variance σ^2
- A single population proportion p

Hypothesis Tests for a Single Population Mean μ

Let μ_0 be a real value that is hypothesized or assumed to be the true value of the population mean μ. There are three types of hypothesis tests:

$H_0: \mu \leq \mu_0$ $H_a: \mu > \mu_0$ (right-tailed test)

$H_0: \mu \geq \mu_0$ $H_a: \mu < \mu_0$ (left-tailed test)

$H_0: \mu = \mu_0$ $H_a: \mu \neq \mu_0$ (two-tailed test)

As with confidence intervals, there are two cases under study:

1. Hypothesis tests on μ when the population variance σ^2 is assumed known

2. Hypothesis tests on μ when the population variance σ^2 is unknown

Case 1. Hypothesis Tests on μ When the Population Variance σ² Is Assumed Known

Assume that the underlying population of interest is normally distributed with known population variance σ^2. $X_1, X_2, \ldots, X_n$ be a random sample from the population, and let $\bar{X}$ represent the sample mean. An appropriate test statistic for this situation is

$$z_0 = \frac{\bar{x} - \mu_0}{\sigma/\sqrt{n}} \tag{6.66}$$

The rejection region, shown in Table 6.8, depends on the alternative hypothesis and level of significance α.

Table 6.8 Rejection regions for a single sample mean, variance known.

Alternative hypothesis	Reject H_0 if
$H_a: \mu > \mu_0$	$z_0 > z_\alpha$
$H_a: \mu < \mu_0$	$z_0 < -z_\alpha$
$H_a: \mu \neq \mu_0$	$z_0 < -z_{\alpha/2}$ or $z_0 > z_{\alpha/2}$

EXAMPLE 6.41

A vendor claims that the average weight of a shipment of parts is 1.84 kg. The customer randomly chooses 64 parts and finds that the sample has an average weight of 1.88 kg. Suppose that the standard deviation of the population is known to be 0.3 kg. Using a level of significance of 0.05, test the hypothesis that the true average weight of the shipment is 1.84 kg. Assume that the weights are normally distributed.

Solution:

Since the population standard deviation is known, the standard normal distribution is used. In addition, since the problem statement gives no indication as to whether the true mean weight is less than or greater than 1.84 kg, a two-sided hypothesis test is appropriate. The steps are as follows:

1. The null and alternative hypotheses are

    $H_0: \mu = 1.84$ $H_a: \mu \neq 1.84$.

2. The level of significance is $\alpha = 0.05$.

3. There are two areas for the rejection region since this is a two-tailed test. The critical values are found from a standard normal table with $\alpha = 0.05$:

    $$z_{\alpha/2} = z_{0.05/2} = z_{0.025} = 1.96 \text{ and } -z_{\alpha/2} = -1.96$$

    Therefore, reject the null hypothesis if the test statistic is greater than 1.96 or less than –1.96.

4. The test statistic is calculated to be:

    $$z_0 = \frac{\bar{x} - \mu_0}{\sigma/\sqrt{n}} = \frac{1.88 - 1.84}{0.30/\sqrt{64}} = 1.07$$

    (Note: This test statistic says the following: the sample mean is roughly 1.07 standard deviations away from the population mean. Is this a large difference? The next step tells us how large is large.)

5 Comparing 1.07 with the critical values in step 3, it can be seen that –1.96 < 1.07 < 1.96. Since the test statistic, 1.07, does not fall into the rejection region, the null hypothesis cannot be rejected at the 0.05 level of significance. The decision is to fail to reject the null hypothesis (weak claim).

6. There is insufficient evidence to conclude that the true mean weight of the shipment is different from 1.84.

Case 2. Hypothesis Tests on μ When the Population Variance σ² Is Unknown

Assume that the underlying population of interest is normally distributed with unknown population variance σ^2. Let $X_1, X_2, \ldots, X_n$ be a random sample from the population, and let $\overline{X}$ represent the sample mean. If the sample size is small, an appropriate test statistic for this situation is

$$t_0 = \frac{\overline{x} - \mu_0}{s / \sqrt{n}} \tag{6.67}$$

which follows a t distribution with $k = n - 1$. The rejection region, shown in Table 6.9, depends on the alternative hypothesis and level of significance α.

It is important to note here that the fact that the null hypothesis is not rejected does not mean it is true. It only indicates that with this sample of data there was not evidence found against the null hypothesis. If a second sample of data is taken, it is possible that the null hypothesis could be rejected.

A summary of the situations outlined for testing the population mean is shown in Table 6.10 (assume the underlying population is normally distributed).

EXAMPLE 6.42

A cutoff saw has been producing parts with a mean length of 4.125 mm. A new blade is installed and the objective is to know whether the mean has decreased. A random sample of 20 parts is selected and their lengths measured. The mean length is 4.120 mm and the sample standard deviation is 0.008 mm. Assume that the population is normally distributed. Using a significance level of 0.10, determine whether the mean length has decreased. Since the population standard deviation is unknown, the t-test will be used.

Solution:

1. The null and alternative hypotheses are

   $H_0: \mu = 4.125$ $H_a: \mu < 4.125$.

2. The level of significance is $\alpha = 0.10$.

3. There is only one rejection region since this is a left-tailed test (again, this is based on the alternative hypothesis). The critical value is found from the t distribution table in Appendix O with $\alpha = 0.10$: $t_{\alpha,k} = t_{0.10,19} = 1.328$. Therefore, reject the null hypothesis if the test statistic is less than -1.328 (since the alternative hypothesis is "less than").

4. The test statistic is calculated to be:

$$t_0 = \frac{\overline{x} - \mu_0}{s / \sqrt{n}} = \frac{4.120 - 4.125}{0.008 / \sqrt{20}} = -2.80$$

5. Comparing -2.80 to the critical value in step 4, it is seen that $-2.80 < -1.328$. Since the test statistic falls into the rejection region, the null hypothesis is rejected at the 0.10 level of significance (strong claim).

6. There is sufficient evidence to indicate that the average length of the part has decreased.

Table 6.9 Rejection regions for a single sample mean, variance unknown.

Alternative hypothesis	Reject H_0 if
$H_a: \mu > \mu_0$	$t_0 > t_{\alpha,k}$
$H_a: \mu < \mu_0$	$t_0 < -t_{\alpha,k}$
$H_a: \mu \neq \mu_0$	$t_0 < -t_{\alpha/2,k}$ or $t_0 > t_{\alpha/2,k}$

Table 6.10 Summary of situations outlined for testing the population mean.

Assumption	Distribution	Test statistic
σ^2 known, population normally distributed	Standard normal distribution	$z_0 = \dfrac{\bar{x} - \mu_0}{\sigma/\sqrt{n}}$
σ^2 unknown and n small ($n \leq 30$), population normally distributed	t distribution	$t_0 = \dfrac{\bar{x} - \mu_0}{s/\sqrt{n}}$
σ^2 unknown and n large (often $n > 40$), population not necessarily normal	Standard normal distribution or t distribution*	$z_0 = \dfrac{\bar{x} - \mu_0}{s/\sqrt{n}}$ or $t_0 = \dfrac{\bar{x} - \mu_0}{s/\sqrt{n}}$

* Recall that as n goes to infinity ($n \to \infty$), the form of the t distribution becomes indistinguishable from the standard normal distribution.

Hypothesis Tests on a Single Population Variance σ^2

The hypothesis testing procedure can be applied in the case of testing a standard or hypothesized value of the population variance. For example, one may be interested in testing the claim that a particular population variance is eight. The null hypothesis is $H_0: \sigma^2 = 8$. Assume that the underlying distribution is normal. Let σ^2 be a real value that is hypothesized or assumed to be the true value of the population variance σ^2. There are three types of hypothesis tests on a population variance:

$H_0: \sigma^2 \leq \sigma_0^2 \qquad H_a: \sigma^2 > \sigma_0^2 \qquad$ (right-tailed test)

$H_0: \sigma^2 \geq \sigma_0^2 \qquad H_a: \sigma^2 < \sigma_0^2 \qquad$ (left-tailed test)

$H_0: \sigma^2 = \sigma_0^2 \qquad H_a: \sigma^2 \neq \sigma_0^2 \qquad$ (two-tailed test)

The chi-square distribution introduced in the "Sampling Distributions" section of this chapter is an appropriate distribution for testing a population variance. The test statistic is given by

$$\chi_0^2 = \frac{(n-1)s^2}{\sigma_0^2} \qquad (6.68)$$

The test statistic follows a chi-square distribution with $k = n - 1$ degrees of freedom, where

- s^2 is the sample variance for a sample taken from the population of interest

- σ_0^2 is the hypothesized value of the variance

- n is the sample size chosen from the population of interest

The hypothesis testing steps outlined earlier also apply to this situation, and the rejection regions are shown in Table 6.11.

The critical values for the chi-square distribution can be found in Appendix J.

Table 6.11   Rejection regions for a single sample hypothesis test on the variance.

Alternative hypothesis	Reject H_0 if
$H_a: \sigma^2 > \sigma_0^2$	$\chi_0^2 > \chi_{\alpha,k}^2$
$H_a: \sigma^2 < \sigma_0^2$	$\chi_0^2 < \chi_{1-\alpha,k}^2$
$H_a: \sigma^2 \neq \sigma_0^2$	$\chi_0^2 < \chi_{1-\alpha/2,k}^2$ or $\chi_0^2 > \chi_{\alpha/2,k}^2$

EXAMPLE 6.43

A process has been running for some time with a variance of 6.25 for a critical dimension. In an effort to improve throughput, a methods engineer increases the drive motor speed. A sample of 13 items is randomly selected from the new process. The variance of the critical dimension in this sample is found to be 6.82. Is there sufficient evidence to conclude that the true process variance has increased? Use $\alpha = 0.05$. Assume that the critical dimension follows a normal distribution.

Solution:

1. The null and alternative hypotheses are

   $H_0: \sigma^2 = 6.25$ $H_1: \sigma^2 > 6.25$

2. The level of significance is $\alpha = 0.05$

3. Since this is a right-tailed test, the null hypothesis is rejected if the test statistic is greater than $\chi_{\alpha,k}^2 = \chi_{0.05,12}^2 = 21.026$

4. The test statistic (using Equation (6.70)) is calculated to be

$$\chi_0^2 = \frac{(n-1)s^2}{\sigma_0^2} = \frac{(13-1)6.82}{6.25} = 13.1$$

5. Since 13.1 < 21.026, the null hypothesis cannot be rejected (weak claim)

6. There is insufficient evidence to conclude that the variance for this critical dimension has increased at the 0.05 level of significance

Hypothesis Tests on a Single Population Proportion p

The hypothesis testing procedure can be applied in the case of testing a standard or hypothesized value of a population proportion. For example, a quality engineer may be interested in testing the claim that a particular population proportion is 0.50. The null hypothesis is then H_0: $p = 0.50$.

Let p_0 be a real value that is hypothesized or assumed to be the true value of the population proportion. There are three types of hypothesis tests on a population proportion:

H_0: $p \leq p_0$ H_a: $p > p_0$ (right-tailed test)

H_0: $p \geq p_0$ H_a: $p < p_0$ (left-tailed test)

H_0: $p = p_0$ H_a: $p \neq p_0$ (two-tailed test)

The null hypothesis is often written simply as H_0: $p = p_0$ for each of the three cases. Either notation is acceptable.

For sufficiently large sample sizes, the normal approximation to the binomial distribution is valid and the test statistic

$$z_0 = \frac{\hat{p} - p_0}{\sqrt{\dfrac{p_0(1 - p_0)}{n}}} \qquad (6.69)$$

follows a standard normal distribution where $\hat{p}$ is the sample proportion and p_0 is the hypothesized value of the population proportion.

If the sample sizes are relatively small, then the appropriate hypothesis test to use is based directly on the binomial distribution. See Devore (2016) for more details on small-sample tests.

The rejection region, shown in Table 6.12, depends on the alternative hypothesis and level of significance α.

Table 6.12   Rejection regions for a single sample hypothesis test on the proportion.

Alternative hypothesis	Reject H_0 if
H_a: $p > p_0$	$z_0 > z_\alpha$
H_a: $p < p_0$	$z_0 < -z_\alpha$
H_a: $p \neq p_0$	$z_0 < -z_{\alpha/2}$ or $z_0 > z_{\alpha/2}$

EXAMPLE 6.44

Billing statements for discharged patients from a particular hospital sometimes contain errors. It is believed that the percentage of billing statements that contain errors is 15%. Out of 1000 billing statements randomly selected from the population, 102 were found to contain errors. Based on this information, can it be concluded that that the proportion of billing statements that contain errors is actually less than 15%? Use a 10% level of significance.

Solution:

For this problem:

- p = the true proportion of billing statements with errors

- x = number of statements with errors, so $x = 102$

- n = sample size, so $n = 1000$

- The sample proportion is then $\hat{p} = \dfrac{x}{n} = \dfrac{102}{1000} = 0.102$

1. The null and alternative hypotheses are

   $H_0: p = 0.15$ $H_a: p < 0.15$

2. The level of significance is $\alpha = 0.10$

3. Since this is a left-tailed test, reject the null hypothesis if the test statistic is less than $-z_\alpha = -z_{0.10} = -1.28$

4. The test statistic (using Equation (6.71)) is

$$z_0 = \frac{\hat{p} - p_0}{\sqrt{\dfrac{p_0(1 - p_0)}{n}}} = \frac{0.102 - 0.15}{\sqrt{\dfrac{0.15(1 - 0.15)}{1000}}} = -4.25$$

5. Since $-4.25 < -1.28$, the null hypothesis is rejected in favor of the alternative at the 0.10 level of significance (strong claim)

6. There is sufficient evidence to conclude that the true percentage of statement errors is less than 15%

Hypothesis Tests and Confidence Intervals for Two Independent Populations

Hypothesis tests and confidence intervals for two independent population means, variances, and proportions are presented in this section.

Hypothesis Tests and Confidence Intervals for Two Independent Population Means μ_1 and μ_2

There are many important cases that involve comparing two populations of interest, such as two processes, two vendors, and so on. Of interest here is testing the difference between two population means $\mu_1 - \mu_2$. One test in particular is that of no difference between the two populations $\mu_1 - \mu_2 = 0$.

Either the standard normal distribution or Student's t distribution can be used. If the population variances are known, use the standard normal distribution. If the population variances are unknown and the sample sizes are relatively small, use Student's t distribution.

The basic assumptions are as follows:

- $X_1, X_2, \ldots, X_{n_1}$ is a random sample from a population with mean μ_1 and variance σ_1^2

- $Y_1, Y_2, \ldots, Y_{n_2}$ is a random sample from a population with mean μ_2 and variance σ_2^2

- The two samples are independent of each other

A good point estimator for $\mu_1 - \mu_2$ would be the difference between the two sample means, $\overline{X} - \overline{Y}$. The expected value and variance for this point estimator are

$$E\left(\overline{X} - \overline{Y}\right) = \mu_1 - \mu_2 \tag{6.70}$$

and

$$V\left(\overline{X} - \overline{Y}\right) = \sigma_{\overline{X}-\overline{Y}}^2 = \frac{\sigma_1^2}{n_1} + \frac{\sigma_2^2}{n_2} \tag{6.71}$$

If it is assumed that the populations are normally distributed, then $\overline{X} - \overline{Y}$ will also be normally distributed. Therefore, the random variable

$$Z = \frac{\left(\overline{X} - \overline{Y}\right) - \left(\mu_1 - \mu_2\right)}{\sqrt{\dfrac{\sigma_1^2}{n_1} + \dfrac{\sigma_2^2}{n_2}}} \tag{6.72}$$

follows a standard normal distribution. As a result, hypothesis tests and confidence intervals can be constructed on the parameter $\mu_1 - \mu_2$.

Case 1. Hypothesis Test on $\mu_1 - \mu_2$, *with Population Variances Known*

Let Δ_0 be a real value that represents the difference between μ_1 and μ_2 that is of interest to be tested. Specifically, the null hypothesis would be H_0: $\mu_1 - \mu_2 = \Delta_0$. For the test of no difference, $\Delta_0 = 0$. The hypothesis tests, test statistic, and rejection regions (Table 6.13) are as follows:

Null hypothesis: H_0: $\mu_1 - \mu_2 = \Delta_0$

Test statistic:
$$z_0 = \frac{\left(\overline{x} - \overline{y}\right) - \Delta_0}{\sqrt{\dfrac{\sigma_1^2}{n_1} + \dfrac{\sigma_2^2}{n_2}}} \tag{6.73}$$

The null hypothesis does not always have to be $\mu_1 - \mu_2 = \Delta_0$; it could be $\leq$ or $\geq$ also. In this case, the null hypothesis is H_0: $\mu_1 - \mu_2 = \Delta_0$.

Table 6.13 Rejection region for a hypothesis test on the means of two independent samples, variance known.

Alternative hypothesis	Reject H_0 if
$H_a: \mu_1 - \mu_2 > \Delta_0$	$z_0 > z_\alpha$
$H_a: \mu_1 - \mu_2 < \Delta_0$	$z_0 < -z_\alpha$
$H_a: \mu_1 - \mu_2 \neq \Delta_0$	$z_0 < -z_{\alpha/2}$ or $z_0 > z_{\alpha/2}$

Example 6.46 illustrates the use of hypothesis testing for the differences between two population means. The steps for the hypothesis tests are identical to the six steps outlined earlier.

EXAMPLE 6.45

Two different formulations of gasoline are being tested to study their road octane numbers. Formulation 1 has a variance octane number of $\sigma_1^2 = 1.45$ while the variance for formulation 2 is $\sigma_2^2 = 1.5$. Ten samples ($n_1 = 10$) are selected from formulation 1 and fifteen samples ($n_2 = 15$) are selected from formulation 2. For sample 1, the average octane number was found to be $\bar{x} = 89$, and for sample 2 the average octane number was found to be $\bar{y} = 91$. Is there significant evidence to indicate that a difference exists between the two formulations? Use a 0.05 level of significance.

Solution:

The parameter of interest is the difference in average octane number, $\mu_1 - \mu_2$. Since there is no indication that $\mu_1 > \mu_2$ or $\mu_1 < \mu_2$, a two-sided test is used.

1. $H_0: \mu_1 - \mu_2 = 0 \qquad H_1: \mu_1 - \mu_2 \neq 0$

2. $\alpha = 0.05$

3. Since this is a two-tailed test and $\alpha = 0.05$, the null hypothesis is rejected if the test statistic is less than $-z_{\alpha/2}$ or greater than $z_{\alpha/2}$, where $z_{\alpha/2} = z_{0.025} = 1.96$

4. The test statistic (using Equation (6.75)) is

$$z_0 = \frac{(\bar{x} - \bar{y}) - \Delta_0}{\sqrt{\dfrac{\sigma_1^2}{n_1} + \dfrac{\sigma_2^2}{n_2}}} = \frac{(89 - 91) - 0}{\sqrt{\dfrac{1.45}{10} + \dfrac{1.5}{15}}} = -4.04$$

5. Since $-4.04 < -1.96$, the null hypothesis is rejected (strong claim)

6. The conclusion is that there is a significant difference in average octane number for the two formulations at the 0.05 level of significance

---

A $100(1 - \alpha)\%$ confidence interval on the parameter $\mu_1 - \mu_2$ is given by

$$(\bar{x} - \bar{y}) - z_{\alpha/2}\sqrt{\frac{\sigma_1^2}{n_1} + \frac{\sigma_2^2}{n_2}} \leq \mu_1 - \mu_2 \leq (\bar{x} - \bar{y}) + z_{\alpha/2}\sqrt{\frac{\sigma_1^2}{n_1} + \frac{\sigma_2^2}{n_2}} \tag{6.74}$$

EXAMPLE 6.46

Reconsider the formulation problem given in the previous example. The 95% confidence interval on $\mu_1 - \mu_2$ is

$$\left(\bar{x} - \bar{y}\right) - z_{\alpha/2}\sqrt{\frac{\sigma_1^2}{n_1} + \frac{\sigma_2^2}{n_2}} \leq \mu_1 - \mu_2 \leq \left(\bar{x} - \bar{y}\right) + z_{\alpha/2}\sqrt{\frac{\sigma_1^2}{n_1} + \frac{\sigma_2^2}{n_2}}$$

$$(89 - 91) - 1.96\sqrt{\frac{1.45}{10} + \frac{1.5}{15}} \leq \mu_1 - \mu_2 \leq (89 - 91) + 1.96\sqrt{\frac{1.45}{10} + \frac{1.5}{15}}$$

$$-2.97 \leq \mu_1 - \mu_2 \leq -1.03$$

There is 95% confidence that the true difference between the average octane numbers lies between –2.97 and –1.03. Note that the hypothesized value $\Delta_0 = 0$ given in the null hypothesis of the previous problem is not contained in this interval. Therefore, it can again be said there is a significant difference in the two population means (i.e., reject the null hypothesis).

Case 2. Hypothesis Test on $\mu_1 - \mu_2$, with Population Variances Unknown

If the sample sizes are relatively large, regardless of the underlying distributions of the populations of interest, the standard normal distribution can be used, as in the case of known variances. The sample variances are used as estimates of the population variances.

If the sample sizes are relatively small and the underlying distributions are normally distributed, then the *t* distribution can be used to conduct hypothesis tests and construct confidence intervals. There are two methods for this situation: the population variances are unknown but assumed roughly equal, and (2) the population variances are unknown and not necessarily equal. The three basic assumptions given earlier still hold for the following methods. Let s_1^2 represent the variance for sample 1 and s_2^2 represent the variance for sample 2.

Method 1. $\sigma_1^2 = \sigma_2^2 = \sigma^2$ (The population variances are unknown but assumed roughly equal.) Since s_1^2 and s_2^2 estimate the same common variance σ^2, yet the sample variances may not be equal, the sample variances can be combined to obtain a single point estimate for σ^2. This is commonly called the pooled variance:

$$s_p^2 = \frac{(n_1 - 1)s_1^2 + (n_2 - 1)s_2^2}{n_1 + n_2 - 2} \tag{6.75}$$

The pooled standard deviation can be found by taking the square root of the pooled variance. The random variable T below

$$T = \frac{\left(\bar{X} - \bar{Y}\right) - \Delta_0}{\sigma\sqrt{\dfrac{1}{n_1} + \dfrac{1}{n_2}}} \tag{6.76}$$

follows a *t* distribution with $k = n_1 + n_2 - 2$ degrees of freedom.

The hypothesis tests, test statistic, and rejection region (Table 6.14) are as follows:

Null hypothesis: $H_0: \mu_1 - \mu_2 = \Delta^0$

Test statistic:
$$t_0 = \frac{(\bar{x} - \bar{y}) - \Delta_0}{s_p\sqrt{\dfrac{1}{n_1} + \dfrac{1}{n_2}}}$$

(6.77)

where $k = n_1 + n_2 - 2$ is the total degrees of freedom.

Table 6.14 Rejection regions for a hypothesis test on the means of two independent samples, variance equal, but unknown.

Alternative hypothesis	Reject H_0 if
$H_a: \mu_1 - \mu_2 > \Delta_0$	$t_0 > t_{\alpha,k}$
$H_a: \mu_1 - \mu_2 < \Delta_0$	$t_0 < -t_{\alpha,k}$
$H_a: \mu_1 - \mu_2 \neq \Delta_0$	$t_0 < -t_{\alpha/2,k}$ or $t_0 > t_{\alpha/2,k}$

EXAMPLE 6.47

Two vendors of a valve diaphragm present significantly different cost quotations. The wall thickness is the critical quality characteristic. Use the following data to determine whether the average thickness of the products from vendor 1 is greater than that from vendor 2. Assume that the populations are normally distributed and that the samples are independent. Furthermore, the population variances are unknown but assumed to be equal. The test is to be conducted at the 0.05 significance level. The wall thickness measurements for both vendors are shown in Table 6.15.

Table 6.15 Wall thickness measurements for two vendors.

Vendor 1:	86	82	91	88	89	85	88	90	84	87	88	83	84	89
Vendor 2:	79	78	82	85	77	86	84	78	80	82	79	76		

Solution:

The necessary summary statistics are:

Vendor 1: $\bar{x} = 86.7$ $s_1 = 2.76$ $n_1 = 14$

Vendor 2: $\bar{y} = 80.5$ $s_2 = 3.26$ $n_2 = 12$

Since the population variances are unknown but assumed equal, the pooled variance and pooled standard deviation should be calculated (using Equation (6.77)):

$$s_p^2 = \frac{(n_1-1)s_1^2 + (n_2-1)s_2^2}{n_1 + n_2 - 2} = \frac{(14-1)(2.76)^2 + (12-1)(3.26)^2}{14+12-2} = 9$$

$$s_p = \sqrt{9} = 3$$

The parameter of interest is the difference in average wall thickness, $\mu_1 - \mu_2$.

1. $H_0: \mu_1 - \mu_2 = 0$ $H_a: \mu_1 - \mu_2 > 0$

2. $\alpha = 0.05$

3. Since this is a right-tailed test and $\alpha = 0.05$, the null hypothesis will be rejected if the test statistic is greater than $t_{\alpha,k}$ where from Appendix O $t_{\alpha,k} = t_{0.05,24} = 1.711$

4. The test statistic is:

$$t_0 = \frac{(\bar{x} - \bar{y}) - \Delta_0}{s_p\sqrt{\frac{1}{n_1} + \frac{1}{n_2}}} = \frac{(86.7 - 80.5) - 0}{3\sqrt{\frac{1}{14} + \frac{1}{12}}} = 5.25$$

5. Since $5.25 > 1.711$, the null hypothesis is rejected (strong claim)

6. The conclusion is that the average thickness of the products from vendor 1 is greater than that from vendor 2 at the 0.05 level of significance

A $100(1 - \alpha)\%$ two-sided confidence interval on the parameter $\mu_1 - \mu_2$ is given by

$$(\bar{x} - \bar{y}) - t_{\alpha/2,k}(s_p)\sqrt{\frac{1}{n_1} + \frac{1}{n_2}} \le \mu_1 - \mu_2 \le (\bar{x} - \bar{y}) + t_{\alpha/2,k}(s_p)\sqrt{\frac{1}{n_1} + \frac{1}{n_2}} \quad (6.78)$$

It is important to note that the test statistic based on the t distribution is robust to the common variance assumption. In addition, it is not necessarily a good idea to do formal testing on the equality of two variances (see Box [1954]).

Method 2. $\sigma_1^2 \ne \sigma_2^2$ (The population variances are unknown and not necessarily equal.) The main differences between methods 1 and 2 are the calculation of the test statistic and the calculation of the degrees of freedom. Since the population variances are not necessarily equal, s_1^2 and s_2^2 and do not estimate a common population variance; s_1^2 is an estimate for σ_1^2, and s_2^2 is an estimate of σ_2^2, and they can be used directly in the test statistic

$$t_0 = \frac{(\bar{x} - \bar{y}) - \Delta_0}{\sqrt{\frac{s_1^2}{n_1} + \frac{s_2^2}{n_2}}} \quad (6.79)$$

This test statistic is based on random variable T, which follows a t distribution with degrees of freedom:

$$v = \frac{\left(\frac{s_1^2}{n_1} + \frac{s_2^2}{n_2}\right)^2}{\frac{\left(s_1^2/n_1\right)^2}{n_1 - 1} + \frac{\left(s_2^2/n_2\right)^2}{n_2 - 1}} \quad (6.80)$$

which is rounded down if it is not an integer value. Devore (2016) recommends using method 2 unless there is strong evidence that the variances of the two populations are equal.

A $100(1 - \alpha)\%$ two-sided confidence interval on the parameter $\mu_1 - \mu_2$ is given by

$$\left(\bar{x} - \bar{y}\right) - t_{\alpha/2,v}\sqrt{\frac{s_1^2}{n_1} + \frac{s_2^2}{n_2}} \leq \mu_1 - \mu_2 \leq \left(\bar{x} - \bar{y}\right) + t_{\alpha/2,v}\sqrt{\frac{s_1^2}{n_1} + \frac{s_2^2}{n_2}} \tag{6.81}$$

Hypothesis Tests and Confidence Intervals for Two Population Variances σ_1^2, σ_2^2

A test on the variances of two populations can be used to determine whether the variance of one is greater than the other. For example, the null hypothesis could be H_0: $\sigma_1^2 = \sigma_2^2$, where σ_1^2 is the variance of population 1 and σ_2^2 is the variance of population 2. This test uses the F distribution, presented in the "Sampling Distributions" section of this chapter.

Let $Y_1, Y_2, \ldots, Y_{n_1}$ be a random sample from a normal distribution with variance σ_1^2, and let $W_1, W_2, \ldots, W_{n_2}$ be a random sample from a normal distribution with variance σ_2^2. Furthermore, assume that the samples are independent of each other and s_1^2 and s_2^2 are the sample variances for Yi's and Wj's, respectively. The random variable

$$F = \frac{s_1^2/\sigma_1^2}{s_2^2/\sigma_2^2} \tag{6.82}$$

follows an F distribution with $k_1 = n_1 - 1$ and $k_2 = n_2 - 1$ degrees of freedom.

The hypothesis tests, test statistic, and rejection regions (Table 6.16) are as follows:

Null hypothesis: H_0: $\sigma_1^2 = \sigma_2^2$

Test statistic: $F_0 = s_1^2/s_2^2$ $\qquad\qquad\qquad\qquad\qquad\qquad\qquad$ (6.83)

The critical values for the F distribution can be found in Appendices F, "F Distribution $F_{0.10}$," G, "F Distribution $F_{0.05}$," and H, "F Distribution $F_{0.01}$." The notation F_{α,k_1,k_2} is the F value with area of α to its right, k_1 represents the numerator degrees of freedom, and k_2 represents the denominator degrees of freedom. A probability from this table represents the area under the curve and to the right of

Table 6.16 Rejection regions for a hypothesis test on two independent variances.

Alternative hypothesis	Reject H_0 if
H_a: $\sigma_1^2 > \sigma_2^2$	$F_0 > F_{\alpha,k_1,k_2}$
H_a: $\sigma_1^2 < \sigma_2^2$	$F_0 < F_{1-\alpha,k_1,k_2}$
H_a: $\sigma_1^2 \neq \sigma_2^2$	$F_0 < F_{1-\alpha/2,k_1,k_2}$ or $F_0 > F_{\alpha/2,k_1,k_2}$

the F value of interest. For example, for a 0.05 level of significance with $k_1 = 15$ and $k_2 = 5$ degrees of freedom, the F value would be $F_{0.05,15,5} = 4.62$. The F table provides values for specific values of α (level of significance). To find critical values when the area to the right is $1 - \alpha$, such as $F_{1-\alpha,k_1,k_2}$, the following relationship is used:

$$F_{1-\alpha,k_1,k_2} = \frac{1}{F_{\alpha,k_2,k_1}} \qquad (6.84)$$

To illustrate, suppose the objective to find a critical value for a left-tailed test where $k_1 = 10$, $k_2 = 8$, and $\alpha = 0.05$. Then $F_{1-\alpha,k_1,k_2} = F_{0.95,10,8}$ and

$$F_{0.95,10,8} = \frac{1}{F_{0.05,8,10}} = \frac{1}{3.07} = 0.326$$

EXAMPLE 6.48

Two chemical companies can supply a particular material. The concentration of an element in this material is important. The mean concentration for both suppliers is approximately the same, but it is suspected that the variability in concentration may differ between the two companies. The standard deviation of concentration in a random sample of $n_1 = 10$ batches produced by company 1 is $s_1 = 3.8$ g/l, while for company 2, a random sample of $n_2 = 16$ batches yields $s_2 = 4.2$ g/l. Using a level of significance of 0.10, the goal is to determine if there is sufficient evidence to conclude that the two population variances differ.

Solution:

Let:

- σ_1^2 be the population variance of the element concentration in the material from company 1

- σ_2^2 be the population variance of the element concentration in the material from company 2

1. The null and alternative hypotheses are

   $H_0: \sigma_1^2 = \sigma_2^2$ $H_1: \sigma_1^2 \neq \sigma_2^2$.

2. The level of significance is $\alpha = 0.10$.

3. There are two rejection regions since this is a two-tailed test. Furthermore, the degrees of freedom are $k_1 = n_1 - 1 = 9$ and $k_2 = n_2 - 1 = 15$. The critical values are

   $$F_{\alpha/2,k_1,k_2} = F_{0.05,9,15} = 2.59$$

   and

   $$F_{0.950,9,15} = \frac{1}{F_{\alpha/2,k_2,k_1}} = \frac{1}{F_{0.05,15,9}} = \frac{1}{3.01} = 0.332$$

   Therefore, reject the null hypothesis if the test statistic is less than 0.332 or greater than 2.59.

Continued

4. The test statistic is

$$F_0 = \frac{s_1^2}{s_2^2} = \frac{(3.8)^2}{(4.2)^2} = 0.819$$

5. Since $0.332 < 0.819 < 2.59$, the null hypothesis cannot be rejected at the 0.10 level of significance (weak claim).

6. There is insufficient evidence to conclude that the variances of the element concentration in this material from the two suppliers are not equal.

A $100(1 - \alpha)\%$ two-sided confidence interval on the parameter σ_1^2/σ_2^2 is given by

$$\frac{s_1^2}{s_2^2} F_{1-\alpha/2,k_1,k_2} \leq \frac{\sigma_1^2}{\sigma_2^2} \leq \frac{s_1^2}{s_2^2} F_{\alpha/2,k_1,k_2} \tag{6.85}$$

The confidence interval on the ratio of the two variances can be used to determine whether there is a significant difference between the two variances. In hypothesis testing the assumption is that the null hypothesis is true, that is, H_0: $\sigma_1^2 = \sigma_2^2$. This equality can be rewritten as

$$\frac{\sigma_1^2}{\sigma_2^2} = 1$$

When constructing a two-sided confidence interval on the ratio of the two variances, the null hypothesis is rejected if the value 1 is not contained within that interval. For example, the 95% two-sided confidence interval on the ratio of variances of the previous example is

$$0.217 \leq \frac{\sigma_1^2}{\sigma_2^2} \leq 2.555$$

Therefore, there is high confidence that the true ratio of the variances lies between 0.217 and 2.555. Since this interval contains the value 1, the conclusion based on the samples is that there is no statistically significant difference between the two variances.

Hypothesis Tests and Confidence Intervals on Two Population Proportions p_1, p_2

There are many situations where one wants to determine whether two populations differ with respect to some proportion of successes or failures. For example, it may be desired to determine whether two machines from the same process are producing the same proportion of nonconforming items. The hypothesis could be H_0: $p_1 - p_2 = 0$, where p_1 is the proportion of successes from population 1 and p_2 is the proportion of successes from population 2. The estimates of p_1 and p_2 are, respectively,

$$\hat{p}_1 = \frac{x_1}{n_1}, \quad \hat{p}_2 = \frac{x_2}{n_2}$$

where

n_1 is the size of the sample chosen from population 1

n_2 is the size of the sample chosen from population 2

x_1 is the number of successes out of a sample of size n_1

x_2 is the number of successes out of a sample of size n_2

The parameter of interest is the difference in the two population proportions $p_1 - p_2$. The point estimator for this parameter is $\hat{p}_1 - \hat{p}_2$. The expected value and variance for the point estimator are

$$E\left(\hat{p}_1 - \hat{p}_2\right) = p_1 - p_2 \tag{6.86}$$

and

$$V\left(\hat{p}_1 - \hat{p}_2\right) = \sigma^2_{\hat{p}_1-\hat{p}_2} = \frac{p_1(1-p_1)}{n_1} + \frac{p_2(1-p_2)}{n_2} \tag{6.87}$$

The random variable

$$z = \frac{(\hat{p}_1 - \hat{p}_2) - (p_1 - p_2)}{\sqrt{\frac{p_1(1-p_1)}{n_1} + \frac{p_2(1-p_2)}{n_2}}} \tag{6.88}$$

follows an approximate standard normal distribution when the approximations described earlier hold for both samples. Under the assumption that the null hypothesis (H_0: $p_1 - p_2 = 0$) is true, then the random variable Z, can be written as

$$z = \frac{(\hat{p}_1 - \hat{p}_2) - 0}{\sqrt{\hat{p}(1-\hat{p})\left(\frac{1}{n_1} + \frac{1}{n_2}\right)}}$$

where $\hat{p}$ is the proportion resulting from the combination of the two samples (estimate of the overall proportion when testing $p_1 = p_2$). The formula is

$$\hat{p} = \frac{x_1 + x_2}{n_1 + n_2} \tag{6.89}$$

The hypothesis tests, test statistic, and rejection regions (Table 6.17) are as follows:

Null hypothesis: H_0: $p_1 - p_2 = 0$

Test statistic: $$z_0 = \frac{(\hat{p}_1 - \hat{p}_2) - 0}{\sqrt{\hat{p}(1-\hat{p})\left(\frac{1}{n_1} + \frac{1}{n_2}\right)}} \tag{6.90}$$

Table 6.17 Rejection regions for a hypothesis test on two independent proportions.

Alternative hypothesis	Reject H_0 if
$H_a: p_1 - p_2 > 0$	$z_0 > z_\alpha$
$H_a: p_1 - p_2 < 0$	$z_0 < -z_\alpha$
$H_a: p_1 - p_2 \neq 0$	$z_0 < -z_{\alpha/2}$ or $z_0 > z_{\alpha/2}$

EXAMPLE 6.49

Two machines produce the same parts. A random sample of 1500 parts from machine 1 has 36 that are nonconforming, and a random sample of 1680 parts from machine 2 has 39 that are nonconforming. Is there evidence to suggest that machine 1 has a higher nonconforming rate than machine 2? Test at the 0.01 level of significance.

Solution:

For this problem:

- p_1 represents the proportion of nonconforming units produced by machine 1

- p_2 represents the proportion of nonconforming units produced by machine 2

- $\hat{p}_1$ is the sample proportion estimating p_1; it is

$$\hat{p}_1 = \frac{x_1}{n_1} = \frac{36}{1500} = 0.024$$

- $\hat{p}_2$ is the sample proportion estimating p_2; it is found to be

$$\hat{p}_2 = \frac{x_2}{n_2} = \frac{39}{1680} = 0.0232$$

- $\hat{p}$ is the proportion resulting from the combination of the two samples (estimate of the overall proportion when testing $p_1 - p_2 = 0$). It is found to be

$$\hat{p} = \frac{x_1 + x_2}{n_1 + n_2} = \frac{36 + 39}{1500 + 1680} = \frac{75}{3180} = 0.0236$$

The parameter of interest is the difference in the two population proportions $p_1 - p_2$.

1. The null and alternative hypotheses are

$$H_0: p_1 - p_2 = 0 \qquad H_a: p_1 - p_2 > 0$$

2. The level of significance is 0.01

3. Since this is a right-tailed test, the null hypothesis will be rejected if the test statistic is greater than $z_\alpha = z_{0.01} = 2.33$

4. The test statistic is

$$z_0 = \frac{(\hat{p}_1 - \hat{p}_2)}{\sqrt{\hat{p}(1-\hat{p})\left(\dfrac{1}{n_1} + \dfrac{1}{n_2}\right)}} = \frac{(0.024 - 0.0232)}{\sqrt{0.0236(1 - 0.0236)\left(\dfrac{1}{1500} + \dfrac{1}{1680}\right)}} = 0.148$$

5. Since 0.148 < 2.33, the null hypothesis cannot be rejected (weak claim)

6. There is insufficient evidence to conclude that machine 1 has a higher nonconforming rate than machine 2 at the 0.01 level of significance

A $100(1 - \alpha)\%$ confidence interval on the parameter $p_1 - p_2$ is

$$(\hat{p}_1 - \hat{p}_2) - z_{\alpha/2}\sqrt{\hat{p}(1-\hat{p})\left(\frac{1}{n_1} + \frac{1}{n_2}\right)} \le p_1 - p_2 \le (\hat{p}_1 - \hat{p}_2) + z_{\alpha/2}\sqrt{\hat{p}(1-\hat{p})\left(\frac{1}{n_1} + \frac{1}{n_2}\right)} \quad (6.91)$$

Paired-comparison Tests

> Define and use paired-comparison
> (parametric) hypothesis tests and interpret
> the results. (Apply)
>
> **Body of Knowledge VI.D.3**

Paired-comparison hypothesis testing involves a two-sample t-test for two samples that are believed to be *dependent,* that is, when an observation from one sample can be logically paired with an observation from the other sample. The pairing of two observations is based on some characteristic they have in common. By pairing the data when necessary, the effect of the common characteristic that may influence the results is reduced.

To illustrate, 40 people are placed on the same diet program. Each person is weighed on day 1 (before weight), put through the program, then weighed again at the end of the program (after weight). The difference between the person's before weight and after weight is recorded. This is a *paired comparison*—pairing each individual person's before weight with their after weight (it would not make sense to compare the before weight of person X with the after weight of person Y, due to individual differences in people).

The data from two samples should be paired when there is a logical relationship between the two observations. Table 6.18 presents heart rates (in beats per minute) for individuals who used two types of exercise equipment, A and B.

There is no indication of whether the heart rates recorded involved five people using both types of equipment or five people using type A and five people using type B. Therefore, there is no indication that the data should be paired from equipment A to equipment B. Consider the set of data in Table 6.19, again representing

Table 6.18 Heart rate data for two types of exercise equipment.

A	161	172	166	189	180
B	155	191	187	174	171

Table 6.19 Heart rate data for paired observations.

Person	1	2	3	4	5
A	161	172	166	189	180
B	155	191	187	174	171

the heart rates of people who used the exercise equipment. Now there is more information that indicates the heart rates have a characteristic in common. Since basal heart rates vary a great deal from person to person, best practice would be to pair the heart rates by person to minimize the effect of individual differences. Therefore, if a significant difference is found, there is a better chance that the difference is due to the type of equipment and not the person using it. If there is any indication that the data should be paired in a particular problem, then pairing should be done (i.e., if in doubt, pair the data).

Suppose there are n independently selected pairs given by $(X_1, Y_1), (X_2, Y_2), \ldots,$ (X_n, Y_n). Furthermore, let $E(X_i) = \mu_1$ and $E(Y_i) = \mu_2$. The paired-comparison test is a test conducted on the differences between the two groups. Define the differences as $D_i = X_i - Y_i$ for all n pairs. Assume the differences D_i are normally distributed with the following parameters:

- Mean difference μ_D, where $\mu_D = \mu_1 - \mu_2$
- Variance of the differences σ_D^2

For a sample of n independently selected pairs (X_i, Y_i), let d_i $(i = 1, -2, \ldots, n)$ represent the actual differences from the sample. The sample mean $\bar{d}$ and sample standard deviation s_d for the differences are, respectively,

$$\bar{d} = \frac{\sum\limits_{i=1}^{n} d_i}{n} \tag{6.92}$$

and

$$s_d = \sqrt{\frac{\sum\limits_{i=1}^{n}\left(d_i - \bar{d}\right)^2}{n-1}} \tag{6.93}$$

It is important to note that once the differences are calculated, the paired t-test is equivalent to the t-test for a single population mean presented earlier. The test statistic that will be used for the paired t-test is

$$t_0 = \frac{\bar{d}}{s_d / \sqrt{n}}$$ (6.94)

which follows a t distribution with $n-1$ degrees of freedom. Follow the six-step procedure for performing a hypothesis test originally introduced in the "Hypothesis Testing" section of this chapter.

EXAMPLE 6.50

Consider the study on two types of exercise equipment given earlier. The following set of data represents heart rates (in beats per minute) for individuals who used the two types of exercise equipment, A and B. The last row represents the differences in heart rate for each person, $d_i = A_i - B_i$ for $i = 1, 2, \ldots, 5$.

Table 6.20 Paired heart rate data with combined differences.

Person	1	2	3	4	5
A	161	172	166	189	180
B	155	191	187	174	171
$d_i = A_i - B_i$	6	−19	−21	15	9

Is there a significant difference in heart rate due to the type of exercise equipment used? Use a 0.05 level of significance. Assume that the differences follow a normal distribution.

Solution:

- Let μ_1 represent the mean heart rate after using equipment A.

- Let μ_2 represent the mean heart rate after using equipment B.

- The logical pairing involves the differences in heart rates for both types of equipment by person. There are $n = 5$ heart rates in each sample.

- Let μ_D represent the true mean difference between the two populations $\mu_D = \mu_1 - \mu_2$.

The necessary summary statistics are

$$\bar{d} = \frac{\sum_{i=1}^{n} d_i}{n} = \frac{6 + (-19) + (-21) + 15 + 9}{5} = -2.0$$

and

$$s_d = \sqrt{\frac{\sum_{i=1}^{n}\left(d_i - \bar{d}\right)^2}{n-1}}$$

$$= \sqrt{\frac{\left(6-(-2.0)\right)^2 + \left(-19-(-2.0)\right)^2 + \left(-21-(-2.0)\right)^2 + \left(15-(-2.0)\right)^2 + \left(9-(-2.0)\right)^2}{5-1}} = 16.76$$

Continued

The steps are:

1. $H_0: \mu_D = 0$ $H_a: \mu_D \neq 0$

2. $\alpha = 0.05$

3. Since this is a two-tailed test, reject H_0 if the test statistic is less than $-t_{\alpha/2,n-1}$ or greater than $t_{\alpha/2,n-1}$ where $t_{\alpha/2,n-1} = t_{0.025,4} = 2.776$

4. Calculate the test statistic:

$$t_0 = \frac{\bar{d}}{s_D/\sqrt{n}} = \frac{-2.0}{16.76/\sqrt{5}} = -0.27$$

5. Since $-2.776 < -0.27 < 2.776$, we fail to reject the null hypothesis (weak claim)

6. There is insufficient evidence to conclude that the type of exercise equipment significantly affects heart rate at the 0.05 level of significance

A $100(1-\alpha)\%$ two-sided confidence interval on the parameter μ_D is given by

$$\bar{d} - t_{\alpha/2,n-1}\left(\frac{s_d}{\sqrt{n}}\right) \leq \mu_D \leq \bar{d} + t_{\alpha/2,n-1}\left(\frac{s_d}{\sqrt{n}}\right) \tag{6.95}$$

The *p*-Value Approach to Hypothesis Testing

Up to this point, hypothesis testing has been presented using the *critical value* (or *fixed significance level) approach* and rejection regions. Critical values are determined based on a stated level of significance (α), among other quantities. The critical value approach is somewhat lacking for two reasons: (1) it does not completely quantify the degree to which a null hypothesis is rejected or not rejected, and (2) it imposes a specific significance level on the practitioner or others making the decision.

For example, suppose a right-tailed test on a population mean with $\alpha = 0.05$ was carried out. It was reported that the critical value found from the t table was $t = 2.306$ and the null hypothesis was rejected—but you are not told the value of the test statistic itself. If you are given no further information, can you determine the value of the test statistic? Obviously the value of the test statistic was greater than 2.306 (since the null hypothesis was rejected), but by how much? There is no indication of whether the test statistic was 2.310 or 10.310 given just this information. In addition, the decision was based on a specific level of significance. If a level of significance was used, but after conducting the test it was determined that a 0.01 level of significance should have been used, new critical values must be determined. In many engineering problems, an acceptable level of significance may be known, but not in every situation.

A second approach that offers some measure of the degree to which the test statistic is significant involves the use of *p*-values. Given the null hypothesis is true, a *p-value* is the smallest level of significance at which the null hypothesis would be rejected. The *p*-value is the probability of obtaining a more extreme value than the observed test statistic. The p-value is also referred to as the observed significance level. A small p-value is evidence against the null hypothesis in favor of the alternative.

For example, suppose H_0: $\mu = 50$ against H_a: $\mu > 50$ and the test statistic is found to be $z_0 = 2.47$. The p-value for this test would be $P(Z > 2.47) = 0.0068$. That is, the probability of a test statistic of 2.47 or more extreme (in this case, larger than 2.47 since this is a right-tailed test) if H_0: $\mu = 50$ is true is 0.0068. This is a highly unlikely event. It is highly unlikely that a test statistic of 2.47 would be obtained if the mean really is 50. But the test statistic was 2.47, so what went wrong? Remember that the claim $\mu = 50$ is a hypothesis that can be proved incorrect (based on collected data). Therefore, the null hypothesis is probably false.

For a predetermined level of significance, the decisions would be as follows:

- If p-value $< \alpha$, reject H_0

- If p-value $\geq \alpha$, fail to reject H_0

Using the p-value approach allows the practitioner flexibility in making decisions. If the significance level is changed for a particular test, no new calculations need to be done to make a decision. The p-value will not change for a test even if the level of significance does.

The p-value is easy to interpret, and most computer software packages will report a p-value for a hypothesis test. Reconsider the wall thickness example for two competing vendors given in Example 6.48.

The parameter of interest is the difference in average wall thickness, $\mu_1 - \mu_2$, and the hypotheses are H_0: $\mu_1 - \mu_2 = 0$ and H_a: $\mu_1 - \mu_2 > 0$. The level of significance was $\alpha = 0.05$, and since the test statistic (5.25) was greater than the critical value (1.711), the null hypothesis would be rejected.

The problem was worked again, this time using a statistical software package, with the output shown in Figure 6.21.

The p-value is given in bold and reported to be 0.000 (this value is most likely some extremely small number very close to zero; so for all practical purposes, the p-value is zero). Since the p-value $< \alpha$ (i.e., 0.000 < 0.05), the null hypothesis is rejected. What is telling about the p-value is that one could easily change the level of significance and be able to make a decision without having to do any further calculations. The p-value will remain 0.000 regardless of the level of significance.

The six-step hypothesis testing procedure given earlier would also apply when using p-values. These steps are as follows:

1. State H_0 and H_a.

2. State α (a common default value is 0.05 if not explicitly stated).

Two-sample T for Vendor1 versus Vendor2

Difference = mu (Vendor1) – mu (Vendor2)

T-Test of difference = 0 (vs >): T-Value = 5.27 P-Value = 0.000 DF = 24

Figure 6.21   Statistical software output of a t-test.

3. Calculate the test statistic.

4. Calculate the p-value.

5. Reject or fail to reject H_0. Reject H_0 if p-value $< \alpha$; otherwise fail to reject H_0.

6. State your conclusions in terms of the problem statement.

The smaller the p-value, the stronger the evidence against the null hypothesis and in favor of the alternative hypothesis. It is important to note that the p-value approach and the critical value approach will lead to the same conclusion for the same problem. This is true as long as all quantities and assumptions are identical when using both approaches. Finally, as with all of the procedures given in this section, it is recommended that the calculations be done using a reliable statistical software package.

Significance Level, Power, Type I and Type II Errors

Since every hypothesis test involves analyzing samples to infer properties of a population, there is some chance that the conclusion may be incorrect, even if the analysis is flawless. These sampling errors are not errors in the usual sense, because they cannot be corrected (without using 100% sampling with no measurement errors). The two possible types of errors that can occur in hypothesis testing are the type I error and type II error, briefly introduced earlier in this section.

A *type I error* occurs when a true null hypothesis is rejected. The probability of committing a type I error is denoted α—the *significance level* in hypothesis testing. The critical values for a hypothesis testing procedure are based on a predetermined level of significance. That is, the maximum allowable probability of rejecting a true null hypothesis (α) is fixed for a particular problem. A *type II error* occurs when a false null hypothesis is not rejected. The probability of committing a type II error is denoted β. A summary of the possible decisions and errors is given in Figure 6.22. Again,

$$\alpha = P(\text{type I error}) = P(\text{rejecting } H_0 \text{ when in fact } H_0 \text{ is true})$$

$$\beta = P(\text{type II error}) = P(\text{failing to reject } H_0 \text{ when in fact } H_0 \text{ is false})$$

In general, it is desirable to have small α and β, but there is often a trade-off. For a fixed sample size in hypothesis testing, decreasing α will result in an increase in β. Because of the way the null and alternative hypotheses are specified in hypothesis testing, it is generally true that committing a type I error is more serious than committing a type II error. Therefore, controlling the probability of committing a type I error (setting α) is often a higher priority than controlling the probability of

		Result of Hypothesis Test	
		Reject H_0	Fail to reject H_0
H_0 is actually	True	Type I error	Correct decision
	False	Correct decision	Type II error

Figure 6.22   Possible decisions and errors in hypothesis testing.

committing a type II error. In fact, it is difficult to specify an exact value of β since that would require knowing the true value of the parameter being tested.

The *power* of a hypothesis test is defined as the probability of correctly rejecting a false null hypothesis. The power is given by $1 - \beta$, since β is the probability of failing to reject the null hypothesis when it is false. The power provides some measure of the test's ability to detect differences. This ability to detect differences is often referred to as the *sensitivity* of the hypothesis test.

Statistical versus Practical Significance

In some situations, it may be possible to detect a statistically significant difference between two populations when there is no practical difference. In hypothesis testing, the goal is to make a decision about a claim or hypothesis. The decision as to whether the null hypothesis is rejected in favor of the alternative hypothesis is based on a sample taken from the population of interest. If the null hypothesis is rejected, there is statistically significant evidence against the null hypothesis in favor of the alternative hypothesis. But statistical significance does not imply practical significance. Rejecting the null hypothesis in favor of the alternative hypothesis by a very small margin may be the result of a relatively large sample size. Large sample sizes will almost always lead to rejection of the null hypothesis.

Consider an automobile manufacturer's claim that one make of car averages 31 miles per gallon (mpg) on the highway. A consumer group tests 75 cars of the same make under identical conditions and finds the average to be 30.6 mpg. One could conduct a hypothesis test of $H_0: \mu = 31$ versus $H_a: \mu < 31$. The sample average is $\bar{x} = 30.6$. If H_0 can be rejected in favor of H_a, there is *statistically significant* evidence to indicate that the true average is less than 31 mpg. But, is 30.6 really different from 31 in the practical sense? In this situation, a statistical significance was found, but not necessarily a practical significance, in the difference between the hypothesized value (31 mpg) and the estimated value (30.6 mpg). Rejecting the null hypothesis in favor of the alternative hypothesis by a very small margin may be the result of a relatively large sample size. Again, large sample sizes can often result in statistically significant results, even though the difference may not be of practical significance. In summary, a rejected null hypothesis implies statistical significance but not necessarily practical significance. Some practitioners prefer using confidence intervals for making decisions since they allow one to see if a practical difference exists.

Analysis of Variance (ANOVA)

> Define use, and interpret ANOVA and interpret the results. (Analyze)
>
> Body of Knowledge VI.D.5

In the previous section, one- and two-sample hypothesis tests were discussed. In the case where the objective is to compare a continuous random variable across more than two samples, the ANOVA procedure can be used. One-way and two-way ANOVA are presented in this section.

One-Way ANOVA

Define use, and interpret ANOVA and interpret the results. (Analyze)

Body of Knowledge VI.D.5

If there is a need to compare more than two samples, the previous tests are not valid. Suppose there is a need to compare a populations. Sometimes the populations are referred to as treatments or levels of a factor. Let $\mu_1, \mu_2, \ldots, \mu_a$ represent the means for the populations. The goal is to determine whether the treatments applied significantly affect the outcome or response of interest.

EXAMPLE 6.51

Alternative energy sources to traditional fossil fuels are in high demand. Several variables are believed to influence the conversion of waste vegetable oil into biodiesel fuel. One variable of interest is the amount of catalyst (%) at three levels—0.6, 1.0, and 1.4—used in the conversion process. The response of interest is conversion rate (wt%) (larger values indicate that more of the waste vegetable oil was successfully converted into useable biodiesel fuel). The experiments are conducted in random order and with the following results shown in Table 6.21.

Table 6.21 Conversion rates for three levels of catalyst.

Catalyst (%)		
0.6	1.0	1.4
71.34	84.62	78.33
76.11	78.21	76.89
73.16	82.39	71.42
76.02	76.55	76.60

In this study:

- Some questions of interest are: Does the amount of catalyst have a significant effect on the conversion rate? If so, which catalyst amount will result in a high conversion rate?

- Catalyst is the *factor of interest* or *independent variable*.

- The factor of interest (catalyst) has three *levels* (0.6%, 1.0%, and 1.4%). Levels may referred to as *treatments* or *groups*. In this example, there are three treatments applied or three groups being studied.

- Conversion rate is the *response of interest* (or *dependent variable*).

- There are four *replicates* ($n = 4$) for each level of catalyst.

Three important assumptions for the use of a one-way ANOVA are as follows:

1. The observations follow a normal distribution (i.e., the populations are normally distributed)

2. The observations are independent

3. The treatments have constant variance (homogeneity of variances)

In summary, the treatment distributions (populations) for all a treatments should be normally distributed, each with the same variance σ^2. An additional assumption that is not always included deals with the number of replicates. It is not necessary that each level of the factor or treatment have the same number of replicates. But large differences in the number of observations from group to group can affect the validity of the analysis. It is assumed that the number of replicates n will be equal or near equal for all treatments. For more details, see Devore (2016), Montgomery and Runger (2013), and Vining and Kowalski (2011).

It should be noted that the ANOVA procedure outlined next is fairly robust to slight departures from these assumptions. The assumptions should always be verified, as will be discussed later in this section.

Suppose there is one factor of interest with a levels of that factor (it could also be said that a treatments are being compared). Let y_{ij} represent the jth response in the ith treatment, where $i = 1, 2, \ldots, a$ and $j = 1, 2, \ldots, n$. For example, the third observation for the second treatment (catalyst amount = 1.0%) given earlier would be denoted $y_{23} = 82.39$. There are a total of $a \times n$ observations in the experiment. A general table of results could be set up as in Table 6.22, where

$y_{i\cdot}$ = the sum of the n observations in the ith treatment (the dot subscript indicates summation over the subscript it replaces)

$y_{\cdot\cdot}$ = the sum of all an observations

$\bar{y}_{i\cdot}$ = average of the n observations in the ith treatment

$\bar{y}_{\cdot\cdot}$ = average of all an observations

A model provides a way to describe the observations (y_{ij}) as a function of the mean for each treatment level (i). The means model is written as

$$y_{ij} = \mu_i + \varepsilon_{ij} \tag{6.96}$$

where μ_i is the mean of the ith treatment level and ε_{ij} is the random error. The hypotheses of interest regarding the means model are

$H_0: \mu_1 = \mu_2 = \ldots = \mu_a$

H_a: at least two of the means differ (that is, $\mu_i \neq \mu_j, i \neq j$)

Table 6.22 A typical table of data for an experiment with one factor.

	Treatment				
	1	**2**	**. . .**	***a***	**Totals**
	y_{11}	y_{21}	$\cdots$	y_{a1}	$y_{.1}$
	y_{12}	y_{22}	$\cdots$	y_{a2}	$y_{.2}$
			$\cdots$		
	y_{1n}	y_{2n}	$\cdots$	y_{an}	$y_{.n}$
Totals	$y_{1.}$	$y_{2.}$	$\cdots$	$y_{a.}$	$y_{..}$
Averages	$\bar{y}_{1.}$	$\bar{y}_{2.}$	$\cdots$	$\bar{y}_{a.}$	$\bar{y}_{..}$

The quantities needed to determine whether a significant difference exists among the treatments (or levels of the factor) are the sum of squares and the degrees of freedom.

The *total sum of squares*, denoted SS_T, is an important quantity that provides a measure of the total overall variability in the response:

$$SS_T = \sum_{i=1}^{a}\sum_{j=1}^{n}\left(y_{ij} - \bar{y}_{..}\right)^2 \tag{6.97}$$

where y_{ij} is a single observation and $\bar{y}_{..}$ is the average of all *an* responses. The total sum of squares can be partitioned into two sources of variability: variability due to the treatments applied ($SS_{\text{Treatments}}$) and variability due to error or unknown sources (SS_E). In other words,

$$SS_T = SS_{\text{Treatments}} + SS_E \tag{6.98}$$

The *sum of squares due to treatments* ($SS_{\text{Treatments}}$) is a portion of the total sum of squares (SS_T). It is a quantity that measures the proportion of total variability that can be explained by or that is due to the different treatments applied:

$$SS_{\text{Treatments}} = n\sum_{i=1}^{a}\left(\bar{y}_{i.} - \bar{y}_{..}\right)^2 \tag{6.99}$$

The *error sum of squares* (SS_E) is that portion of the total sum of squares (SS_T) that represents the inherent variability. This is variability that is not due to the treatments applied or levels used. In conducting an experiment involving a single factor, it is assumed that all variables (other than the treatments) that could possibly influence the response are held constant; any variability that cannot be attributed to the treatment is said to be error. Under these conditions the "leftover" variability is considered inherent. For example, if temperature is known to possibly influence the conversion rate in the previous example, but temperature is not of interest at this point, temperature would be held (this is the temperature of a water bath in the reaction experiment) at a constant and only vary the factor that is of interest (such as a catalyst). The error sum of squares can be found by:

$$SS_E = SS_T - SS_{\text{Treatments}}$$

It is important to note that if the goal is to show that the treatments cause a significant effect on the response, then the variability due to treatments should be to be large as compared with the inherent variability. It is desirable to have the variability due to error or unknown sources be as small as possible (i.e., SS_E should be small).

A *ratio* involving the $SS_{\text{Treatments}}$ and SS_E is used to reject or fail to reject the hypothesis of interest that all treatment means are equal:

$$H_0: \mu_1 = \mu_2 = \ldots = \mu_a$$

This ratio involving the $SS_{\text{Treatments}}$ and SS_E (whose exact calculations will be shown next) should be significantly large to reject the null hypothesis. A large value of the ratio indicates that most of the total variability is attributed to the treatments applied and is not just variability due to error. If the error variability was comparable to (or larger than) the variability due to treatments, this would indicate that there is very little difference in treatments applied and that most of the variability is uncontrollable.

Degrees of freedom are associated with each source of variability. The degrees of freedom are necessary values in the computation of a test statistic and are as follows:

- The total degrees of freedom are $an - 1$

- For a treatments, the degrees of freedom are $a - 1$

- The degrees of freedom for error are $a(n - 1)$

- The total degrees of freedom can be partitioned into degrees of freedom for treatments and degrees of freedom for error:

$$an - 1 = a - 1 + a(n - 1)$$

The degrees of freedom are used in the ratio involving the sums of squares discussed previously. The sum of squares divided by the appropriate degrees of freedom provides a measure of variability adjusted for sample size and number of treatments in the study. These resulting measures are referred to as *mean squares* (MS). Under H_0, they are estimates of the error variance. The *mean square for treatments* is

$$MS_{\text{Treatments}} = \frac{SS_{\text{Treatments}}}{a - 1} \tag{6.100}$$

The error mean square is

$$MS_E = \frac{SS_E}{a(n - 1)} \tag{6.101}$$

Now, the two mean squares can be directly compared. If $MS_{\text{Treatments}} > MS_E$, then there may be evidence that the treatments have a significant effect on the response. The ratio of the mean squares can be used as a test statistic to make a decision about rejecting or failing to reject the null hypothesis H_0. The ratio is the test statistic, denoted by F_0:

$$F_0 = \frac{\mathrm{MS}_{\mathrm{Treatments}}}{\mathrm{MS}_E} \qquad (6.102)$$

which can be shown to follow an F distribution with $k_1 = a - 1$ and $k_2 = a(n - 1)$ degrees of freedom. If F_0 is large, then there may be evidence that the different treatments significantly affect the response of interest.

Recall the section on testing two population variances. The F distribution was appropriate for modeling the ratio of two variances. Therefore, the test statistic F_0 will be compared with an appropriate critical value found from the F distribution (Appendices F, G, and H). The appropriate critical value is given by $F_{\alpha,a-1,a(n-1)}$, where α is the probability of a type I error (discussed in previous sections), $a - 1$ is the degrees of freedom for the numerator of F_0, and $a(n - 1)$ is the degrees of freedom for the denominator of F_0. Therefore, if $F_0 > F_{\alpha,a-1,a(n-1)}$, the null hypothesis will be rejected and it will be concluded that the treatments or levels are significantly different at the α level of significance. The null hypothesis is only rejected for large F_0 since a large ratio indicates that the variability due to the treatments is larger than the variability due to error (i.e., $\mathrm{MS}_{\mathrm{Treatments}} \gg \mathrm{MS}_E$).

The p-values previously discussed can also be calculated for the F test given here. The same interpretation would apply: if the p-value $< \alpha$, then reject the null hypothesis; otherwise, fail to reject the null hypothesis. The p-values are easy to interpret and are provided by most statistical software packages when conducting an ANOVA.

The degrees of freedom (df), sum of squares (SS), mean squares (MS), F value, and p-value are often summarized in an ANOVA table. Table 6.23 is a one-way ANOVA table.

The calculations and the resulting ANOVA table can be easily obtained using modern computer software or the formulas given in this section. Software packages that have statistical capabilities will automatically report some form of this ANOVA table.

Let's return to the conversion rate of biodiesel fuel example presented at the beginning of this section. In this example, the null and alternative hypotheses can be set up and the results of an ANOVA table presented through using a commercially available and reliable statistical package.

Table 6.23   One-way ANOVA table.

Source of variability	df	SS	MS	F	p-value
Treatments	$a - 1$	$\mathrm{SS}_{\mathrm{Treatments}}$	$\mathrm{MS}_{\mathrm{Treatments}}$	F_0	$P(F > F_0)$
Error	$a(n - 1)$	SS_E	MS_E		
Total	$an - 1$	SS_T			

EXAMPLE 6.52

The treatment of interest is the amount of catalyst (%) and the response is conversion rate. Is there significant evidence to conclude that the amount of catalyst significantly affects the conversion rate?

Solution:

The null and alternative hypotheses are

$H_0: \mu_1 = \mu_2 = \mu_3$

H_a: at least two μ_i are different, for $i \neq j$

Before a formal analysis is conducted on the data, it is often informative to display the results graphically. The box plot is one such appropriate graphical display. Box plots for catalyst amount are shown in Figure 6.23.

Based on the box plots, it appears that the catalyst amount of 1.0% results in higher conversion rates than either 0.6% or 1.4%. There does not appear to be a difference in conversion rate between catalyst amounts of 0.6% and 1.4%. Since interpretation of the graphical displays can be subjective, a more formal analysis such as an ANOVA would be more reliable. The ANOVA table is shown in Table 6.24.

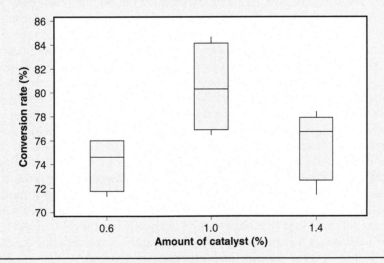

Figure 6.23 Box plots for catalyst amount.

Table 6.24 ANOVA table for conversion rate data.

Source of variability	df	SS	MS	F	p-value
Catalyst	2	84.92	42.46	4.50	0.044
Error	9	85.01	9.45		
Total	11	169.93			

The p-value is reported as 0.044. Since the p-value is small, the null hypothesis is rejected so it can be concluded that there is a difference in mean conversion rate for at least one pair of catalysts.

At this point, the assumptions given earlier should be verified. Some simple tools can be used to verify that the normality and constant variance assumptions are valid. To assess normality, a normal probability plot of the observations can be constructed. A simple method for assessing constant variance is to examine the standard deviations of each treatment. A quick and dirty rule of thumb is that the constant variance assumption is plausible as long as the largest treatment standard deviation is not much more than two times the smallest treatment standard deviation. (See Devore [2016] for more details on these and other methods.) More formal methods for assessing constant variance involve analyzing residuals. These methods will be discussed in later sections.

To adequately assess independence, the order in which the data were collected must be known. Without the order, it is difficult to determine the validity of the independence assumption. In addition, if the experiment was conducted randomly (carried out randomly) it is often assumed that this randomization will minimize any dependency among the observations.

Two-Way ANOVA

The *two-way ANOVA* hypothesis test can be used when there are two factors of interest in the experiment. In the biodiesel fuel example there was one factor (catalyst amount) with three levels. When more than one factor is under investigation in an experiment, a factorial experiment should be used. A *factorial experiment* is one where all possible combinations of the factor levels are investigated. To illustrate, suppose there are two factors A and B with levels a and b, respectively. In a full-factorial experiment, there would be ab total combinations, which are the treatments of interest. It is desired to determine the differences among the levels of factor A, the differences among the levels of factor B, and whether an interaction exists between the two factors. An interaction between factors can be demonstrated graphically. Figure 6.24 represents the interaction plots of two factors A and B, where A has two levels ($a = 2$) and B has three levels ($b = 3$). Figure 6.24a indicates that there is no significant interaction between factors A and B. Notice that moving across the levels of factor B, the levels of factor A maintain identical patterns. Figure 6.24b, on the other hand, indicates a significant interaction between factors A and B. Notice that by changing from level 1 to level 2 of factor A, the response is quite different. By changing the level of factor A, and keeping factor B at level 2, for example, the response has changed.

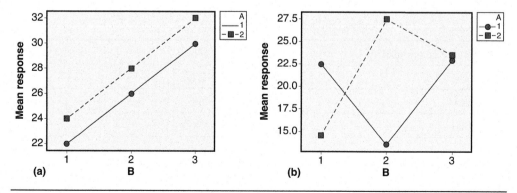

Figure 6.24 Interaction plots of factors A and B.

When analyzing two-factor experiments, the effects to be analyzed are the main effects of factor A, the main effects of factor B, and the interaction between them.

EXAMPLE 6.53

Reconsider the biodiesel fuel example given earlier; now a second factor is of interest. Along with the catalyst, the temperature of the water bath for the process is also of interest. There are two temperatures, 30°C and 60°C. Two replicates of each combination of catalyst and temperature are recorded, with the results shown in Table 6.25.

Table 6.25 Conversion rates for experiment with two factors.

		Catalyst (%)		
		0.6	**1.0**	**1.4**
Temperature	30	75.22, 76.81	83.10, 79.55	69.24, 71.64
	60	77.01, 75.39	75.33, 72.67	72.00, 74.57

In this study:

- Some questions of interest are: Does the amount of catalyst have a significant effect on conversion rate? Does temperature have a significant effect on conversion rate? Is there a significant interaction between temperature and the amount of catalyst?

- Catalyst and temperature are the *factors of interest* or *independent variables*.

- The factor "catalyst" has three *levels* (0.6%, 1.0%, and 1.4%). The factor "temperature" has two *levels* (30°C and 60°C).

- Conversion rate is the *response of interest* (or *dependent variable*).

- There are two *replicates* ($n = 2$) for each combination of catalyst and temperature.

Suppose there are two factors of interest, A and B, with a and b levels, respectively. Furthermore, suppose there are n replicates for each combination ab. The total sum of squares (SS_T) can be calculated for the two-way table and it can be partitioned into four sources of variability:

$$SS_T = SS_A + SS_B + SS_{AB} + SS_E \tag{6.103}$$

where SS_A is the sum of squares for factor A, SS_B is the sum of squares for factor B, SS_{AB} is the sum of squares for the interaction AB, and SS_E is the error sum of squares. The mean squares can be calculated and an ANOVA table created (see Table 6.26).

The numerator and denominator degrees of freedom needed to find the appropriate critical value or calculate the p-value will vary depending on which factor is being tested. Consider factor A: the correct degrees of freedom needed to find the appropriate critical value are $(a - 1)$, $ab(n - 1)$ (i.e., the degrees of freedom for the

Table 6.26 Two-way ANOVA table.

Source of variability	df	SS	MS	F	p-value
Factor A	$a - 1$	SS_A	MS_A	$F_0 = \dfrac{MS_A}{MS_E}$	$P(F > F_0)$
Factor B	$b - 1$	SS_B	MS_B	$F_0 = \dfrac{MS_B}{MS_E}$	$P(F > F_0)$
AB interaction	$(a - 1)(b - 1)$	SS_{AB}	MS_{AB}	$F_0 = \dfrac{MS_{AB}}{MS_E}$	$P(F > F_0)$
Error	$ab(n - 1)$	SS_E	MS_E		
Total	$abn - 1$	SS_T			

numerator of F_0 and the degrees of freedom for the denominator of F_0). As with the one-way ANOVA, the F-statistic measures the ratio between the effect and the experimental error. If the variation due to the effect is a sufficiently large multiple of the error, the effect is considered statistically significant. Using p-values, this means that the null hypothesis would be rejected if the p-value $< \alpha$.

EXAMPLE 6.54

Reconsider the conversion rate example with two factors of interest, catalyst and temperature. The resulting ANOVA table is shown in Table 6.27.

Using p-values, one would conclude that the amount of catalyst has a significant effect on the conversion rate (p-value = 0.009). But there is insufficient evidence to conclude that temperature has a significant effect on the conversion rate (p-value = 0.209). Finally, it appears that there is a significant interaction between catalyst and temperature (p-value = 0.016).

The interaction plot is shown in Figure 6.25. There is a clear indication that a significant interaction exists between temperature and catalyst. If the goal is to maximize conversion rate, it appears that 1.0% catalyst and a temperature of 30°C would be a good choice.

Table 6.27 ANOVA table for conversion rate example with two factors of interest.

Source of variability	df	SS	MS	F	p-value
Catalyst	2	72.104	36.0520	11.63	0.009
Temperature	1	6.149	6.1490	1.98	0.209
Catalyst × temperature interaction	2	55.635	27.8174	8.97	0.016
Error	6	18.598	3.0996		
Total	11	152.486			

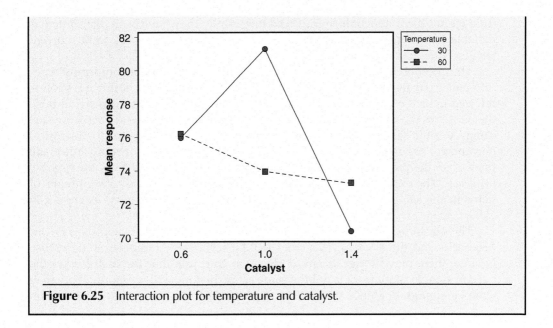

Figure 6.25 Interaction plot for temperature and catalyst.

The details of the general notation and formulas are not presented here, but the reader is encouraged to see Devore (2016); Montgomery and Runger (2013); Montgomery, Runger, and Hubele (2010); or Vining and Kowalski (2011).

As a final note on the two-way ANOVA, it is important to realize that if each combination of the factors consists of only one observation ($n = 1$), you cannot estimate the two-factor interaction. When $n = 1$, there will not be enough degrees of freedom left over for error, the important quantity MS_E cannot be estimated, and MS_E is needed to calculate the test statistic. If it is acceptable to only estimate the main factors (A and B), then the interaction is removed (not tested) and the SS_{AB} and degrees of freedom for the interaction are moved into error. If the interaction is possibly important, then it is recommended that at least two replicates for each combination of factors be collected.

Goodness-of-fit Tests

> Define and use chi square and other
> goodness-of-fit tests, and understand the
> results. (Apply)
>
> **Body of Knowledge VI.D.4**

Chi-square and other goodness-of-fit tests help determine whether a discrete sample has been drawn from a known population. The probability distribution may be of a specific form, such as the Poisson, binomial, geometric, and so on, or it may be simply a table of outcomes and their assumed probabilities. For example, suppose that all rejected products have exactly one of four types of nonconformities (that render them nonconforming), and historically they have been distributed as in Table 6.28. Data on rejected parts for a randomly selected week in the current year are shown in Table 6.29.

The question to be answered is this: Is the distribution of nonconformity types different from the historical distribution? The test that answers this question is referred to as the χ^2 *goodness-of-fit test.* To get a feel for this test, construct a table that displays the number of nonconforming units that would be expected in each category if the sample exactly followed the historical percentages (the historical percentages are used as estimates of the probabilities that the nonconformities are present on the product). The expected number will be referred to as the *expected frequency.* The expected frequency is found by multiplying the total number of items in the sample *n* by the probability for a particular category, as shown in Table 6.30.

The question to be answered is whether the difference between the *expected frequencies* and the *observed frequencies* will be sufficiently large. If the difference is large, there may be significant evidence to conclude that the distribution the current sample came from is not the same as the historical distribution; there may even be enough evidence to conclude that the historical (assumed) distribution

Table 6.28 Historical percentages of nonconformities for rejected products.

Nonconformity	Percentage of nonconforming products
Paint run	16%
Paint blister	28%
Decal crooked	42%
Door cracked	14%
Total	100%

Table 6.29 Number of nonconformities for a random week.

Nonconformity	Number of nonconforming products
Paint run	27
Paint blister	60
Decal crooked	100
Door cracked	21
Total	208

Table 6.30 Observed and expected frequencies for nonconformity data.

Nonconformity	Observed frequency (O_i)	Probability (p_i)	Expected frequency (E_i) [$E_i = np_i$]
Paint run	27	0.16	33.28
Paint blister	60	0.28	58.24
Decal crooked	100	0.42	87.36
Door cracked	21	0.14	29.12
Total	$n = 208$	1	

is no longer valid. The test statistic that can be used to determine whether the assumed distribution is still valid is

$$\chi_0^2 = \sum_{i=1}^{k} \frac{\left(O_i - E_i\right)^2}{E_i} \tag{6.104}$$

It can be shown that the test statistic follows a chi-square distribution with $k - 1$ degrees of freedom (where k = number of categories). Let p_i represent the proportion of the population that falls into the ith category, for $i = 1, 2, \ldots, k$. Let $p_{i,0}$ represent the hypothesized value of p_i. The null and alternative hypotheses would be

$H_0: p_1 = p_{1,0}; p_2 = p_{2,0}; \ldots ; p_k = p_{k,0}$

$H_a: p_i \neq p_{i,0}$ for at least one $i = 1, 2, \ldots, k$

The procedure for conducting a goodness-of-fit test is as follows:

1. Determine the null and alternative hypotheses.

2. State the level of significance α.

3. Determine the rejection region. For this test the critical value is $\chi_{\alpha,k-1}^2$.

4. Calculate the test statistic.

5. If $\chi_0^2 \geq \chi_{\alpha,k-1}^2$, reject H_0; otherwise fail to reject H_0.

6. State the conclusions in terms of the problem statement.

EXAMPLE 6.55

The goodness-of-fit test will be executed for the problem involving nonconforming products using a 5% level of significance.

1. $H_0: p_1 = 0.16; p_2 = 0.28; p_3 = 0.42; p_4 = 0.14$

   $H_a: p_i \neq p_{i,0}$ for at least one i = 1, 2, ..., 4

Continued

2. $\alpha = 0.05$

3. For this test the critical value is $\chi^2_{\alpha, k-1} = \chi^2_{0.05,3} = 7.815$

4. Calculate the test statistic:

$$\chi^2_0 = \sum_{i=1}^{k} \frac{(O_i - E_i)^2}{E_i} = \frac{(27 - 33.28)^2}{33.28} + \frac{(60 - 58.24)^2}{58.24} + \frac{(100 - 87.36)^2}{87.36} + \frac{(21 - 29.12)^2}{29.12}$$

$$= 5.33$$

5. Since 5.33 < 7.815, we fail to reject H_0 (weak claim)

6. The conclusion is that the data do not indicate that there has been a change in the proportion of observed nonconforming products when compared with historical proportions, at the 0.05 level of significance

The chi-square goodness-of-fit test is valid as long as the expected frequencies are not too small. Some recommendations for a minimum value have included 3, 4, and 5. Other recommendations have been that some of the expected frequencies can be as small as 1 or 2 as long as most of the expected frequencies exceed 5. For more details on other applications of the chi-square test and further recommendations, see Devore (2016), Montgomery and Runger (2013), and Vining and Kowalski (2011).

Contingency Tables

Define and use contingency tables to evaluate statistical significance. (Apply)

Body of Knowledge VI.D.6

In this section, a test concerning count data will be presented. Suppose a sample of n items has been collected and each item can be classified into two different categories at the same time. Data that can be classified according to two different criteria (or factors) can be displayed in a *two-way contingency table*. In cases such as this, it is often of interest to determine whether the two categories are statistically independent of one another. For example, consider the population of high school graduates. It may be of interest to determine whether the hourly wage for an entry-level job is independent of graduating from high school.

Suppose there are r levels of factor 1 and c levels of factor 2. Each criterion can have several different levels. An $r \times c$ *contingency table* could be written as in Table 6.31, where

- The r rows represent the levels of the first factor

- The c columns represent the levels of the second factor

- O_{ij} represents the number of observations that fall into category i of factor 1 and category j of factor 2, where $i = 1, 2, \ldots, r$ and $j = 1, 2, \ldots c$

Table 6.31 A generic contingency table.

		Columns			
		1	2	...	c
Rows	1	O_{11}	O_{12}	...	O_{1c}
	2	O_{21}	O_{22}	...	O_{2c}
	:	:	:	...	:
	r	O_{r1}	O_{r2}	...	O_{rc}

EXAMPLE 6.56

A company operates two machines on three different shifts. The company wants to determine if machine breakdowns that occur during operation are *independent* of the shift on which the machine is used. The data are recorded in a 2×3 contingency table, shown in Table 6.32.

Table 6.32 A contingency table for machine breakdown.

	Shift		
Machine	1	2	3
1	30	40	20
2	30	40	10

In this study:

- $r = 2$, the number of machines.

- $c = 3$, the number of shifts.

- O_{ij} represents the number of breakdowns that occur on the ith machine when used on the jth shift. For example $O_{12} = 40$. Therefore, 40 breakdowns have been recorded on machine 1 when it was used on the second shift.

The objective here is determining whether the two factors are independent of one another.

The *expected frequencies* are calculated based on the assumption that the two factors of interest are independent of one another. Denote the expected frequencies as E_{ij} (for $i = 1, 2, \ldots, r$ and $j = 1, 2, \ldots, c$). Calculate the expected frequencies for each entry in the contingency table using $E_{ij} = na_ib_j$, where

- n = total number of observations, that is, $n = O_{11} + O_{12} + \ldots + O_{rc}$

- a_i is the probability that a randomly selected observation will fall into the ith category of factor 1 (the row factor) and is found using the following formula:

$$a_i = \frac{\sum_{j=1}^{c} O_{ij}}{n} \qquad (6.105)$$

(Summing over the columns for the *i*th row)

- b_j is the probability that a randomly selected observation will fall into the *j*th category of factor 2 (the column factor) and is found using the following formula:

$$b_j = \frac{\sum_{i=1}^{r} O_{ij}}{n} \qquad (6.106)$$

(Summing over the rows for the *j*th column)

If the two factors are independent, then one would expect the observed frequency and the expected frequency for each cell to be similar. This assumption can be tested using the test statistic

$$\chi_o^2 = \sum_{i=1}^{r} \sum_{j=1}^{c} \frac{(O_{ij} - E_{ij})^2}{E_{ij}} \qquad (6.107)$$

which follows a chi-square distribution with $(r - 1)(c - 1)$ degrees of freedom. The test statistic can be compared with a critical value from the chi-square distribution with $(r - 1)(c - 1)$ degrees of freedom and a significance level α. The critical value is denoted $\chi^2_{\alpha,(r-1)(c-1)}$. If the test statistic is greater than the critical value, it can be concluded there is enough evidence that the two factors are not independent. The test is valid as long as the expected frequency of each cell is at least five.

EXAMPLE 6.57

A company operates two machines on three different shifts. The company wants to determine if machine breakdowns are *independent* of shift. The data are shown in Table 6.33.

Solution:

Calculate the expected frequency for each cell, where $n = 30 + 40 + 20 + 30 + 40 + 10 = 170$. The row probabilities (probabilities associated with the machines) are:

Machine 1: $a_1 = (30 + 40 + 20)/170 = 90/170 = 0.529$

Machine 2: $a_2 = (30 + 40 + 10)/170 = 80/170 = 0.471$

The column probabilities (probabilities associated with the shifts) are found as follows:

Machine 1: $b_1 = (30 + 30)/170 = 60/170 = 0.353$

Machine 2: $b_2 = (40 + 40)/170 = 80/170 = 0.471$

Machine 3: $b_3 = (20 + 10)/170 = 30/170 = 0.176$

Expected frequency computations for two of the six cells are

$E_{11} = na_1b_1 = 170(90/170)(60/170) = 31.765$

$E_{23} = na_2b_3 = 170(80/170)(30/170) = 14.118$

The expected frequencies for all six cells are provided in Table 6.33.

Table 6.33 Expected frequencies for machine breakdown.

	Shift		
Machine	1	2	3
1	31.765	42.353	15.882
2	28.235	37.647	14.118

The test statistic is

$$\chi_0^2 = \sum\sum \frac{(O_{ij} - E_{ij})^2}{E_{ij}}$$

$$= \frac{(30-31.765)^2}{31.765} + \frac{(40-42.353)^2}{42.353} + \ldots + \frac{(10-14.118)^2}{14.118}$$

$$= 2.755$$

With $\alpha = 0.05$ and degrees of freedom $(r-1)(c-1) = 2$, the critical value is $\chi_{\alpha,(r-1)(c-1)}^2 = \chi_{0.05,2}^2 = 5.99$. Since $2.755 < 5.99$, we fail to reject the hypothesis of independence. Breakdown of a particular machine appears to be independent of which shift is using the machine.

RELATIONSHIPS BETWEEN VARIABLES

This section covers four kinds of relationships between variables: simple linear correlation, linear regression, multiple linear regression, and time series analysis.

Simple Linear Correlation

> Calculate the correlation coefficient and its confidence interval, and illustrate a hypothesis for correlation statistics. (Apply)
>
> **Body of Knowledge VI.E.2**

Correlation measures the strength of the linear relationship between two variables. A *linear* relationship exists between two variables if one variable increases as the other increases or decreases. Graphically, this will be seen if the values of the two variables plot along a straight line. One of the parameters that defines the relationship between variables is the *population correlation coefficient* ρ. The population correlation coefficient is often unknown and can be estimated using sample data. Suppose x and y are jointly normally distributed random variables. The sample correlation coefficient, denoted r, can be used as the estimate of the population correlation coefficient ρ. The sample correlation coefficient is

$$r = \frac{S_{xy}}{\sqrt{S_{xx}}\sqrt{S_{yy}}} \tag{6.108}$$

where

$$S_{xy} = \sum_{i=1}^{n}(x_i - \bar{x})(y_i - \bar{y}) = \sum_{i=1}^{n}x_i y_i - \frac{\left(\sum_{i=1}^{n}x_i\right)\left(\sum_{i=1}^{n}y_i\right)}{n} \tag{6.109}$$

$$S_{xx} = \sum_{i=1}^{n}(x_i - \bar{x})^2 = \sum_{i=1}^{n}x_i^2 - \frac{\left(\sum_{i=1}^{n}x_i\right)^2}{n} \tag{6.110}$$

$$S_{yy} = \sum_{i=1}^{n}(y_i - \bar{y})^2 = \sum_{i=1}^{n}y_i^2 - \frac{\left(\sum_{i=1}^{n}y_i\right)^2}{n} \tag{6.111}$$

The sample correlation coefficient r measures the strength of the linear relationship and has the following properties:

- $1 \le r \le 1$; the closer the value is to -1 or 1, the stronger the linear relationship
  - If r is negative, this indicates that as one variable is increasing, the other is decreasing
  - If r is positive, this indicates that both variables are increasing or both variables are decreasing
- If $r = 0$, then there is no linear relationship between the two variables
- r has no units attached to it, such as pounds, inches, feet, and so on

Figure 6.26 illustrates two variables x and y. Figure 6.26a displays two random variables that are *positively correlated.* In this case, the value of r is positive and near 1. Figure 6.26b displays two random variables that are *negatively correlated.* In this case, the value of r is negative and near -1. Figure 6.26c displays two variables that are not linearly related at all. In this situation, there does appear to be some relationship between x and y, but it is not linear. Therefore, the correlation coefficient r would be zero.

There is a direct relationship between the correlation coefficient and the slope of a simple linear model. The sign on the correlation coefficient is the same as the sign on the slope. This will be discussed further in the next section.

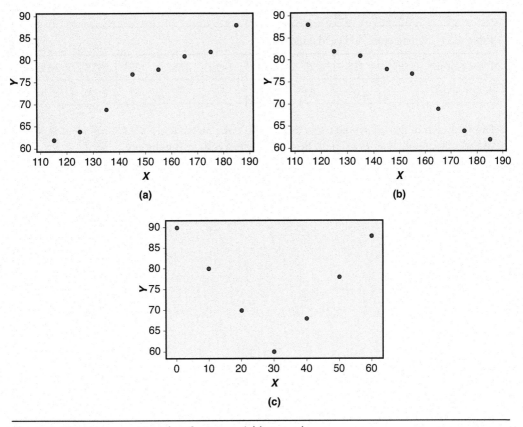

Figure 6.26 Various scatter plots for two variables x and y.

There is some subjectiveness in the interpretation of the correlation coefficient estimate. If $-0.6 \le r \le 0.6$, for example, there is not always agreement as to whether the association between the two variables is significantly correlated. A t-test on the population correlation coefficient can be conducted to determine the statistical significance of the correlation. For complete details on testing the significance of the population correlation coefficient, see Devore (2016); Montgomery and Runger (2013); Montgomery, Runger, and Hubele (2010); or Kutner et al. (2004).

EXAMPLE 6.58

When data have been collected relating two variables, it is often useful to find an equation that models the relationship. Then the value of the dependent variable can be predicted for a given value of the independent variable. For example, suppose a chemical engineer is investigating the relationship between the operating temperature of a process and product yield. In this case, it might be useful to control the operating temperature (independent variable) to control or predict yield (dependent variable). For this example, eight readings are taken, and shown in Table 6.34. In an actual application more data would be desirable.

Continued

Table 6.34 Temperature and yield data.

Temperature, °C (x)	115	125	135	145	155	165	175	185
Yield, % (y)	62	64	69	77	78	81	82	88

The first step in the investigation is to plot the data, as in Figure 6.27, to determine if it seems reasonable to approximate the relationship with a straight line.

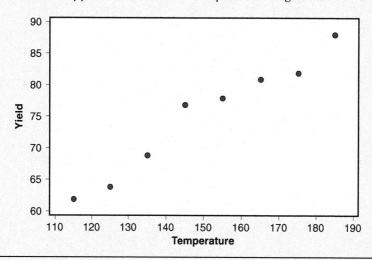

Figure 6.27 Scatter plot of temperature and yield.

For these data, the sums of squares needed to determine the sample correlation coefficient

$$S_{xy} = \sum_{i=1}^{n} x_i y_i - \frac{\left(\sum_{i=1}^{n} x_i\right)\left(\sum_{i=1}^{n} y_i\right)}{n} = 1545$$

$$S_{xx} = \sum_{i=1}^{n} x_i^2 - \frac{\left(\sum_{i=1}^{n} x_i\right)^2}{n} = 4200$$

$$S_{yy} = \sum_{i=1}^{n} y_i^2 - \frac{\left(\sum_{i=1}^{n} y_i\right)^2}{n} = 592.875$$

resulting in the below calculation

$$r = \frac{S_{xy}}{\sqrt{S_{xx}}\sqrt{S_{yy}}} = \frac{1545}{\sqrt{4200}\sqrt{592.875}} = 0.979$$

The sample correlation coefficient of 0.979 indicates that there is a very strong positive linear relationship between temperature and yield.

Linear Regression

> Calculate simple linear regression models.
> Illustrate hypothesis tests for regression
> statistics. Use linear regression models for
> estimation and prediction. (Apply)
>
> **Body of Knowledge VI.E.1**

Linear regression models are important statistical tools developed to relate two or more variables of interest. This relationship often takes the form of a linear equation or linear model. In this section, simple linear regression is presented. *Simple linear regression* is the situation where there are exactly two variables:

- One independent variable (often denoted by x)

- One dependent variable (often denoted by y)

Although a perfect straight line cannot be drawn through these points in Example 6.60, the trend looks linear. The next step is to find an equation that best fits the data. Before creating regression lines for particular problems, some assumptions and basic definitions must be presented.

Notation and Definitions

Reconsider the scatter plot in Figure 6.27. The scatter plot indicates that the two variables may be linearly related. This is indicated by the fact that the observations fall approximately along a straight line. A *simple linear regression model* is one that characterizes a linear relationship between the response of interest y and an independent (explanatory or regressor) variable x:

$$y = \beta_0 + \beta_1 x + \varepsilon \tag{6.112}$$

where β_0 and β_1 are called *regression coefficients* and ε represents a *random error term* (recall that the data will rarely lie exactly along a straight line, so when a straight line is fit to the data, there will be some error).

Let $x_1, x_2, \ldots, x_n$ represent real values of the independent variable (also called an explanatory variable) and $y_1, y_2, \ldots, y_n$ represent real values of the dependent variable (also called the response). The sample consists of n pairs of data (x_1, y_1), $(x_2, y_2), \ldots, (x_n, y_n)$. The general model can be written in terms of the individual observations:

$$y_i = \beta_0 + \beta_1 x_i + \varepsilon_i, \text{ for } i = 1, 2, \ldots, n \tag{6.113}$$

For the simple linear regression model:

- The coefficients β_0 and β_1 are parameters that define the mathematical relationship between the independent and dependent variables. β_0 is the intercept and β_1 is the slope.

- The *intercept* is the value of y when $x = 0$. This is the height at which the regression line crosses the y-axis.

- The *slope* represents the change in the response for every one unit change in the independent variable x.

Given a series of values for an independent variable x and the corresponding dependent variable y, point estimates for β_0 and β_1 can be calculated. The point estimates are denoted b_0 and b_1. Once the point estimates are obtained, a fitted regression line can be given by

$$\hat{y}_i = b_0 + b_1 x_i \tag{6.114}$$

where $\hat{y}_i$ is the predicted value of the response for a given value of the independent variable.

Estimating the Parameters β_0 and β_1 and Making Predictions

The statistics b_0 and b_1 need to be calculated in such a way that the resulting fitted line will provide predicted values that will be close to the actual value for each value of x. One method for calculating b_0 and b_1 is based on minimizing the error between the actual value of y and the predicted value of y for each pair of data, that is, $e_i = y_i - \hat{y}_i$. This is an appropriate method since a goal of simple linear regression is to make predictions after fitting a model between the independent variable and the response. A method frequently employed is the least squares method. The formulas for finding b_1 and b_0 are as follows:

$$b_1 = \frac{S_{xy}}{S_{xx}} \tag{6.115}$$

$$b_0 = \bar{y} - b_1 \bar{x} \tag{6.116}$$

where S_{xy} and S_{xx} were defined earlier. Equations (6.115) and (6.116) are often referred to as the *least squares estimates*. These formulas result in estimates that will give us a best-fitting line. By "best fitting," it is meant that the line with these estimates for the coefficients will result in the smallest error sum of squares.

Let e_i represent the error associated with the ith observation $e_i = y_i - \hat{y}_i$ for $i = 1, 2, \ldots, n$ (a realized value of the error is referred to as a *residual*). Ideally, a fitted line will be produced that will minimize the n errors as much as possible. More specifically, the fitted regression line should minimize the quantity

$$SS_E = \sum_{i=1}^{n} e_i^2 \tag{6.117}$$

(the error sum of squares). The formulas for b_0 and b_1 given previously, in Equations (6.115) and (6.116), respectively, result in a fitted line that will make this quantity as small as possible. In fact, there are no other estimates of β_0 and β_1 that will result in a smaller error sum of squares.

EXAMPLE 6.59

Reconsider the yield data from Example 6.60. Temperature is the independent variable x and yield is the response y. We want to fit a regression line relating temperature to yield.

The necessary calculations for b_1 and b_0 are:

$$n = 8$$

$$\sum_{i=1}^{8} x_i = 115 + 125 + \ldots + 185 = 1200 \qquad \sum_{i=1}^{8} x_i^2 = 115^2 + 125^2 + \ldots + 185^2 = 184,200$$

$$\sum_{i=1}^{8} y_i = 62 + 64 + \ldots + 88 = 601 \qquad \sum_{i=1}^{n} x_i y_i = 115(62) + 125(64) + \ldots + 185(88) = 91,695$$

$$\bar{x} = 150 \qquad \bar{y} = 75.125$$

Calculate b_1 and b_0 (using Equations (6.116) and (6.117)):

$$S_{xy} = \sum_{i=1}^{n} x_i y_i - \frac{\left(\sum_{i=1}^{n} x_i\right)\left(\sum_{i=1}^{n} y_i\right)}{n} = 91,695 - \frac{(1200)(601)}{8} = 1545$$

$$S_{xx} = \sum_{i=1}^{n} x_i^2 - \frac{\left(\sum_{i=1}^{n} x_i\right)^2}{n} = 184,200 - \frac{(1200)^2}{8} = 4200$$

$$b_1 = \frac{S_{xy}}{S_{xx}} = \frac{1545}{4200} = 0.368$$

$$b_0 = \bar{y} - b_1\bar{x} = 75.125 - 0.368(150) = 19.9$$

The final fitted regression line is then

$$\hat{y} = 19.9 + 0.368$$

The fitted regression line is plotted along with the original data in Figure 6.28.

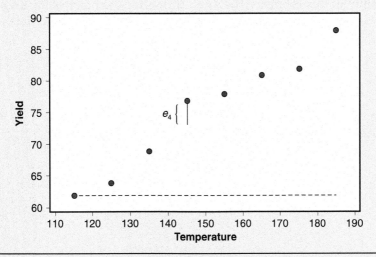

Figure 6.28 Scatter plot and fitted regression line for the yield data.

The fitted regression line represents the predicted value $\hat{y}$ for each value of x. Graphically, the residuals mentioned earlier are the vertical differences between the actual value of y and the predicted value of y for each value of x. The vertical line represents the residual for $x_4 = 145$ ($e_4 = y_4 - \hat{y}_4 = 77 - 73.26 = 3.74$).

The fitted regression model is often used to make predictions of new or future observations for the response. Let x_0 be a value of the independent variable. The point estimator of the new value, y_0, is given using Equation (6.116) by

$$\hat{y}_0 = b_0 + b_1 x_0$$

For example, suppose it is desired to predict the yield for a temperature of 150°C. The predicted value of the yield would be:

$$\hat{y}_0 = 19.9 + 0.368 x_0$$

$$= 19.9 + 0.368(150)$$

$$= 75.14\%$$

Because the value is a single point estimate calculated from sample data, there is variability or error in this prediction. It is sometimes of interest to construct an interval estimate for a future observation. A prediction interval provides a measure of the estimate and error of prediction. For complete details on prediction intervals, see Devore (2016); Montgomery and Runger (2013); Montgomery, Runger, and Hubele (2010); Kutner et al. (2004); or Vining and Kowalski (2011).

The equation for the regression line is based on observed data. Therefore, predictions of new observations with X values outside the range of original data (x_{min}, x_{max}) should be used with caution. This is called *extrapolation*.

Hypothesis Testing in Simple Linear Regression

Fitting a simple linear regression model involves a sample of data. As a result, there will naturally be some error in the estimates of the coefficients β_0 and β_1. Recall that when estimating a population mean with a sample mean there is some variability in this estimate. The same is true for the point estimates of the coefficients b_0 and b_1. The expected value and variance of the point estimate of β_0 are

$$E(b_0) = \beta_0 \tag{6.118}$$

$$V(b_0) = \sigma^2 \left[\frac{1}{n} + \frac{\bar{x}^2}{S_{xx}} \right] \tag{6.119}$$

The expected value and variance for the point estimate of β_1 are

$$E(b_1) = \beta_1 \tag{6.120}$$

$$V(b_1) = \frac{\sigma^2}{S_{xx}} \tag{6.121}$$

where S_{xx} was defined in Equation (6.111) and σ^2 is the error variance (also referred to as the process variability). An estimate of σ^2 is

$$\hat{\sigma}^2 = \frac{SS_E}{n-2} = MS_E \tag{6.122}$$

where $n - 2$ is the error degrees of freedom and SS_E represents the error sum of squares defined previously:

$$SS_E = \sum_{i=1}^{n}(y_i - \hat{y}_i)^2 = \sum_{i=1}^{n}e_i^2 \tag{6.123}$$

The standard errors for b_0 and b_1 are

$$s.e.(b_0) = \sqrt{V(b_0)} = \sqrt{\sigma^2\left[\frac{1}{n} + \frac{\bar{x}^2}{S_{xx}}\right]} \tag{6.124}$$

$$s.e.(b_1) = \sqrt{V(b_1)} = \sqrt{\frac{\sigma^2}{S_{xx}}} \tag{6.125}$$

An important test in simple linear regression is a test on the coefficient β_1. In particular, a test on the significance of regression would involve testing $\beta_1 = 0$. If $\beta_1 = 0$, then Equation (6.114) would be

$$y = \beta_0 + \beta_1 x + \varepsilon$$

$$= \beta_0 + \varepsilon$$

which indicates no significant linear relationship between x and y.

A t-test can be conducted on the slope β_1. The hypotheses of interest are

$H_0: \beta_1 = 0$

$H_a: \beta_1 \neq 0$

The test statistic is

$$t_0 = \frac{b_1 - 0}{\sqrt{\dfrac{\hat{\sigma}^2}{S_{xx}}}} \tag{6.126}$$

A large value of t_0 would lead to rejection of the null hypothesis. An appropriate critical value is $t_{\alpha/2,n-2}$, found from the t table in Appendix O. If a p-value is calculated, the null hypothesis would be rejected if the p-value is small (p-value $< \alpha$), and would indicate a significant linear relationship between x and y.

A t-test can also be conducted on the intercept β_0. The hypotheses of interest are

$H_0: \beta_0 = 0$

$H_a: \beta_0 \neq 0$

The test statistic is

$$t_0 = \frac{b_0 - 0}{\sqrt{\hat{\sigma}^2 \left[\dfrac{1}{n} + \dfrac{\bar{x}^2}{S_{xx}} \right]}} \qquad (6.127)$$

A large value of t_0 would lead to rejection of the null hypothesis. An appropriate critical value is $t_{\alpha/2, n-2}$, found from the t table in Appendix O. If a p-value is calculated, the null hypothesis would be rejected if the p-value is small (p-value $< \alpha$).

The calculations do not need to be done by hand. A statistical software package can be used to carry out all the necessary calculations.

EXAMPLE 6.60

Reconsider the yield and temperature data. The hypotheses of interest are

$$H_0: \beta_1 = 0 \text{ versus } H_a: \beta_1 \neq 0$$

and

$$H_0: \beta_0 = 0 \text{ versus } H_a: \beta_0 \neq 0$$

The output from a particular statistical package for this problem is:

```
Predictor      Coef    SE Coef        T        P
Constant     19.946      4.735     4.21    0.006
x           0.36786    0.03120    11.79    0.000
```

The output can be interpreted as follows:

- The row "Constant" is the hypothesis test on the intercept: $H_0: \beta_0 = 0$ versus $H_a: \beta_0 \neq 0$.

- The row "x" is the hypothesis test on the slope: $H_0: \beta_1 = 0$ versus $H_a: \beta_1 \neq 0$.

- The column labeled "Coef" contains the point estimates for each parameter, that is, $b_0 = 19.946$ and $b_1 = 0.36786$.

- The column labeled "SE Coef" provides the standard error of each estimate, that is, s.e.(b_0) = 4.735 and s.e.(b_1) = 0.0312.

- The column labeled "T" represents the test statistic for the intercept and slope; $t_0 = 4.21$ (test on the intercept) and $t_0 = 11.79$ (test on the slope).

- The last column, labeled "P," contains the p-value for each parameter.

The p-value for testing $\beta_1 = 0$ is 0.000. Since this value is small, the hypothesis that $\beta_1 = 0$ can be rejected and it can be concluded that the slope is not zero. That is, there appears to be a statistically significant linear relationship between temperature and yield.

The test on the intercept $\beta_0 = 0$ also indicates that the intercept is significant. If we fail to reject the null hypothesis $\beta_0 = 0$, it is often left to the practitioner to determine if it makes practical sense to leave the intercept in the model.

The $100(1 - \alpha)\%$ two-sided confidence interval on the intercept is given by

$$b_0 - t_{\alpha/2, n-2} \text{s.e.}(b_0) \leq \beta_0 \leq b_0 + t_{\alpha/2, n-2} \text{s.e.}(b_0) \qquad (6.128)$$

The $100(1 - \alpha)\%$ two-sided confidence interval on the slope is given by

$$b_1 - t_{\alpha/2,n-2}\text{s.e.}(b_1) \le \beta_1 \le b_1 + t_{\alpha/2,n-2}\text{s.e.}(b_1) \tag{6.129}$$

EXAMPLE 6.61

For the yield and temperature data, it is desired to construct 95% confidence intervals on the slope and intercept. In this case, the value $t_{\alpha/2,n-2} = t_{0.025,6} = 2.447$ and the resulting confidence intervals are

$$b_0 - t_{\alpha/2,n-2}\text{s.e.}(b_0) \le \beta_0 \le b_0 + t_{\alpha/2,n-2}\text{s.e.}(b_0)$$

$$19.946 - 2.447(4.735) \le \beta_0 \le 19.946 + 2.447(4.735)$$

$$8.36 \le \beta_0 \le 31.53$$

and

$$b_1 - t_{\alpha/2,n-2}\text{s.e.}(b_1) \le \beta_0 \le b_1 + t_{\alpha/2,n-2}\text{s.e.}(b_1)$$

$$0.368 - 2.447(0.0312) \le \beta_1 \le 0.368 - 2.447(0.0312)$$

$$0.292 \le \beta_1 \le 0.444$$

The confidence intervals do not contain zero, so there is evidence to indicate that the slope and intercept are both nonzero. Again, since the 95% confidence interval on β_1 does not contain zero, there is evidence to indicate that there is a significant linear relationship between temperature and yield.

Test for Significance of Regression Using ANOVA

ANOVA can also be used to test for significance of regression. The null and alternative hypotheses of interest are H_0: $\beta_1 = 0$ and H_a: $\beta_1 \ne 0$, respectively. Note that only the test on the slope will determine significance of regression. The *total sum of squares* (SS_T) is a measure of the total variability. SS_T can be partitioned into two sources of variability: (1) the regression line that has been fit and (2) error. This is similar to the total sum of squares discussed in the "Analysis of Variance" section of this chapter The *error sum of squares* (also referred to as the residual sum of squares) defined in this section is a measure of the unexplained variability in the responses y. The variability due to the regression model that has been fit is the *regression sum of squares* (SS_R). The partition is

$$SS_T = SS_R + SS_E \tag{6.130}$$

Where

$$S_{yy} = \sum_{i=1}^{n}(y_i - \bar{y})^2 = \sum_{i=1}^{n}y_i^2 - \frac{\left(\sum_{i=1}^{n}y_i\right)^2}{n}$$

$$SS_R = \sum_{i=1}^{n}(\hat{y}_i - \bar{y})^2 \tag{6.131}$$

And

$$\mathrm{SS}_E = \sum_{i=1}^{n}(y_i - \hat{y}_i)^2 = \sum_{i=1}^{n}e_i^2$$

It is desirable to have the regression sum of squares be large in comparison with the error sum of squares. A large value of SS_R would indicate that most of the variability in the response can be explained by the regression model that has been fit. As seen in the "Analysis of Variance" section of this chapter, one has to take into account the sample size and adjust the sum of squares using the appropriate degrees of freedom. An ANOVA table can be constructed (see Table 6.35).

If critical values are used, the null hypothesis would be rejected if $F_0 > F_{\alpha,1,n-2}$. The critical value is found from the F table in Appendix G.

Table 6.35 ANOVA table for testing significance of regression.

Source	df	SS	MS	F	p-value
Regression	1	SS_R	$\mathrm{MS}_R = \mathrm{SS}_R/1$	$F_0 = \mathrm{MS}_R/\mathrm{MS}_E$	$P(F > F_0)$
Error	$n-2$	SS_E	$\mathrm{MS}_E = \mathrm{SS}_E/(n-2)$		
Total	$n-1$	SS_T			

EXAMPLE 6.62

The ANOVA table associated with the test for significance of regression based on the model fit is given below. The null and alternative hypotheses are

$H_0: \beta_1 = 0$

$H_a: \beta_1 \neq 0$

Table 6.36 ANOVA table for temperature and yield regression model.

Source	df	SS	MS	F	p-value
Regression	1	568.34	568.34	138.98	0.000
Error	6	24.54	4.09		
Total	7	592.87			

Since the p-value is approximately zero, the null hypothesis would be rejected, and it would again be concluded that there is a statistically significant linear relationship between yield and temperature. If critical values are used, the critical value is $F_{0.05,1,6} = 5.99$ (assuming a 0.05 level of significance). Since $138.98 > 5.99$, the null hypothesis is again rejected.

The ANOVA is useful not only for testing the significance of regression but also for providing an estimate of $\hat{\sigma}^2$. Specifically, $\hat{\sigma}^2 = MS_E$. In this problem, $\hat{\sigma}^2 = MS_E = 4.09$.

Coefficient of Determination

The *coefficient of determination* R^2 gives a measure of the adequacy of the current regression model for a particular set of data. It is the proportion of the total variability in the response that can be explained by the regression line. The coefficient of determination for the simple linear regression model can be computed by taking the square of the correlation coefficient r. (Often the notation R^2 is used for this value even though correlation coefficient is denoted by lowercase r.) Since $-1 \le r \le 1$, then $0 \le R^2 \le 1$. In general, the coefficient of determination can be calculated for any linear regression model by

$$R^2 = \frac{SS_R}{SS_T} = 1 - \frac{SS_E}{SS_T} \qquad (6.132)$$

EXAMPLE 6.63

For the yield and temperature problem, the coefficient of determination is

$$R^2 = \frac{SS_R}{SS_T} = \frac{568.34}{592.87} = 0.959$$

It is concluded that approximately 95.9% of the total variability in the response (yield) can be explained by the regression model involving temperature.

Assumptions in Regression Analysis

There are several assumptions in linear regression. For the most part, the least squares approach and the results or conclusions drawn from the data are fairly *robust* to these assumptions; that is, it takes a substantial deviation from the norm to affect the results. The assumptions for the least squares approach to regression analysis are as follows:

1. The errors e_i are independent

2. The errors e_i are normally distributed with mean zero

3. The errors e_i have constant variance σ^2

The assumptions can be checked using residual analysis. Residuals plotted against the fitted values $\hat{y}$ or against the independent variable x can provide some information about the validity of the constant variance assumption. A normal probability plot of residuals can be used to assess the assumption of normality. The independence assumption can be verified by examining a plot of the residuals against the time sequence—if the time sequence is known. With the exception of the normal probability plot of the residuals, all residual plots should exhibit no obvious patterns in the residuals. If the residuals fall along a straight line in the normal probability plot, then the normality assumption is assumed to be valid. Caution should be used when interpreting residual plots for small sets of data. For small sample sizes, patterns on residual plots can often occur by chance. Keep in mind that the least squares method is fairly robust to slight departures from these assumptions. Residual analysis is further discussed in the "Design and Analysis of Experiments" section of this chapter.

Time Series Analysis

Define, describe, and use time-series analysis, including moving average to identify trends and seasonal or cyclical variation. (Apply)

Body of Knowledge VI.E.3

Time series analysis in mathematical statistics involves mathematical techniques for determining cycles and trends in data over time. Two specific tools are discussed in this section:

- Moving average smoothing

- Trend analysis

Moving average smoothing and trend analysis are two methods of analyzing data. There are other methods, but they are beyond the scope of this discussion.

Run charts display a plot of data obtained on sequential samples taken from a process. This plot has an x-axis of sequence or time. The y-axis is that of the measurement taken on the sample. For example, the rate of non-mission-capable equipment or systems due to maintenance issues (NMCM) is important to monitor. Figure 6.29 displays the monthly NMCM rates over a two-year period.

Note that in this case there might be some sort of cycle present in the NMCM rate. The process may not have a random pattern of NMCM rates around the average rate. The scale or time period of the x-axis must be very well understood to correctly interpret the run chart.

The *control chart*, which will be discussed in the "Statistical Process Control" section of this chapter, is a special type of run chart. The control chart has a center or central line (the mean) drawn in to facilitate the ability to see the data move back and forth across this line. When the measurement for one sample tends to be dependent on the measurement for the previous sample, these data are called *auto-correlated*. As will be shown in the next section, one assumption necessary for control charts to be valid is that the observations are independently distributed. When autocorrelation is present in the data, standard control charts do not work well in monitoring the process. Typical modeling techniques such as linear regression are also no longer valid because autocorrelated data are not independent, one of the

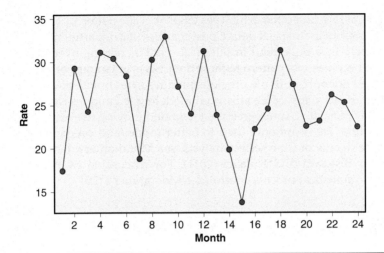

Figure 6.29   Run chart for NMCM rate.

key assumptions of linear regression models. Suppose there are n measurements taken in some time sequence. A measure of sample autocorrelation is given by

$$r_k = \frac{\sum_{t=1}^{n-k}\left(x_t - \overline{x}\right)\left(x_{t+k} - \overline{x}\right)}{\sum_{t=1}^{n}\left(x_t - \overline{x}\right)^2}, \text{ for } k = 0, 1, \ldots, K \qquad (6.133)$$

where

k represents the number of time periods between measurements

$\overline{x}$ is the average of all measurements

x_t is the measurement taken at time t

x_{t+k} is the measurement taken at time $t + k$

K is the total number of time periods

For example, if it is believed that measurements taken one after another are autocorrelated, then $k = 1$. In many problems, it may be necessary to compute r_k for several values of k, where an autocorrelation plot can be used to identify the value of k. See Bisgaard and Kulahci (2011) for more information on autocorrelation plots.

Detecting autocorrelation can be accomplished using several methods (e.g., graphically, as described above). Two analytic methods include moving average smoothing and trend analysis. *Moving average smoothing* involves smoothing the data over a short interval of time. Consecutive observations in a series are averaged over a chosen window of time to remove as much noise as possible from the system. Moving average is discussed as part of the discussion on control charts. *Trend analysis* fits a general trend model to time series data and provides forecasts. Some models commonly fit include the linear, quadratic, exponential, and S-curve. Both methods work well when no seasonal component is present in the data.

Time series data often exhibit seasonal or cyclic patterns. This type of behavior is often present in financial data. Consider sales of a department store, for example. While there may be a trend in sales (sales are increasing over time), there is also likely to be a seasonal pattern to these data. Sales in January of the current year are correlated not only with the previous month's sales but also with sales in January of the previous years. More advanced modeling techniques can take advantage of this cyclic behavior. Autoregressive integrated moving average (ARIMA) models, for example, are commonly used to better model and predict seasonal data. For complete details of time series analysis, see Montgomery, Jennings, and Kulahci (2015) or Bisgaard and Kulahci (2011). For discussion of autocorrelation with respect to statistical process control, see Montgomery (2013).

STATISTICAL PROCESS CONTROL (SPC)

This section covers several aspects of statistical process control: objectives and benefits, common and special causes of variation, selection of variable, rational subgrouping, control charts, control chart analysis, and short-run SPC.

Objectives and Benefits

> Identify and explain the objectives and benefits of SPC. (Understand)
>
> **Body of Knowledge VI.F.1**

Statistical process control (SPC) is quantitative problem solving consisting of diagnostic techniques to assist in locating problem sources and prescriptive techniques to help solve problems. Many of these techniques are based on statistical principles.

A *process* is any repeatable sequence of events or operations leading to either a tangible or an intangible outcome. The use of SPC will show that a process is either in statistical control (i.e., the process variation appears to be random) or out of statistical control (i.e., the process exhibits nonrandom variation). SPC also makes it possible to determine whether the process is improving.

SPC is a tool for communicating information to engineering, product operations, and quality control personnel. The principal elements of a successful SPC framework are analysis (to understand the process), methods (to measure the process), and leadership (to change the process).

Several benefits can be attributed to SPC. Continuous improvement and maintenance of quality and productivity can be achieved, and process complexity can be reduced. By identifying and reducing process complexity, errors will be reduced and productivity improved through the substitution of sampling for 100% inspection. SPC also provides a common internal language for management, supervision, quality assurance/control, and product operations to discuss problems, solutions, decisions, and actions.

Common and Special Causes of Variation

> Describe, identify, and distinguish between
> these types of causes. (Analyze)
>
> **Body of Knowledge VI.F.2**

Every process has variation. The sources of process variation can be divided into two categories: special and common. *Common cause variation* is that which is inherent in the process and generally is not controllable by process operators. Examples of common causes include variation in raw materials and variation in ambient temperature and humidity. In the case of service processes, common causes typically include such things as variation in input data, variations in customer load, and variation in computer operations. Some authors refer to common cause variation as *natural variation*.

Special causes of variation include unusual events that, when detected, can usually be removed or adjusted. Examples include tool wear, gross changes in raw materials, and broken equipment. Special causes are sometimes called *assignable* causes.

A principal problem in process management is the separation of special and common causes. If the process operator tries to adjust a process in response to common cause variation, the result is usually more variation rather than less. This is sometimes called *overadjustment* or *overcontrol*. If a process operator fails to respond to the presence of a special cause of variation, this cause is likely to produce additional process variation. This is referred to as *underadjustment* or *undercontrol*.

The principal purpose of control charts is to help the process operator recognize the presence of special causes so that appropriate action can be taken. Control charts are discussed in detail in the sections that follow.

Selection of Variable

> Identify and select variable characteristics for
> monitoring by control charts. (Analyze)
>
> **Body of Knowledge VI.F.3**

When a control chart is to be used, a variable (or variables) must be selected for monitoring. In a new process, there may be many different quality characteristics to monitor. However, as the process becomes more stable, the number of monitored characteristics will most likely be reduced.

Sometimes the variable of interest is the most critical dimension of the product. Contractual requirements with a customer sometimes specify the variable(s) to be monitored via a control chart. If the root cause of the assignable variation is known, an input variable, such as voltage or air pressure, may be monitored. It is possible to monitor several variables on separate control charts. But it is also useful to monitor two or more characteristics using a single control chart (multivariate control chart). Ultimately, the selection of the quality characteristic to be charted depends on experience and judgment.

Rational Subgrouping

Define and apply the principles of rational subgrouping. (Apply)

Body of Knowledge VI.F.4

The selection of samples is important in the construction of control charts. The method used to select samples for a control chart must be logical or rational. In general, *rational subgrouping* involves selecting samples such that if assignable causes of variation are present in the system, there should be a greater probability of variation between successive samples while the variation within the sample is kept small.

Samples frequently consist of parts that are produced successively or consecutively by the same process, to minimize the within-sample variation. The next sample is chosen later so that any process shifts that have occurred will be displayed on the chart as between-sample variation. Choosing the rational subgroup requires care to make sure the same process is producing each item.

In some instances it is more appropriate to select the sample *over the entire interval* since the last sample was chosen. This approach to rational subgrouping is effective in detecting shifts that may occur between samples taken consecutively. The sample represents all units produced since the last sample was taken. In general, the subgroup is a random sample of units selected over the entire interval since the last subgroup was selected.

Caution should be used when interpreting control charts where the subgroups are units randomly selected over an interval. It is possible to make even an out-of-control process appear to be in control simply by increasing the interval between selected units.

Control Charts

Identify, select, construct, and use various control charts, including –R, –s, individuals and moving range (ImR or XmR), moving average and moving range (MamR), p, np, c, and u. (Analyze)

Body of Knowledge VI.F.5

Control charts are the most common tool for monitoring a quality characteristic of interest. Walter A. Shewhart introduced the concept of control charts in the 1920s. Because of his work, several control charts monitoring a single quality characteristic of interest are referred to as Shewhart control charts. Control charts can be used for monitoring individual observations or subgroups. Different types of control charts are used for continuous versus discrete data, but all the charts can be used to monitor for changes or trends in the quality characteristics of interest.

In this section, control charts for variables data and attributes data are presented, including the following:

- $\bar{x}$ and R control charts

- $\bar{x}$ and s control charts

- Individuals control charts

- Fraction nonconforming control charts

- Control charts for nonconformities

For each of these control charts, distribution assumptions must be satisfied. For example, the $\bar{x}$ charts are based on the assumption that $\bar{x}$ follows a normal distribution. The Shewhart control charts are sensitive to this assumption. If the normality assumption is violated, the overall performance of these charts can be very poor and result in incorrect signals.

Control limits are calculated based on data from the process. Formulas for control limits and examples of each are given in this section. The formulas are repeated in Appendix A, "Control Limit Formulas." Several constants are needed in the formulas. These appear as subscripted letters, such as A_2. The values of these constants are given in Appendix B, "Constants for Control Charts." When calculating control limits, it is prudent to collect as much data as practical. Many authorities specify at least 25 samples. The examples in the following sections use fewer samples for simplicity. It is desirable for the sample size to be held constant if possible.

Variables Control Charts

The most used control charts for variables (continuous) subgroup data are the $\bar{x}$ and R chart and the $\bar{x}$ and s chart. The $\bar{x}$ chart monitors the mean of the process while the R chart and s chart monitor the process variability.

$\bar{x}$ and R Charts

Suppose there are m subgroups each of size n chosen at random from a particular process (see Table 6.37). The sample mean and range for each subgroup are also given in Table 6.37.

The statistic $\bar{\bar{x}}$ is the grand average and is the best estimate of the true process mean μ. $\bar{R}$ is the average range and will be used to estimate the process variability and to construct control charts. The upper control limit (UCL), center line (CL), and lower control limit (LCL) for the $\bar{x}$ control chart are

$$\text{UCL} = \bar{\bar{x}} + A_2\bar{R}$$

$$\text{CL} = \bar{\bar{x}} \qquad (6.134)$$

$$\text{LCL} = \bar{\bar{x}} - A_2\bar{R}$$

The UCL, CL, and LCL for the R control chart are

$$\text{UCL} = D_4\bar{R}$$

$$\text{CL} = \bar{R} \qquad (6.135)$$

$$\text{LCL} = D_3\bar{R}$$

A_2, D_3, and D_4 are constants that depend on the sample size n. They can be found in Appendix B. Derivations of these constants can be found in Montgomery (2013).

Table 6.37 General notation for subgroup data.

Subgroup, i	Measurements	$\bar{x}_i$	$R_i = x_{(\max i)} - x_{(\min i)}$
1	$x_{11}, x_{21}, \ldots, x_{n1}$	$\bar{x}_1$	R_1
2	$x_{12}, x_{22}, \ldots, x_{n2}$	$\bar{x}_2$	R_2
3	$x_{13}, x_{23}, \ldots, x_{n3}$	$\bar{x}_3$	R_3
.	.	.	.
.	.	.	.
.	.	.	.
m	$x_{1m}, x_{2m}, \ldots, x_{nm}$	$\bar{x}_m$	R_m
		$\bar{\bar{x}} = \dfrac{\sum\limits_{i=1}^{m} \bar{x}_i}{m}$	$\bar{R} = \dfrac{\sum\limits_{i=1}^{m} R_i}{m}$

EXAMPLE 6.64

The turnaround time for complete blood count analysis from the laboratory to the emergency room at a local hospital is an important quality characteristic to be monitored. Turnaround times were recorded over 20 days in a one-month period. Four specimens were randomly selected per day and the turnaround times (in minutes) recorded. The times as well as the subgroup averages and ranges are given in Table 6.38. The grand average and average range are given in the last row of Table 6.38.

Table 6.38 Turnaround time data for $\bar{x}$ and R charts.

Day	x_1	x_2	x_3	x_4	$\bar{x}_i$	R_i
1	83	49	65	78	68.75	34
2	81	77	75	76	77.25	6
3	71	67	44	58	60.00	27
4	92	53	93	74	78.00	40
5	75	58	90	51	68.50	39
6	70	79	87	49	71.25	38
7	74	50	68	45	59.25	29
8	80	66	75	64	71.25	16
9	80	63	72	81	74.00	18
10	90	77	92	64	80.75	28
11	75	51	89	74	72.25	38
12	64	65	88	59	69.00	29
13	97	57	88	76	79.50	40
14	84	62	55	68	67.25	29
15	76	63	70	66	68.75	13
16	62	68	66	55	62.75	13
17	73	77	91	83	81.00	18
18	65	65	84	46	65.00	38
19	73	64	84	71	73.00	20
20	75	88	65	93	80.25	28
					$\bar{\bar{x}} = 71.39$	$\bar{R} = 27.05$

From Appendix B, with $n = 4$, $A_2 = 0.729$, $D_3 = 0$, and $D_4 = 2.282$. The control limits for the $\bar{x}$ control chart are

$$UCL = \bar{\bar{x}} + A_2\bar{R} = 71.39 + 0.729(27.05) = 91.11$$

$$CL = \bar{\bar{x}} = 71.39$$

$$LCL = \bar{\bar{x}} - A_2\bar{R} = 71.39 - 0.729(27.05) = 51.67$$

Continued

The control limits for the R control chart are

$$\text{UCL} = D_4\bar{R} = 2.282(27.05) = 61.73$$

$$\text{CL} = \bar{R} = 27.05$$

$$\text{LCL} = D_3\bar{R} = 0(27.05) = 0$$

The $\bar{x}$ and R control charts for turnaround times are displayed in Figure 6.30.

There are no points that plot outside the control limits on either chart. There also do not appear to be any obvious patterns on the $\bar{x}$ control chart. The process appears to be in control. More discussion of interpretation of control charts is provided in the "Control Chart Analysis" section of this chapter.

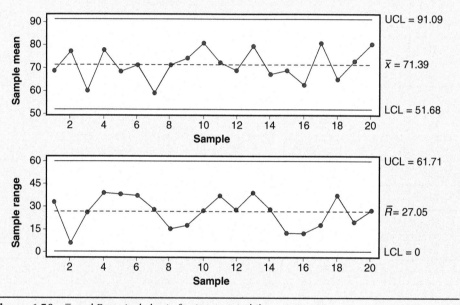

Figure 6.30 $\bar{x}$ and R control charts for turnaround times.

$\bar{x}$ and s Charts

Whenever possible, the sample standard deviation should be used instead of the range in estimating the process variability. When the sample size n is large, say $n > 10$, the sample standard deviation is a better estimate of the true process standard deviation than the range. As n increases, the range R loses statistical efficiency and becomes less precise. The sample standard deviation is also a better estimator for the process standard deviation for nonconstant sample sizes.

The development of the $\bar{x}$ and s control chart is similar to development of the $\bar{x}$ and R control chart. In this case, the subgroup standard deviation is calculated instead of the range. Suppose $x_{i1}, x_{i2}, \ldots, x_{in}$ represent a sample of size n for any subgroup i. The formula for the sample standard deviation of subgroup i is

$$s_i = \sqrt{\frac{\sum_{j=1}^{n}(x_{ij} - \bar{x})^2}{n-1}} \tag{6.136}$$

The average standard deviation for all m subgroups is

$$\bar{s} = \frac{\sum_{i=1}^{m} s_i}{m} \tag{6.137}$$

The control limits and center line for the $\bar{x}$ control chart are then

$$UCL = \bar{\bar{x}} + A_3\bar{s}$$
$$CL = \bar{\bar{x}} \tag{6.138}$$
$$LCL = \bar{\bar{x}} - A_3\bar{s}$$

The control limits and center line for the s chart are

$$UCL = B_4\bar{s}$$
$$CL = \bar{s} \tag{6.139}$$
$$LCL = B_3\bar{s}$$

where A_3, B_3, and B_4 are constants that depend on the sample size n. They can be found in Appendix B.

EXAMPLE 6.65

Reconsider the turnaround time data from the previous example. Instead of the range for each day (subgroup), the standard deviation is calculated. The subgroup averages will not change. The sample standard deviations and average standard deviations are given in Table 6.39.

Table 6.39 Turnaround time data for $\bar{x}$ and s charts.

Day	x_1	x_2	x_3	x_4	$\bar{x}_i$	s_i
1	83	49	65	78	68.75	15.20
2	81	77	75	76	77.25	2.63
3	71	67	44	58	60.00	11.97
4	92	53	93	74	78.00	18.81
5	75	58	90	51	68.50	17.52

Continued

Table 6.39 Turnaround time data for $\bar{x}$ and s charts. (Continued)

Day	x_1	x_2	x_3	x_4	$\bar{x}_i$	s_i
6	70	79	87	49	71.25	16.38
7	74	50	68	45	59.25	13.94
8	80	66	75	64	71.25	7.54
9	80	63	72	81	74.00	8.37
10	90	77	92	64	80.75	13.00
11	75	51	89	74	72.25	15.73
12	64	65	88	59	69.00	12.94
13	97	57	88	76	79.50	17.29
14	84	62	55	68	67.25	12.37
15	76	63	70	66	68.75	5.62
16	62	68	66	55	62.75	5.74
17	73	77	91	83	81.00	7.83
18	65	65	84	46	65.00	15.51
19	73	64	84	71	73.00	8.29
20	75	88	65	93	80.25	12.69
					$\bar{\bar{x}} = 71.39$	$\bar{s} = 11.97$

The control limits and center line for the $\bar{x}$ control chart are

$$\mathrm{UCL} = \bar{\bar{x}} + A_3\bar{s} = 71.39 + 1.628(11.97) = 90.88$$

$$\mathrm{CL} = \bar{\bar{x}} = 71.39$$

$$\mathrm{LCL} = \bar{\bar{x}} - A_3\bar{s} = 71.39 - 1.628(11.97) = 51.90$$

The control limits and center line for the s chart are

$$\mathrm{UCL} = B_4\bar{s} = 2.266(11.97) = 27.12$$

$$\mathrm{CL} = \bar{s} = 11.97$$

$$\mathrm{LCL} = B_3\bar{s} = 0(11.97) = 0$$

where $A_3 = 1.628$, $B_3 = 0$, and $B_4 = 2.266$, from Appendix B with $n = 4$. The $\bar{x}$ and s control charts are displayed in Figure 6.31.

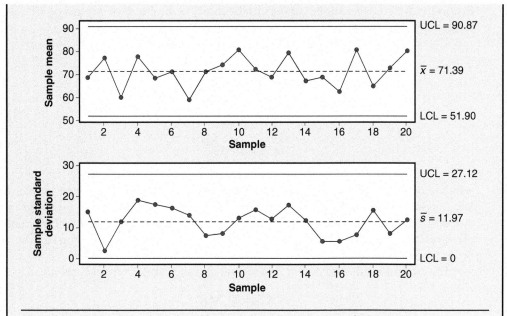

Figure 6.31 $\bar{x}$ and s control charts for complete blood count analysis turnaround times.

The process appears to be in control since there are no obvious trends or patterns and points plot within the control limits on both charts.

Individuals Control Charts

Many practical applications exist in which the subgroup consists of a single observation ($n = 1$). Examples include very slow processes or processes in which the measurement is very expensive to obtain, such as with destructive tests. An *individuals control chart* for variable data is appropriate for this type of situation.

The individuals control chart uses the *moving range* of two successive subgroups to estimate process variability (see Montgomery [2013] for a detailed discussion of moving range and individuals control charts in general). The moving range is given by

$$\text{MR}_i = |x_i - x_{i-1}| \qquad (6.140)$$

For m subgroups of size $n = 1$ each, $m - 1$ moving ranges are defined as $\text{MR}_2 = |x_2 - x_1|$, $\text{MR}_3 = |x_3 - x_2|$, ..., $\text{MR}_m = |x_m - x_{m-1}|$. The *average moving range* is simply

$$\overline{\text{MR}} = \frac{\displaystyle\sum_{i=2}^{m}\text{MR}_i}{m-1} \qquad (6.141)$$

Division is done by $m - 1$ since only $m - 1$ moving range values are calculated (there is no moving range for subgroup 1). Control charts are constructed for the individual observations (individuals chart) and the moving range of the subgroups (MR chart).

The control limits and center line of the x (or individuals) control chart are

$$UCL = \bar{x} + 3\frac{\overline{MR}}{d_2}$$

$$CL = \bar{x} \qquad (6.142)$$

$$LCL = \bar{x} - 3\frac{\overline{MR}}{d_2}$$

where d_2 is a constant that depends on the number of observations used to calculate the moving range for each subgroup (i.e., $n = 2$). Values for d_2 can be found in Appendix B. The control chart for individuals is constructed by plotting the actual observation x_i, the control limits, and the center line against the subgroup (or time) order.

The control limits and center line for the moving range control chart are

$$UCL = D_4\overline{MR}$$

$$CL = \overline{MR} \qquad (6.143)$$

$$LCL = D_3\overline{MR}$$

where D_3 and D_4 are constants found in Appendix B for $n = 2$. The moving range control chart is constructed by plotting the $m - 1$ moving ranges, the control limits, and the center line against the subgroup (or time) order.

EXAMPLE 6.66

Packages of a particular instant dry food are filled by a machine and weighed. The weights (in ounces) for 15 successive packages have been collected and are displayed in Table 6.40. The engineer wishes to determine whether the filling process is indeed in control.

To illustrate, consider the first moving range at subgroup 2:

$$MR_2 = |x_2 - x_1| = |19.92 - 19.85| = 0.07$$

The remaining moving ranges are calculated accordingly and are given in Table 6.40. The control limits and center line for the individuals chart with moving ranges of size 2 are

$$UCL = 19.954 + 3\frac{0.39}{1.128} = 20.991$$

$$CL = 19.954$$

$$LCL = 19.954 - 3\frac{0.39}{1.128} = 18.917$$

Table 6.40 Weights for dry food packages.

Bottle	Weight (x_i)	Moving range
1	19.85	—
2	19.92	0.07
3	19.93	0.01
4	19.26	0.67
5	20.36	1.10
6	19.96	0.40
7	19.87	0.09
8	19.80	0.07
9	20.40	0.60
10	19.98	0.42
11	20.17	0.19
12	19.81	0.36
13	20.21	0.40
14	19.64	0.57
15	20.15	0.51
	$\bar{x} = 19.954$	$\overline{\text{MR}} = 0.39$

The control limits and center line for the moving range chart are

$$\text{UCL} = 3.267(0.39) = 1.274$$
$$\text{CL} = 0.39$$
$$\text{LCL} = 0(0.39) = 0$$

The control charts for individual observations and for the moving range are displayed in Figure 6.32.

Examining these control charts, the process does not appear to be out of statistical control.

Continued

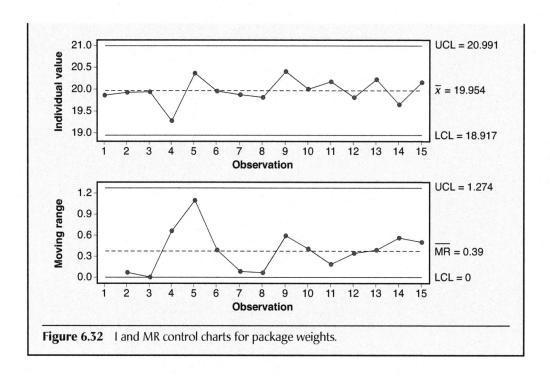

Figure 6.32   I and MR control charts for package weights.

It is important to note that the moving range control chart cannot be interpreted in the same way as the *R* chart presented earlier, with respect to patterns or trends. Patterns or trends identified on the moving range chart do not necessarily indicate that the process is out of control. The moving ranges are *correlated*. There is a natural dependency between successive MR_i values.

Attributes Control Charts

Attributes control charts are used for discrete or count data. In many scenarios the quality characteristic of interest is simply a classification of the measurement into a single category. For example, manufactured products may be measured but classified only as defective/nondefective, conforming/nonconforming, or pass/fail. Other situations may involve monitoring the number of nonconformities on an item. For example, billing statements may be examined for errors such as incorrect name, missing information, and incorrect amounts or type of service identified. Variables control charts are not appropriate for many of these situations. Control charts for data that can be classified are *attributes control charts.* The following are examples of attributes control charts:

- Fraction nonconforming control charts (*p* charts)
- Number nonconforming control charts (*np* charts)
- Control charts for nonconformities (*c* and *u* control charts)

Control charts for nonconformities are similar to those for the number of nonconforming items, discussed in the previous section. The *p* chart and *np* chart represent the fraction of nonconforming items. When the variable of interest is the number of nonconformities per unit, the p and np charts are not appropriate. For p and np charts, it was noted that the number of nonconforming units could not exceed the number of units being investigated in the subgroup, that is, $X \le n$. For monitoring nonconformities, there is no such restriction. In this case, nonconformities are counted per unit. There could be an infinite (countably infinite) number of nonconformities on a unit or units. More than one of these errors may occur on any one unit. Control charts for nonconformities are the c chart and the u chart.

The p Chart

For the fraction nonconforming control charts, the quality characteristic of interest can be placed into one of exactly two categories. These categories may be pass/fail, conforming/nonconforming, and so on. For simplification, the term "nonconforming" will be used as a general reference regardless of the final categories to be used. The notation to be used is as follows:

- n—number of items examined (lot size, sample size).

- m—number of subgroups.

- X—number of nonconforming items found in the sample of size n, where $X \le n$.

- p—probability that any one item of interest will be nonconforming. This parameter is often unknown and must be estimated.

- $\hat{p}$—sample fraction nonconforming. By definition, this is

$$\hat{p} = \frac{X}{n}$$

and is calculated for each of the m subgroups.

- $\bar{p}$—average fraction nonconforming. By definition,

$$\bar{p} = \frac{\sum_{i=1}^{m} \hat{p}_i}{m} \tag{6.144}$$

and is an estimate of p, defined above.

The p *chart* is used to monitor the proportion nonconforming directly. The control limits and center line (when p is unknown) are

$$\text{UCL} = \bar{p} + 3\sqrt{\frac{\bar{p}(1-\bar{p})}{n}}$$

$$\text{CL} = \bar{p} \tag{6.145}$$

$$\text{LCL} = \bar{p} - 3\sqrt{\frac{\bar{p}(1-\bar{p})}{n}}$$

Note that if the LCL is computed to be less than zero, it is set at zero.

The control limits, center line, and individual sample fraction nonconforming $\hat{p}_i$ are plotted against the subgroup number m. If any of the fraction nonconforming lie outside the control limits, the process is considered out of control. Patterns or trends would also be an indication of possible out-of-control situations.

It is not necessary that the sample sizes be equal for all subgroups. For example, suppose surgeries that result in surgical site infections are monitored at a particular hospital. The number of surgeries performed each month is examined, and those resulting in surgical infections are recorded. Typical data for a 12-month period are given in Table 6.41.

Table 6.41 Surgical site infection rates.

Month	Surgeries	Surgical infection
1	57	8
2	62	6
3	66	1
4	57	2
5	69	2
6	63	6
7	55	10
8	56	6
9	54	9
10	62	3
11	65	4
12	69	5

EXAMPLE 6.67

A small bank collects data on the number of weekly account activities that are recorded in error. Over a 12-week period, 1000 account activities are randomly selected and examined for the number that are in error. The bank would like to monitor the proportion of errors being committed, by establishing control charts.

The fraction in error $\hat{p}_i$ for each week must be computed. The fraction in error for each week is given in Table 6.42 for $n = 1000$. The average fraction in error $\bar{p}$ is found to be

$$\bar{p} = \frac{\sum_{i=1}^{12}\hat{p}_i}{12} = 0.01042$$

Table 6.42 Errors in account activities.

Week	Number of errors	$\hat{p}_i$
1	6	0.006
2	11	0.011
3	4	0.004
4	10	0.010
5	5	0.005
6	30	0.030
7	9	0.009
8	8	0.008
9	12	0.012
10	7	0.007
11	12	0.012
12	11	0.011

The control limits and center line for the p chart are

$$UCL = \bar{p} + 3\sqrt{\frac{\bar{p}(1-\bar{p})}{n}} = 0.01042 + 3\sqrt{\frac{0.01042(1-0.01042)}{1000}} = 0.020052$$

$$CL = 0.01042$$

$$LCL = \bar{p} - 3\sqrt{\frac{\bar{p}(1-\bar{p})}{n}} = 0.01042 - 3\sqrt{\frac{0.01042(1-0.01042)}{1000}} = 0.00078$$

The resulting p chart is displayed in Figure 6.33. There is a single point that plots beyond the upper control limit. This point should be investigated to determine if it is truly an unusual point. If it is found to be unusual and the assignable cause identified, the point can be removed and the center line and control limits recalculated. Suppose in this case that the cause for the outlier in week 6 was identified and a revised control chart constructed. The revised control chart is shown in Figure 6.34. Notice that the control limits and center line have been updated while the fraction in error for week 6 is still plotted on the graph. On a revised control chart, the removed point is used only as a placeholder.

Continued

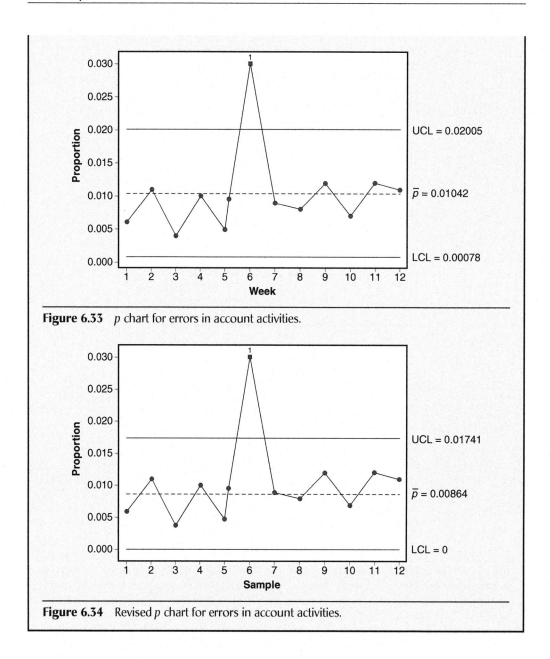

Figure 6.33 *p* chart for errors in account activities.

Figure 6.34 Revised *p* chart for errors in account activities.

The sample size is variable, and there are two ways to calculate the control limits:

- Use the same formulas for the control limits given earlier, using the average sample size as an estimate for n

- Use the actual sample sizes and construct varying control limits

For the surgical infection rates, varying control limits were used. The control chart is displayed in Figure 6.35.

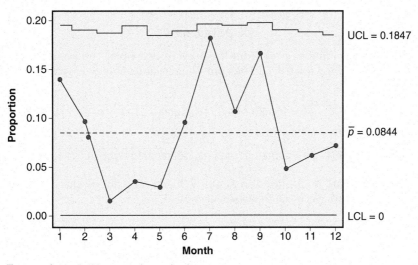

Figure 6.35 p chart for surgical site infection rate using varying sample sizes.

The np Chart

The np chart is a variation of the p chart, with the actual number of nonconforming items plotted on the chart. The np chart and the p chart for the same problem will provide identical information. That is, if the p chart indicates that a process is out of control, then the np chart will also indicate that the same process is out of control. One of the reasons the np chart is an attractive alternative to the p chart is ease of interpretation.

The average fraction nonconforming $\bar{p}$ is the only value that must be estimated before constructing the control limits. It can be found without having to calculate the sample fraction nonconforming values ($\hat{p}_i$). For the np chart, the average fraction nonconforming can be calculated as

$$\bar{p} = \frac{\sum_{i=1}^{m} X_i}{mn} \tag{6.146}$$

The control limits and center line are then

$$\mathrm{UCL} = n\bar{p} + 3\sqrt{n\bar{p}(1-\bar{p})}$$

$$\mathrm{CL} = n\bar{p} \tag{6.147}$$

$$\mathrm{LCL} = n\bar{p} - 3\sqrt{n\bar{p}(1-\bar{p})}$$

The control limits, center line, and number of nonconforming items X_i are plotted against the subgroup. Interpretation of the np chart is identical to that of the p chart.

EXAMPLE 6.68

Reconsider the accounts in error from the previous example. The average fraction in error was found to be $\bar{p} = 0.01042$. The control limits and center line for the np control chart are

$$\mathrm{UCL} = n\bar{p} + 3\sqrt{n\bar{p}(1-\bar{p})} = 1000(0.01042) + 3\sqrt{1000(0.01042)(1-0.01042)} = 20.05$$

$$\mathrm{CL} = n\bar{p} = 1000(0.01042) = 10.42$$

$$\mathrm{LCL} = n\bar{p} - 3\sqrt{n\bar{p}(1-\bar{p})} = 1000(0.01042) - 3\sqrt{1000(0.01042)(1-0.01042)} = 0.787$$

The np control chart is displayed in Figure 6.36. As with the p chart, the np chart indicates that the process is out of statistical control.

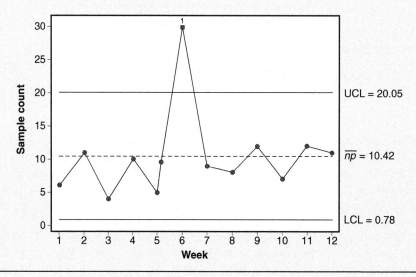

Figure 6.36 np control chart for errors in account activities.

The *c* Chart

If the subgroup size n is constant from subgroup to subgroup, the *c chart* is an appropriate control chart for nonconformities. For the *c* chart:

- n = number of units inspected, sample size (this can be size $n = 1$ or greater)

- m = number of subgroups

- X = number of nonconformities per unit inspected or per subgroup

- $\bar{c}$ = average number of nonconformities:

$$\bar{c} = \frac{\displaystyle\sum_{i=1}^{m} X_i}{m} \tag{6.148}$$

The control limits and center line for the c chart are

$$UCL = \bar{c} + 3\sqrt{\bar{c}}$$
$$CL = \bar{c}$$
$$LCL = \bar{c} - 3\sqrt{\bar{c}}$$

(6.149)

EXAMPLE 6.69

Billing statements for a local hospital are being examined for errors. Twenty billing statements are randomly chosen each day over a 24-day period and examined for missing information, incorrect amounts, and wrong type of service identified. The number of errors (nonconformities) is given in Table 6.43.

Table 6.43 Errors on hospital billing statements.

Day	Number of errors	Day	Number of errors
1	4	13	10
2	18	14	13
3	14	15	3
4	7	16	12
5	7	17	17
6	8	18	13
7	16	19	9
8	6	20	17
9	10	21	9
10	12	22	9
11	9	23	6
12	8	24	10

The average number of errors is

$$\bar{c} = \frac{\sum_{i=1}^{m} X_i}{m} = \frac{4 + 18 + \ldots + 10}{24} = 10.29$$

The control limits and center line for the c chart is

$$UCL = \bar{c} + 3\sqrt{\bar{c}} = 10.29 + 3\sqrt{10.29} = 19.91$$
$$CL = \bar{c} = 10.29$$
$$LCL = \bar{c} - 3\sqrt{\bar{c}} = 10.29 - 3\sqrt{10.29} = 0.67$$

Continued

The *c* chart is displayed in Figure 6.37. The process appears to be in statistical control.

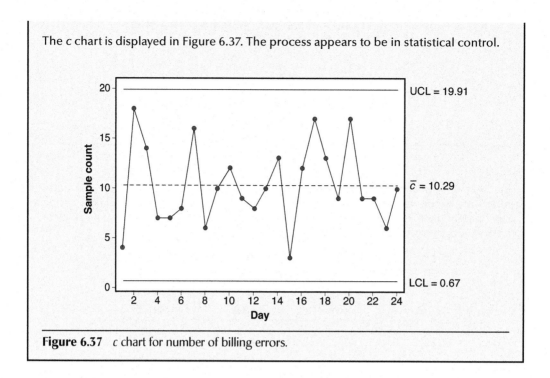

Figure 6.37 *c* chart for number of billing errors.

The *u* Chart

The *c* chart monitors the number of nonconformities. The *u chart*, on the other hand, monitors the *average* number of nonconformities. Like the *p* and *np* charts, the resulting *c* and *u* charts for constant sample size will provide identical results. It is not necessary for the sample size to be constant from subgroup to subgroup for the *u* chart. Let *ui* be the average number of nonconformities for the *i*th subgroup ($i = 1, 2, \ldots, m$), where

$$u_i = \frac{X_i}{n} \tag{6.150}$$

Also, let $\bar{u}$ represent the overall average number of nonconformities per unit, that is,

$$\bar{u} = \frac{\sum\limits_{i=1}^{m} u_i}{m} \tag{6.151}$$

The control limits and center line for the average number of nonconformities are

$$UCL = \bar{u} + 3\sqrt{\frac{\bar{u}}{n}}$$

$$CL = \bar{u} \tag{6.152}$$

$$LCL = \bar{u} - 3\sqrt{\frac{\bar{u}}{n}}$$

The control limits, center line, and u_i are plotted on the control chart against the subgroup.

EXAMPLE 6.70

Reconsider the errors on billing statements example. The average number of non-conformities u_i for each day, in which 20 billing statements were collected, is given in Table 6.44.

Table 6.44 Billing statement errors for a 24-day period.

Day	Number of errors	u_i	Day	Number of errors	u_i
1	4	0.20	13	10	0.50
2	18	0.90	14	13	0.65
3	14	0.70	15	3	0.15
4	7	0.35	16	12	0.60
5	7	0.35	17	17	0.85
6	8	0.40	18	13	0.65
7	16	0.80	19	9	0.45
8	6	0.30	20	17	0.85
9	10	0.50	21	9	0.45
10	12	0.60	22	9	0.45
11	9	0.45	23	6	0.30
12	8	0.40	24	10	0.50

The overall average number of nonconformities per unit is then

$$\bar{u} = \frac{\sum_{i=1}^{m} u_i}{m} = \frac{0.20 + 0.90 + \ldots + 0.50}{24} = 0.515$$

The control limits and center line for the u chart are

$$UCL = \bar{u} + 3\sqrt{\frac{\bar{u}}{n}} = 0.515 + 3\sqrt{\frac{0.515}{20}} = 0.996$$

$$CL = \bar{u} = 0.515$$

$$LCL = \bar{u} - 3\sqrt{\frac{\bar{u}}{n}} = 0.515 - 3\sqrt{\frac{0.515}{20}} = 0.033$$

Continued

The *u* control chart is displayed in Figure 6.38. Again, the process does not appear to be out of statistical control.

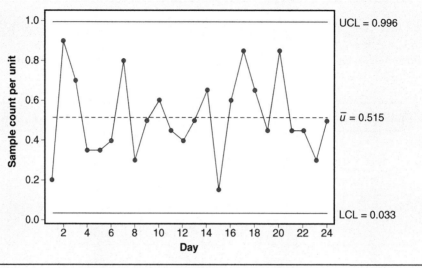

Figure 6.38 *u* chart for billing statement errors.

Moving Average Control Chart

The MA control chart uses a moving average of a certain span (not necessarily consecutive observations). However, the moving average is an unweighted average of the observations. Suppose there are n observations, $x_1, x_2, \ldots, x_n$, selected from the process with mean μ_0 and standard deviation σ. Furthermore, suppose a moving average of span w is of interest. The moving average statistic at time i can be written as

$$\text{MA}_i = \frac{x_i + x_{i-1} + \ldots + x_{i-w+1}}{w} \tag{6.153}$$

The values of MA_i are plotted on a control chart with control limits and center line:

$$\text{UCL} = \mu_0 + \frac{3\sigma}{\sqrt{w}}$$
$$\text{CL} = \mu_0 \tag{6.154}$$
$$\text{LCL} = \mu_0 - \frac{3\sigma}{\sqrt{w}}$$

The MA chart may be suitable for the following situations:

- When data are collected periodically or when it may take some time to produce a single item

- When it is desirable to dampen the effects of overcontrol

- When it is necessary to detect shifts in the process that are smaller than what a Shewhart chart can detect

Choosing a Control Chart

The selection of a control chart is based on the type of data and the size of the subgroup used. Selecting an incorrect type of control chart for a given type of data or subgroup size could lead to an incorrect signal in the control chart. Figure 6.39 depicts a flowchart for the identification of the correct control chart based on the type of data and subgroup size.

Attribute data, also known as discrete data, such as the number of defective units or defective parts, uses c charts, U charts, NP charts, and P charts. The first two are used for the number of defects with c charts used when the subgroup size is constant and a U chart are used when the subgroup size varies. The latter two are used for the number of detective units, with NP charts used if the subgroup size is constant and P charts used if the subgroup size varies.

Continuous data, also known as variable data, such as measurement results, is plotted on an $\bar{x}$ and mR chart, $\bar{x}$ and R chart, or an $\bar{x}$ and S chart. An $\bar{x}$ and mR chart is used when the subgroup size is one. There are two possible control charts for continuous data when the subgroup size is greater than one. An $\bar{x}$ and R chart is used if the subgroup size is greater than one, but equal to eight or less and an $\bar{x}$ and S chart is used if the subgroup sizes is greater than eight. In other words, if the subgroup size is greater than one and the data is continuous, an $\bar{x}$ and R chart is used if the subgroup size is less than nine and an $\bar{x}$ and S chart is used if the subgroup size is equal to nine or greater than nine.

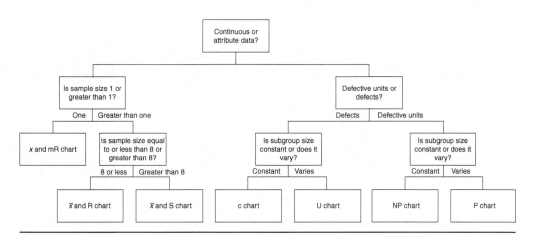

Figure 6.39   Flowchart for control chart selection.

Source: Based on © 2022, M. Barsalou. Originally published in *Quality Progress*, February 2022.

Control Chart Analysis

> Read and interpret control charts and use
> rules for determining statistical control.
> (Evaluate)
>
> **Body of Knowledge VI.F.6**

A critical tool in the analysis of charted data is the process log. The process log may be a separate document or it may be maintained as part of the control chart itself. Entries in the log should include all changes in the process and its environment, including maintenance, raw materials, adjustments, tooling, fixturing, and so on.

Each of the control limit formulas discussed in the previous section uses data from the process. Although it is not always obvious from the formulas, the upper and lower limits are placed at $\pm 3\sigma$ from the average. The use of three-sigma limits is a direct result of the underlying assumption of normality. It can be shown that if the underlying distribution is normal, then approximately 99.7% of all the data will lie within three standard deviations of the mean. Therefore, an observation that falls beyond three standard deviations from the mean would be flagged as unusual since the probability of this occurring is 0.003 and may be an indication of an out-of-control process. Since the Shewhart control charts are based on the normality assumption, it is common to use three standard deviations in the construction of the control limits for these charts. For the EWMA control chart, if $L = 3$ and $\lambda = 1$, then the control limits would reduce to the standard Shewhart control limits. But it has been shown that values other than $L = 3$ and $\lambda = 1$ can result in well-performing control charts, especially for detecting small shifts in the process parameter.

It should be noted that the probability of a point falling inside or outside three standard deviations is somewhat theoretical because no process runs as if its output were randomly selected numbers from some historical distribution. It is enough to say that when a point falls outside the control limits, the probability is quite high that the process has changed. When the probability is very high that a point *did not* come from the distribution used to calculate the control limits, the process is said to be *out of statistical control.* Unfortunately, this is often abbreviated to "out of control," which seems to imply some wild action on the part of the process. In reality, the out-of-statistical-control condition is often very subtle and would perhaps not be detected without the control chart. This, in fact, is one of the main values of the control chart: it detects changes in a process that would not otherwise be noticed. This may permit adjustment or other action on the process before serious damage is done.

One of the hazards of using a control chart without proper training is the tendency to react to a point that is not right on target by adjusting the process, even though the chart does not indicate that the process has changed. If an adjustment is made whenever a point is not exactly on target, it may tend to destabilize a stable process. In the ideal situation, a process should not need adjustment except when the chart indicates it is out of statistical control. W. Edwards Deming (1986) states that "the function of a control chart is to minimize the net economic loss from . . . overadjustment and underadjustment."

Many events are very unlikely to occur unless the process has changed, and thus serve as statistical indicators of process change. The lists of rules that reflect these statistical indicators vary somewhat from textbook to textbook, but two of the most widely used lists of rules are the eight rules used by the software package Minitab and the six rules listed by the AIAG in its SPC manual.

The eight Minitab rules are as follows:

1. One point more than 3σ from the center line (either side)

2. Nine points in a row on the same side of the center line

3. Six points in a row, all increasing or all decreasing

4. Fourteen points in a row, alternating up and down

5. Two out of three points more than 2σ from the center line (same side)

6. Four out of five points more than 1σ from the center line (same side)

7. Fifteen points in a row within 1σ of the center line (either side)

8. Eight points in a row more than 1σ from the center line (either side)

In the third edition of its SPC manual, the AIAG provides a list of special cause criteria that is identical to Minitab's list except for rule 2, which says:

2. Seven points in a row on one side of the center line

The AIAG SPC manual emphasizes that "the decision as to which criteria to use depends on the process being studied/controlled." CQEs may find it useful to generate additional tests for particular situations. If, for instance, an increase in values represents a safety hazard, it would not be necessary to wait for the specified number of successively increasing points to take action. The $\pm 3\sigma$ location for the control limits is somewhat arbitrary and could conceivably be adjusted based on the economic trade-off between the costs of not taking action when an out-of-control condition occurs and the costs of taking action when an out-of-control condition has not occurred. In general, moving the control limits up and down can be a source of additional problems, and it would be better in most cases to put that energy into reducing variation.

Sensitizing rules should always be used with caution. Although sensitizing rules can improve a Shewhart chart's ability to detect small shifts, they can seriously degrade the performance of the chart when the process is indeed in control. Control chart performance is often measured by the *average run length* (ARL), which is defined as the number of cycles, time periods, or samples that elapse before the process signals out-of-control. If the process is in control, the ARL will preferably be large. If the process is out of control, a small ARL is desirable. When several sensitizing rules are used simultaneously on a control chart, the in-control ARL can become unacceptably small. For example, suppose that independent process data are being monitored using a standard Shewhart control chart. For an in-control process, the ARL is approximately 370. However, the Shewhart control chart with Western Electric rules (Western Electric [1956]) has an in-control ARL of approximately 91 (see Champ and Woodall [1987]). Thus, even if the process is in statistical control, the sensitizing rules may lead to more false alarms than the standard Shewhart control chart with no sensitizing rules.

The important issue, of course, is not the exact wording of the rules so much as the action that takes place once the unusual event has occurred. The first step always should be to ascertain that the point is calculated and plotted correctly. If possible, a double check should be made on the measurement itself. For variables charts, the range section should be analyzed first. Increases in the range values represent increased variation between the readings within an individual sample. Possible causes include bearings, tooling, or fixtures. In the case of cutoff operations, for instance, if the part is pushed against a backstop for measurement, the backstop could have become "rubbery." Changes in the averages chart represent some sort of shift in the process. Frequent causes are tool wear, changes in raw materials, and changes in measurement systems or process parameters such as machine settings, voltages, pneumatic pressure, and so on. It is useful to construct a list of things to check when certain chart characteristics occur. Such a list can come from a discussion among experienced personnel as well as from data from a process log.

In some cases the events on the out-of-control lists represent improved situations. For instance, the process is considered out of control if too many points are in the middle third of the control limit area. Recall that the control chart tests are used to help determine whether the current values come from the distribution that was used to calculate the control limits. If too many points are grouped around the center line, the points probably come from a different distribution. The process should be investigated to determine what changed and to see whether this change can be perpetuated. If a log is maintained for the process, it may be possible to find changes that correspond to the time that the improvement occurred. Experience is the best teacher when it comes to chart interpretation. Efforts should be made to document a body of knowledge about each process.

Finally, note that a control chart is really a graphical hypothesis test. The null hypothesis is that the process has not changed, and as each point is plotted, the chart is examined to determine whether there is sufficient evidence to reject the null hypothesis and conclude that the process has changed. The significance level varies somewhat with the chart test employed.

For an overview of research on control charting methods for process monitoring and improvement, see Woodall and Montgomery (1999, 2014). Also, see Woodall (2017) for an in-depth review of Phase I SPC analysis, which includes discussion aimed at bridging the gap between theory and practice. Vining (2009) describes the differences between Phase I and Phase II analysis in SPC.

Additional references on SPC can be found in Capizzi (2015); Chakraborti, Human, and Graham (2008); Hawkins and Wu (2014); and Trip and Does (2010). For a detailed case study using SPC, see Godfrey, Russell, and Betz-Stablein (2016), where the authors present an application of control charts to monitor chronic kidney failure in patients.

Short-Run Statistical Process Control

> Identify and define short-run SPC rules.
> (Understand)
>
> **Body of Knowledge VI.F.7**

The control charts presented to this point apply to processes that are considered long, continuous production runs. These charts are not appropriate for short production runs. Short production runs are commonplace and include processes that produce built-to-order product or quick turnaround production. Short-run control charts should be considered when data are collected infrequently or aperiodically. They may be used with historical target or current target values, attribute or variable data, and individual or subgrouped averages. Standardized control charts are commonly used to monitor short production runs. A simple illustration for attribute data will be presented. For complete details on short production runs, see Montgomery (2013).

The short-run control charts for attribute data are actually *standardized control charts*. The attribute for the control chart of interest is standardized and plotted on a control chart. To illustrate, consider the standardized value using the number of nonconformities (i.e., c chart). The standardized value is

$$Z_i = \frac{c_i - \bar{c}}{\sqrt{\bar{c}}}$$
(6.155)

which follows a standard normal distribution. The following properties of *all* standardized control charts apply:

- Each data point is standardized

- The standardized random variable Z_i has a standard normal distribution

- The center line for all standardized charts is zero

- The control limits for all the standardized charts are –3 and 3

EXAMPLE 6.71

Nonconformities are counted on 10 printed circuit boards. The boards come from a short production run. The nonconformities are given in Table 6.45.

Table 6.45   Number of nonconformities for printed circuit boards.

Printed circuit board	Number of nonconformities
1	4
2	0
3	1
4	3
5	6
6	3
7	1
8	0
9	5
10	2
Total	25

PROCESS AND PERFORMANCE CAPABILITY

This section addresses four aspects of process and performance capability: process capability studies, process performance versus specifications, process capability indices, and process performance indices.

Process Capability Studies

> Define, describe, calculate, and use process capability studies, including identifying characteristics, specifications and tolerances, developing sampling plans for such studies, and establishing statistical control. (Analyze)
>
> **Body of Knowledge VI.G.1**

The purpose of a capability study is to determine whether a process is capable of meeting certain requirements. Capability of a process can be evaluated through determination of a probability distribution, its shape, center, and spread. Tools such as histograms, probability plots, and stem-and-leaf plots can be used to evaluate process capability without having stated specification limits for the quality characteristic of interest.

Process capability is often investigated with respect to given specifications. In theory, a capability study should be performed for every product dimension and every quality characteristic. In practice, however, people familiar with a process usually can identify the few characteristics that merit a full capability study, i.e., those characteristics that experience has shown to be difficult to hold to specification. For example, suppose a customer requires certain process outputs to be 45–55, such as:

- The arrival time for a delivery vehicle must be between 45 and 55 minutes after the hour

- Manufactured pumps must produce between 45 psi and 55 psi

- The plating thickness must be from 45 to 55 mm

In these instances, the 45–55 requirement is called the specification, which typically is inclusive of the endpoints.

Bothe (1997) identifies six major activities as parts of a process capability study:

1. Verifying process stability

2. Estimating process parameters

3. Measuring process capability

4. Comparing actual capability to desired capability

5. Making a decision concerning process changes

6. Reporting the results of the study with recommendations

These six areas are not unique and may require several different methods to complete any one activity. For example, control charts and designed experiments can be implemented to estimate process capability. In addition, Montgomery (2013) recommends the use of histograms and probability plotting in addition to process capability ratios (presented in this section) as techniques useful in determining the capability of a process.

The first step in conducting a capability study is to verify that the process is stable. A *stable* process can be thought of as a process without special causes of variation present. Process stability can be determined by using a control chart. The process is stable if the chart shows that no special causes are present after an appropriate number of points have been plotted. A key phrase in the previous sentence is "appropriate number of points." Although authorities disagree on the number of points needed, 20–30 points are commonly used. However, the more points you plot, the higher the confidence you can have in the stability conclusion.

The second step in conducting a capability study is to determine whether it is reasonable to assume that the process data come from a normal distribution. To do this, a normal probability plot or histogram could be constructed using the original readings (not the averages) from the control chart. If the histogram looks normal, with most points grouped around a single peak and fairly symmetric tails on each side, you may assume that the data constitute a sample drawn from an approximately normal population. Using a normal probability plot, it can be concluded that the normality assumption is satisfied if the data fall along a straight line. Again, the more data you use, the higher the confidence you can have in this conclusion. The normality assumption is necessary for the results of a process capability study (process capability ratios, discussed next) to be considered valid. If the data are non-normal, a transformation to induce normality may be necessary. Kotz and Lovelace (1998) also discuss process capability indices that can be used for non-normal distributions. For information about a hypothesis test to check if data are normally distributed, refer to Devore (2016) or Montgomery and Runger (2013).

If the data are normally distributed, the next step is to use the normal distribution to estimate process capability. The most common method is to use the data from a control chart to estimate μ and σ. The sampling plan is then the same as that used for the control chart. Once the chart exhibits statistical control, the values of $\bar{\bar{x}}$ and $\bar{R}$ calculated from the control chart are used in the capability analysis formulas. This process is similar when using $\bar{\bar{x}}$ and s charts, and individuals and MR charts.

Process Performance Versus Specifications

> Distinguish between natural process limits
> and specification limits, and calculate percent
> defective, defects per million opportunities
> (DPMO), and parts per million (PPM). (Analyze)
>
> **Body of Knowledge VI.G.2**

This section covers the capability of a process in relation to specification limits. The capability of a process could be described by the fraction of units that fall outside the specification limits. To estimate the capability, an estimate the process standard deviation, σ, is needed for an in-control process. Depending on the type of control chart used to monitor the process, σ is estimated as

$$\hat{\sigma} = \frac{\bar{R}}{d_2} \tag{6.156}$$

for an $\bar{x}$ and R chart,

$$\hat{\sigma} = \frac{\bar{s}}{c_4} \tag{6.157}$$

for an $\bar{x}$ and s chart, and

$$\hat{\sigma} = \frac{\overline{MR}}{d_2} \tag{6.158}$$

for an individuals and MR chart. To illustrate, consider Example 6.72.

EXAMPLE 6.72

A dimension has specifications of 2.125 ± 0.005. Data from the process indicate that the distribution is normally distributed, and the $\bar{x}$ and R control chart indicates that the process is stable. The control chart used a sample of size five and it is found that $\bar{\bar{x}} = 2.1261$ and $\bar{R} = 0.0055$. Determine what fraction of the manufactured product will have this particular dimension outside the specification limits.

Solution:

Let X represent the dimension of the quality characteristic of interest. What is needed is the fraction of the manufactured product that will have this particular dimension outside the specification limits; this can be written as $1 - (2.120 < X < 2.130)$. Since X is normally distributed, the standard normal distribution can be used to determine this fraction. The best point estimate for μ is $\bar{\bar{x}} = 2.1261$. The point estimate for process standard deviation σ is computed as

$$\hat{\sigma} = \frac{\bar{R}}{d_2} = \frac{0.0055}{2.326} = 0.00236$$

The constant d_2 can be found in Appendix B for $n = 5$.

The estimated fraction that *does* conform to specifications is

$$P(2.120 < X < 2.130) = P\left(\frac{2.120 - 2.1261}{0.00236} < \frac{X - \bar{\bar{x}}}{\hat{\sigma}} < \frac{2.130 - 2.1261}{0.00236}\right)$$

$$= P(-2.58 < Z < 1.65)$$

$$= P(Z < 1.65) - P(Z < -2.58)$$

$$= 0.9505 - 0.0049$$

$$= 0.9456$$

Therefore, the fraction that is *nonconforming* is $1 - 0.9456 = 0.0544$. Approximately 5.44% of the products will fall outside specification for this quality characteristic.

Control Limits, Specification Limits, and Natural Tolerance Limits

It should be noted that there is a significant difference between control limits, specification limits, and natural tolerance limits. Control limits are determined by the natural tolerance of the process, while specification limits are determined externally—usually by management, engineers, customers, and so on. There is no relationship between specification limits and control limits. Suppose the sample mean $\bar{x}$ is being monitored, where the population of interest is normally distributed with mean μ and standard deviation σ. The different limits could be written as follows:

Natural limits: $\mu \pm 3\sigma$

Control limits: $\bar{x} \pm 3\dfrac{\sigma}{\sqrt{n}}$ (6.159)

Specification limits: [LSL, USL] (determined externally)

Defective Parts per Million Opportunities

The following section will cover several metrics of process capability for variables data. When a process is measured as attribute data, however, alternate metrics must be used. One of the most frequent measures for process performance is parts per million (ppm) defective. The ppm measures the number of defective/nonconforming parts in one million parts produced.

Another metric used to measure process capability for attributes is defects per million opportunities (DPMO), which is estimated as

$$\text{DPMO} = \left(\frac{\text{Total number of defects}}{(\text{Number of units})(\text{Number of opportunities/unit})}\right)(1{,}000{,}000) \quad (6.160)$$

An *opportunity* is defined as the number of potential chances within a unit for a defect to occur (Montgomery 2013). DPMO differs from ppm in that ppm measures the number of nonconforming parts while DPMO measures the number of nonconformities. These metrics are the same when the number of opportunities per unit is equal to one. DPMO is useful because it can be used to compare the quality of different products, provided that the number of opportunities for defects has been thoroughly determined (Kubiak 2009).

EXAMPLE 6.73

Consider the hospital billing data, where 20 billing statements were randomly selected over a 24-day period. Suppose that each billing statement has 12 opportunities for a mistake (a defect) to occur. Estimate DPMO for this scenario.

There were 245 total defects in this time period and (20)(24) = 480 billing statements examined.

$$\text{DPMO} = \left(\frac{245}{(480)(12)}\right)(1{,}000{,}000) = 42{,}534.72$$

For additional information on common process performance metrics, see Montgomery (2013) and Kubiak (2009).

Process Capability Indices

> Define, select, and calculate Cp, Cpk, Cpm, and Cr, and evaluate process capability.
> (Evaluate)
>
> **Body of Knowledge VI.G.3**

Various capability indices have been developed to try to quantify process capability in a single number. The stability and normality requirements discussed earlier must be met for these measures to be effective. Four such indices are C_p, C_r, C_{pk}, and C_{pm}.

C_p and C_r

C_p compares the tolerance (the width of the engineering specifications) with the natural process tolerance. C_p is given by

$$C_p = \frac{USL - LSL}{6\sigma} \tag{6.161}$$

where LSL is the lower specification limit and USL is the upper specification limit. The true process standard deviation σ is usually unknown and must be estimated from the sample data. The sample standard deviation s can be used if control charts are used in the analysis. The estimate of C_p is

$$\hat{C}_p = \frac{USL - LSL}{6\hat{\sigma}} \tag{6.162}$$

Consider the example which involved a quality characteristic with specification limits set at 2.125 ± 0.005 and $\hat{\sigma} = 0.00236$. The estimate of C_p, is

$$\hat{C}_p = \frac{USL - LSL}{6\hat{\sigma}} = \frac{2.130 - 2.120}{6(0.00236)} = 0.706$$

Generally, it is desirable for $C_p > 1$. Based on this analysis, the process does not appear to be capable.

The C_r measure is simply the inverse of C_p, that is, $C_r = 1/C_p$. An estimate of C_r, which is also referred to as the PTR, is

$$\hat{C}_r = \frac{6\hat{\sigma}}{USL - LSL} \tag{6.163}$$

A simple interpretation of C_r is the percentage of the tolerance (or specification band) that is used up by the process. Consider the example again where it was found that $\hat{C}_p = 0.706$. Then $\hat{C}_r = 1/0.706 = 1.416$. This value can be interpreted that the process uses 141.6% of the specification band, giving further evidence that this is not a capable process. This ratio is sometimes referred to as the capability ratio, and smaller values are better.

C_{pk}

The capability measure C_{pk} penalizes a process whose mean is off center. C_{pk} takes into account process centering and is given by

$$C_{pk} = \min\left[\frac{\text{USL} - \mu}{3\sigma}, \frac{\mu - \text{LSL}}{3\sigma}\right] \tag{6.164}$$

It is desirable to have a value of $C_{pk} > 1$, which indicates that the process exceeds the stated minimum requirement. An estimate of C_{pk} is

$$\hat{C}_{pk} = \min\left[\frac{\text{USL} - \bar{\bar{x}}}{3\hat{\sigma}}, \frac{\bar{\bar{x}} - \text{LSL}}{3\hat{\sigma}}\right] \tag{6.165}$$

For this example,

$$\hat{C}_{pk} = \min\left[\frac{\text{USL} - \bar{\bar{x}}}{3\hat{\sigma}}, \frac{\bar{\bar{x}} - \text{LSL}}{3\hat{\sigma}}\right]$$

$$= \min\left[\frac{2.130 - 2.1261}{3(0.00236)}, \frac{2.1261 - 2.120}{3(0.00236)}\right]$$

$$= \min[0.551, 0.862]$$

$$= 0.551$$

Historically, a C_{pk} value of 1.0 or larger was considered capable. This would be equivalent to stating that the natural process limits lie inside the tolerance limits. More recently, quality requirements have become more stringent, and many customers require C_{pk} values of 1.33, 1.66, or 2.00.

C_{pm}

The previous measure, C_{pk}, was developed to take into account centering of the process. However, studies have shown that a large value of C_{pk} does not necessarily indicate that the location of the process mean is centered between the LSL and USL. The C_{pm} metric was developed to provide a better measure of centering and is given by

$$C_{pm} = \frac{\text{USL} - \text{LSL}}{6\sqrt{(\mu - T)^2 + \sigma^2}} \tag{6.166}$$

An estimate is then

$$\hat{C}_{pm} = \frac{\text{USL} - \text{LSL}}{6\sqrt{(\bar{\bar{x}} - T)^2 + \hat{\sigma}^2}} \tag{6.167}$$

where T is the process target. Again, the estimates of μ and σ are obtained from control charts.

Interpreting Process Capability Ratios

The assumptions underlying C_p, C_r, C_{pk}, and C_{pm} are critical to accurately interpret their respective values and the capability of the process. As discussed at the beginning of this section, the process must be stable and the population normally distributed to correctly interpret process capability. Proper interpretation of C_p requires the process mean to be centered between the LSL and USL as well. Several studies have discussed the implications of violating these assumptions. In general, it has been shown that these indices are highly sensitive to their assumptions. See, for example, Somerville and Montgomery (1996).

When the process is not centered, $C_{pk} < C_p$. Therefore, C_p is said to measure the potential capability of a process while C_{pk} measures the actual capability. A process is considered capable when the process capability ratios are greater than 1, and incapable when they are less than 1. A process with $C_p = 1$ and both an LSL and a USL results in 2700 ppm defective. A process with $C_p = 1.50$ and both an LSL and a USL results in 7 ppm defective (Montgomery 2013). Therefore, the larger the capability ratio, the better. Six sigma processes require process capability ratios equal to 2 (Perez-Wilson 1997). Table 6.46 displays recommended minimum values of process capability ratios for different processes.

The point estimators for the capability indices given in this section have some degree of error or variability associated with them. It has been recommended that confidence intervals on the process capability indices be constructed to quantify the precision associated with the point estimators. The reader is encouraged to see Kotz and Lovelace (1998) for complete details of the point estimators for and confidence intervals on these and other capability indices.

Table 6.46 Recommended minimum values of the process capability ratio.

	Two-sided specifications	One-sided specifications
Existing processes	1.33	1.25
New processes	1.50	1.45
Safety, strength, or critical parameter, existing process	1.50	1.45
Safety, strength, or critical parameter, new process	1.67	1.60

Source: D. C. Montgomery, *Introduction to Statistical Quality Control*, 7th ed. (Hoboken, NJ: John Wiley & Sons, 2013).

Process Performance Indices

> Define, select, and calculate Pp and Ppk, and
> evaluate process performance. (Evaluate)
>
> **Body of Knowledge VI.G.4**

Performance indices provide a picture of current process operation and have been used for comparison and prioritization of improvement efforts. Two such performance indices are P_p and P_{pk}. The performance indices have been recommended for use when the process is *not* in statistical control. The formulas for P_p and P_{pk} are equivalent to those for C_p and C_{pk}, respectively, except that the sample standard deviation is used instead of σ.

Some practitioners recommend the use of P_p and P_{pk} when the process is not in control. This is a somewhat controversial position because an out-of-control process is unpredictable. Montgomery (2013) states, "The process performance indices P_p and P_{pk} are actually more than a step backwards. They are a waste of engineering and management effort—they tell you nothing." Wheeler (2004) disagrees with Montgomery and uses P_p and P_{pk} to calculate what he refers to as the effective cost of production. The reader is encouraged to see Kotz and Lovelace (1998) for more discussion on performance and capability indices.

In general, the longer the time span over which the data are collected, the more valid the capability analysis. The analysis of data collected over a few hours can provide information about the process during those hours and may be useful for comparison purposes during process improvement efforts. Using control charts for process capability allows for the evaluation of both short-term and long-term process capability. For example, $\bar{x}$ and R charts provide both instantaneous variability and variability over time.

Once again, verifying the normality of a process is important. If the underlying distribution is not normal, the indices described in this chapter may not be valid. Various transformations and alternative indices have been proposed when the distribution is non-normal. See Kotz and Lovelace (1998), Luceño (1996), Montgomery (2013), and Rodriquez (1992) for details on dealing with non-normality and process capability.

DESIGN AND ANALYSIS OF EXPERIMENTS

Experiments are an essential part of research and process and product development. It is important to correctly design and implement any experiment to obtain statistically valid results. All experiments can be considered "designed" experiments, but some of them may be designed poorly. Positive results can be achieved when a statistically designed experiment is developed and implemented correctly. Some of the results of a good experimental design include the following:

- Improvement in process yield
- Reduction in process variability (closer conformance to nominal or target requirements is often achieved)
- Reduction in design and development time
- Reduction in operation costs

The purpose of conducting a statistically designed experiment is to gain as much relevant information as possible with a minimum amount of cost (cost includes time, money, resources, and so on). Therefore, it is important to construct and carry out an *efficient* designed experiment. An efficiently designed experiment is one that includes the minimum number of runs and minimizes the amount of resources, personnel, and time utilized. Most statistically designed experiments are efficient and economical. Experiments that are not statistically designed are often expensive and inefficient and can often result in a waste of resources.

Before discussing the actual design and implementation of valid experiments, some important terminology must be introduced.

Terminology

Define terms such as dependent and independent variables, factors, levels, response, treatment, error, and replication. (Understand)

Body of Knowledge VI.H.1

This section provides definitions for several important terms. Figure 6.40 depicts the general process of a system.

In experimental design, the *dependent variable* or *response*, y, is the result or outcome of interest of the experiment, for example, yield of a process, time to complete a task, and taste score.

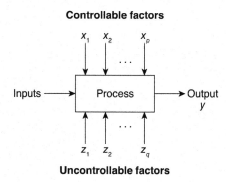

Figure 6.40 General system process.

Source: D. C. Montgomery, *Design and Analysis of Experiments*, 9th ed. (New York: John Wiley & Sons, 2017).

In experimental design, the *independent variables*, x's, sometimes referred to as *treatments* or *factors*, are chosen by the experimenter or practitioner to determine what effect, if any, they will have on the outcome of the experiment. Examples include the following:

- Type of gasoline (such as standard, plus, or super)
- Condensation temperature and its effect on yield
- Carbonation level in a test of a soft-drink taste
- Supplier of raw material in a manufacturing process

Factors can be *quantitative* (e.g., temperature, amount of fertilizer per acre) or *qualitative* (e.g., technician, different additives, supplier, or type of keyboard).

There may be more than one factor under investigation in any one experiment. In addition, factors can take on one of several roles. For example, *control factors* are process inputs to be controlled in actual production. These factors can be adjusted in practice to affect the output of a process. *Noise factors,* on the other hand, z's, can be controlled during the experiment but are allowed to vary naturally in actual production. These factors are difficult to control in practice and can introduce variability into the response of interest. Understanding the effect of noise factors on the response can aid in reducing this variability in practice while not completely removing it. Examples of noise factors include humidity within a manufacturing plant, ambient temperature, and how a product is used in practice.

Levels in experimental design refers to the levels of the factors—for example, temperature levels of 200°C, 300°C, and 400°C; cooking times of one hour or two hours; two suppliers, A and B; and percent additive of 0.2%, 0.5%, and 0.8%.

A *treatment* in experimental design refers to a combination of the levels of each factor assigned to an experimental unit. This is sometimes called a *treatment combination.* To illustrate, consider an experiment on the breaking strength of a material. Two factors of interest are the machine (M1, M2, M3) on which the material is produced and the technician (T1, T2) using the machine. One treatment combination would be technician 2 using machine 1 (T2M1). "Treatment" is a term left over from the early days of experimental design and its roots in agricultural experimentation.

Factorial designs are those where all treatment combinations of the factors are carried out. Suppose an experiment involves three factors, A, B, and C, with three, five, and two levels investigated, respectively. A full-factorial design would consist of $3 \times 5 \times 2 = 30$ treatment combinations.

Error in experimental design has several meanings. In any experimental situation, error could represent errors in experimentation, errors of measurement, variation in materials or factors in general, or the effect of noise factors on the response, for example. *Experimental error* is the variability that is observed when a treatment combination is repeated, that is, replicated.

The objective of a designed experiment is to generate knowledge about a product or process. The experiment seeks to find the effect a set of independent variables has on a set of dependent variables. Mathematically this relationship can be denoted $y = f(x) + \varepsilon$, where x is an independent variable and y is the dependent variable (although there will most likely be more than one independent variable). For example, suppose a machine operator who can adjust the feed, speed, and coolant temperature wishes to find the settings that will produce the best surface finish. The feed, speed, and coolant temperature are the *independent variables* or *factors*. Surface finish is the *dependent variable* or *response* and its value depends on the values of the independent variables. Independent variables may also be thought of as input variables, and dependent variables as output variables. There may be additional independent variables, such as the hardness of the material or humidity of the room, that have an effect on the dependent variable. These factors are considered *noise factors* since they may induce variability in the surface finish but cannot necessarily be controlled in actual production. In this example, the experimental design may specify that the speed will be set at 1300 rev/min for part of the experiment and at 1800 rev/min for the remainder. These values are referred to as the *levels* of the speed factor. The team decides to test each factor at two levels, as follows:

- Feed (F): 0.01 and 0.04 in/rev

- Speed (S): 1300 and 1800 rev/min

- Coolant temperature (C): 100°F and 140°F

A full-factorial design for the three factors will be used. A full-factorial experiment tests all possible combinations of levels and factors, using one run for each combination. The total number of combinations is given by L^F, where F represents the number of factors of interest, each with L levels. In this situation, the number of treatment combinations is $2^3 = 8$. The team develops a data collection sheet listing those eight experiments, with room for recording five replicates ($n = 5$) for each run (see Table 6.47).

As the data are collected, the values are recorded as shown in Table 6.48. These data are also referred to as the response values since they show how the process or product responds to various treatments.

Note that the five values for a particular run are not all the same. This may be due to drift in the factor levels, variation in the measurement system, and/or the

Table 6.47   A 2^3 full-factorial data collection table.

Run	F	S	C	1	2	3	4	5
1	0.01	1300	100					
2	0.01	1300	140					
3	0.01	1800	100					
4	0.01	1800	140					
5	0.04	1300	100					
6	0.04	1300	140					
7	0.04	1800	100					
8	0.04	1800	140					

Table 6.48   A 2^3 full-factorial data collection table with data.

Run	F	S	C	1	2	3	4	5
1	0.01	1300	100	10.1	10.0	10.2	9.8	9.9
2	0.01	1300	140	3.0	4.0	3.0	5.0	5.0
3	0.01	1800	100	6.5	7.0	5.3	5.0	6.2
4	0.01	1800	140	1.0	3.0	3.0	1.0	2.0
5	0.04	1300	100	5.0	7.0	9.0	8.0	6.0
6	0.04	1300	140	4.0	7.0	5.0	6.0	8.0
7	0.04	1800	100	5.8	6.0	6.1	6.2	5.9
8	0.04	1800	140	3.1	2.9	3.0	2.9	3.1

influence of noise factors. The variation observed in the readings for a particular run is referred to as *experimental error*. If the number of replications is decreased, the calculation of experimental error is less accurate, although the experiment has a lower total cost. If all the factors that impact the dependent variable are included in the experiment and all measurements are exact, replication is not needed and a very efficient experiment could be conducted. Thus, the accurate determination of experimental error and cost are competing design properties.

Once the data are collected as shown in Table 6.48, it may be useful to find the average of the five replication responses for each run. These averages are shown in Table 6.49.

Table 6.49   A 2^3 full-factorial data collection table with run averages.

Run	F	S	C	Average surface finish reading
1	0.01	1300	100	10
2	0.01	1300	140	4
3	0.01	1800	100	6
4	0.01	1800	140	2
5	0.04	1300	100	7
6	0.04	1300	140	6
7	0.04	1800	100	6
8	0.04	1800	140	3

Planning and Organizing Experiments

> Identify the basic elements of designed experiments, including determining the experiment objective, selecting factors, responses, and measurement methods, and choosing the appropriate design. (Analyze)
>
> **Body of Knowledge VI.H.2**

There is a general process of designing and analyzing an experiment. Table 6.50 provides the seven steps associated with planning, designing, conducting, and analyzing an experiment. This section provides some details on the steps in this process.

Planning and Organizing a Designed Experiment

Planning and organizing a designed experiment is just as important as conducting the experiment and analyzing the results. Important steps in planning and organizing experiments are the first three steps in Table 6.50.

The team making these types of choices and decisions should include engineers, technicians, management, customers, statisticians, and others who have firsthand knowledge of and experience with the process under study. It is important to ensure that the experiment is conducted as planned. Errors that occur as the experiment is carried out or errors in the measurements could deliver invalid results.

When preparing to conduct an experiment, one first asks, "What question are we seeking to answer?" In the example illustrated in the previous section, the objective was to find the combination of process settings that minimizes the surface finish reading.

The objective of a designed experiment is considered the goal of the experiment. Recognition of and statement of the problem is the first step in designing a successful experiment. Although stating the objective of the problem may seem obvious, it is not always given due consideration in the initial stages of planning the experiment.

The response (or responses) of interest is the outputs to be measured. The responses should represent all aspects of quality, productivity, and functionality. What factors might significantly affect the response? In most processes a very large number of variables could be measured of which only a few have any real impact on the response. Initially, many factors should be included and screening experiments carried out to eliminate those factors that do not significantly affect the response. One task in designing an experiment is to maximize the chance of including the significant variables in the design and leaving out those that have little impact.

The levels of the factors should also be given serious consideration. The span or scope of the experimental conditions will have an impact on one's ability to determine the significance of a factor. For example, should the range of temperature be

Table 6.50 Guidelines for designing an experiment.

1. Recognition of and statement of the problem	⎫
2. Selection of the response variable*	Pre-experimental planning
3. Choice of factors, levels, and ranges*	⎭
4. Choice of experimental design	
5. Performing the experiment	
6. Statistical analysis of the data	
7. Conclusions and recommendations	

Source: D. C. Montgomery, *Design and Analysis of Experiments*, 9th ed. (New York: John Wiley & Sons, 2017).
*In practice, steps 2 and 3 are often done simultaneously or in reverse order.

from 100°C to 200°C or from 125°C to 175°C for a particular problem? If the range is too narrow, important effects could be completely missed.

Once the objective of the experiment has been determined and factors and levels selected, an appropriate measurement system is chosen. The measurement method is determined by the response that has been decided on. For example, if the outcome measured is placed into one of several possible categories (categorical data), the response that will be modeled or used in the analysis would be quite different than if the measured outcome is continuous. The measurement system must be appropriate for the type of response of interest and can only be determined by people familiar with the process and output. Regardless of the type of response, methods exist that can adequately address these issues. This is discussed in the "Design Principles" section of this chapter.

Choice of Design

Once the objective of the experiment has been decided on, the factors, levels, and responses determined, and the method of measurement chosen, the next step is to choose the type of design to be used. This is step 4. The choice of design will depend on the previous steps (stating the objective, choosing factors, levels, and responses, and determining the measurement method). Other important considerations include the size of the design that is acceptable, the number of replicates, the run order of the design, and whether blocking is involved. Many standard statistical packages aid the practitioner in determining an appropriate design. In choosing the appropriate design, the objective of the experiment should always be kept in mind. Therefore, rather than designing a massive experiment involving many variables and levels, it is usually best to begin with more modest screening designs whose purpose is to determine the variables and levels that need further study.

Analysis of Results

Designed experiments, when conducted properly, can lead to very reliable results that provide insight into the important factors and optimal level settings. Properly designed experiments and the results of appropriate analysis easily lend themselves to sequential experimentation for more detailed understanding and modeling of the process. The analysis of the results involves some very straight-forward but important steps:

- Exploratory and graphical analysis. Simple plots and tables of the data can provide insight into the process.

- Model fitting. Mathematical models of the form $y = f(x) + \varepsilon$ are built and provide a relationship between the response and the independent variables.

- Fine-tuning the model. Not all independent variables will be significantly related to the response. Several analysis steps can be taken to remove terms from the fitted model that have no significant effect on the response.

- Model diagnostics. Assumptions should be verified. The use of plots (such as residual plots) is useful in this step.

- Refining the model. This step is necessary if any of the assumptions are violated. Model refitting may be necessary, or a new form of the model investigated.

In the next several sections, various basic designs and analysis techniques are presented. Complete details on these and other aspects of experimental designs can be found in Montgomery (2017).

Design Principles

> Define and apply the principles of power and sample size, balance, replication, order, efficiency, randomization, blocking, interaction, and confounding. (Apply)
>
> **Body of Knowledge VI.H.3**

Once the experiment is planned and carried out, and the outcomes recorded, appropriate analysis is necessary to make final decisions on factors, factor settings, and prediction. Some analysis techniques are described at the end of this section.

Randomization

Randomization in experimental design is the ordering of the treatment combinations in a sequence that will reduce the effect of uncontrolled variables that might affect the dependent variable. Randomization will reduce the effect of unwanted nuisance factors that are not part of the experiment but may influence the results.

Returning to the surface finish example given earlier, there are eight treatments with five replications per treatment. This produces 40 tests or treatments. The tests from this design should be performed in random order. This is referred to as a *completely randomized design.* For the surface finish example, suppose the machine used in the process has some temperature effect; that is, machine temperature increases the longer the machine is running and can possibly affect the surface finish. Furthermore, suppose the treatment combinations are carried out in order. If machine temperature does have an effect on surface finish, and the factor "feed rate" is found to be statistically significant, it is not completely known whether the significant effect is really due to the change in feed rate or due to the temperature of the machine. These two factors could very well be confounded. *Confounding* in experimental design is the term used to signify that the effect of one independent variable is indistinguishable from the effect of another independent variable or combination of independent variables (interactions). The 40 tests in the surface finish example may be randomized in two possible ways:

1. Number the tests from 1 to 40 and randomize those numbers to obtain the order in which tests are performed. This is referred to as a completely randomized design.

2. Randomize the run order, but once a run is set up, make all five replicates for that run.

Although it usually requires more time and effort, the first method is better. To see that this is true, suppose time of day is a noise factor such that products made before noon are different from those made after noon. By randomizing, the time effect of when the product is made is minimized. In this way, if significant effects of the factors are identified, thee is more confidence that the effect is due to the changes made in the controllable factors rather than outside, often uncontrollable, factors.

Replication

In experimental design, *replication* is the repetition of the basic experiment. This involves a complete reset of the factor levels and repeating the experiment. Replication provides an estimate of experimental error and leads to more precise estimates of the factor effects. It should be noted that multiple measurements of a treatment combination do not necessarily constitute replication. There is a significant difference between true replication and *repeated measures.*

Blocking/Local Control of Error

There are many instances when a factor may affect the response of interest but it is not a factor of interest. These factors are often referred to as *nuisance* factors. For example, suppose the 40 tests in the surface finish example cannot be conducted during one shift, but must be carried out over two shifts. In addition, it is believed that the shift may have an effect on surface finish. The team would be concerned about the impact the shift difference could have on the results.

Randomization can often reduce the effects of a nuisance factor when there is no way of controlling this factor in practice. If the nuisance factor is known and can be controlled for purposes of experimentation, then the factor can be taken into account during testing. A technique called *blocking* can be used to reduce variability transmitted by a nuisance factor. By removing the influence of this factor, the statistical analysis is more likely to reveal whether the factor of interest is truly significant or not. The simplest form of blocking is pairing, used to compare two dependent samples.

Blocking is one form of R. A. Fisher's concept of local control of error. In general, *local control* refers to grouping experimental units in such a way that units within the group are homogeneous. This type of control aids in eliminating the variability or noise due to inactive or extraneous factors. Local control also includes the use of covariates when blocking is not possible in an experiment.

Designed Experiments and Statistical Control

There has been considerable debate about the use of designed experiments in industry if the process under investigation is not known to be in statistical control. Some researchers have argued that the process must be in statistical control before conducting legitimate industrial experiments, while others have argued that statistical control is not necessary (see Bisgaard [2008]). Research by R. A. Fisher first published in 1925 showed that statistical control was not a prerequisite for implementing designed experiments when replication, blocking, and randomization were key components of the experimentation. Arguments have been made to the effect that Fisher's results, while applicable in agricultural experiments, do not apply in industrial settings.

Anyone involved in conducting experiments should read the *Quality Engineering* article by Søren Bisgaard (2008). Statistical control and designed experiments are discussed in detail by Bisgaard, with discussion of his article provided by G. Geoffrey Vining, Thomas P. Ryan, George E. P. Box, Donald J. Wheeler, and Douglas C. Montgomery.* The article and discussions are a must-read for practitioners and researchers alike and provide numerous references for further reading. Simpson, Listak, and Hutto (2013) also provide recommendations for planning and assessing well-designed experiments.

Full-Factorial Experiments

> Construct full-factorial designs and use computational and graphical methods to analyze the significance of results. (Analyze)
>
> **Body of Knowledge VI.H.4**

In full-factorial experiments all possible combinations of the levels of factors are investigated. The two-factor factorial was introduced in the "Analysis of Variance" section of this chapter when discussing the two-way ANOVA. Consider an

---

*These discussions are found in *Quality Engineering* (vol. 20, no. 2, 2008) as follows: Vining, 151–53, doi:10.1080/08982110701866198; Ryan, 154–57, doi:10.1080/08982110801894892; Box, 158–59, doi:10.1080/08982110801890148; Wheeler, 160–64, doi:10.1080/08982110801924509; Montgomery, 165–68, doi:10.1080/08982110801894900; Bisgaard (rejoinder), 169–76, doi:10.1080/08982110801973118.

experiment that involves exactly two factors of interest, A and B, where there are a levels of factor A, b levels of factor B, and n replicates at each combination of A and B. The general model that would describe the response of interest y is given as

$$y_{ijk} = \mu + \tau_i + \beta_j + (\tau\beta)_{ij} + \varepsilon_{ijk} \text{ for } i = 1, 2, \ldots, a;$$
$$j = 1, 2, \ldots, b; \text{ and } k = 1, 2, \ldots, n$$

(6.168)

where

y_{ijk} = the kth response at the combination of the ith level of A and the jth level of B

μ = the overall mean effect

τ_i = the parameter for the effect of the ith level of A

β_j = the parameter for the effect of the jth level of B

$(\tau\beta)_{ij}$ = the parameter for the effect of the ijth level of the interaction between A and B

ε_{ijk} = the error

The following hypotheses are of interest:

H_0: $\tau_1 = \tau_2 = \ldots = \tau_a = 0$ (the effect for each level of A is zero)

H_a: $\tau_i \neq 0$, for at least one i

H_0: $\beta_1 = \beta_2 = \ldots = \beta_b = 0$ (the effect for each level of B is zero)

H_1: $\beta_j \neq 0$, for at least one j

H_0: $(\tau\beta)_{11} = (\tau\beta)_{12} = \ldots = (\tau\beta)_{ab} = 0$ (no significant interaction between A and B)

H_a: $(\tau\beta)_{ij} \neq 0$ for at least one i and one j

The sums of squares, degrees of freedom, mean squares, test statistics, and p-values can be calculated using a reliable statistical software package. The resulting ANOVA table would look like Table 6.51.

It should be noted that the ANOVA approach is not the only method for testing the significance of the effects and interactions. If each factor has exactly two levels, it is common to examine the results of t-tests on the coefficients representing each factor and interaction. To build a model as recommended, t-tests can be very useful.

Two-Level Factorial Designs

A special type of factorial design that receives a great deal of attention is a design where all factors are run at exactly two levels. If there are k factors, the design is a 2^k factorial design. The number of experimental runs (or observations) is 2^k. For example, consider the surface finish illustration given earlier. There are three factors of interest: feed rate, speed, and coolant temperature, each at two levels. A full-factorial design consists of $2^3 = 8$ runs or treatment combinations.

Table 6.51 ANOVA table for two-factor factorial experiment.

Source of variation	df	SS	MS	F	p-value
Factor A	$a-1$	SS_A	$MS_A = \dfrac{SS_A}{a-1}$	$F_0 = \dfrac{MS_A}{MS_E}$	$P(F > F_0)$
Factor B	$b-1$	SS_B	$MS_B = \dfrac{SS_B}{b-1}$	$F_0 = \dfrac{MS_B}{MS_E}$	$P(F > F_0)$
AB interaction	$(a-1)(b-1)$	SS_{AB}	$MS_{AB} = \dfrac{SS_{AB}}{(a-1)(b-1)}$	$F_0 = \dfrac{MS_{AB}}{MS_E}$	$P(F > F_0)$
Error	$ab(n-1)$	SS_E	$MS_E = \dfrac{SS_E}{ab(n-1)}$		
Total	$abn-1$	SS_T			

The two levels of each factor can be coded as –1 and 1, the low and high levels of each factor, respectively. Consider an experiment with two factors A and B, each at two levels, shown in Table 6.52.

There would be a total of four combinations, and it is desired to determine whether A, B, or AB is significant. The combinations can be written in Table 6.53. To obtain the column for the levels of the AB interaction, multiply column A and column B.

Table 6.52 Coded factor levels.

	A	B
Low	–1	–1
High	1	1

Table 6.53 Combinations for terms in a two-factor interaction model.

Run	A	B	AB	Responses
1	–1	–1	1	$y_{11}, y_{12}, \cdots y_{1n}$
2	–1	1	–1	$y_{21}, y_{22}, \cdots y_{2n}$
3	1	–1	–1	$y_{31}, y_{32}, \cdots y_{3n}$
4	1	1	1	$y_{41}, y_{42}, \cdots y_{4n}$

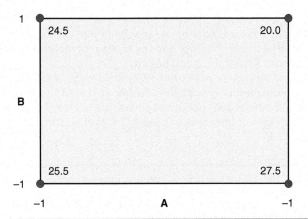

Figure 6.41   All possible combinations of two factors A and B, with two levels each.

Suppose there are two replicates for each run and the average response is calculated. Geometrically, the data can be displayed on a square for the factors as shown in Figure 6.41.

Each corner of the square represents a run or treatment combination. The values at the corners represent the average response of each combination. For example, at the low level of A and the high level of B the average response is 24.5.

Standard analysis techniques can be applied to the special case of factors with only two levels. The estimation of the main factors and interaction will be examined using an example. The effect estimate is calculated as the average response at the high (+1) level minus the average response at the low (–1) level. The main effect provides a measure of how each individual factor (main factors such as A, B, and C) affects the response moving from one level of the factor to the next. The estimated effect for each factor is simply the difference in the average response at the high level of the factor and the average response at the low level of the factor. The term "estimated effect" is denoted by *ee*. Main effects plots can be useful for examining the change in the factor effects from the low to high levels. See Montgomery (2017) for further details.

EXAMPLE 6.74

In an article by Lee and Awbi (2004), the authors discuss the effect internal partitioning of office space has on room air ventilation. In the design of modern office buildings, it is important to consider the air quality in a room. For office buildings it is desirable to construct a highly energy-efficient building, often with an open-space floor plan. With open-space construction, internal partitions are introduced to design the office to fit the current needs of the company. With internal partitioning, the layout can easily be restructured for different occupants. However, the air ventilation system is designed for open-space rooms. When interferences are introduced (such as office furniture, wall partitions, and so on) the air quality can be significantly affected. In the study on the effect of internal partitioning on room air quality, three factors are of interest: partition location (A), partition height (B), and gap underneath (C). The partition locations are chosen at 40% and 60% of the room length from the left end of the room. The partition

Continued

heights are chosen as 60% and 80% of the room height. The factor "gap underneath" represents the space between the floor and the bottom of the partition. Gap is set at 0% of the room height and 10% of the room height.

One response of interest is ventilation effectiveness y_v, a scaleless quantity that is a function of contamination concentration. Larger values of y_v indicate better ventilation effectiveness. The tests are conducted on a small scale model test room with the length, width, and height of the room measured in meters. The factors and their levels are given in Table 6.54.

Table 6.54 Factor levels for ventilation experiment.

Factor	Low level (–1)	High level (+1)
Partition length (A)	40%	60%
Partition height (B)	60%	80%
Gap underneath (C)	0%	10%

Suppose a similar experiment was conducted using these factors to test their effect on ventilation effectiveness. The design used was a 2^3 factorial in two replicates, with results given in Table 6.55 (factors are coded). A complete randomization of the treatments for all 16 runs was carried out.

Table 6.55 Partitioning effect on ventilation effectiveness.

Treatment	A	B	C	y_v
1	–1	–1	–1	2.227, 1.874
2	1	–1	–1	2.134, 2.252
3	–1	1	–1	1.470, 1.404
4	1	1	–1	2.091, 2.270
5	–1	–1	1	2.073, 1.825
6	1	–1	1	2.162, 2.480
7	–1	1	1	1.615, 1.558
8	1	1	1	2.157, 2.169

Graphically, the results can be displayed using the average response for each treatment. Figure 6.42 displays a cube plot for the three factors: partition length (A), partition height (B), and gap underneath (C).

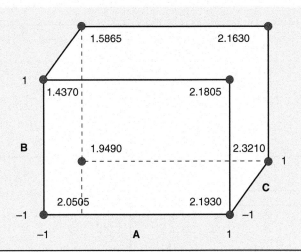

Figure 6.42   Cube plot for partition length, partition height, and gap underneath.

Consider the estimated effect of gap underneath. The average response at the high level (+1) of C (gap underneath) is

$$C_{+1} = \frac{2.073 + 1.825 + 2.162 + 2.480 + 1.615 + 1.558 + 2.157 + 2.169}{8} = 2.005$$

The average at the low level (−1) of C is

$$C_{-1} = \frac{2.227 + 1.874 + 2.134 + 2.252 + 1.470 + 1.404 + 2.091 + 2.270}{8} = 1.965$$

The estimated effect of C (gap underneath) on ventilation effectiveness is then

$$ee(C) = C_{+1} - C_{-1} = 2.005 - 1.965 = 0.04$$

The estimated effect for C shows that as the gap underneath the partition is changed from 0% to 10%, the average ventilation effectiveness increases by 0.04. The estimated effects of partition length and partition height are calculated similarly and found to be 0.46 and −0.29, respectively. Main effects plots for partition length, partition height, and gap underneath are displayed in Figure 6.43.

It appears that there is a significant difference between the levels of factor A and the levels of factor B, but not necessarily between the levels of factor C.

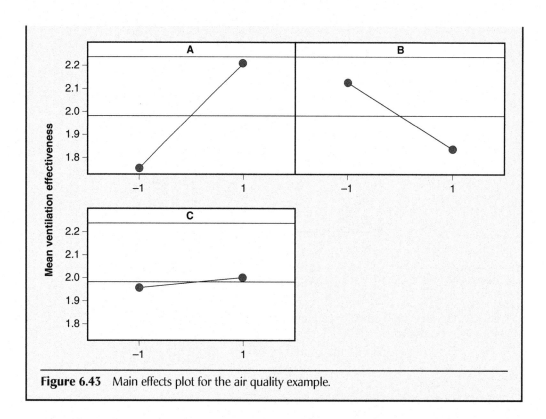

Figure 6.43 Main effects plot for the air quality example.

Using this definition of main effect, the larger the absolute value of the main effect, the more influence that factor has on the quality characteristic. It is possible that the perceived difference between high and low results is not statistically significant. This would occur if the experimental error were so large that it would be impossible to determine whether the difference between the high and low levels is due to a real difference in the dependent variable or due to experimental error. This may be determined by using ANOVA procedures and/or t-tests.

For analysis of data from an experiment, the null hypothesis is that changing the factor level does not make a difference in the dependent variable. The α risk is the probability that the analysis will show that there is a significant difference when there is not. The β risk is the probability that the analysis will show that there is no significant difference when there is. The power of the experiment is defined as $1 - \beta$, so the higher the power of the experiment, the lower the β risk. In general, a higher number of replications or a larger sample size provides a more precise estimate of experimental error, which in turn reduces the β risk.

An *interaction* in experimental design describes the change in the response when two or more factors are interdependent. Interactions are discussed in some detail in the "Statistical Decision-Making section of this chapter and also further in this section with respect to factorial designs. Interactions may exist between the factors of interest, and this interaction effect must be determined as was done with the main effects. The interactions in the example include the two-factor interactions and the three-factor interaction: partition length by partition height (AB), partition length by gap underneath (AC), partition height by gap underneath (BC), and partition length by partition height by gap underneath (ABC).

Again, the objective to find the average difference in the response between the high level and the low level of each interaction. What is considered a "high" and "low" level for an interaction? The levels of the interactions are simply the results of the levels of the main effects. In coded form the high and low levels of each interaction can be labeled simply by multiplying the levels of each factor involved in the interaction. For example, if A is set at its low level (A = –1) and B is set at its high level (B = 1), then the corresponding level of the interaction AB would be –1 (since –1 × 1 = –1). This is simply a label that is convenient for determining the low and high levels of each interaction and is a result of the geometry of the design. The table for the main effects and interactions for the 2^3 full-factorial design is given in Table 6.56. Notice that any column multiplied by itself results in a column of +1's only. When a column consists of 1's only, it is called the *identity column* and denoted *I*. For example, A × A = *I*.

The estimated effects of the interactions can be easily calculated. See Table 6.56 for the rows associated with AB at the high and low levels. For example, the average response at the high level of the interaction AB (partition length and partition height) is

$$AB_{+1} = \frac{2.227 + 1.874 + 2.091 + 2.270 + 2.073 + 1.825 + 2.157 + 2.169}{8} = 2.08575$$

The average response at the low level of AB is

$$AB_{-1} = \frac{2.134 + 2.252 + 1.470 + 1.404 + 2.162 + 2.480 + 1.615 + 1.558}{8} = 1.884375$$

The estimated effect of the AB interaction is then

$$ee(AB) = AB_{+1} - AB_{-1} = 2.08575 - 1.884375 = 0.2014$$

Table 6.56 Main effect and interaction table for the ventilation factorial design.

Treatment	A	B	C	AB	AC	BC	ABC	y_v
1	–1	–1	–1	1	1	1	–1	2.227, 1.874
2	1	–1	–1	–1	–1	1	1	2.134, 2.252
3	–1	1	–1	–1	1	–1	1	1.470, 1.404
4	1	1	–1	1	–1	–1	–1	2.091, 2.270
5	–1	–1	1	1	–1	–1	1	2.073, 1.825
6	1	–1	1	–1	1	–1	–1	2.162, 2.480
7	–1	1	1	–1	–1	1	–1	1.615, 1.558
8	1	1	1	1	1	1	1	2.157, 2.169

The remaining interaction effects can be estimated similarly. The estimated effects for all the main effects and interactions are given in Table 6.57.

Interaction plots, discussed in the "Analysis of Variance" section of this chapter, are often useful for examining the two-factor interactions. The interaction plots for this example are given in Figures 6.44 through 6.46.

Based on the interaction plot in Figure 6.44, it is possible that a significant interaction exists between partition length (A) and partition height (B) because the lines are not parallel. Figure 6.45 indicates that there does not appear to be an interaction between partition length (A) and gap underneath (C). There appears to be a weak interaction between partition height (B) and gap underneath (C), which is indicated by the slightly nonparallel lines in Figure 6.46. However, the plots are somewhat subjective, and more statistically based evidence is needed.

Whether the effects are statistically significant can be determined using the ANOVA approach, a model-fitting approach, or both. The ANOVA approach will be looked at first.

In the ANOVA approach, sums of squares are calculated for each effect and the experimental error. The degree of freedom for factors with exactly two levels (−1, +1) is 1 (the number of levels minus 1 as with all factorial designs). The sums

Table 6.57 Estimated effects for the air quality example.

Factor	Estimated effect (*ee*)	Factor	Estimated effect (*ee*)
A	0.459	AC	0.016
B	−0.287	BC	0.026
C	0.040	ABC	−0.099
AB	0.201		

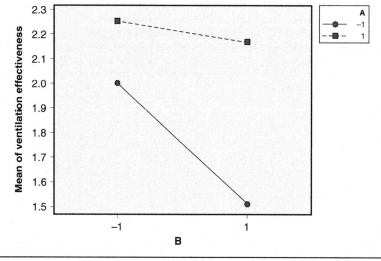

Figure 6.44 Interaction plot for partition length and partition height.

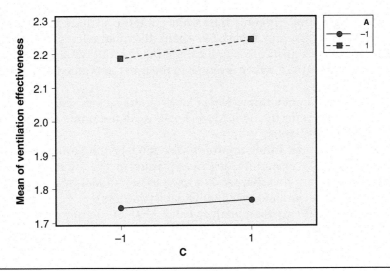

Figure 6.45 Interaction plot for partition length and gap underneath.

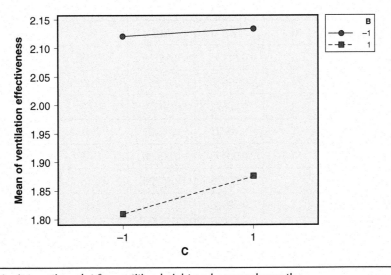

Figure 6.46 Interaction plot for partition height and gap underneath.

of squares for each factor can be found easily using the estimated effects and can be shown to be

$$SS_{Factor} = n2^{(k-2)}ee^2 \qquad (6.169)$$

where n is the number of replicates and k is the number of factors. Test statistics can be calculated for each factor and each interaction. All this information can be summarized in an ANOVA table. The ANOVA table for this example is given in Table 6.58, where degrees of freedom for error are $2^k(n-1)$ and total degrees of freedom are $n2^k - 1$. Based on the results of the ANOVA, it appears that factors A and B and the interaction AB are significant. This is evident by the small p-values for each of these terms. Based on these results, the analysis should be carried out again but with only the significant terms included. The results for the new analysis are given in Table 6.59. Again, the main effects of A and B and the interaction AB are statistically significant. From the ANOVA in Table 6.59 it is seen that $\hat{\sigma}^2 = MS_E = 0.01832$, which is less than the previous value using the full model (see Table 6.58).

The analyst can determine which levels of the factors will result in large values for ventilation effectiveness. More details on determining these levels are provided later in this chapter.

Next is the model-fitting approach. The model-fitting approach is simply the regression analysis procedure described earlier in the "Relationships Between Variables" section of this chapter. It is used to fit a model relating the dependent variable (response) and independent variables (factors).

Model fitting (regression analysis) and ANOVA are not necessarily separate approaches. An ANOVA is often reported when the regression approach is used

Table 6.58   ANOVA table for the ventilation example.

Source	df	SS	MS	F	p-value
A	1	0.84135	0.84135	39.48	0.000
B	1	0.32862	0.32862	15.42	0.004
C	1	0.00628	0.00628	0.29	0.602
AB	1	0.16221	0.16221	7.61	0.025
AC	1	0.00098	0.00098	0.05	0.836
BC	1	0.00278	0.00278	0.13	0.727
ABC	1	0.03930	0.03930	1.84	0.211
Error	8	0.17048	0.02131		
Total	15	1.55199			

Table 6.59   ANOVA table for the ventilation example, with only statistically significant terms.

Source	df	SS	MS	F	p-value
A	1	0.84135	0.84135	45.93	0.000
B	1	0.32862	0.32862	17.94	0.001
AB	1	0.16221	0.16221	8.86	0.012
Error	12	0.21982	0.01832		
Total	15	1.55199			

to study the effects of the factors and interactions on the response. A model relating the independent variables and dependent variable (response) can be given by

$$y = \beta_0 + \beta_1 x_1 + \beta_2 x_2 + \ldots + \beta_k x_k + \varepsilon$$

where y is the response of interest and $x_1, x_2, \ldots, x_k$ represent the independent variables. In factorial designs, the independent variables are the factors such as A, B, and C and the interactions among the factors AB, AC, BC, and ABC. To illustrate, let x_1 represent factor A, x_2 represent factor B, and so on. Note that the convention to let $x_1 x_2$ represent the AB interaction, for example, is used. The coefficients β_i on each term can be tested using t-tests, as done in the "Relationships Between Variables" section of this chapter. The null hypothesis of interest is H_0: $\beta_i = 0$ for all i. Results of the t-test for the air quality example are given in Table 6.60.

The "Effect" column displays the estimated effects for the main effects and interactions. From the p-values for the t-tests, it can again be concluded that partition length (A), partition height (B), and the interaction between the two factors (AB) are significant. The analysis should be rerun involving only the terms found significant. A model relating ventilation effectiveness to partition length, partition height, and the interaction can now be fit. The column labeled "Coef" provides the estimates of the coefficients in the regression model

$$\hat{y} = 1.9851 + 0.2293 x_1 - 0.1433 x_2 + 0.1007 x_1 x_2$$

where x_1 represents partition length, x_2 represents partition height, and $x_1 x_2$ represents the interaction between the two factors. It should also be noted that the coefficient estimates are one-half of the estimated effects. The fitted model above is in coded form. That is, if it is desired to make predictions for certain levels of the factors, one would use the notation (−1, 1) to plug into the equation. For example,

Table 6.60 t-tests for factors and interactions for the air quality example.

Term	Effect	Coef	SE Coef	t	p-value
Constant	—	1.9851	0.03649	54.39	0.000
A	0.4586	0.2293	0.03649	6.28	0.000
B	−0.2866	−0.1433	0.03649	−3.93	0.004
C	0.0396	0.0198	0.03649	0.54	0.602
AB	0.2014	0.1007	0.03649	2.76	0.025
AC	0.0156	0.0078	0.03649	0.21	0.836
BC	0.0264	0.0132	0.03649	0.36	0.727
ABC	−0.0991	−0.0496	0.03649	−1.36	0.211

If the objective is to predict the ventilation effectiveness for the low levels of A and B, then $x_1 = -1$ and $x_2 = -1$ in the fitted model:

$$\hat{y} = 1.9851 + 0.2293x_1 - 0.1433x_2 + 0.1007x_1x_2$$
$$= 1.9851 + 0.2293(-1) - 0.1433(-1) + 0.1007(-1)(-1)$$
$$= 2.0$$

The model can also be written in terms of the actual levels of the factors. It is recommended that the model fitting be done using a reliable statistical software package. The model using the actual levels can be shown to be

$$\hat{y} = 5.366 - 0.048A - 0.065B + 0.001AB$$

The predicted value when partition length and partition height are at their low levels is found by replacing A and B with the actual levels of the factors. For A at its low level (40) and B at its low level (60), the predicted value is

$$\hat{y} = 5.366 - 0.048A - 0.065B + 0.001AB$$
$$= 5.366 - 0.048(40) - 0.065(60) + 0.001(40)(60)$$
$$= 2.0$$

The difference between this estimate and the one from the model in coded units is strictly due to round-off error. Either model can be used to fit the data. In addition, the actual levels in this example are left as percentage values such as 40 and not converted to decimal form such as 0.40. This was only by choice. Using a statistical package, the lower level and upper level of partition length could be stated as 0.40 and 0.60, respectively, but in this case the choice was to use 40 and 60. The same main effects and interaction would still be found to be significant.

Once the model has been refined so that it contains only those terms that are statistically significant, the three assumptions of normality, independence, and constant variance should be investigated. If the order in which the treatments were carried out was not recorded, the independence assumption will be difficult to verify. Hopefully, by randomizing all 16 runs while all extraneous factors are held constant there is no significant problem with dependency. Again, it is desirable to actually be able to check this assumption.

Recall that the residuals are defined as $e_i = y_i - \hat{y}_i$, where the predicted values are found as shown previously. The 16 residuals can be calculated and analyzed through residual plots. The normal probability plot of the residuals is shown in Figure 6.47. The residuals appear to generally fall along a straight line, so the normality assumption does not appear to be violated. The residuals plotted against the significant factors are displayed in Figure 6.48 and Figure 6.49. There does not appear to be a problem with constant variance across the factor level because the vertical spread of the residuals for each factor level is approximately the same in both figures.

Now that the significant terms are identified and the necessary assumptions have been shown to be satisfied, the next step is to determine the optimal settings for the significant factors. In this example, a goal is to maximize the ventilation effectiveness. There are several ways to determine these settings. Two graphical methods will be discussed.

A useful graphical display of the fitted model is a contour plot. The contour plot for the fitted model in coded form is shown in Figure 6.50. A *contour plot*

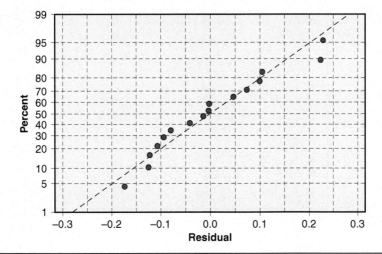

Figure 6.47 Normal probability plot of the residuals for the air quality example.

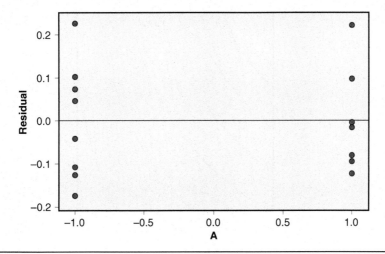

Figure 6.48 Residuals plotted against levels of factor A (partition length).

displays constant values of the predicted response (contours) over the range of the significant factors. Notice that the contour lines are curved; this is the result of a significant interaction between the two factors. For this example, it is clear that the lower right-hand corner of the contour plot displays higher values of ventilation effectiveness. If the goal is to maximize ventilation effectiveness, it appears that factor A (partition length) should be set at its high level (60%) while factor B (partition height) should be set at its low level (60%).

Main effects plots and interaction plots are also useful graphical displays of the results. Since the two main effects found significant are involved in a significant interaction, it is the interaction plot that should be examined. In fact, if the factors are involved in a significant interaction but only the main effects plots of these factors are examined, it is possible to choose less than optimal settings of the factors.

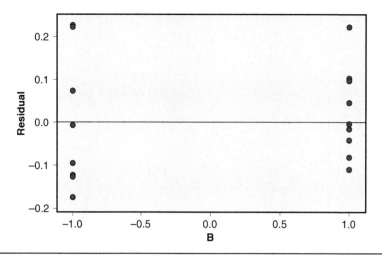

Figure 6.49 Residuals plotted against factor B (partition height).

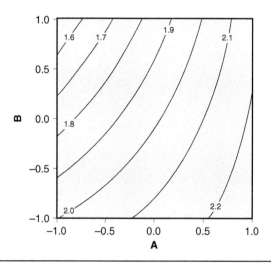

Figure 6.50 Contour plot for the air quality example.

Recall the interaction plot of factors A and B. The highest ventilation effectiveness occurs at the low level of B (partition height) and high level of A (partition length).

The reader is encouraged to consult Devore (2016); Montgomery and Runger (2013); Montgomery, Runger, and Hubele (2010); Vining and Kowalski (2011); and Myers, Montgomery, and Anderson-Cook (2016) for more details on methods for determining acceptable levels of the significant factors.

2^k Designs with a Single Replicate

Often it is not possible or economical to obtain more than a single replicate for a designed experiment (i.e., $n = 1$). When this is the case, it is not possible to test the significance of all the effects. There is no internal estimate of error since there is no replication. Specifically, there are no degrees of freedom left over for error to estimate the process variability σ^2. The total degrees of freedom for a design with a single replicate are $2^k - 1$. Each main effect and interaction is given one degree of freedom. For example, suppose that in the ventilation effectiveness example there is only one replicate. The total number of runs would be eight, and the total degrees of freedom would be $2^k - 1 = 8 - 1 = 7$. Furthermore, there are three main effects (A, B, and C) and four interactions (AB, AC, BC, and ABC). Since every effect has one degree of freedom, all of the degrees of freedom are used. There are no degrees of freedom for error. t-tests and the ANOVA method cannot be carried out.

To address this issue, several approaches can be employed. These approaches are often based on the *sparsity-of-effects principle*. That is, an assumption is made that some higher-order interactions are *negligible* (orders higher than two-factor interactions), and the system being investigated is believed to be dominated by the main effects and the low-order interactions. Under this assumption the degrees of freedom for the higher-order interactions are pooled into error degrees of freedom. Any sums of squares these interactions may have had get pooled into error sums of squares.

If there is any indication that one or more of the higher-order interactions are significant, then the pooling approach is not appropriate. A different method of analysis that is often used is examination of a normal probability plot of the estimated effects. This approach was suggested by Daniel (1959) and is available in most statistical software packages. Effects that are not significant (or are negligible) are said to be normally distributed with mean zero and variance σ^2. When plotted on a normal probability plot, estimated effects that are negligible will tend to fall along a straight line. The negligible effects are pooled into error and the degrees of freedom assigned to error.

EXAMPLE 6.75

Consider the air quality scenario presented earlier. Suppose that only one replicate was obtained for each of the eight runs. Data typical of this experiment are shown in Table 6.61.

Table 6.61 A single replicate of the air quality example.

Treatment	A	B	C	AB	AC	BC	ABC	y_v
1	−1	−1	−1	1	1	1	−1	2.135
2	1	−1	−1	−1	−1	1	1	2.015
3	−1	1	−1	−1	1	−1	1	1.520
4	1	1	−1	1	−1	−1	−1	1.999
5	−1	−1	1	1	−1	−1	1	1.998
6	1	−1	1	−1	1	−1	−1	2.103
7	−1	1	1	−1	−1	1	−1	1.624
8	1	1	1	1	1	1	1	2.135

Continued

The estimated effects for the main factors and all of the interactions can still be calculated using the formulas given previously. The estimated effects are then plotted on a normal probability plot (sometimes a standardized value of the effects will be plotted). The normal probability plot of the estimated effects is displayed in Figure 6.51.

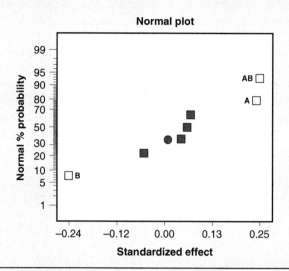

Figure 6.51 Normal probability plot of the estimated effects for the air quality example.

The normal probability plot of the effects (the effects have been "standardized") indicates that the main effects A and B and the interaction AB may be significant. An analysis could then be carried out on A, B, and AB. An analysis is conducted on the three terms with all other terms pooled into error. The results of t-tests on the effects are shown in Table 6.62.

Model fitting and residual analysis can be completed similarly to the case of more than one replicate. An analysis of variance can also be conducted with A, B, and the AB interaction as the only terms in the model.

Table 6.62 *t*-test results for the air quality example.

Term	Effect	Coef	SE Coef	*t*	*p*-value
Constant	—	1.9411	0.02953	65.72	0.000
A	0.2438	0.1219	0.02953	4.13	0.015
B	−0.2432	−0.1216	0.02953	−4.12	0.015
AB	0.2512	0.1256	0.02953	4.25	0.013

The methods and procedures outlined in this section can be used for any number of factors at two levels each. A drawback to the use of 2^k full-factorial designs is that the design size becomes prohibitively large as the number of factors increases. For example, even if there are only seven factors each at two levels, the number of experimental runs would be $2^7 = 128$, without replication. It is not unusual, especially in screening experiments, to have six, seven, or more factors of interest being investigated. In these cases, it is often very useful to run experiments involving fractions of the full-factorial design. These designs are commonly referred to as fractional factorial designs and are discussed in the next section.

Two-Level Fractional Factorial Experiments

> Construct two-level fractional factorial designs and apply computational and graphical methods to analyze the significance of results. (Analyze)
>
> Body of Knowledge VI.H.5

Fractional factorial designs are those where only a fraction of the full-factorial design is used. Fractional factorial designs are economic alternatives to the full-factorial designs as the number of factors increases. Screening experiments often involve a large number of factors, so full-factorials are not always practical or economical.

Half-fractions of a 2^k are designs that consist of half of the standard 2^k design. Half-fractions are usually denoted 2^{k-1} (one-half of the $2^k = 2^k/2 = 2^{k-1}$).

EXAMPLE 6.76

Consider an experiment with six factors each at two levels. A full-factorial design consists of $2^6 = 64$ combinations or runs. A full 2^6 experimental design is in many instances prohibitively large. However, 32 experimental runs may be more economical. In this case, one-half of the runs from the full 2^6 can be chosen. The resulting design is referred to as a 2^{6-1} design. Runs selected from the full-factorial are not chosen at random. More on this later in this section.

In some instances, a half-fraction may still be too large and impractical. It may be more economical to use designs that are one-fourth, or possibly one-eighth, the size of the full-factorial. The general notation for a fractional factorial design is denoted as 2^{k-p}, where $1/2^p$ represents the fraction of the full-factorial.

EXAMPLE 6.77

A screening experiment is going to be conducted involving 10 factors each at two levels. A full-factorial design with a single replicate would still require $2^{10} = 1024$ runs. The experimenters can afford to do no more than 40 runs initially for screening. A fraction of the full-factorial that could be used and still meet the size requirements would be a 2^{10-5} design, which would require only 32 experimental runs ($2^{10-5} = 2^5 = 32$).

When conducting an experiment with k factors, the interest is in not only the significance of each factor but also the interactions between the factors. If a full-factorial could be implemented, then all main effects of interest and all two-factor interactions are fully estimable. However, when employing fractional factorial designs, the design size is reduced, and not all interactions of interest may be estimable separately from main effects or other interactions. Some of the interactions and/or main effects may be confounded or aliased with one another, making it difficult to determine which factor or interaction is truly significant.

The identity column will be very useful in fractional factorial designs. If any column in the design is multiplied by the identity column, the result is the original column. For example, $A \times I = A$. The ABC interaction is a *generator* and would be used to generate the column for one of the main factors. ABC is often referred to as a *word*.

An important characteristic of fractional factorial designs is the defining relation. The *defining relation* is one that contains all possible "words" whose signs do not change in the experiment. For example, from Table 6.63 the interaction column ABC consists of all +1's. Therefore, ABC would be a word in the defining relation. Since it is the only column with the signs unchanged, it is the only word in the defining relation. In this problem, the defining relation would be $I = ABC$. All aliases are found through the defining relation. For example, the alias for factor A is

$$A \cdot I = A \cdot ABC = BC$$

Therefore, factor A is aliased with the BC interaction. The other aliases are found similarly:

$$B \cdot I = B \cdot ABC = AC$$

$$C \cdot I = C \cdot ABC = AB$$

EXAMPLE 6.78

A study is going to be conducted involving three factors each at two levels. Suppose there are funds to conduct four treatments and not the eight that would make up a full 2^3 factorial design. A half-fraction of the 2^3 design would seem like a natural choice and would be called a 2^{3-1} design. A 2^{3-1} design and all columns for the interactions are given in Table 6.63.

Table 6.63 Main effects and interactions table for a 2^{3-1} design.

Run	A	B	C	AB	AC	BC	ABC
1	–1	–1	1	1	–1	–1	1
2	1	–1	–1	–1	–1	1	1
3	–1	1	–1	–1	1	–1	1
4	1	1	1	1	1	1	1

Notice that the column for factor C and the column for the AB interaction are identical. It would be said that factor C is aliased or confounded with the AB interaction, that is, C = AB. Also notice in the table that the column for the ABC interaction contains only the high level of the interaction. It would be said that ABC is equal to the identity column (I = ABC).

The configuration in Table 6.63 guarantees that none of the main factors have identical columns (therefore they are not aliased or confounded with one another). But main effects are aliased with two-factor interactions. If it is believed that the AB interaction may be significant, then a different design (with more runs) would have to be used.

The 2^{3-1} design is said to be of resolution III. *Resolution III* designs are those where main effects are aliased with two-factor interactions. More on this later in this section.

Resolution IV or higher designs are desirable, since they guarantee that the main effects will be clear of (not aliased with) other main effects and two-factor interactions. The obvious drawback to resolution IV designs is that two-factor interactions are aliased with other two-factor interactions. Suppose one executes the 2^{4-1} design, analyze the results, and determine that all main effects and the two-factor interaction AB are found to be statistically significant. With resolution IV designs, it is unknown for sure that AB is truly significant or if the two-factor interaction it is aliased with (here AB = CD) is significant. There are methods for breaking these aliases that involve adding a subset of new experimental runs. See Box, Hunter, and Hunter (2005) or Montgomery (2017) for more details on breaking these aliases (also referred to as "de-aliasing").

EXAMPLE 6.79

A study is going to be conducted involving four factors each at two levels. Suppose there are funds to conduct eight treatments and not the 16 that would make up a full 2^4 factorial design. A half-fraction of the 2^4 design would seem like a natural choice. The half-fraction of the 2^4 is the 2^{4-1} design and would contain 2^3 = 8 runs. One possible fraction is displayed in Table 6.64.

Continued

Table 6.64 Half-fraction of a 2^4 factorial design.

Run	A	B	C	D
1	−1	−1	−1	−1
2	1	−1	−1	1
3	−1	1	−1	1
4	1	1	−1	−1
5	−1	−1	1	1
6	1	−1	1	−1
7	−1	1	1	−1
8	1	1	1	1

In this study a full 2^3 design was constructed for factors A, B, and C. Column D was generated from the three-factor interaction ABC, that is, D = ABC. In this example ABC is the generator and the defining relation is I = ABCD. This design is said to be of *resolution IV*. Resolution IV designs are those where main effects are aliased with three-factor interactions, and two-factor interactions are aliased with other two-factor interactions. Using the defining relation I = ABCD all of the aliases can be obtained. For the main effects:

$$A = BCD$$

$$B = ACD$$

$$C = ABD$$

$$D = ABC$$

For the two-factor interactions:

$$AB = AB \cdot I = AB \cdot ABCD = CD$$

$$AC = AC \cdot I = AC \cdot ABCD = BD$$

$$AD = AD \cdot I = AD \cdot ABCD = BC$$

The following are some of the properties for experimental design:

1. Resolution III designs have main effects confounded with two-factor interactions

2. Resolution IV designs have main effects confounded with three-factor interactions and two-factor interactions confounded with each other

3. Resolution V designs have two-factor interactions confounded with three-factor interactions only

---

EXAMPLE 6.80

Consider an experiment involving six factors where only 16 runs can be used. A full-factorial design in 16 runs is a 2^4 design. This design is referred to as a 2^{6-2} fractional factorial design.

A 2^4 full-factorial design could be constructed for four of the six factors, but the remaining two factor columns would have to be *generated*. Let A, B, C, D, E, and F represent the six factors. Suppose a full-factorial design is constructed for A, B, C, and D. It can be shown that two generators needed for E and F could be E = ABC and F = BCD. The resulting defining relation would be I = ABCE = BCDF = ADEF. The last "word," ADEF, is found by multiplying the two original generators, ABCE and BCDF (see Box, Hunter, and Hunter [2005] or Montgomery [2017] for more details). The resolution of this design is IV.

In general, the resolution of a design can always be determined from a complete defining relation. By definition, the resolution of a design is equal to the length of the smallest word in the defining relation. For example, consider a 2^{7-2} design with factors A, B, C, D, E, F, and G. The complete defining relation for this design using the generators F = ABCD and G = ABDE can be shown to be

$$I = ABCDF = ABDEG = CEFG$$

The length of the smallest word is four, so the design is of resolution IV.

There are numerous approaches and methods involving fractional factorial designs. The reader is encouraged to see Box, Hunter, and Hunter (2005); Ledolter and Swersey (2007); and Montgomery (2017) for complete details and examples of full and fractional factorial designs and their applications.

Chapter 7
Risk Management

RISK FUNDAMENTALS

Per ISO 31000:2018, risk is defined as:

"Effect of uncertainty on objectives"

It means that any potential effect due to any cause, which leads to deviation from expectation, is risk. In organizational enterprise terms, the effect of not meeting objectives is the consequence of risk. These objectives may be safety-related, performance-related, or related to failure reduction.

ISO 31000:2018 defines *risk management* as "coordinated activities to direct and control an organization with regard to risk." Quality and risk management are integral parts of any organization. Quality risk can be simply defined as the effect of uncertainty on quality objectives.

Products, services, systems, and organizations continually face a multitude of risks that may hamper their functioning and lead to a variety of failures. These risks may be operational, commercial, environmental, technological, financial, or even social and cultural. Quality, depending on the context, can interface with one or many of these areas. In today's world, management of risk is not only an aspiration but a necessity for a successful organization to maintain its profits and reputation.

> Define, describe, and apply risk terminology such as risk, risk management, severity, occurrence, detection, and risk-based thinking. (Analyze)
>
> **Body of Knowledge VII.A.1**

For additional definitions and descriptions of risk terminology, refer to the rest of this chapter, the "Reliability," "Safety," and "Hazard Assessment Tools" sections of Chapter 3, and the Glossary.

Risk Hierarchy

> Understand and apply various types of
> enterprise (strategic, software, business,
> regulatory, medical, audit), operational
> (supplier, supply chain, safety, project,
> manufacturing, operations, service, quality
> system), and product (design, process, use,
> safety) risk management. (Apply)
>
> **Body of Knowledge VII.A.2**

On a basic level, holistic organizational risk strategy is based on the following three pillars (see Figure 7.1):

1. Product-, process-, or service-level risk management

2. Enterprise risk management

3. Operational risk management

Product-, process-, or service-level risk management focuses on managing the day-to-day ground-level risks in terms of the specific end deliverables of the organization to its customers. *Enterprise risk management* is the coordinated approach for centralized management of risks and their cascade from the strategic mission level. *Operational risk management* is the coordination and control of all risky activities

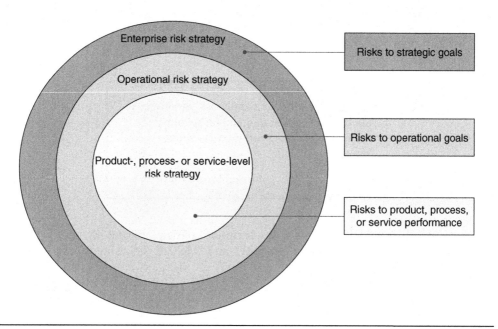

Figure 7.1   Risk management pillars.

of the system at the operational business unit or functional level to successfully achieve the predefined expected operational outputs and objectives.

The aim of all risk management activities is the following:

- Realistic assessment of the organizational objectives and path to their achievement

- Prevention of undesired outcomes

- Continuous improvement

- Value sustenance and value addition

Except for the focus on suppliers, most of the risk management activities within the purview of a quality engineer will fall within the "product, process or service" rung of risk management. Here, usually the focus is on risk reduction and risk avoidance. However, it is important to understand that there are various other levels within the organization where decisions relating to risks are potentially taken, even if they are not documented or identified as such. More importantly, these decisions will affect risk management at other levels.

Quality management emphasizes creating products and services with desirable characteristics that satisfy the customers need and, where possible, delight the customer. Quality risk management is focused on the evaluation of potential events that may impact the objective of achieving quality (in whichever way the word "quality" is defined by the organization). ISO 31000:2018 lists several risk management elements of a well-functioning system. It states that risk management should be:

a. **Integrated.** Risk management is an integral part of all organizational activities.

b. **Structured and comprehensive.** A structured and comprehensive approach to risk management contributes to consistent and comparable results.

c. **Customized.** The risk management framework and process are customized and proportionate to the organization's external and internal context related to its objectives.

d. **Inclusive.** Appropriate and timely involvement of stakeholders enables their knowledge, views and perceptions to be considered. This results in improved awareness and informed risk management.

e. **Dynamic.** Risks can emerge, change, or disappear as an organization's external and internal context changes. Risk management anticipates, detects, acknowledges, and responds to those changes and events in an appropriate and timely manner.

f. **Best available information.** The inputs to risk management are based on historical and current information, as well as on future expectations. Risk management explicitly takes into account any limitations and uncertainties associated with such information and expectations. Information should be timely, clear and available to relevant stakeholders.

g. **Human and cultural factors.** Human behavior and culture significantly influence all aspects of risk management at each level and stage.

h. **Continual improvement.** Risk management is continually improved through learning and experience.

The Process Approach

ISO 9001, the global standard for quality management focuses on the *process approach*. The *process approach* is an organizational strategy of managing and controlling a process and various interacting subprocesses within the organization. Any activity that has an input and output is a process. If a process is converting an input to an output, it means there are certain sets of sub-activities within the process that enable this change.

The realization of outputs of the process is contingent not only on the inputs but also on the actual "processing" step, whereby the activities convert the input to output. The success of this set of activities depends on overcoming resistance, barriers, or hurdles and monitoring their output and modulating parameters to ensure desired output.

A risk-based process approach focuses on anticipation of the resistance, barriers, and hurdles—and their preemptive mitigation to an acceptable level—such that the desired level of output is maintained (see Figure 7.2). Resistance, barriers, and hurdles can be hazards, hazardous situations, faults, or failures that hamper operability and negatively affect the process outputs. To control the process, one must understand its hazards and anticipate the outcome of the realization of hazards on the process outcome.

This can be accomplished by incorporating risk management by using the PDCA approach:

- Risk planning to ensure a systematic scheme or framework for realization of risk management activities

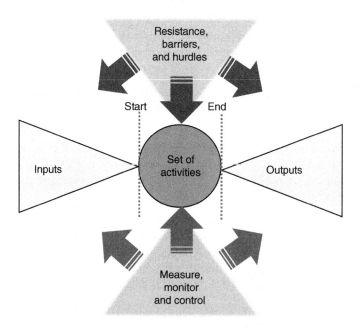

Figure 7.2 Risk-based process approach.

- Risk identification by analyzing the set of activities within the process and its critical points

- Risk analysis and prioritization to consider preventive mitigations or level of risk acceptance

- Risk monitoring and control to keep an eye out for pain points and emergent issues

Thus, risk management, PDCA, and the process approach are all part of quality management and feed into and from one another (see Figure 7.3).

Risk-based thinking is a *philosophy* and not a set of tools. Risk-based thinking will not automatically follow by simply creating a risk analysis document or a risk manager position within a company. Risk-based thinking must be tied and aligned to the culture of a company, such that its objectives, whether they be individual or organizational, incorporate this approach.

ISO 9001:2015 removed the earlier preventive action clause and introduced risk-based thinking, which, by nature, is preventive in spirit. By practicing risk mitigation by design in its true form, the designers of products, processes, and services adopt a risk-based mindset to preemptively mitigate subsystem-specific, foreseeable risks. This results in low-risk products, processes, and services, which in turn allow greater tolerances for operational and subsequently strategic risks. Safe products and processes may encourage positive risk taking by engendering confidence in top management, which in turn will lead them to strategically leverage strengths to capitalize on business opportunities. Thus, risk managed at one level allows for opportunities for value creation at other levels. Mismanaged risks will lead to reduction in value because risks may magnify as they shift through levels.

The essence of risk-based thinking is to inculcate a mindset that leads to foreseeing threats and opportunities and estimate them with an objective level of certainty such that targeted modifications and controls can be built into the design and surveillance of systems.

Figure 7.3 Confluence of risk management, process approach, and PDCA with quality management.

ISO 9001 and Risk Management

ISO 9001 is the international standard that specifies requirements for a quality management system (QMS). Organizations across the globe pursue certification to this standard, which is used to demonstrate commitment to quality along with consistent customer-focused value creation and sustenance in the products and services created or marketed by the organization.

In Clause 0.1, ISO 9001:2015 mentions that the standard employs the PDCA cycle and risk-based thinking. It goes on to say:[1]

> "Risk-based thinking enables an organization to determine the factors that could cause its processes and its quality management system to deviate from the planned results, to put in place preventive controls to minimize negative effects and to make maximum use of opportunities as they arise."

ISO 9001, in its 2015 version, also removed the section on preventive actions. The idea is that life-cycle risk identification, analysis, evaluation modification, and monitoring, which are outcomes of the risk management process, are, by nature, preventive. And this includes calibration, maintenance, human factors engineering, and other such quality systems activities, whether in the design, manufacturing, or distribution experience of products or processes.

The standard draws attention to the risks associated with organizational contexts and objectives. It specifically mentions the risks again in the following clauses:[2]

Clause 4.4.1

The organization shall determine the processes needed for the quality management system and their application throughout the organization, and shall address the risks and opportunities as determined with requirements of Clause 6.1.

Clause 5.1.1

The top management shall demonstrate leadership and commitment with respect to quality management system by promoting the use of process approach and risk-based thinking.

Clause 5.1.2

Top management shall demonstrate leadership and commitment with respect to customer focus by ensuring that the risks and opportunities that can affect conformity of products and services and the ability to enhance customer satisfaction are determined and addressed.

Clause 6.1

When planning for the quality management system, the organization shall consider the issues referred to in 4.1 and the requirements referred to in 4.2 and determine the risks and opportunities that need to be addressed to:

a) give assurance that the quality management system can achieve its intended result(s);

b) enhance desirable effects;

c) prevent, or reduce, undesired effects;

d) achieve improvement.

Clause 6.1.2

The organization shall plan:

a) actions to address these risks and opportunities;

b) how to:

1) integrate and implement the actions into its quality management system processes (see 4.4);

2) evaluate the effectiveness of these actions.

Actions taken to address risks and opportunities shall be proportionate to the potential impact on the conformity of products and services.

NOTE 1 Options to address risks can include avoiding risk, taking risk in order to pursue an opportunity, eliminating the risk source, changing the likelihood or consequences, sharing the risk, or retaining risk by informed decision.

NOTE 2 Opportunities can lead to the adoption of new practices, launching new products, opening new markets, addressing new clients, building partnerships, using new technology and other desirable and viable possibilities to address the organization's or its customers' needs.

Clause 9.1.3

The organization shall analyse and evaluate appropriate data and information arising from monitoring and measurement. The results of analysis shall be used to evaluate the effectiveness of actions taken to address risks and opportunities.

Clause 9.3.2

The management review shall be planned and carried out taking into consideration the effectiveness of actions taken to address risks and opportunities.

Clause 10.2.1

When a nonconformity occurs, including any arising from complaints, the organization shall update risks and opportunities determined during planning, if necessary.

The focus of these clauses is summarized in Table 7.1.

The standard expects the risk management to stem from the organizational leadership, which echoes the foundational message of enterprise risk management. On the other end of the spectrum, the standard also expects in Clause 5 that a risk affecting conformity of products must be identified and addressed,

Table 7.1   Risk focus of ISO 9001:2015 clauses.

Clause	Focus
4.4.1	QMS processes should address the upside and downside of risks
5.1.1	Enterprise support for risk-based thinking
5.1.2	Product- and service-level risk management
6.1	Ensuring outcomes of risk management through QMS planning
6.1.2	Integration of QMS and risk management; focus on the upside of risk as opportunity
9.1.3	Monitoring of risk outcomes
9.3.2	Risk oversight by leadership
10.2.1	Post-market / life-cycle risk management

thus covering the whole gamut of the hierarchical risk spectrum discussed earlier. Implicitly, one may interpret that the standard is asking the organization to implement risk management at various levels corresponding the quality activities that the level, which may include strategic, operational, and program, product, and service level via scope/context setting, risk assessments, risk evaluations, and risk treatment as shown in Figure 7.4.

It should be clarified that the standard is not explicitly asking for a formal risk management process, and that certification to this standard may not be contingent on such a requirement. It simply directs attention toward risk management—a set of practices and techniques that can significantly accelerate the accomplishment of the same goals as ISO 9001 in a structured fashion that:

1. Improves organizational governance

2. Establishes and sustains a continual improvement culture and framework

3. Enables evidence-based decision making

4. Improves customer satisfaction

5. Ensures consistent quality by accomplishing all of the above

Risk and Opportunity in ISO 9001

In section 0.3.3, the standard mentions:

"Opportunities can arise as a result of a situation favourable to achieving an intended result, for example, a set of circumstances that allows the organization to attract customers, develop new products and services, reduce waste or improve productivity. Actions to address opportunities can also include consideration of associated risks. Risk is the effect of uncertainty and any such uncertainty can have positive or negative effects. A positive

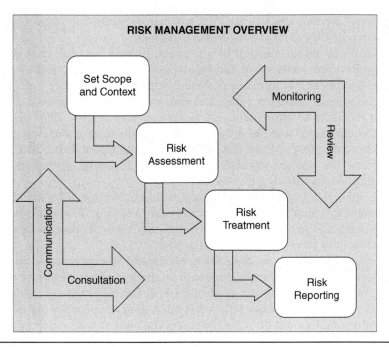

Figure 7.4 Risk management process overview.

deviation arising from a risk can provide an opportunity, but not all positive effects of risk result in opportunities."

The standard addresses the fact that positive deviations arise from risk and must be considered. Risks may not always have a negative outcome and is not always to be avoided. Opportunities more often arise at the enterprise and the operational levels of risk management as shown in Figure 7.1.

Risk Management Process

ISO 31000:2018 divides the risk assessment process into three distinct and sequential phases:

1. Risk identification
2. Risk analysis
3. Risk evaluation

At all levels of risk management, the risk assessment is an activating phase that is the crux of the risk management process and that will require significant resources.

The risk identification process, as discussed earlier, deals with finding, recognizing, and describing the risks. The risk analysis process deals with understanding the risk in terms of its constituent factors, which are usually probability and consequence. The risk evaluation process deals with comparing the results of the risk analysis process with the predefined criteria to check acceptability of the risk.

Figure 7.5 is from ISO 31000:2018, which clarifies the interaction of these three processes with other risk management processes.

Once a preliminary design of a product, process, service, or system is finalized, the first risk assessment can be started. It is important not to wait for the final design freeze but perform preliminary risk analysis early on. The closer to the requirements-gathering phase the risk analysis is performed, the easier and cheaper it will be to implement risk modification measures. The concept of risk-based thinking is to have not only the designers thinking about potential hazards and their consequences from the first stroke of their pencils but also the process owners and the finance, marketing, clinical, engineering, operations, and other relevant functions thinking the same way.

The goal is to inculcate risk-based thinking among all stakeholders from design stage 0, which starts with requirements gathering. To ensure successful risk management, risk professionals must holistically view the process at all times and not narrow their focus on one specific aspect.

A common mistake is detailed analysis and documentation in the design phase followed by change of ownership in the live production phase where the threads of risk monitoring and control are lost. The root cause of this problem is a defect in the risk management plan that often does not identify interfacing, cross-over responsibilities and does not empower the owners with correct guidance and

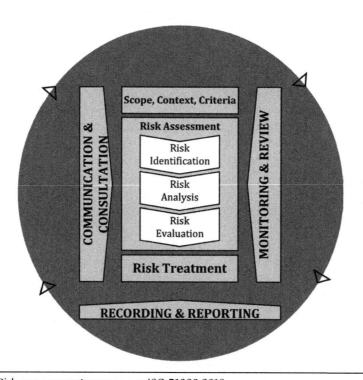

Figure 7.5   Risk management process per ISO 31000:2018.

Source: Reproduced by permission from ISO, *Risk Management–Risk Assessment Techniques*, 31010:2019, 2019, https://www.iso.org/standard/72140.html. International Organization for Standardization, Geneva, Switzerland.

information to realize efficient risk management practices. Such interfacing problems can also arise in the risk assessment process between the identification, analysis, and evaluation phases. Thus, sufficient clarity in terms of responsibilities and outputs of various stakeholders must be provided in the risk management plan.

Risk assessment, is only a subsystem of the whole risk management process, which includes *communication and consultation* with relevant stakeholders and *monitoring and review* of the identified and evaluated risks.

RISK PLANNING AND ASSESSMENT

Risk management should be integrated across an organization regardless of a centralized or decentralized approach. Depending on the company culture, risk can also be treated from a preventive (proactive) approach. Historically, risk management teams have taken such an approach. This preventive approach to risk expects risk events and is able to treat them, both as potential opportunities for success rather than failure, and to catch and control the deleterious risks when the necessary "reactive" mode is needed. This chapter will cover risk events from both the proactive and reactive standpoints. It is up to the individual or organization to decide which approach is best.

A decentralized risk management approach involves treating risk as a discipline or process. For example, every product or process could incorporate a risk assessment that is used to identify, analyze, evaluate, and monitor risk. Alternatively, risk could be managed from a single department that oversees all risk management activities across the organization.

Regardless of the way in which risk management is incorporated into an organization, it is important to have a plan or policy in place. Planning is crucial for setting ground rules and objectives, identifying key stakeholders, and selecting key methods for risk analysis. Every step of the risk management process should be decided and documented during the planning phase. This subject will be covered in detail in the following section.

Risk Management Plan

> Analyze and interpret a risk management plan and its components (objectives, risk criteria, stakeholder identification, and team member roles/responsibilities) to identify and prioritize risks. (Analyze)
>
> **Body of Knowledge VII.B.1**

Risk planning in an enterprise context is an important piece in priming the organization for risk management activities. Planning begins with a *gap analysis*, which is a comparison of the current state with the desired future state.

For tactical, process-specific risk management planning, the following questions could be asked to uncover gaps:

1. Are the current risk planning, risk identification, risk assessment, and risk treatment and response processes enough?

2. Are the current risk processes inclusive?

3. Do the current risk processes add value?

4. What is the risk competency of the organization?

5. What process steps could be improved, added, or deleted?

6. Are the resources enough for the present state?

7. What resources will be needed for the future state?

The tactical plan for risk management must be determined with the organizational risk maturity in mind. This plan should include common consent on the following:

1. Scope and context of the risk process in its entirety throughout the life cycle (inclusions and exclusions must be listed), especially on the following:

   a. Methods and sources of data gathering and risk identification

   b. Methods of risk assessment

   c. Criteria for risk evaluation and prioritization

   d. Criteria for risk acceptability

2. Resources (human and financial) and resource development

3. Team member and stakeholder roles and responsibilities

4. Reporting structure and cascading levels of decision making

5. Timelines of deliverables

6. Risk repository (or risk register) and its document controls

7. A general idea of the risk appetite and attitude

8. Risk review methods (periodic and ad hoc)

9. Risk escalation pathways

10. Contingencies

When conducting risk assessments for complex products, processes, and systems, a separate document must be prepared that defines how the activities of risk management will be conducted. This document is not generic, but it may be similar within similar product families. It specifically details the approaches, methodologies, and tools used.

The following should be considered for inclusion in the risk management plan:

1. **Stakeholder roles and responsibilities.** The clarity of responsibilities of the stakeholder is critical to ensure the success of risk management.

Stakeholder roles and responsibilities should be defined by phases
to ensure that there are no gaps in understanding of the roles in pre-
completion, post-completion, and sustenance phases. Some stakeholders
will be risk owners, while some will be approvers; others may just need
to be informed and kept in the loop. This clarification is important and
must be referred to in the plan. A RACI matrix maybe used for this
purpose. See Chapter 1 for additional information on the RACI diagram.

2. **Definition of probability and severity (impact).** Tabulation of different
   levels of probability and severity per a standard or customized scale
   is preferable. There are various scales available for qualitatively
   or quantitatively classifying probability and impact. Quantitative
   probability scalars may be derived from historical product data, or
   estimated for new products from data from similar products. (The terms
   probability, occurrence, and likelihood are often used interchangeably.)

3. **Risk acceptability criteria.** Such criteria should be clearly defined
   before a risk management project is approved. It can be visualized in
   the risk matrix of probability and severity in terms of color, often in
   2, 3, or 4 categories. For example, if there are two impact categories,
   perhaps they would be "Low" and "High," or "acceptable" and
   "unacceptable." If three categories, perhaps they would be "acceptable"
   ("Low"), "undesirable" ("Medium"), and "intolerable" ("High"). Some
   criteria have up to five levels, e.g., very low, low, medium, high, and
   very high. See Tables 7.3 and 7.4 for examples. This nomenclature is
   somewhat standard, and often used and understood. However, it is
   important to define the criteria words used, as well as any actions
   needed to accompany risk impact ratings such categories. One example
   might be: "To accept a product or process with one or more intolerable
   ratings, a senior medical officer (product) or senior manufacturing
   officer (process) must approve an explanatory risk-benefit document
   accompanying the risk analysis." Be sure further description as
   necessary for clarity is approved in the Risk Management File.

4. **Hazard categories.** Categorization essentially means grouping the risks.
   A hazard-based categorization lends itself to easy grouping in terms
   of expected failures and in terms of causes of failure. In the project
   management discipline, a risk breakdown structure is sometimes used
   to satisfy this criterion. In other sectors, product-, commodity-, or
   service-based groupings may be used.

5. **Budget including proposed cost reserves and approval chain for
   usage.** The monies needed to realize risk management activities must be
   properly budgeted to ensure timely and effective responses. An estimate
   must be made early in the process and approved by the management
   such that an acceptable cost baseline is established. As the risk
   management process progresses, realistic and practical changes must be
   made to this estimate. For the foreseeable risks for which no mitigations
   have been performed and which may prove to be a financial burden
   if they are realized, a contingency reserve must be set. The trigger and
   approval chain for such reserves must be established in the plan.

6. **Stakeholder tolerances.** Stakeholder tolerances are important to assess since the risk responses will be based on risk thresholds, which, in large part, are essentially stakeholder risk thresholds. More risk means more opportunity but may also mean more chances of loss (financial or reputational). Depending on the industry, these thresholds may differ, but they also may change based on maturity and outlook of the organization or company. Therefore, a note should be made in the plan regarding the set thresholds since they become the early baseline for risk mitigations and responses.

7. **Frequency of tracking, reporting, and review.** Risk management is an iterative process and relies on effective feedback and feedforward loops of information and data sharing. The data must be analyzed, and usable information must be disseminated to risk owners and other stakeholders. The frequency of review meetings and templates for tracking must be decided in the plan.

In addition, depending on the organization's need, the plan should consider methods for determining aggregate risks (at various hierarchical levels of risk management) and measures to verify the effectiveness of implementation of risk treatments and modifications.

The following is a sample risk management plan:

1. Description of the system

    a. Objectives/intended use/characteristics

    b. Dependencies

    c. Stakeholder analysis

2. Risk management scope and objectives

    a. Prioritization of objectives/characteristics

    b. Scales for probability and severity

    c. Definition of risk and risk trigger conditions

3. Risk management methodology

    a. Interface with organizational methods of risk management

    b. Risk taxonomy and metalanguage

    c. Key deliverables

4. Risk management organization

    a. Roles and responsibilities

    b. Rules of escalation

    c. Budget

    d. Schedule

    e. Reporting

   5. Tools and techniques

       a. Description of tools and techniques for risk identification

       b. Description of tools and techniques for risk analysis

       c. Description of tools and techniques for risk control and monitoring

       d. Documentation and storage requirements

       e. System requirements

   6. Communications

       a. Dissemination of information

       b. Pre-launch reporting

       c. Post-market/post-launch surveillance (early and steady-state)

       d. Audience and nature of communication

   7. Criteria for success

Risk Assessment

> Apply categorization methods and evaluation tools to assess risk such as failure mode and effects analysis. Identify and apply evaluation metrics including the use of risk matrices, risk priority numbers, and acceptability criteria. (Analyze)
>
> **Body of Knowledge VII.B.2**

There are three main components of risk assessment: identification, analysis, and evaluation. These components collectively help establish a form of risk syntax or statements. A generic form of risk syntax is the following:

Because of <defined cause>, <an uncertain event> may occur, which would lead to <effect on the objective>.

Once a risk has been identified and analyzed, expected outcomes can be postulated, followed by events that may occur as a result. In this section, tools are provided that will help in the process of creating risk statements and outcomes.

Risk Identification

Risk identification is the process of determining which risks affect the end goals, intended uses, or objectives. This determination in the risk-identification phase involves finding, defining, and documenting these risks.

The purpose of risk identification is to identify all possible risks, whether current risks, possible future risks, risks that are not currently under the organization's control, or risks that may occur due to results of an accumulation of factors or steps in the process.

The questions to be answered during the risk identification process are as follows:

- What could affect us?

- What could go wrong?

To answer these questions, the risks must be broken down into specific and sensible individual line items.

The key to the success of risk management lies here at this first step: *What level of specificity do you use to document the risk?* A simple technique for this is to follow the *generic risk syntax:*

Because of <defined cause>, <an uncertain event> may occur, which would lead to <effect on the objective>.

The cause-and-effect loop must be clarified for the risk line to lend itself to proper usage. Another idea is to organize the cause, hazardous situation, effect, and classification (threat, failure, or opportunity) in separate columns as in Table 7.2.

Neutral terms have been used here to emphasize that there can be positive and negative aspects of risk. In certain industries, like medical devices, a risk may be specifically categorized in technical terms as *failure mode or hazardous situation* and a negative effect may be a *harm.*

As greater details are populated during the risk-identification exercise, it must be noted that some causes, effects, and risks will show up again and again. This is because one risk or failure may have more than one cause and, upon occurrence, could have more than one effect.

Risk Analysis

The risk analysis phase entails qualitative, semiquantitative, or quantitative impact analysis of the risks identified in the risk identification phase. It is the second part of the overall risk assessment process of identification, analysis, and evaluation.

ISO 31000:2018 defines the purpose of the risk analysis phase as follows:[3]

"To comprehend the nature of risk and its characteristics including, where appropriate, the level of risk."

Table 7.2. Tabular organization of cause, hazardous situation, effect, classification and risk line item.

Hazard	Cause	Hazardous Situation	Effect	Classification	Risk
Icy road	Worn tires	Driving car on icy roads	Crash	Threat	Due to driving with worn tires on icy roads, the car can slip and crash

This phase requires an understanding of the nature of the risk such that it can be profiled in terms of probability and consequence (severity or magnitude) and eventually be assigned a risk level. Each and every risk must undergo this process. Risk evaluation that follows the analysis phase uses this analyzed nature of risk and considers it in the context of the organization's willingness to accept the risk.

Risk analysis consists of two main things:

1. Defining the risk in usable terms—this usually means in terms of probability and consequence

2. Measuring the risk for relative comparison

The analysis is carried out by resolving the risk into its constituents of likelihood and consequence. Consequence analysis and assessment of likelihood by assignation of probability or occurrence rating together comprises the risk analysis phase as shown in Figure 7.6.

While consequence analysis ensures accurate assignation of the impact of the risk, and probability assessment ensures assignation of a probabilistic occurrence value, both operations cannot be conducted in isolation. Sometimes the identified risks may lead to one or multiple consequences. The probabilities of these consequences will mostly be different and must be assessed accordingly.

Look back at the risk syntax used in the risk identification phase (shown in Figure 7.7):

Due to <cause>, <risk> can occur, which will lead to <effect>.

Depending on the context within which the organization, system, or product or service operates, various root causes may give rise to various conditions. These conditions may mature into multiple effects or consequences with differing probabilities, thus giving rise to risks. While probability and consequence have

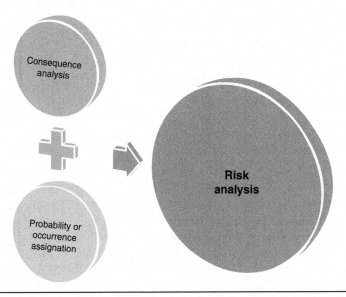

Figure 7.6 Consequence analysis and occurrence assignment comprise risk analysis.

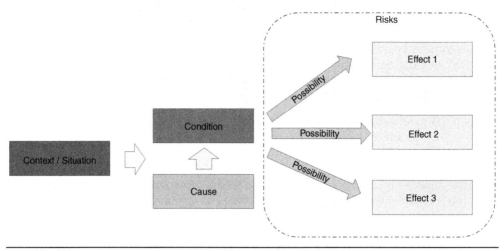

Figure 7.7   Usage of risk metalanguage.

been considered, risk analysis must also consider the complexity of the situation at hand and interconnectivity of risk factors.

The aim of the risk analysis phase is the following:

> To analyze the nature of risk by breaking it down into its constituent hazards, consequences, and probabilities and comparing them with an objective baseline in absolute or relative terms.

Risk Evaluation

The process of risk evaluation is performed by comparing the estimated risk against the baseline criteria initially set to determine the risk acceptability. It is the exercise of assessing action for estimated risks based on their respective significance to the objectives in terms of concerned product, service, process, or business.

ISO 31000:2018 mentions the following:

> "Risk evaluation involves comparing the results of the risk analysis with the established risk criteria to determine where additional action is required. This can lead to a decision to:
>
> — do nothing further;
> — consider risk treatment options;
> — undertake further analysis to better understand the risk;
> — maintain existing controls;
> — reconsider objectives."

The risk is estimated by identifying the severity of the consequence of the event and the probability of occurrence of the consequence. The most critical aspect of risk evaluation is the risk acceptability criteria. It is required to have the risk acceptability criteria before starting the risk management process. The criteria used to determine whether the risk is acceptable must be defined based on the organizational willingness to accept the level of risk. This is informed by the risk tolerance and risk appetite, which should have a baseline in the true product, process, and business risk to all stakeholders.

There are different methods followed in determining the acceptability criteria based on the organizational context, nature of risks, external environment, and known stakeholder concerns. The willingness to accept the risk for a thermometer is very different from that for a life-sustaining device. The risk of death or injury will not be accepted for the use of a thermometer, but a risk of injury or burn from a life-sustaining device may be accepted if it makes a difference between life and death.

Regulations or standards also could determine the level of acceptability for each product type. It is a good practice to document the rationale for the selection of a particular acceptance criteria. The manufacturer either could choose single acceptance criteria for all products or could have different criteria for different products based on the unique context and environment of operation.

After each risk is determined (i.e., the occurrence/probability) and the consequence is estimated, the level of the risk is charted on the risk matrix. This level is now compared with the earlier set value of the acceptability criteria and checked for acceptability based on RPN, risk levels, or other methods. If the risk is not acceptable, risk reduction is in order by applying appropriate risk control or mitigation measures—the lower the risk appetite, the more the controls.

In the risk matrix, the color changes correspond to a heat map, which usually shows the varying risk levels. In Table 7.3, three levels of risk (low, medium, high) are shown. The number of impact levels, number of probability levels, demarcation between risk levels, and the number of risk levels are the prerogative of the organization and are dependent on the context within which the organization operates, risk appetite, and available resources for risk management activities.

The levels of risk can be seen as levels of tolerance or in terms of acceptability or non-acceptability. These risk levels are sometimes known as risk criticality levels. Commonly, three levels of low, medium, and high are used, but five-level criticality scales of very low, low, medium, high, and very high and similar classifications are also acceptable. The important thing to remember is that the criticality levels must provide the right balance between grading of the risks according to their magnitude and separating them out in terms of acceptability. Thus, decision rules must be defined for each risk level.

Table 7.3 A 5x5 risk matrix.

		Impact level				
		Level 1	Level 2	Level 3	Level 4	Level 5
Probability level	Level 5	Medium	Medium	High	High	High
	Level 4	Low	Medium	High	High	High
	Level 3	Low	Medium	Medium	High	High
	Level 2	Low	Low	Medium	Medium	Medium
	Level 1	Low	Low	Low	Low	Low

Decision rules decide which levels of risk are acceptable and which levels are not. This is where the key to the heat map is decided. In the matrix shown above, the rules in Table 7.4 may apply.

The decision rules may also choose to use a risk index number to decide on the level of criticality. The risk index number is a risk index compiled using a scoring approach with the logic shown below:

Risk index number = Probability level × Impact level

The levels of probability and severity of impact are graded on a linear or weighted ordinal scale. In either case, an increasing number can be used to denote increasing magnitude. In Table 7.5 the ordinal probability level is multiplied by the impact level to get a risk index number.

Now, based on the risk index number, the decisions shown in Table 7.6 or 7.7 may be chosen to apply.

The type of risk matrix and the decision rules to be used should be defined in the risk management plan. ISO 31010:2019 provides the following caveat:

> "If the highest consequence is deemed to be tolerable at some low likelihood then the lowest step on the likelihood scale should represent an acceptable likelihood for the highest defined consequence (otherwise all activities with the highest consequence are defined as intolerable and cannot be made tolerable)."

Table 7.4 Risk levels and decision rules.

Risk criticality level	Decision rule
High	Generally unacceptable—needs concurrence of top management
Medium	Reduce as low as reasonably practicable (ALARP) or for medical devices, as far as possible (AFAP)
Low	Acceptable risk—monitor and trend

Table 7.5 Risk matrix populated using probability x impact.

		Severity level				
		Grade I (1)	Grade II (2)	Grade III (3)	Grade IV (4)	Grade V (5)
Probability level	Frequent (5)	5	10	15	20	25
	Probable (4)	4	8	12	16	20
	Occasional (3)	3	6	9	12	15
	Remote (2)	2	4	6	8	10
	Improbable (1)	1	2	3	4	5

Table 7.6 Risk criticality levels and risk index number.

Risk criticality level	Risk index number	Decision rule
High	>10	Unacceptable risk (intolerable)—needs concurrence of top management
Medium	From 5 to 10	Tolerable risk but reduce/mitigate to ALARP or AFAP
Low	Less than 5	Acceptable risk (tolerable)—monitor and trend

Table 7.7 Risk matrix coded for risk levels by acceptability decisions.

		Severity level				
		Grade I (1)	Grade II (2)	Grade III (3)	Grade IV (4)	Grade V (5)
Probability level	Frequent (5)	Medium	Medium	High	High	High
	Probable (4)	Low	Medium	High	High	High
	Occasional (3)	Low	Medium	Medium	High	High
	Remote (2)	Low	Low	Medium	Medium	Medium
	Improbable (1)	Low	Low	Low	Low	Low

This means that one must not shun high-risk pathways but instead aim to reduce the risk as much as possible to an acceptable level. The lowest probability level must correspond to the acceptability level for the highest consequence.

The choice of risk matrix must be governed by its purpose, which is assessment of a risk by assignation of a risk criticality level or rating to all identified risks to check the level of acceptability. Here, risks are being "bucketed" for prioritization based on their similar nature.

The goals of using a risk matrix are the following:

1. To have a consistent analysis method for risks

2. To have a method that assigns risk levels based on the same characteristics of probability and consequence for all risks

3. To be a visual tool for risk criticality estimation

4. To be a comparative tool to rank risks that have the most and least influence on objectives

5. To be a tool to assess changes in risk levels or ratings as the consequence or probability of a risk changes through the life cycle.

6. To aid in risk prioritization

Table 7.8 Action priority rating levels.

Action Priority (AP) for DFMEA and PFMEA							
Action Priority is based on combinations of Severity, Occurrence, and Detection ratings in order to prioritize actions for risk reduction							Blank until filled in by user
Effect	**S**	**Prediction of Failure Cause Occurring**	**O**	**Ability to Detect**	**D**	**ACTION PRIORITY (AP)**	**Comments**
Product or Plant Effect Very High	9-10	Very high	8-10	Low-Very-low	7-10	H	
				Moderate	5-6	H	
				High	2-4	H	
				Very high	1	H	
		High	6-7	Low-Very-low	7-10	H	
				Moderate	5-6	H	
				High	2-4	H	
				Very high	1	H	
		Moderate	4-5	Low-Very-low	7-10	H	
				Moderate	5-6	H	
				High	2-4	H	
				Very high	1	M	
		Low	2-3	Low-Very-low	7-10	H	
				Moderate	5-6	M	
				High	2-4	L	
				Very high	1	L	
		Very low	1	Very high – Very low	1-10	L	
Product or Plant Effect High	7-8	Very high	8-10	Low-Very-low	7-10	H	
				Moderate	5-6	H	
				High	2-4	H	
				Very high	1	H	
		High	6-7	Low-Very-low	7-10	H	
				Moderate	5-6	H	
				High	2-4	H	
				Very high	1	M	

Table 7.8 Action priority rating levels. (Continued)

Action Priority (AP) for DFMEA and PFMEA							
Action Priority is based on combinations of Severity, Occurrence, and Detection ratings in order to prioritize actions for risk reduction							Blank until filled in by user
Effect	S	Prediction of Failure Cause Occurring	O	Ability to Detect	D	ACTION PRIORITY (AP)	Comments
		Moderate	4-5	Low-Very-low	7-10	H	
				Moderate	5-6	M	
				High	2-4	M	
				Very high	1	M	
		Low	2-3	Low-Very-low	7-10	M	
				Moderate	5-6	M	
				High	2-4	L	
				Very high	1	L	
		Very low	1	Very high – Very low	1-10	L	
Product of Plant Effect Moderate	4-6	Very high	8-10	Low-Very-low	7-10	H	
				Moderate	5-6	H	
				High	2-4	M	
				Very high	1	M	
		High	6-7	Low-Very-low	7-10	M	
				Moderate	5-6	M	
				High	2-4	M	
				Very high	1	L	
		Moderate	4-5	Low-Very-low	7-10	M	
				Moderate	5-6	L	
				High	2-4	L	
				Very high	1	L	
		Low	2-3	Low-Very-low	7-10	L	
				Moderate	5-6	L	
				High	2-4	L	
				Very high	1	L	

(continued)

Table 7.8 Action priority rating levels. (Continued)

Action Priority (AP) for DFMEA and PFMEA							
Action Priority is based on combinations of Severity, Occurrence, and Detection ratings in order to prioritize actions for risk reduction							Blank until filled in by user
Effect	**S**	**Prediction of Failure Cause Occurring**	**O**	**Ability to Detect**	**D**	**ACTION PRIORITY (AP)**	**Comments**
		Very low	1	Very high – Very low	1-10	L	
Product or Plant Effect Low	2-3	Very high	8-10	Low-Very-low	7-10	M	
				Moderate	5-6	M	
				High	2-4	L	
				Very high	1	L	
		High	6-7	Low-Very-low	7-10	L	
				Moderate	5-6	L	
				High	2-4	L	
				Very high	1	L	
		Moderate	4-5	Low-Very-low	7-10	L	
				Moderate	5-6	L	
				High	2-4	L	
				Very high	1	L	
		Low	2-3	Low-Very-low	7-10	L	
				Moderate	5-6	L	
				High	2-4	L	
				Very high	1	L	
		Very low	1	Very high – Very low	1-10	L	
No discernable effect	1	Very low – Very high	1-10	Very high – Very low	1-10	L	

The decision for risk acceptability is always the organization's prerogative. Some guidance in the right direction can be obtained by reviewing historically similar risks (especially similar risks for similar products/processes/service/businesses), acceptable risk in the state of art, yardstick or generally accepted gold standard product (process or service), international standards, regulatory guidance, scientific evidence, industry benchmarking, and best practices.

Risk acceptability with a focus on prevention can also employ usage of Action Priority ratings as detailed in AIAG VDA FMEA 2019 handbook (see Table 7.8 below). Action Priority ratings can help guide the mitigation actions focused on severity and occurrence scales (similar to the Risk Matrix approach) and also display the detection rating without obfuscating the final risk level.

Stakeholder communication is the key to defining risk acceptability criteria as stakeholder risk appetites majorly feed into the organizational risk appetite, which largely dictates the level of acceptability along with the points listed earlier. There are four major outcomes of the risk evaluation process, as shown in Figure 7.8 and discussed below.

1. Risk acceptance for low risks or for risks for which the organization has a high tolerance.

2. Further analysis for medium-, high-, or medium-high-level risks needing greater analytical understanding before their magnitude and resulting impact can be evaluated.

3. Risk mitigation is the most common operation performed on all risks that are not acceptable in this stage. Here begins the assessment of risk treatments.

4. In case of certain high or very high risks in which it is amply clear without any detailed analysis that the risk control or mitigation will be fruitless or too straining, the organization must reassess the need for the objective that is the cause of the risk. These are the cases where cost-benefit to risk-benefit analysis may show a negative outlook. Top management is usually involved in the decision to reconsider already set objectives.

Now that the risk has been evaluated against baseline criteria and candidates for risk review have been prioritized, these risks undergo a risk treatment, which is detailed in the next section.

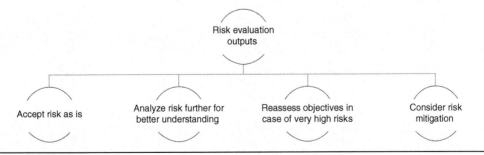

Figure 7.8 Outcomes of the risk evaluation process.

RISK TREATMENT, CONTROL, AND MONITORING

Identification and Documentation

> Identify risks, gaps, and controls and
> document with tools such as a risk register.
> (Analyze)
>
> Body of Knowledge VII.C.1

The storage of risk information in a secure and retrievable location is critical to the success of risk management. The vehicle for risk repository should be addressed in the planning phase itself to suit the methods of and the tools for risk assessments. This repository can be a physical paper or virtual document, but it must be a revision-controlled manuscript that is able to be continually updated and approved. These documents are sometimes referred to as risk registers, risk tables, or hazard logs.

The documentation starts in the risk identification phase, where the list of identified hazards or risks or failure modes is created. This is usually the first column of the risk register or table. Since this is the first building block of the risk documentation process, (although usually not required) it may be of value to identify, along with the risk, certain accompanying information, such as the "date identified," "identified by," "current oversight," "ownership," and so on. Along with the identification of the risk, the expected outcome of the risk must also be documented in words.

With identification of the risk, the brainstorming team can be challenged with identification of the cause of the identified risk. Fault trees, discussed in Chapter 5, are valuable for such cause identification and documentation. This is important information and must be documented for two reasons:

1. There might be disagreement among stakeholders regarding the root cause in later stages of risk management

2. This information is critical for risk modification/risk treatment

Then, the information regarding the risk assessment itself in terms of occurrence and impact should be documented. The expected outcome of the risk in the risk identification stage can be used to judge the impact of the risk. Specifically, the results of risk analysis, evaluation, and proposed controls should be documented in separate columns. As required, the risk levels (and accompanying priorities) must be documented as well.

The resulting modification of the risks, each by line item, should be identified and documented for every identified risk. The risk response action should be documented next to the modification.

Finally, the owner of the risk (and the associated response) should be identified and documented for future reference. There must be one more column to document the actual outcome or effect of the risk upon realization for future assessment purposes.

Thus, a simple risk repository should contain the following:

1. List of risks, failure modes, or hazards (and expected outcomes)
2. Causes of risks
3. Probability of occurrence
4. Impact or severity or consequence
5. Priority or risk levels
6. Risk response
7. Risk owner
8. Actual outcome, if and when available

It is always useful to document the reassessment of risk after risk modification in terms of new modified probability, occurrence, and risk level. Separate columns can be added for this activity.

Specific tools like FMEA, hazard analysis and critical control points (HACCP), and hazard and operability study (HAZOP) have a risk register inherent in their respective worksheets.

To conclude, it is important to have a documented and centralized risk repository to ensure the following:

1. Agreed-upon risks, responses, and owners are documented
2. The documentation is readily available to all stakeholders
3. The documentation can be referred to in case of disagreements
4. The documentation can be referenced to review modifications and associated actions
5. New emergent risks can be documented and assessed as needed
6. To add to body of knowledge of organization risk management for reference in the future

While the risk repository can be physical or virtual, it is important to ensure Good Documentation Practices (GDP) in the following regards:

1. The document is easily retrievable with properly defined protocols for access
2. The document has appropriate change-control precautions and safeguards in place
3. Approval authority in case of changes is identified in the risk management plan along with method of electronic or physical signatures
4. A document with built-in calculations (e.g., MS Excel sheet) has its calculations validated during design
5. The document is revision controlled with revision history available to relevant users

Risk Management System Evaluation

> Apply auditing techniques and testing of controls to evaluate a risk management system. (Apply)
>
> **Body of Knowledge VII.C.2**

Risk auditing is performed to verify that the known sources of risk are under control. Risk auditing is also often called risk monitoring. Audits are used to verify that risk treatment and mitigation plans are effective. They can also be helpful in identifying new risks.

A common method of verification is to examine current documents and records. This emphasizes the fact that risk management is an ongoing process; documentation resulting from methods such as an FMEA must be continuously maintained and updated as the process and/or treatment plans change. Another way to verify how risks are being controlled is by observing the process in person, interviewing subjects, or testing the process or product to ensure the appropriate mitigation plans are in place (Russell 2013). Goals when testing the process or product include ensuring that risk assessment results match or mirror the actual results. Early feedback can occur if aggressive "Post-Market Surveillance" (PMS) is employed to "pull" early field product or process results into analysis. For product PMS, this can be ensured when those give "beta" or few early distributed products are given to select "thought leaders" to use or review with mandatory feedback required to pull product or process use information into analysis for ease of use, product problems, recommendations, etc. This yields expedient assurance that actual results mirror pre-release risk assessment results.

In addition, ISO 31000:2018, Risk management—principles and guidelines, is an international standard on risk management. While organizations cannot be certified under this standard, it does provide guidance on internal and external audit programs.

When performing risk-based audits, it is recommended to audit both for compliance and effectiveness wherein improvement opportunities can be identified for your organization. An example of a risk-based audit schedule would include a) changes to or new customer requirements, b) supplier issues, c) technology, d) new or revised regulatory requirements, e) process changes, f) risk metrics properly acquired and analyzed, and g) design changes. Note: When performing a risk-based audit on design controls, it is important to ensure the risk is mitigated as early on in the design and development phase as possible. This as well as risk re-assessment triggers should be clearly defined.

As stated above regarding FMEA's being continuously maintained and updated, it is also important to review in detail the content of the FMEA to ensure it aligns with the requirements stated ISO 31000:2018, Risk management—principles and guidelines or in the case of Medical Devices, ISO 14971:2019, Application of Risk Management to Medical Devices. The completion of a FMEA alone does not necessarily ensure compliance.

Refer to Chapter 2 for more information on auditing.

Risk Treatment Strategies

> Understand and apply risk treatment
> strategies, such as avoid, mitigate, transfer,
> and accept. (Analyze)
>
> **Body of Knowledge VII.C.3**

The aim of risk treatment or risk modification is to determine a set of actions to be applied to the evaluated and prioritized risks. This will ensure that the organizational objectives are successfully achieved by attempting to change the existing risk profile or exposure. Since risk has already been characterized in terms of impact and probability, risk treatment involves the following techniques for typical risks, commonly known as threats or negative risks:

1. Reduction in the probability of occurrence

2. Reduction in the magnitude of impact

3. A decrease in the liability from risk realization

4. Elimination of probability of occurrence (usually occurring only with new design)

The first two measures are risk mitigation measures whereby response planning is conducted to ensure a decrease in risk exposure. Risk mitigation is defined as a reduction in the risk level to an acceptable limit. It involves taking certain actions that result in system change that allows the reduction of impact or occurrence.

The third measure falls under the category of risk transfer. Risk transfer means taking steps to transfer all or part of the impact of the risk outside the organization such that when the risk is realized, the fallout or at least a part of it (commercial, financial, etc.) is absorbed by another party.

The fourth measure falls under the category of risk avoidance. Risk avoidance means taking steps to ensure that the probability of occurrence of the risk is zero. This usually involves a major foundational change (such as a design change completely eliminating the threat) and either significantly more resources for realization of the objective or abandonment of a specific objective. Avoidance is recommended when either the risk exposure is too large for the organization to sustain, and an impact will likely cripple the organization, or the risk attitude is too averse.

If none of the above are chosen, then the risk is accepted as-is without any reduction. This is often the case with low-level risks. Risks can be accepted in two ways:

1. Passive acceptance: a reactive approach with no contingency planning. As the risk materializes, the response is decided ad hoc

2. Active acceptance: a proactive approach where risk control measures are thought out as part of the treatment and control plan. It involves

anticipating the risk and preparing for the contingency to minimize negative risk impact.

In case the mitigative efforts for a high-level risk are too resource-consuming, a decision may still be made to accept the risk. In such cases, the acceptance should always be supported by a strong contingency plan. In many cases, this decision rests with the leadership since the impact and exposure of a high-priority risk are usually significant.

Figure 7.9 shows the potential risk responses to the risk of getting into an accident while driving in the snow to pick up groceries.

For positive risks or opportunities, the following avenues are available for risk treatment:

1. Increasing the probability of occurrence

2. Increasing the magnitude of impact

3. Eliminating the probability of nonoccurrence

4. Sharing ownership of risk to ensure realization of maximum benefit

The first two measures fall under risk enhancement. The organization is using a dedicated strategy to ensure that the possibility of a positive impact is as high as possible. In doing so, the exposure to risk is increased in an attempt to affect the realization of the positive event.

The third measure talks about risk exploitation. This means that every measure is taken to ensure that the positive risk is realized. Risk exploitation is the opposite of risk avoidance and means that the organizational strategy is set such that the risk is realized 100%.

There are two kinds of risk exploitation:

1. Direct exploitation creates the system structure specifically to ensure realization of opportunity. This may include specific design and process

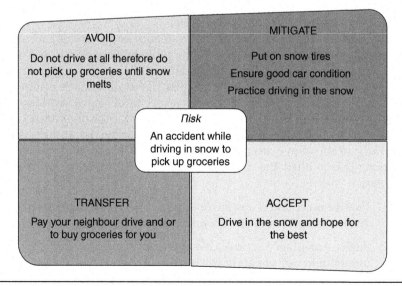

Figure 7.9 Four options for risk treatment or modification.

changes in the manufacturing sector or inclusion of specific objectives in scope in project management or inclusion of specific investment portfolios in the financial sector.

2. Indirect exploitation means steering the system to ensure realization of positive risk without a major change in initial objectives and functional structure built to support those objectives. This is a bottom-up approach to risk exploitation as opposed to the direct top-down approach.

The fourth point is risk sharing. At times, one organization is unable to ensure an effective positive risk realization strategy despite devoting significant resources. Due to the global and variegated nature of businesses, it becomes incumbent at times to seek a partnership with another organization for mutual benefit. In risk sharing, an organization sacrifices some ownership of the risk (and the return) to another organization to ensure higher chances of occurrence of positive impact. For example, multinational companies often form joint ventures with local companies when entering a new market.

The risk responses to negative and positive risks are summarized in Figure 7.10.

Risk Monitoring

Apply risk monitoring techniques such as, complaint tracking, trending, and post-market surveillance. (Analyze)

Body of Knowledge VII.C.4

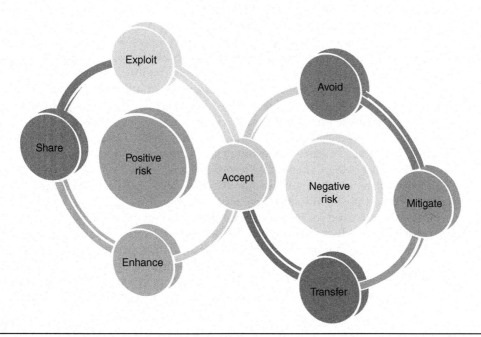

Figure 7.10 Risk responses to opportunities (positive risks) and threats (negative risks)

The risks that have been identified, analyzed, evaluated, and treated fall in the following categories:

1. Mitigated or enhanced

2. Avoided or exploited

3. Transferred or shared

4. Accepted

These are the possible outputs of the risk response plans for the evaluated risks. It does not mean that these risks have been 100% treated. A response plan for risk mitigation may be anticipated to reduce risk by 80%, but will it really do so? How accurate are our predictions about risk and our response to it? Since there is a subjective and predictive aspect to risk assessment and treatment, systems need to be put in place to monitor and verify the assessment and treatment as more real-world data and evidence become available to ensure that the risks stay stable at predefined levels.

The monitoring phase of risk management is where real-world data are used to track the risks and/or their constituents to ensure that the risks are behaving in the manner anticipated during risk treatment and response planning. Risk monitoring can be accomplished in two ways:

1. Reassessment of risks after treatment and continually throughout the life cycle

2. Tracking by using key risk indicators

All risks need not be reassessed continually. An organization must prioritize which risks are to be reassessed and set schedules or conditions for their reassessment throughout the life cycle. Precipitating events like complaints, defects, losses, warranty claims, and service requests can be used as checkpoints to reassess risks at discrete times to ensure acceptable risk profiles.

There may be an "Alpha" group of few early users who are asked a series of questions about their use of the product, such as (1) ease of use, (2) physical issues with handling, (3), areas of confusion when handling the product, (4) recommendations for improvements, (5) comparisons of other similar products, or (6) problems with the product that might cause users to avoid the product or go to competitors. These are only a sample of potential questions, and they must be asked and answered early during initial product use to ensure considerations such as (1) accuracy of early risk estimates, (2) uncovering serious or unexpected issues in product design, (3) helping to remove ambiguity in product use, or even (4) comparing the product with competitive products. This can form the basis of post-market and post-production risk monitoring.

There arises a need for indicators that inform about the status of the risk without the need to conduct full risk reassessments every time. The assessments mentioned above are executed early in the product distribution and continued with normal periodicity after an early analysis shows trending data from the indicators has stabilized. The trending status of these indicators can act as a flag for investigations, which may result in complete or partial risk reassessments.

A risk indicator is simply a metric that *indicates* the state of the level of risk. It is important to note that not all indicators show the exact level of risk exposure; most indicators usually provide just a trend of the drivers, causes, or intermediary effects of risk.

Not all risks are the same. The most important risks are categorized as key risks and the indicators for these key risks are known as key risk indicators (KRIs). These are defined as:

> A metric that provides a leading or lagging indication of the current state of risk exposure on key objectives. KRIs can be used to continually assess current and predict potential future risk exposure.

The KRIs should have a strong relationship with the key performance indicators (KPIs) of the organization's goals. The KPIs are metrics that are quantifiable measurements to assess performance of a specific process, product, system, or function.

ISO 31000:2018 says that[4]:

> "The results of monitoring and review should be incorporated throughout the organization's performance management, measurement and reporting activities."

KPIs are metrics that help gauge performance of the organization in terms of achievement of objectives. If an objective has a KPI, then it is highly likely that a KRI can be defined for that objective. If a risk has assigned controls because of risk treatment, then the risk indicator can become a metric to assess the effectiveness of the treatment.

Leading indicators are measurements of an element that influences the risk performance, while lagging indicators are actual measurements of the major components of the risk performance itself.

Leading indicators have predictive value, while lagging indicators are outputs of events that have already occurred, which help set future strategy. Some metrics can act as leading or lagging indicators based on the measured parameter, which may be an input to one process and an output of another.

The KRIs must be able to present the risk exposure qualitatively or quantitatively by having a strong relationship with the risk, its intermediate output, or its drivers.

In Figure 7.11, there are two choices for risk monitoring:

1. Reassess risk for every manufacturing issue, supply chain issue, inspection issue, and complaint issue as these events occur

2. Define performance of each risk in terms of its main driver and assign a KRI to track the risk

For point 2, consider the operational goal of "production of defect-free product." Assume the KPI for this is 99.5% final yield. The risks related to this goal are the following:

Risk One: Due to manufacturing process issues, process steps A, C, and D are inefficient, which has led to an increase in nonconformances during sampling.

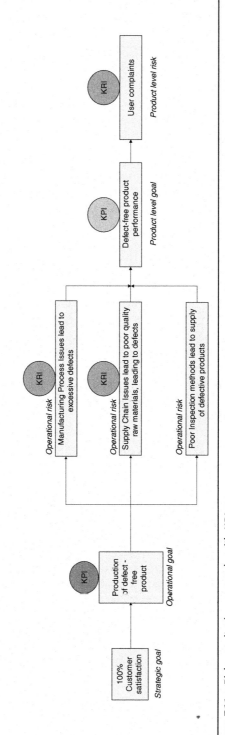

Figure 7.11   Risk monitoring example with KRIs.

Risk Two: Due to supply chain issues, raw materials X and Y are being sourced from new suppliers who are barely able to meet tolerance levels, leading to a high in-process scrap rate.

Risk Three: Due to loose and nonstandard inspection methods, the product is sometimes not inspected for all features, leading to an increase in defective products being shipped out.

Now, there should have been probabilities and impacts assigned for these risks from an operational standpoint, and these risks should have had mitigations in place. If this original risk were to be reassessed, one may notice an increase in probability and impact and realize that the risk exposure has increased and the mitigation has failed, or one may see a minor change that does not increase the risk level.

Another method to monitor these risks is to use KRIs. The indicator that would most closely state the health of the process would be the following:

For Risk One: Nonconformance rate

For Risk Two: Incoming inspection reject rate and raw material scrap rate

For Risk Three: Product complaint rate

A rise in nonconformance and scrap rate is both a leading indicator for user complaints and a lagging indicator for a poor production process. User complaints are a lagging indicator for poor product performance.

The KRIs could vary in their specificity. They might be very focused on one aspect, or they may be an amalgamation of various sub-indicators. For example, an organization with very high sensitivity to consumer complaints may choose to have that as a specific KRI against a performance indicator of customer satisfaction. Another organization may choose to create a balanced scorecard for quality and include consumer complaints as a line item along with separate data for manufacturing defects, supplier issues, delivery timeliness, service satisfaction, and so on and assign an overall score that becomes an amalgamated KRI.

Indicators can be top down, which are high-level composite indicators constituted of multiple sub-indicators to show the health of a greater operational or strategic goal. They can also be bottom up, where increased specificity can be afforded to monitor the exposure on a functional product, process, or service level. One way to evaluate processes for risk sources, therefore for potential sources/causes of risks would be Fault trees, in which each of the major "Hazards" (possible sources of harm to the process) are listed "Top-Down" in Fault trees as parts (causes) of the Fault tree, then analyzed for potential controls to reduce the probability of occurrence.

Regardless of the type of indicator used, it must always be ensured that it helps to identify, monitor as much as possible, and quantify the elements of the risk exposure. It must be noted that some KRIs will be more accurate in their representation of the actual risk than others.

Some KRIs may represent the frequency of events, which informs the probability assignation of the risk, and some may use elements from the impact assignation.

The benefits of KRIs are the following:

1. They can be easily converted to charts and trends

2. They are easily associated with objectives through KPIs

3. They can be shown on visual dashboards or converted to scorecards

4. Trending of KRIs can help predict future risk breaches

5. They allow risk monitoring without reassessing the risk every single time

6. They test the effectiveness of the risk treatment

7. They act as a bellwether for risk breaches

8. They can be hierarchically defined

Mitigation Planning

Apply and interpret risk mitigation plan.
(Analyze)

Body of Knowledge VII.C.5

The goal of risk response planning is to choose and implement risk treatment options to address the evaluated and prioritized risks. The previous sections covered available risk treatments in detail and presented that the decision to avoid, mitigate, transfer, accept, exploit, enhance, or share risk is a critical risk treatment step. It is clear that, when choosing an option, the risk attitudes of the stakeholders, risk tolerance of the organization, organizational obligations, competitor performance, market perceptions, and regulatory, legal, or compliance commitments must be taken into consideration.

Once the decision for how to treat risk has been made, practical options must be considered for realizing this decision. The viability of treatment must be assessed before it is implemented to ensure its effectiveness and to ensure that new unacceptable risks are not introduced as a part of the treatment plan. Figure 7.12 summarizes the risk response planning process with its inputs and outputs. The following is a discussion in additional detail.

The response planning starts by assessing the available treatment options for the prioritized risks based on communication and consultation. The rationale for the selection of the treatment must be documented. The expected actions and outcomes of the selected treatment must be assessed and documented as well; this is the expected change in the risk as a result of the applied treatment.

The actual treatment itself may require resources and an action plan for deployment. Thus, relevant process owners and responsible persons must be identified to actuate the treatment effectively and in a timely manner. Finally, the risk should be monitored continually after application of the treatment. For effective monitoring, performance measures must be defined such that verification of effectiveness of treatment can be carried out.

A risk response plan at a minimum must consist of the following:

1. Identification of the type of treatment and justification

2. Identification of the treatment actions and a plan for implementation

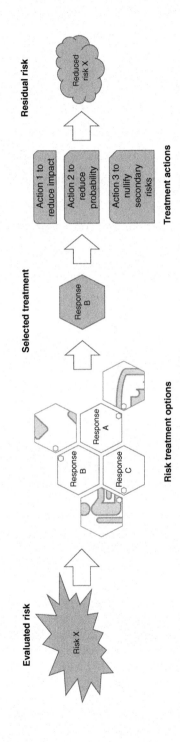

Figure 7.12 Risk response planning process.

3. Expected outcome/benefit of the treatment

4. Measures to monitor the effectiveness of the treatment

5. Risk reassessment after treatment

A detailed risk response plan should ideally consist of the following:

1. List of all available risk treatments for every prioritized risk

2. Justification for selection of one treatment over another

3. Testing the chosen treatment for effectiveness

4. Checking the treatment as a source of secondary negative risks

5. Conducting a stakeholder review of the treatment

6. Documenting the scope of the treatment

7. Documenting assumptions and constraints of the treatment

8. Documenting the resource requirements of the treatments

9. Plan of action for treatment implementation, including schedule and timing (one time or staggered)

10. Risk reassessment after treatment is over

11. Documented level of residual risk acceptability

12. Performance monitoring

13. Plan actions in case of treatment failure

The Concept of Secondary Risk

The risk treatments must be analyzed for their outcomes and effects in terms of additional risks that may be generated when they are implemented. It is very common for a response to a risk to either result in some change in other risks or result in new risks. The risks that are engendered by risk responses to already assessed or unassessed risks are known as *secondary risks*. If such risks arise, one must either choose another risk response or assess the secondary risk to check its acceptability and to understand its drivers and mitigators.

The Concept of Residual Risk

Residual risk is the risk that remains after a satisfactory application of risk treatment. Analysis of the residual risk is the key to understand the current and realistic risk profile. This analysis must be continual to ensure that the risk profile is maintained. For example, consumer behaviors may change over time, which would invalidate certain assumptions that were valid a few years ago.

As another example, a medical device could be repurposed for a procedure it was not intended for. Initially, the manufacturer acknowledged the risk and due to its low occurrence decided that a warning on a label was a sufficient mitigation. With changing surgical techniques, doctors found it more and more useful to repurpose the device, thereby increasing the occurrence rate. Thus, a new and stronger risk response would now be needed from the manufacturer.

The level of acceptability of the residual risk must be assessed with the same techniques used to assess the level of original risk. The risk matrix again proves useful here since the levels of risks are already charted on a matrix and the change in impact and probability levels after the treatment can be objectively assessed in terms of risk levels or ratings as shown in Figure 7.13.

The Concept of Inherent Risk

The natural level of raw, untreated risk associated with any activity is known as *inherent risk*. After a risk undergoes treatment, the remaining risk is residual risk. The word "residual" originates from the reduction of risk, as shown in Figure 7.14.

Most times, it is not possible to mitigate all risk, and some level of residual risk always remains. It is valuable to discuss these cases to understand the level of mitigation afforded by risk treatments. The source of risks is often a hazard, and to totally remove a risk would be to remove the hazard that causes the risk. Since this is not always possible, there is always a component of inherent risk that remains. Untreatable inherent risk is shown in Figure 7.15.

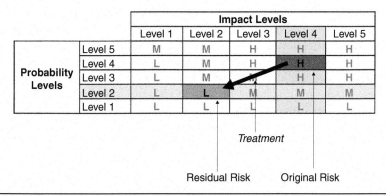

Figure 7.13 From original risk to residual risk.

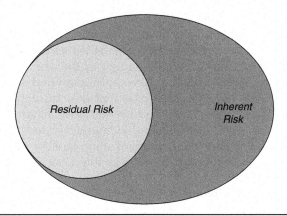

Figure 7.14 Residual risk and inherent risk.

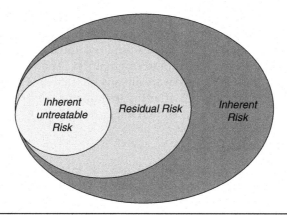

Figure 7.15   Untreatable risk, residual risk, and inherent risk.

For example, however powerful the grip of a tire can be made for traction, if a car is driven on ice or through tracts of accumulating snow, there is always a risk of slipping. This is because the snow or ice is the hazard and leads to the hazardous situation of low friction when a rubber tire is driven on it. There are numerous ways to reduce slippage, but there will always be a small inherent untreatable risk present unless one decides to avoid risk and just not drive the car in snow at all.

Similarly, every medical procedure has inherent risks. If a surgery is performed, there is risk of infection since a 100% sterile environment is difficult to guarantee. There is an obvious hazard, but the operation proceeds despite the hazard with the attempt to reduce the initial inherent risks by taking multiple precautions.

This understanding helps modulate risk treatment efforts. Recognizing the untreatable risks prevents people from excessively spending resources in the wrong place. Consensus from stakeholders must always be gained before a portion of risk is deemed untreatable.

Contingency Planning

When there is no treatment of the risk planned and the risks are accepted as is, the organization must proactively prepare a strategy to deal with those risks as they manifest themselves. This active acceptance of risk and planning actions for foreseen risks when they present themselves is known as *contingency planning*. A contingency plan should mitigate the negative effects of the risk and should clarify the type and level of action along with responsibilities for execution.

Sometimes an amount of money known as the contingency reserve is kept aside for these untreated risks that have been identified and evaluated but not mitigated. There may be unforeseen risks that arise during the system life cycle, and these must also be dealt with to ensure sustained achievement of goals. Since these emergent risks were neither identified nor evaluated, their response will be reactive in nature. It means that the organization must be sufficiently agile to triage resources at the first sign of these risks to ensure that they do not have an adverse impact.

The risk response planning process is summarized in Figure 7.16.

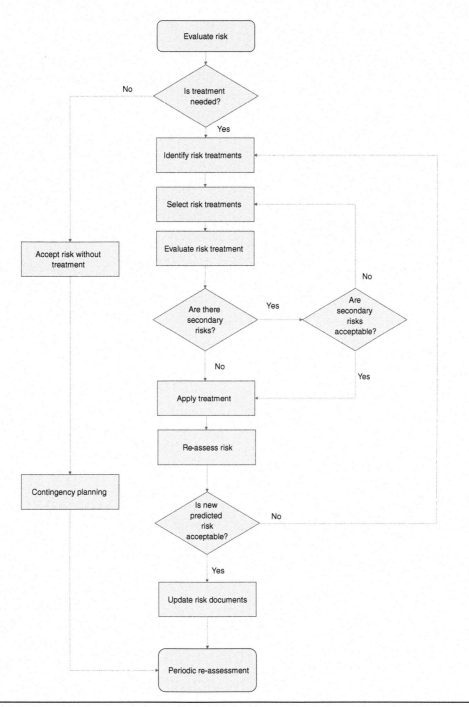

Figure 7.16 Flowchart for risk response planning process.

For additional information on risk management and risk analysis, see Pinto and Garvey (2012) and Wang and Roush (2000). Luko (2013) discusses common risk management terminology and standards for risk management.

Appendix A
Control Limit Formulas

VARIABLES CHARTS

$\bar{x}$ and R chart: *Averages Chart*: $\bar{\bar{x}} \pm A_2\bar{R}$ *Range Chart*: $\text{LCL} = D_3\bar{R}$ $\text{UCL} = D_4\bar{R}$

$\bar{x}$ and s chart: *Averages Chart*: $\bar{\bar{x}} \pm A_3\bar{s}$ *Std. Dev. Chart*: $\text{LCL} = B_3\bar{s}$ $\text{UCL} = B_4\bar{s}$

Individuals and Moving Range Chart (two-value moving window):

Individuals Chart: $\bar{x} \pm 2.66\bar{R}$ *Moving Range*: $\text{UCL} = 3.267\bar{R}$

Moving Average and Moving Range (two-value moving window):

Moving Average: $\bar{\bar{x}} \pm 1.88\bar{R}$ *Moving Range*: $\text{UCL} = 3.267\bar{R}$

ATTRIBUTES CHARTS

p chart: $\bar{p} \pm 3\sqrt{\dfrac{\bar{p}(1-\bar{p})}{n}}$

np chart: $n\bar{p} \pm 3\sqrt{n\bar{p}(1-\bar{p})}$

c chart: $\bar{c} \pm 3\sqrt{\bar{c}}$

u chart: $\bar{u} \pm 3\sqrt{\dfrac{\bar{u}}{n}}$

Appendix B
Constants for Control Charts

Subgroup size n	A_2	d_2	D_3	D_4	A_3	C_4	B_3	B_4	E_2	A_2 for median charts
2	1.880	1.128	0	3.267	2.659	0.798	0	3.267	2.660	1.880
3	1.023	1.693	0	2.574	1.954	0.886	0	2.568	1.772	1.187
4	0.729	2.059	0	2.282	1.628	0.921	0	2.266	1.457	0.796
5	0.577	2.326	0	2.114	1.427	0.940	0	2.089	1.290	0.691
6	0.483	2.534	0	2.004	1.287	0.952	0.030	1.970	1.184	0.548
7	0.419	2.704	0.076	1.924	1.182	0.959	0.118	1.882	1.109	0.508
8	0.373	2.847	0.136	1.864	1.099	0.965	0.185	1.815	1.054	0.433
9	0.337	2.970	0.184	1.816	1.032	0.969	0.239	1.761	1.010	0.412
10	0.308	3.078	0.223	1.777	0.975	0.973	0.284	1.716	0.975	0.362

Appendix C
Statistical Tolerance Factors for at Least 99% of the Population

("k-Values")

	One-sided tolerance Confidence level				Two-sided tolerance Confidence level		
n	0.90	0.95	0.99	*n*	0.90	0.95	0.99
10	3.532	3.981	5.075	10	3.959	4.433	5.594
11	3.444	3.852	4.828	11	3.849	4.277	5.308
12	3.371	3.747	4.633	12	3.758	4.150	5.079
13	3.310	3.659	4.472	13	3.682	4.044	4.893
14	3.257	3.585	4.336	14	3.618	3.955	4.737
15	3.212	3.520	4.224	15	3.562	3.878	4.605
16	3.172	3.463	4.124	16	3.514	3.812	4.492
17	3.136	3.415	4.038	17	3.471	3.754	4.393
18	3.106	3.370	3.961	18	3.433	3.702	4.307
19	3.078	3.331	3.893	19	3.399	3.656	4.230
20	3.052	3.295	3.832	20	3.368	3.615	4.161
21	3.028	3.262	3.776	21	3.340	3.577	4.100
22	3.007	3.233	3.727	22	3.315	3.543	4.044
23	2.987	3.206	3.680	23	3.292	3.512	3.993
24	2.969	3.181	3.638	24	3.270	3.483	3.947
25	2.952	3.158	3.601	25	3.251	3.457	3.904
30	2.884	3.064	3.446	30	3.170	3.350	3.733
40	2.793	2.941	3.250	40	3.066	3.213	3.518
50	2.735	2.863	3.124	50	3.001	3.126	3.385

Appendix D
Standard Normal Distribution
for Selected Z-Values

Z	Area to left of Z	Area to right of Z	Parts per million right of Z
0	0.5000000	0.5000000	500000.0002
0.1	0.5398279	0.4601721	460172.1045
0.2	0.5792597	0.4207403	420740.3128
0.3	0.6179114	0.3820886	382088.6425
0.4	0.6554217	0.3445783	344578.3034
0.5	0.6914625	0.3085375	308537.5326
0.6	0.7257469	0.2742531	274253.0649
0.7	0.7580364	0.2419636	241963.5785
0.8	0.7881447	0.2118553	211855.3339
0.9	0.8159399	0.1840601	184060.0917
1	0.8413447	0.1586553	158655.2598
1.1	0.8643339	0.1356661	135666.1015
1.2	0.8849303	0.1150697	115069.7317
1.3	0.9031995	0.0968005	96800.5495
1.4	0.9192433	0.0807567	80756.71126
1.5	0.9331928	0.0668072	66807.22879
1.6	0.9452007	0.0547993	54799.28945
1.7	0.9554346	0.0445654	44565.43178
1.8	0.9640697	0.0359303	35930.26551
1.9	0.9712835	0.0287165	28716.49286
2	0.9772499	0.0227501	22750.06204
2.1	0.9821356	0.0178644	17864.35742
2.2	0.9860966	0.0139034	13903.39891
2.3	0.9892759	0.0107241	10724.08106
2.4	0.9918025	8.1975289×10^{-3}	8197.528869
2.5	0.9937903	6.2096799×10^{-3}	6209.679859
2.6	0.9953388	4.6612218×10^{-3}	4661.221783

Continued

Z	Area to left of Z	Area to right of Z	Parts per million right of Z
2.7	0.9965330	3.4670231E-03	3467.023053
2.8	0.9974448	2.5551906E-03	2555.190642
2.9	0.9981341	1.8658801E-03	1865.88014
3	0.9986500	1.3499672E-03	1349.967223
3.1	0.9990323	9.6767124E-04	967.6712356
3.2	0.9993128	6.8720208E-04	687.2020808
3.3	0.9995165	4.8348254E-04	483.4825366
3.4	0.9996630	3.3698082E-04	336.9808229
3.5	0.9997673	2.3267337E-04	232.6733737
3.6	0.9998409	1.5914571E-04	159.1457138
3.7	0.9998922	1.0783015E-04	107.8301454
3.8	0.9999276	7.2372434E-05	72.37243427
3.9	0.9999519	4.8115519E-05	48.11551887
4	0.9999683	3.1686035E-05	31.68603461
4.1	0.9999793	2.0668716E-05	20.66871577
4.2	0.9999866	1.3354097E-05	13.35409733
4.3	0.9999915	8.5460212E-06	8.546021191
4.4	0.9999946	5.4169531E-06	5.416953054
4.5	0.9999966	3.4008031E-06	3.400803062
4.6	0.9999979	2.1146434E-06	2.114643376
4.7	0.9999987	1.3023157E-06	1.302315654
4.8	0.9999992	7.9435267E-07	0.794352669
4.9	0.9999995	4.7986955E-07	0.479869547
5	0.9999997	2.8710500E-07	0.287105
5.1	0.9999998	1.7012231E-07	0.170122314
5.2	0.9999999	9.9834400E-08	0.0998344
5.3	0.9999999	5.8022066E-08	0.058022066
5.4	1.0000000	3.3396123E-08	0.033396123
5.5	1.0000000	1.9036399E-08	0.019036399
5.6	1.0000000	1.0746217E-08	0.010746217
5.7	1.0000000	6.0076532E-09	0.006007653
5.8	1.0000000	3.3260517E-09	0.003326052
5.9	1.0000000	1.8235793E-09	0.001823579
6	1.0000000	9.9012187E-10	0.000990122

Appendix E
Areas under Standard Normal Distribution to the Left of Z-Values

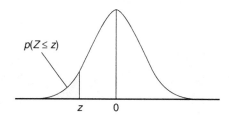

$p(Z \le z)$

z	−0.09	−0.08	−0.07	−0.06	−0.05	−0.04	−0.03	−0.02	−0.01	−0.00
−3.5	0.0002	0.0002	0.0002	0.0002	0.0002	0.0002	0.0002	0.0002	0.0002	0.0002
−3.4	0.0002	0.0003	0.0003	0.0003	0.0003	0.0003	0.0003	0.0003	0.0003	0.0003
−3.3	0.0003	0.0004	0.0004	0.0004	0.0004	0.0004	0.0004	0.0005	0.0005	0.0005
−3.2	0.0005	0.0005	0.0005	0.0006	0.0006	0.0006	0.0006	0.0006	0.0007	0.0007
−3.1	0.0007	0.0007	0.0008	0.0008	0.0008	0.0008	0.0009	0.0009	0.0009	0.0010
−3.0	0.0010	0.0010	0.0011	0.0011	0.0011	0.0012	0.0012	0.0013	0.0013	0.0013
−2.9	0.0014	0.0014	0.0015	0.0015	0.0016	0.0016	0.0017	0.0018	0.0018	0.0019
−2.8	0.0019	0.0020	0.0021	0.0021	0.0022	0.0023	0.0023	0.0024	0.0025	0.0026
−2.7	0.0026	0.0027	0.0028	0.0029	0.0030	0.0031	0.0032	0.0033	0.0034	0.0035
−2.6	0.0036	0.0037	0.0038	0.0039	0.0040	0.0041	0.0043	0.0044	0.0045	0.0047
−2.5	0.0048	0.0049	0.0051	0.0052	0.0054	0.0055	0.0057	0.0059	0.0060	0.0062
−2.4	0.0064	0.0066	0.0068	0.0069	0.0071	0.0073	0.0075	0.0078	0.0080	0.0082
−2.3	0.0084	0.0087	0.0089	0.0091	0.0094	0.0096	0.0099	0.0102	0.0104	0.0107
−2.2	0.0110	0.0113	0.0116	0.0119	0.0122	0.0125	0.0129	0.0132	0.0136	0.0139
−2.1	0.0143	0.0146	0.0150	0.0154	0.0158	0.0162	0.0166	0.0170	0.0174	0.0179
−2.0	0.0183	0.0188	0.0192	0.0197	0.0202	0.0207	0.0212	0.0217	0.0222	0.0228
−1.9	0.0233	0.0239	0.0244	0.0250	0.0256	0.0262	0.0268	0.0274	0.0281	0.0287
−1.8	0.0294	0.0301	0.0307	0.0314	0.0322	0.0329	0.0336	0.0344	0.0351	0.0359
−1.7	0.0367	0.0375	0.0384	0.0392	0.0401	0.0409	0.0418	0.0427	0.0436	0.0446
−1.6	0.0455	0.0465	0.0475	0.0485	0.0495	0.0505	0.0516	0.0526	0.0537	0.0548
−1.5	0.0559	0.0571	0.0582	0.0594	0.0606	0.0618	0.0630	0.0643	0.0655	0.0668

Continued

z	−0.09	−0.08	−0.07	−0.06	−0.05	−0.04	−0.03	−0.02	−0.01	−0.00
−1.4	0.0681	0.0694	0.0708	0.0721	0.0735	0.0749	0.0764	0.0778	0.0793	0.0808
−1.3	0.0823	0.0838	0.0853	0.0869	0.0885	0.0901	0.0918	0.0934	0.0951	0.0968
−1.2	0.0985	0.1003	0.1020	0.1038	0.1056	0.1075	0.1093	0.1112	0.1131	0.1151
−1.1	0.1170	0.1190	0.1210	0.1230	0.1251	0.1271	0.1292	0.1314	0.1335	0.1357
−1.0	0.1379	0.1401	0.1423	0.1446	0.1469	0.1492	0.1515	0.1539	0.1562	0.1587
−0.9	0.1611	0.1635	0.1660	0.1685	0.1711	0.1736	0.1762	0.1788	0.1814	0.1841
−0.8	0.1867	0.1894	0.1922	0.1949	0.1977	0.2005	0.2033	0.2061	0.2090	0.2119
−0.7	0.2148	0.2177	0.2206	0.2236	0.2266	0.2296	0.2327	0.2358	0.2389	0.2420
−0.6	0.2451	0.2483	0.2514	0.2546	0.2578	0.2611	0.2643	0.2676	0.2709	0.2743
−0.5	0.2776	0.2810	0.2843	0.2877	0.2912	0.2946	0.2981	0.3015	0.3050	0.3085
−0.4	0.3121	0.3156	0.3192	0.3228	0.3264	0.3300	0.3336	0.3372	0.3409	0.3446
−0.3	0.3483	0.3520	0.3557	0.3594	0.3632	0.3669	0.3707	0.3745	0.3783	0.3821
−0.2	0.3859	0.3897	0.3936	0.3974	0.4013	0.4052	0.4090	0.4129	0.4168	0.4207
−0.1	0.4247	0.4286	0.4325	0.4364	0.4404	0.4443	0.4483	0.4522	0.4562	0.4602
0.0	0.4641	0.4681	0.4721	0.4761	0.4801	0.4840	0.4880	0.4920	0.4960	0.5000

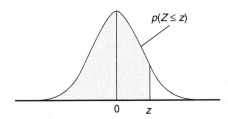

$p(Z \leq z)$

z	0.00	0.01	0.02	0.03	0.04	0.05	0.06	0.07	0.08	0.09
0.0	0.5000	0.5040	0.5080	0.5120	0.5160	0.5199	0.5239	0.5279	0.5319	0.5359
0.1	0.5398	0.5438	0.5478	0.5517	0.5557	0.5596	0.5636	0.5675	0.5714	0.5753
0.2	0.5793	0.5832	0.5871	0.5910	0.5948	0.5987	0.6026	0.6064	0.6103	0.6141
0.3	0.6179	0.6217	0.6255	0.6293	0.6331	0.6368	0.6406	0.6443	0.6480	0.6517
0.4	0.6554	0.6591	0.6628	0.6664	0.6700	0.6736	0.6772	0.6808	0.6844	0.6879
0.5	0.6915	0.6950	0.6985	0.7019	0.7054	0.7088	0.7123	0.7157	0.7190	0.7224
0.6	0.7257	0.7291	0.7324	0.7357	0.7389	0.7422	0.7454	0.7486	0.7517	0.7549
0.7	0.7580	0.7611	0.7642	0.7673	0.7704	0.7734	0.7764	0.7794	0.7823	0.7852
0.8	0.7881	0.7910	0.7939	0.7967	0.7995	0.8023	0.8051	0.8078	0.8106	0.8133
0.9	0.8159	0.8186	0.8212	0.8238	0.8264	0.8289	0.8315	0.8340	0.8365	0.8389
1.0	0.8413	0.8438	0.8461	0.8485	0.8508	0.8531	0.8554	0.8577	0.8599	0.8621

Continued

Continued

z	0.00	0.01	0.02	0.03	0.04	0.05	0.06	0.07	0.08	0.09
1.1	0.8643	0.8665	0.8686	0.8708	0.8729	0.8749	0.8770	0.8790	0.8810	0.8830
1.2	0.8849	0.8869	0.8888	0.8907	0.8925	0.8944	0.8962	0.8980	0.8997	0.9015
1.3	0.9032	0.9049	0.9066	0.9082	0.9099	0.9115	0.9131	0.9147	0.9162	0.9177
1.4	0.9192	0.9207	0.9222	0.9236	0.9251	0.9265	0.9279	0.9292	0.9306	0.9319
1.5	0.9332	0.9345	0.9357	0.9370	0.9382	0.9394	0.9406	0.9418	0.9429	0.9441
1.6	0.9452	0.9463	0.9474	0.9484	0.9495	0.9505	0.9515	0.9525	0.9535	0.9545
1.7	0.9554	0.9564	0.9573	0.9582	0.9591	0.9599	0.9608	0.9616	0.9625	0.9633
1.8	0.9641	0.9649	0.9656	0.9664	0.9671	0.9678	0.9686	0.9693	0.9699	0.9706
1.9	0.9713	0.9719	0.9726	0.9732	0.9738	0.9744	0.9750	0.9756	0.9761	0.9767
2.0	0.9772	0.9778	0.9783	0.9788	0.9793	0.9798	0.9803	0.9808	0.9812	0.9817
2.1	0.9821	0.9826	0.9830	0.9834	0.9838	0.9842	0.9846	0.9850	0.9854	0.9857
2.2	0.9861	0.9864	0.9868	0.9871	0.9875	0.9878	0.9881	0.9884	0.9887	0.9890
2.3	0.9893	0.9896	0.9898	0.9901	0.9904	0.9906	0.9909	0.9911	0.9913	0.9916
2.4	0.9918	0.9920	0.9922	0.9925	0.9927	0.9929	0.9931	0.9932	0.9934	0.9936
2.5	0.9938	0.9940	0.9941	0.9943	0.9945	0.9946	0.9948	0.9949	0.9951	0.9952
2.6	0.9953	0.9955	0.9956	0.9957	0.9959	0.9960	0.9961	0.9962	0.9963	0.9964
2.7	0.9965	0.9966	0.9967	0.9968	0.9969	0.9970	0.9971	0.9972	0.9973	0.9974
2.8	0.9974	0.9975	0.9976	0.9977	0.9977	0.9978	0.9979	0.9979	0.9980	0.9981
2.9	0.9981	0.9982	0.9982	0.9983	0.9984	0.9984	0.9985	0.9985	0.9986	0.9986
3.0	0.9987	0.9987	0.9987	0.9988	0.9988	0.9989	0.9989	0.9989	0.9990	0.9990
3.1	0.9990	0.9991	0.9991	0.9991	0.9992	0.9992	0.9992	0.9992	0.9993	0.9993
3.2	0.9993	0.9993	0.9994	0.9994	0.9994	0.9994	0.9994	0.9995	0.9995	0.9995
3.3	0.9995	0.9995	0.9995	0.9996	0.9996	0.9996	0.9996	0.9996	0.9996	0.9997
3.4	0.9997	0.9997	0.9997	0.9997	0.9997	0.9997	0.9997	0.9997	0.9997	0.9998
3.5	0.9998	0.9998	0.9998	0.9998	0.9998	0.9998	0.9998	0.9998	0.9998	0.9998

Appendix F
F Distribution $F_{0.10}$

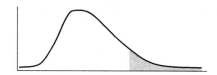

F distribution $F_{0.10}$

		Numerator degrees of freedom									
	1	**2**	**3**	**4**	**5**	**6**	**7**	**8**	**9**	**10**	**11**
1	39.86	49.50	53.59	55.83	57.24	58.20	58.91	59.44	59.86	60.19	60.47
2	8.53	9.00	9.16	9.24	9.29	9.33	9.35	9.37	9.38	9.39	9.40
3	5.54	5.46	5.39	5.34	5.31	5.28	5.27	5.25	5.24	5.23	5.22
4	4.54	4.32	4.19	4.11	4.05	4.01	3.98	3.95	3.94	3.92	3.91
5	4.06	3.78	3.62	3.52	3.45	3.40	3.37	3.34	3.32	3.30	3.28
6	3.78	3.46	3.29	3.18	3.11	3.05	3.01	2.98	2.96	2.94	2.92
7	3.59	3.26	3.07	2.96	2.88	2.83	2.78	2.75	2.72	2.70	2.68
8	3.46	3.11	2.92	2.81	2.73	2.67	2.62	2.59	2.56	2.54	2.52
9	3.36	3.01	2.81	2.69	2.61	2.55	2.51	2.47	2.44	2.42	2.40
10	3.29	2.92	2.73	2.61	2.52	2.46	2.41	2.38	2.35	2.32	2.30
11	3.23	2.86	2.66	2.54	2.45	2.39	2.34	2.30	2.27	2.25	2.23
12	3.18	2.81	2.61	2.48	2.39	2.33	2.28	2.24	2.21	2.19	2.17
13	3.14	2.76	2.56	2.43	2.35	2.28	2.23	2.20	2.16	2.14	2.12
14	3.10	2.73	2.52	2.39	2.31	2.24	2.19	2.15	2.12	2.10	2.07
15	3.07	2.70	2.49	2.36	2.27	2.21	2.16	2.12	2.09	2.06	2.04
16	3.05	2.67	2.46	2.33	2.24	2.18	2.13	2.09	2.06	2.03	2.01
17	3.03	2.64	2.44	2.31	2.22	2.15	2.10	2.06	2.03	2.00	1.98
18	3.01	2.62	2.42	2.29	2.20	2.13	2.08	2.04	2.00	1.98	1.95
19	2.99	2.61	2.40	2.27	2.18	2.11	2.06	2.02	1.98	1.96	1.93
20	2.97	2.59	2.38	2.25	2.16	2.09	2.04	2.00	1.96	1.94	1.91
21	2.96	2.57	2.36	2.23	2.14	2.08	2.02	1.98	1.95	1.92	1.90
22	2.95	2.56	2.35	2.22	2.13	2.06	2.01	1.97	1.93	1.90	1.88
23	2.94	2.55	2.34	2.21	2.11	2.05	1.99	1.95	1.92	1.89	1.87
24	2.93	2.54	2.33	2.19	2.10	2.04	1.98	1.94	1.91	1.88	1.85
25	2.92	2.53	2.32	2.18	2.09	2.02	1.97	1.93	1.89	1.87	1.84
26	2.91	2.52	2.31	2.17	2.08	2.01	1.96	1.92	1.88	1.86	1.83
27	2.90	2.51	2.30	2.17	2.07	2.00	1.95	1.91	1.87	1.85	1.82
28	2.89	2.50	2.29	2.16	2.06	2.00	1.94	1.90	1.87	1.84	1.81
29	2.89	2.50	2.28	2.15	2.06	1.99	1.93	1.89	1.86	1.83	1.80
30	2.88	2.49	2.28	2.14	2.05	1.98	1.93	1.88	1.85	1.82	1.79
40	2.84	2.44	2.23	2.09	2.00	1.93	1.87	1.83	1.79	1.76	1.74
60	2.79	2.39	2.18	2.04	1.95	1.87	1.82	1.77	1.74	1.71	1.68
100	2.76	2.36	2.14	2.00	1.91	1.83	1.78	1.73	1.69	1.66	1.64

Denominator degrees of freedom

F distribution $F_{0.10}$ *(continued)*

		Numerator degrees of freedom										
		12	**13**	**14**	**15**	**16**	**17**	**18**	**19**	**20**	**21**	**22**
Denominator degrees of freedom	**1**	60.71	60.90	61.07	61.22	61.35	61.46	61.57	61.66	61.74	61.81	61.88
	2	9.41	9.41	9.42	9.42	9.43	9.43	9.44	9.44	9.44	9.44	9.45
	3	5.22	5.21	5.20	5.20	5.20	5.19	5.19	5.19	5.18	5.18	5.18
	4	3.90	3.89	3.88	3.87	3.86	3.86	3.85	3.85	3.84	3.84	3.84
	5	3.27	3.26	3.25	3.24	3.23	3.22	3.22	3.21	3.21	3.20	3.20
	6	2.90	2.89	2.88	2.87	2.86	2.85	2.85	2.84	2.84	2.83	2.83
	7	2.67	2.65	2.64	2.63	2.62	2.61	2.61	2.60	2.59	2.59	2.58
	8	2.50	2.49	2.48	2.46	2.45	2.45	2.44	2.43	2.42	2.42	2.41
	9	2.38	2.36	2.35	2.34	2.33	2.32	2.31	2.30	2.30	2.29	2.29
	10	2.28	2.27	2.26	2.24	2.23	2.22	2.22	2.21	2.20	2.19	2.19
	11	2.21	2.19	2.18	2.17	2.16	2.15	2.14	2.13	2.12	2.12	2.11
	12	2.15	2.13	2.12	2.10	2.09	2.08	2.08	2.07	2.06	2.05	2.05
	13	2.10	2.08	2.07	2.05	2.04	2.03	2.02	2.01	2.01	2.00	1.99
	14	2.05	2.04	2.02	2.01	2.00	1.99	1.98	1.97	1.96	1.96	1.95
	15	2.02	2.00	1.99	1.97	1.96	1.95	1.94	1.93	1.92	1.92	1.91
	16	1.99	1.97	1.95	1.94	1.93	1.92	1.91	1.90	1.89	1.88	1.88
	17	1.96	1.94	1.93	1.91	1.90	1.89	1.88	1.87	1.86	1.86	1.85
	18	1.93	1.92	1.90	1.89	1.87	1.86	1.85	1.84	1.84	1.83	1.82
	19	1.91	1.89	1.88	1.86	1.85	1.84	1.83	1.82	1.81	1.81	1.80
	20	1.89	1.87	1.86	1.84	1.83	1.82	1.81	1.80	1.79	1.79	1.78
	21	1.87	1.86	1.84	1.83	1.81	1.80	1.79	1.78	1.78	1.77	1.76
	22	1.86	1.84	1.83	1.81	1.80	1.79	1.78	1.77	1.76	1.75	1.74
	23	1.84	1.83	1.81	1.80	1.78	1.77	1.76	1.75	1.74	1.74	1.73
	24	1.83	1.81	1.80	1.78	1.77	1.76	1.75	1.74	1.73	1.72	1.71
	25	1.82	1.80	1.79	1.77	1.76	1.75	1.74	1.73	1.72	1.71	1.70
	26	1.81	1.79	1.77	1.76	1.75	1.73	1.72	1.71	1.71	1.70	1.69
	27	1.80	1.78	1.76	1.75	1.74	1.72	1.71	1.70	1.70	1.69	1.68
	28	1.79	1.77	1.75	1.74	1.73	1.71	1.70	1.69	1.69	1.68	1.67
	29	1.78	1.76	1.75	1.73	1.72	1.71	1.69	1.68	1.68	1.67	1.66
	30	1.77	1.75	1.74	1.72	1.71	1.70	1.69	1.68	1.67	1.66	1.65
	40	1.71	1.70	1.68	1.66	1.65	1.64	1.62	1.61	1.61	1.60	1.59
	60	1.66	1.64	1.62	1.60	1.59	1.58	1.56	1.55	1.54	1.53	1.53
	100	1.61	1.59	1.57	1.56	1.54	1.53	1.52	1.50	1.49	1.48	1.48

Continued

F distribution F$_{0.10}$ *(continued)*

					Numerator degrees of freedom						
	23	24	25	26	27	28	29	30	40	60	100
1	61.94	62.00	62.05	62.10	62.15	62.19	62.23	62.26	62.53	62.79	63.01
2	9.45	9.45	9.45	9.45	9.45	9.46	9.46	9.46	9.47	9.47	9.48
3	5.18	5.18	5.17	5.17	5.17	5.17	5.17	5.17	5.16	5.15	5.14
4	3.83	3.83	3.83	3.83	3.82	3.82	3.82	3.82	3.80	3.79	3.78
5	3.19	3.19	3.19	3.18	3.18	3.18	3.18	3.17	3.16	3.14	3.13
6	2.82	2.82	2.81	2.81	2.81	2.81	2.80	2.80	2.78	2.76	2.75
7	2.58	2.58	2.57	2.57	2.56	2.56	2.56	2.56	2.54	2.51	2.50
8	2.41	2.40	2.40	2.40	2.39	2.39	2.39	2.38	2.36	2.34	2.32
9	2.28	2.28	2.27	2.27	2.26	2.26	2.26	2.25	2.23	2.21	2.19
10	2.18	2.18	2.17	2.17	2.17	2.16	2.16	2.16	2.13	2.11	2.09
11	2.11	2.10	2.10	2.09	2.09	2.08	2.08	2.08	2.05	2.03	2.01
12	2.04	2.04	2.03	2.03	2.02	2.02	2.01	2.01	1.99	1.96	1.94
13	1.99	1.98	1.98	1.97	1.97	1.96	1.96	1.96	1.93	1.90	1.88
14	1.94	1.94	1.93	1.93	1.92	1.92	1.92	1.91	1.89	1.86	1.83
15	1.90	1.90	1.89	1.89	1.88	1.88	1.88	1.87	1.85	1.82	1.79
16	1.87	1.87	1.86	1.86	1.85	1.85	1.84	1.84	1.81	1.78	1.76
17	1.84	1.84	1.83	1.83	1.82	1.82	1.81	1.81	1.78	1.75	1.73
18	1.82	1.81	1.80	1.80	1.80	1.79	1.79	1.78	1.75	1.72	1.70
19	1.79	1.79	1.78	1.78	1.77	1.77	1.76	1.76	1.73	1.70	1.67
20	1.77	1.77	1.76	1.76	1.75	1.75	1.74	1.74	1.71	1.68	1.65
21	1.75	1.75	1.74	1.74	1.73	1.73	1.72	1.72	1.69	1.66	1.63
22	1.74	1.73	1.73	1.72	1.72	1.71	1.71	1.70	1.67	1.64	1.61
23	1.72	1.72	1.71	1.70	1.70	1.69	1.69	1.69	1.66	1.62	1.59
24	1.71	1.70	1.70	1.69	1.69	1.68	1.68	1.67	1.64	1.61	1.58
25	1.70	1.69	1.68	1.68	1.67	1.67	1.66	1.66	1.63	1.59	1.56
26	1.68	1.68	1.67	1.67	1.66	1.66	1.65	1.65	1.61	1.58	1.55
27	1.67	1.67	1.66	1.65	1.65	1.64	1.64	1.64	1.60	1.57	1.54
28	1.66	1.66	1.65	1.64	1.64	1.63	1.63	1.63	1.59	1.56	1.53
29	1.65	1.65	1.64	1.63	1.63	1.62	1.62	1.62	1.58	1.55	1.52
30	1.64	1.64	1.63	1.63	1.62	1.62	1.61	1.61	1.57	1.54	1.51
40	1.58	1.57	1.57	1.56	1.56	1.55	1.55	1.54	1.51	1.47	1.43
60	1.52	1.51	1.50	1.50	1.49	1.49	1.48	1.48	1.44	1.40	1.36
100	1.47	1.46	1.45	1.45	1.44	1.43	1.43	1.42	1.38	1.34	1.29

Denominator degrees of freedom (row labels along left edge)

Appendix G
F Distribution $F_{0.05}$

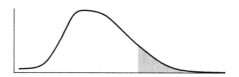

F distribution $F_{0.05}$

		Numerator degrees of freedom									
	1	**2**	**3**	**4**	**5**	**6**	**7**	**8**	**9**	**10**	**11**
1	161.4	199.5	215.7	224.6	230.2	234.0	236.8	238.9	240.5	241.9	243.0
2	18.51	19.00	19.16	19.25	19.30	19.33	19.35	19.37	19.38	19.40	19.40
3	10.13	9.55	9.28	9.12	9.01	8.94	8.89	8.85	8.81	8.79	8.76
4	7.71	6.94	6.59	6.39	6.26	6.16	6.09	6.04	6.00	5.96	5.94
5	6.61	5.79	5.41	5.19	5.05	4.95	4.88	4.82	4.77	4.74	4.70
6	5.99	5.14	4.76	4.53	4.39	4.28	4.21	4.15	4.10	4.06	4.03
7	5.59	4.74	4.35	4.12	3.97	3.87	3.79	3.73	3.68	3.64	3.60
8	5.32	4.46	4.07	3.84	3.69	3.58	3.50	3.44	3.39	3.35	3.31
9	5.12	4.26	3.86	3.63	3.48	3.37	3.29	3.23	3.18	3.14	3.10
10	4.96	4.10	3.71	3.48	3.33	3.22	3.14	3.07	3.02	2.98	2.94
11	4.84	3.98	3.59	3.36	3.20	3.09	3.01	2.95	2.90	2.85	2.82
12	4.75	3.89	3.49	3.26	3.11	3.00	2.91	2.85	2.80	2.75	2.72
13	4.67	3.81	3.41	3.18	3.03	2.92	2.83	2.77	2.71	2.67	2.63
14	4.60	3.74	3.34	3.11	2.96	2.85	2.76	2.70	2.65	2.60	2.57
15	4.54	3.68	3.29	3.06	2.90	2.79	2.71	2.64	2.59	2.54	2.51
16	4.49	3.63	3.24	3.01	2.85	2.74	2.66	2.59	2.54	2.49	2.46
17	4.45	3.59	3.20	2.96	2.81	2.70	2.61	2.55	2.49	2.45	2.41
18	4.41	3.55	3.16	2.93	2.77	2.66	2.58	2.51	2.46	2.41	2.37
19	4.38	3.52	3.13	2.90	2.74	2.63	2.54	2.48	2.42	2.38	2.34
20	4.35	3.49	3.10	2.87	2.71	2.60	2.51	2.45	2.39	2.35	2.31
21	4.32	3.47	3.07	2.84	2.68	2.57	2.49	2.42	2.37	2.32	2.28
22	4.30	3.44	3.05	2.82	2.66	2.55	2.46	2.40	2.34	2.30	2.26
23	4.28	3.42	3.03	2.80	2.64	2.53	2.44	2.37	2.32	2.27	2.24
24	4.26	3.40	3.01	2.78	2.62	2.51	2.42	2.36	2.30	2.25	2.22
25	4.24	3.39	2.99	2.76	2.60	2.49	2.40	2.34	2.28	2.24	2.20
26	4.23	3.37	2.98	2.74	2.59	2.47	2.39	2.32	2.27	2.22	2.18
27	4.21	3.35	2.96	2.73	2.57	2.46	2.37	2.31	2.25	2.20	2.17
28	4.20	3.34	2.95	2.71	2.56	2.45	2.36	2.29	2.24	2.19	2.15
29	4.18	3.33	2.93	2.70	2.55	2.43	2.35	2.28	2.22	2.18	2.14
30	4.17	3.32	2.92	2.69	2.53	2.42	2.33	2.27	2.21	2.16	2.13
40	4.08	3.23	2.84	2.61	2.45	2.34	2.25	2.18	2.12	2.08	2.04
60	4.00	3.15	2.76	2.53	2.37	2.25	2.17	2.10	2.04	1.99	1.95
100	3.94	3.09	2.70	2.46	2.31	2.19	2.10	2.03	1.97	1.93	1.89

Denominator degrees of freedom

F distribution $F_{0.05}$ *(continued)*

		Numerator degrees of freedom										
		12	**13**	**14**	**15**	**16**	**17**	**18**	**19**	**20**	**21**	**22**
Denominator degrees of freedom	**1**	243.9	244.7	245.4	245.9	246.5	246.9	247.3	247.7	248.0	248.3	248.6
	2	19.41	19.42	19.42	19.43	19.43	19.44	19.44	19.44	19.45	19.45	19.45
	3	8.74	8.73	8.71	8.70	8.69	8.68	8.67	8.67	8.66	8.65	8.65
	4	5.91	5.89	5.87	5.86	5.84	5.83	5.82	5.81	5.80	5.79	5.79
	5	4.68	4.66	4.64	4.62	4.60	4.59	4.58	4.57	4.56	4.55	4.54
	6	4.00	3.98	3.96	3.94	3.92	3.91	3.90	3.88	3.87	3.86	3.86
	7	3.57	3.55	3.53	3.51	3.49	3.48	3.47	3.46	3.44	3.43	3.43
	8	3.28	3.26	3.24	3.22	3.20	3.19	3.17	3.16	3.15	3.14	3.13
	9	3.07	3.05	3.03	3.01	2.99	2.97	2.96	2.95	2.94	2.93	2.92
	10	2.91	2.89	2.86	2.85	2.83	2.81	2.80	2.79	2.77	2.76	2.75
	11	2.79	2.76	2.74	2.72	2.70	2.69	2.67	2.66	2.65	2.64	2.63
	12	2.69	2.66	2.64	2.62	2.60	2.58	2.57	2.56	2.54	2.53	2.52
	13	2.60	2.58	2.55	2.53	2.51	2.50	2.48	2.47	2.46	2.45	2.44
	14	2.53	2.51	2.48	2.46	2.44	2.43	2.41	2.40	2.39	2.38	2.37
	15	2.48	2.45	2.42	2.40	2.38	2.37	2.35	2.34	2.33	2.32	2.31
	16	2.42	2.40	2.37	2.35	2.33	2.32	2.30	2.29	2.28	2.26	2.25
	17	2.38	2.35	2.33	2.31	2.29	2.27	2.26	2.24	2.23	2.22	2.21
	18	2.34	2.31	2.29	2.27	2.25	2.23	2.22	2.20	2.19	2.18	2.17
	19	2.31	2.28	2.26	2.23	2.21	2.20	2.18	2.17	2.16	2.14	2.13
	20	2.28	2.25	2.22	2.20	2.18	2.17	2.15	2.14	2.12	2.11	2.10
	21	2.25	2.22	2.20	2.18	2.16	2.14	2.12	2.11	2.10	2.08	2.07
	22	2.23	2.20	2.17	2.15	2.13	2.11	2.10	2.08	2.07	2.06	2.05
	23	2.20	2.18	2.15	2.13	2.11	2.09	2.08	2.06	2.05	2.04	2.02
	24	2.18	2.15	2.13	2.11	2.09	2.07	2.05	2.04	2.03	2.01	2.00
	25	2.16	2.14	2.11	2.09	2.07	2.05	2.04	2.02	2.01	2.00	1.98
	26	2.15	2.12	2.09	2.07	2.05	2.03	2.02	2.00	1.99	1.98	1.97
	27	2.13	2.10	2.08	2.06	2.04	2.02	2.00	1.99	1.97	1.96	1.95
	28	2.12	2.09	2.06	2.04	2.02	2.00	1.99	1.97	1.96	1.95	1.93
	29	2.10	2.08	2.05	2.03	2.01	1.99	1.97	1.96	1.94	1.93	1.92
	30	2.09	2.06	2.04	2.01	1.99	1.98	1.96	1.95	1.93	1.92	1.91
	40	2.00	1.97	1.95	1.92	1.90	1.89	1.87	1.85	1.84	1.83	1.81
	60	1.92	1.89	1.86	1.84	1.82	1.80	1.78	1.76	1.75	1.73	1.72
	100	1.85	1.82	1.79	1.77	1.75	1.73	1.71	1.69	1.68	1.66	1.65

Continued

F distribution F$_{0.05}$ *(continued)*

		Numerator degrees of freedom										
		23	24	25	26	27	28	29	30	40	60	100
	1	248.8	249.1	249.3	249.5	249.6	249.8	250.0	250.1	251.1	252.2	253.0
	2	19.45	19.45	19.46	19.46	19.46	19.46	19.46	19.46	19.47	19.48	19.49
	3	8.64	8.64	8.63	8.63	8.63	8.62	8.62	8.62	8.59	8.57	8.55
	4	5.78	5.77	5.77	5.76	5.76	5.75	5.75	5.75	5.72	5.69	5.66
	5	4.53	4.53	4.52	4.52	4.51	4.50	4.50	4.50	4.46	4.43	4.41
	6	3.85	3.84	3.83	3.83	3.82	3.82	3.81	3.81	3.77	3.74	3.71
	7	3.42	3.41	3.40	3.40	3.39	3.39	3.38	3.38	3.34	3.30	3.27
	8	3.12	3.12	3.11	3.10	3.10	3.09	3.08	3.08	3.04	3.01	2.97
	9	2.91	2.90	2.89	2.89	2.88	2.87	2.87	2.86	2.83	2.79	2.76
	10	2.75	2.74	2.73	2.72	2.72	2.71	2.70	2.70	2.66	2.62	2.59
Denominator degrees of freedom	11	2.62	2.61	2.60	2.59	2.59	2.58	2.58	2.57	2.53	2.49	2.46
	12	2.51	2.51	2.50	2.49	2.48	2.48	2.47	2.47	2.43	2.38	2.35
	13	2.43	2.42	2.41	2.41	2.40	2.39	2.39	2.38	2.34	2.30	2.26
	14	2.36	2.35	2.34	2.33	2.33	2.32	2.31	2.31	2.27	2.22	2.19
	15	2.30	2.29	2.28	2.27	2.27	2.26	2.25	2.25	2.20	2.16	2.12
	16	2.24	2.24	2.23	2.22	2.21	2.21	2.20	2.19	2.15	2.11	2.07
	17	2.20	2.19	2.18	2.17	2.17	2.16	2.15	2.15	2.10	2.06	2.02
	18	2.16	2.15	2.14	2.13	2.13	2.12	2.11	2.11	2.06	2.02	1.98
	19	2.12	2.11	2.11	2.10	2.09	2.08	2.08	2.07	2.03	1.98	1.94
	20	2.09	2.08	2.07	2.07	2.06	2.05	2.05	2.04	1.99	1.95	1.91
	21	2.06	2.05	2.05	2.04	2.03	2.02	2.02	2.01	1.96	1.92	1.88
	22	2.04	2.03	2.02	2.01	2.00	2.00	1.99	1.98	1.94	1.89	1.85
	23	2.01	2.01	2.00	1.99	1.98	1.97	1.97	1.96	1.91	1.86	1.82
	24	1.99	1.98	1.97	1.97	1.96	1.95	1.95	1.94	1.89	1.84	1.80
	25	1.97	1.96	1.96	1.95	1.94	1.93	1.93	1.92	1.87	1.82	1.78
	26	1.96	1.95	1.94	1.93	1.92	1.91	1.91	1.90	1.85	1.80	1.76
	27	1.94	1.93	1.92	1.91	1.90	1.90	1.89	1.88	1.84	1.79	1.74
	28	1.92	1.91	1.91	1.90	1.89	1.88	1.88	1.87	1.82	1.77	1.73
	29	1.91	1.90	1.89	1.88	1.88	1.87	1.86	1.85	1.81	1.75	1.71
	30	1.90	1.89	1.88	1.87	1.86	1.85	1.85	1.84	1.79	1.74	1.70
	40	1.80	1.79	1.78	1.77	1.77	1.76	1.75	1.74	1.69	1.64	1.59
	60	1.71	1.70	1.69	1.68	1.67	1.66	1.66	1.65	1.59	1.53	1.48
	100	1.64	1.63	1.62	1.61	1.60	1.59	1.58	1.57	1.52	1.45	1.39

Appendix H
F Distribution $F_{0.01}$

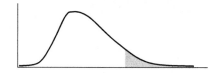

F distribution F$_{0.01}$

		Numerator degrees of freedom									
	1	**2**	**3**	**4**	**5**	**6**	**7**	**8**	**9**	**10**	**11**
1	4052	4999	5404	5624	5764	5859	5928	5981	6022	6056	6083
2	98.5	99	99.16	99.25	99.3	99.33	99.36	99.38	99.39	99.4	99.41
3	34.12	30.82	29.46	28.71	28.24	27.91	27.67	27.49	27.34	27.23	27.13
4	21.2	18	16.69	15.98	15.52	15.21	14.98	14.8	14.66	14.55	14.45
5	16.26	13.27	12.06	11.39	10.97	10.67	10.46	10.29	10.16	10.05	9.963
6	13.75	10.92	9.78	9.148	8.746	8.466	8.26	8.102	7.976	7.874	7.79
7	12.25	9.547	8.451	7.847	7.46	7.191	6.993	6.84	6.719	6.62	6.538
8	11.26	8.649	7.591	7.006	6.632	6.371	6.178	6.029	5.911	5.814	5.734
9	10.56	8.022	6.992	6.422	6.057	5.802	5.613	5.467	5.351	5.257	5.178
10	10.04	7.559	6.552	5.994	5.636	5.386	5.2	5.057	4.942	4.849	4.772
11	9.646	7.206	6.217	5.668	5.316	5.069	4.886	4.744	4.632	4.539	4.462
12	9.33	6.927	5.953	5.412	5.064	4.821	4.64	4.499	4.388	4.296	4.22
13	9.074	6.701	5.739	5.205	4.862	4.62	4.441	4.302	4.191	4.1	4.025
14	8.862	6.515	5.564	5.035	4.695	4.456	4.278	4.14	4.03	3.939	3.864
15	8.683	6.359	5.417	4.893	4.556	4.318	4.142	4.004	3.895	3.805	3.73
16	8.531	6.226	5.292	4.773	4.437	4.202	4.026	3.89	3.78	3.691	3.616
17	8.4	6.112	5.185	4.669	4.336	4.101	3.927	3.791	3.682	3.593	3.518
18	8.285	6.013	5.092	4.579	4.248	4.015	3.841	3.705	3.597	3.508	3.434
19	8.185	5.926	5.01	4.5	4.171	3.939	3.765	3.631	3.523	3.434	3.36
20	8.096	5.849	4.938	4.431	4.103	3.871	3.699	3.564	3.457	3.368	3.294
21	8.017	5.78	4.874	4.369	4.042	3.812	3.64	3.506	3.398	3.31	3.236
22	7.945	5.719	4.817	4.313	3.988	3.758	3.587	3.453	3.346	3.258	3.184
23	7.881	5.664	4.765	4.264	3.939	3.71	3.539	3.406	3.299	3.211	3.137
24	7.823	5.614	4.718	4.218	3.895	3.667	3.496	3.363	3.256	3.168	3.094
25	7.77	5.568	4.675	4.177	3.855	3.627	3.457	3.324	3.217	3.129	3.056
26	7.721	5.526	4.637	4.14	3.818	3.591	3.421	3.288	3.182	3.094	3.021
27	7.677	5.488	4.601	4.106	3.785	3.558	3.388	3.256	3.149	3.062	2.988
28	7.636	5.453	4.568	4.074	3.754	3.528	3.358	3.226	3.12	3.032	2.959
29	7.598	5.42	4.538	4.045	3.725	3.499	3.33	3.198	3.092	3.005	2.931
30	7.562	5.39	4.51	4.018	3.699	3.473	3.305	3.173	3.067	2.979	2.906
40	7.314	5.178	4.313	3.828	3.514	3.291	3.124	2.993	2.888	2.801	2.727
60	7.077	4.977	4.126	3.649	3.339	3.119	2.953	2.823	2.718	2.632	2.559
100	6.895	4.824	3.984	3.513	3.206	2.988	2.823	2.694	2.59	2.503	2.43

Denominator degrees of freedom

F distribution $F_{0.01}$ *(continued)*

		Numerator degrees of freedom									
	12	**13**	**14**	**15**	**16**	**17**	**18**	**19**	**20**	**21**	**22**
1	6107	6126	6143	6157	6170	6181	6191	6201	6208.7	6216.1	6223.1
2	99.42	99.42	99.43	99.43	99.44	99.44	99.44	99.45	99.448	99.451	99.455
3	27.05	26.98	26.92	26.87	26.83	26.79	26.75	26.72	26.69	26.664	26.639
4	14.37	14.31	14.25	14.2	14.15	14.11	14.08	14.05	14.019	13.994	13.97
5	9.888	9.825	9.77	9.722	9.68	9.643	9.609	9.58	9.5527	9.5281	9.5058
6	7.718	7.657	7.605	7.559	7.519	7.483	7.451	7.422	7.3958	7.3721	7.3506
7	6.469	6.41	6.359	6.314	6.275	6.24	6.209	6.181	6.1555	6.1324	6.1113
8	5.667	5.609	5.559	5.515	5.477	5.442	5.412	5.384	5.3591	5.3365	5.3157
9	5.111	5.055	5.005	4.962	4.924	4.89	4.86	4.833	4.808	4.7855	4.7651
10	4.706	4.65	4.601	4.558	4.52	4.487	4.457	4.43	4.4054	4.3831	4.3628
11	4.397	4.342	4.293	4.251	4.213	4.18	4.15	4.123	4.099	4.0769	4.0566
12	4.155	4.1	4.052	4.01	3.972	3.939	3.91	3.883	3.8584	3.8363	3.8161
13	3.96	3.905	3.857	3.815	3.778	3.745	3.716	3.689	3.6646	3.6425	3.6223
14	3.8	3.745	3.698	3.656	3.619	3.586	3.556	3.529	3.5052	3.4832	3.463
15	3.666	3.612	3.564	3.522	3.485	3.452	3.423	3.396	3.3719	3.3498	3.3297
16	3.553	3.498	3.451	3.409	3.372	3.339	3.31	3.283	3.2587	3.2367	3.2165
17	3.455	3.401	3.353	3.312	3.275	3.242	3.212	3.186	3.1615	3.1394	3.1192
18	3.371	3.316	3.269	3.227	3.19	3.158	3.128	3.101	3.0771	3.055	3.0348
19	3.297	3.242	3.195	3.153	3.116	3.084	3.054	3.027	3.0031	2.981	2.9607
20	3.231	3.177	3.13	3.088	3.051	3.018	2.989	2.962	2.9377	2.9156	2.8953
21	3.173	3.119	3.072	3.03	2.993	2.96	2.931	2.904	2.8795	2.8574	2.837
22	3.121	3.067	3.019	2.978	2.941	2.908	2.879	2.852	2.8274	2.8052	2.7849
23	3.074	3.02	2.973	2.931	2.894	2.861	2.832	2.805	2.7805	2.7582	2.7378
24	3.032	2.977	2.93	2.889	2.852	2.819	2.789	2.762	2.738	2.7157	2.6953
25	2.993	2.939	2.892	2.85	2.813	2.78	2.751	2.724	2.6993	2.677	2.6565
26	2.958	2.904	2.857	2.815	2.778	2.745	2.715	2.688	2.664	2.6416	2.6211
27	2.926	2.872	2.824	2.783	2.746	2.713	2.683	2.656	2.6316	2.609	2.5886
28	2.896	2.842	2.795	2.753	2.716	2.683	2.653	2.626	2.6018	2.5793	2.5587
29	2.868	2.814	2.767	2.726	2.689	2.656	2.626	2.599	2.5742	2.5517	2.5311
30	2.843	2.789	2.742	2.7	2.663	2.63	2.6	2.573	2.5487	2.5262	2.5055
40	2.665	2.611	2.563	2.522	2.484	2.451	2.421	2.394	2.3689	2.3461	2.3252
60	2.496	2.442	2.394	2.352	2.315	2.281	2.251	2.223	2.1978	2.1747	2.1533
10	2.368	2.313	2.265	2.223	2.185	2.151	2.12	2.092	2.0666	2.0431	2.0214

Continued

F distribution $F_{0.01}$ *(continued)*

Denominator degrees of freedom	Numerator degrees of freedom										
	23	24	25	26	27	28	29	30	40	60	100
1	6228.7	6234.3	6239.9	6244.5	6249.2	6252.9	6257.1	6260.4	6286.4	6313	6333.9
2	99.455	99.455	99.459	99.462	99.462	99.462	99.462	99.466	99.477	99.484	99.491
3	26.617	26.597	26.579	26.562	26.546	26.531	26.517	26.504	26.411	26.316	26.241
4	13.949	13.929	13.911	13.894	13.878	13.864	13.85	13.838	13.745	13.652	13.577
5	9.4853	9.4665	9.4492	9.4331	9.4183	9.4044	9.3914	9.3794	9.2912	9.202	9.13
6	7.3309	7.3128	7.296	7.2805	7.2661	7.2528	7.2403	7.2286	7.1432	7.0568	6.9867
7	6.092	6.0743	6.0579	6.0428	6.0287	6.0156	6.0035	5.992	5.9084	5.8236	5.7546
8	5.2967	5.2793	5.2631	5.2482	5.2344	5.2214	5.2094	5.1981	5.1156	5.0316	4.9633
9	4.7463	4.729	4.713	4.6982	4.6845	4.6717	4.6598	4.6486	4.5667	4.4831	4.415
10	4.3441	4.3269	4.3111	4.2963	4.2827	4.27	4.2582	4.2469	4.1653	4.0819	4.0137
11	4.038	4.0209	4.0051	3.9904	3.9768	3.9641	3.9522	3.9411	3.8596	3.7761	3.7077
12	3.7976	3.7805	3.7647	3.7501	3.7364	3.7238	3.7119	3.7008	3.6192	3.5355	3.4668
13	3.6038	3.5868	3.571	3.5563	3.5427	3.53	3.5182	3.507	3.4253	3.3413	3.2723
14	3.4445	3.4274	3.4116	3.3969	3.3833	3.3706	3.3587	3.3476	3.2657	3.1813	3.1118
15	3.3111	3.294	3.2782	3.2636	3.2499	3.2372	3.2253	3.2141	3.1319	3.0471	2.9772
16	3.1979	3.1808	3.165	3.1503	3.1366	3.1238	3.1119	3.1007	3.0182	2.933	2.8627
17	3.1006	3.0835	3.0676	3.0529	3.0392	3.0264	3.0145	3.0032	2.9204	2.8348	2.7639
18	3.0161	2.999	2.9831	2.9683	2.9546	2.9418	2.9298	2.9185	2.8354	2.7493	2.6779
19	2.9421	2.9249	2.9089	2.8942	2.8804	2.8675	2.8555	2.8442	2.7608	2.6742	2.6023
20	2.8766	2.8594	2.8434	2.8286	2.8148	2.8019	2.7898	2.7785	2.6947	2.6077	2.5353
21	2.8183	2.801	2.785	2.7702	2.7563	2.7434	2.7313	2.72	2.6359	2.5484	2.4755
22	2.7661	2.7488	2.7328	2.7179	2.704	2.691	2.6789	2.6675	2.5831	2.4951	2.4218
23	2.7191	2.7017	2.6857	2.6707	2.6568	2.6438	2.6316	2.6202	2.5355	2.4471	2.3732
24	2.6764	2.6591	2.643	2.628	2.614	2.601	2.5888	2.5773	2.4923	2.4035	2.3291
25	2.6377	2.6203	2.6041	2.5891	2.5751	2.562	2.5498	2.5383	2.453	2.3637	2.2888
26	2.6022	2.5848	2.5686	2.5535	2.5395	2.5264	2.5142	2.5026	2.417	2.3273	2.2519
27	2.5697	2.5522	2.536	2.5209	2.5069	2.4937	2.4814	2.4699	2.384	2.2938	2.218
28	2.5398	2.5223	2.506	2.4909	2.4768	2.4636	2.4513	2.4397	2.3535	2.2629	2.1867
29	2.5121	2.4946	2.4783	2.4631	2.449	2.4358	2.4234	2.4118	2.3253	2.2344	2.1577
30	2.4865	2.4689	2.4526	2.4374	2.4233	2.41	2.3976	2.386	2.2992	2.2079	2.1307
40	2.3059	2.288	2.2714	2.2559	2.2415	2.228	2.2153	2.2034	2.1142	2.0194	1.9383
60	2.1336	2.1154	2.0984	2.0825	2.0677	2.0538	2.0408	2.0285	1.936	1.8363	1.7493
100	2.0012	1.9826	1.9651	1.9489	1.9337	1.9194	1.9059	1.8933	1.7972	1.6918	1.5977

Appendix I
Binomial Distribution

Probability of x or fewer occurrences in a sample of size n

Binomial distribution

n	x	0.01	0.02	0.03	0.04	0.05	0.06	0.07	0.08	0.09	0.10	0.15	0.20	0.25	0.30	0.35	0.40	0.45	0.50
2	0	0.980	0.960	0.941	0.922	0.903	0.884	0.865	0.846	0.828	0.810	0.723	0.640	0.563	0.490	0.423	0.360	0.303	0.250
2	1	1.000	1.000	0.999	0.998	0.998	0.996	0.995	0.994	0.992	0.990	0.978	0.960	0.938	0.910	0.878	0.840	0.798	0.750
3	0	0.970	0.941	0.913	0.885	0.857	0.831	0.804	0.779	0.754	0.729	0.614	0.512	0.422	0.343	0.275	0.216	0.166	0.125
3	1	1.000	0.999	0.997	0.995	0.993	0.990	0.986	0.982	0.977	0.972	0.939	0.896	0.844	0.784	0.718	0.648	0.575	0.500
3	2	1.000	1.000	1.000	1.000	1.000	1.000	1.000	0.999	0.999	0.999	0.997	0.992	0.984	0.973	0.957	0.936	0.909	0.875
4	0	0.961	0.922	0.885	0.849	0.815	0.781	0.748	0.716	0.686	0.656	0.522	0.410	0.316	0.240	0.179	0.130	0.092	0.063
4	1	0.999	0.998	0.995	0.991	0.986	0.980	0.973	0.966	0.957	0.948	0.890	0.819	0.738	0.652	0.563	0.475	0.391	0.313
4	2	1.000	1.000	1.000	1.000	1.000	0.999	0.999	0.998	0.997	0.996	0.988	0.973	0.949	0.916	0.874	0.821	0.759	0.688
4	3	1.000	1.000	1.000	1.000	1.000	1.000	1.000	1.000	1.000	1.000	0.999	0.998	0.996	0.992	0.985	0.974	0.959	0.938
5	0	0.951	0.904	0.859	0.815	0.774	0.734	0.696	0.659	0.624	0.590	0.444	0.328	0.237	0.168	0.116	0.078	0.050	0.031
5	1	0.999	0.996	0.992	0.985	0.977	0.968	0.958	0.946	0.933	0.919	0.835	0.737	0.633	0.528	0.428	0.337	0.256	0.188
5	2	1.000	1.000	1.000	0.999	0.999	0.998	0.997	0.995	0.994	0.991	0.973	0.942	0.896	0.837	0.765	0.683	0.593	0.500
5	3	1.000	1.000	1.000	1.000	1.000	1.000	1.000	1.000	1.000	1.000	0.998	0.993	0.984	0.969	0.946	0.913	0.869	0.813
5	4	1.000	1.000	1.000	1.000	1.000	1.000	1.000	1.000	1.000	1.000	1.000	1.000	0.999	0.998	0.995	0.990	0.982	0.969
6	0	0.941	0.886	0.833	0.783	0.735	0.690	0.647	0.606	0.568	0.531	0.377	0.262	0.178	0.118	0.075	0.047	0.028	0.016
6	1	0.999	0.994	0.988	0.978	0.967	0.954	0.939	0.923	0.905	0.886	0.776	0.655	0.534	0.420	0.319	0.233	0.164	0.109
6	2	1.000	1.000	0.999	0.999	0.998	0.996	0.994	0.991	0.988	0.984	0.953	0.901	0.831	0.744	0.647	0.544	0.442	0.344
6	3	1.000	1.000	1.000	1.000	1.000	1.000	1.000	0.999	0.999	0.999	0.994	0.983	0.962	0.930	0.883	0.821	0.745	0.656
6	4	1.000	1.000	1.000	1.000	1.000	1.000	1.000	1.000	1.000	1.000	0.998	0.995	0.989	0.978	0.959	0.931	0.891
6	5	1.000	1.000	1.000	1.000	1.000	1.000	1.000	1.000	1.000	1.000	1.000	1.000	1.000	0.999	0.998	0.996	0.992	0.984
7	0	0.932	0.868	0.808	0.751	0.698	0.648	0.602	0.558	0.517	0.478	0.321	0.210	0.133	0.082	0.049	0.028	0.015	0.008
7	1	0.998	0.992	0.983	0.971	0.956	0.938	0.919	0.897	0.875	0.850	0.717	0.577	0.445	0.329	0.234	0.159	0.102	0.063
7	2	1.000	1.000	0.999	0.998	0.996	0.994	0.990	0.986	0.981	0.974	0.926	0.852	0.756	0.647	0.532	0.420	0.316	0.227
7	3	1.000	1.000	1.000	1.000	1.000	1.000	0.999	0.999	0.998	0.997	0.988	0.967	0.929	0.874	0.800	0.710	0.608	0.500
7	4	1.000	1.000	1.000	1.000	1.000	1.000	1.000	1.000	1.000	1.000	0.999	0.995	0.987	0.971	0.944	0.904	0.847	0.773
7	5	1.000	1.000	1.000	1.000	1.000	1.000	1.000	1.000	1.000	1.000	1.000	1.000	0.999	0.996	0.991	0.981	0.964	0.938
7	6	1.000	1.000	1.000	1.000	1.000	1.000	1.000	1.000	1.000	1.000	1.000	1.000	1.000	1.000	0.999	0.998	0.996	0.992

Continued

591

Binomial distribution *(continued)*

n	x	0.01	0.02	0.03	0.04	0.05	0.06	0.07	0.08	0.09	0.10	0.15	0.20	0.25	0.30	0.35	0.40	0.45	0.50
8	0	0.923	0.851	0.784	0.721	0.663	0.610	0.560	0.513	0.470	0.430	0.272	0.168	0.100	0.058	0.032	0.017	0.008	0.004
8	1	0.997	0.990	0.978	0.962	0.943	0.921	0.897	0.870	0.842	0.813	0.657	0.503	0.367	0.255	0.169	0.106	0.063	0.035
8	2	1.000	1.000	0.999	0.997	0.994	0.990	0.985	0.979	0.971	0.962	0.895	0.797	0.679	0.552	0.428	0.315	0.220	0.145
8	3	1.000	1.000	1.000	1.000	1.000	0.999	0.999	0.998	0.997	0.995	0.979	0.944	0.886	0.806	0.706	0.594	0.477	0.363
8	4	1.000	1.000	1.000	1.000	1.000	1.000	1.000	1.000	1.000	1.000	0.997	0.990	0.973	0.942	0.894	0.826	0.740	0.637
8	5	1.000	1.000	1.000	1.000	1.000	1.000	1.000	1.000	1.000	1.000	1.000	0.999	0.996	0.989	0.975	0.950	0.912	0.855
8	6	1.000	1.000	1.000	1.000	1.000	1.000	1.000	1.000	1.000	1.000	1.000	1.000	1.000	0.999	0.996	0.991	0.982	0.965
8	7	1.000	1.000	1.000	1.000	1.000	1.000	1.000	1.000	1.000	1.000	1.000	1.000	1.000	1.000	1.000	0.999	0.998	0.996
9	0	0.914	0.834	0.760	0.693	0.630	0.573	0.520	0.472	0.428	0.387	0.232	0.134	0.075	0.040	0.021	0.010	0.005	0.002
9	1	0.997	0.987	0.972	0.952	0.929	0.902	0.873	0.842	0.809	0.775	0.599	0.436	0.300	0.196	0.121	0.071	0.039	0.020
9	2	1.000	0.999	0.998	0.996	0.992	0.986	0.979	0.970	0.960	0.947	0.859	0.738	0.601	0.463	0.337	0.232	0.150	0.090
9	3	1.000	1.000	1.000	1.000	0.999	0.999	0.998	0.996	0.994	0.992	0.966	0.914	0.834	0.730	0.609	0.483	0.361	0.254
9	4	1.000	1.000	1.000	1.000	1.000	1.000	1.000	1.000	0.999	0.999	0.994	0.980	0.951	0.901	0.828	0.733	0.621	0.500
9	5	1.000	1.000	1.000	1.000	1.000	1.000	1.000	1.000	1.000	1.000	0.999	0.997	0.990	0.975	0.946	0.901	0.834	0.746
9	6	1.000	1.000	1.000	1.000	1.000	1.000	1.000	1.000	1.000	1.000	1.000	1.000	0.999	0.996	0.989	0.975	0.950	0.910
9	7	1.000	1.000	1.000	1.000	1.000	1.000	1.000	1.000	1.000	1.000	1.000	1.000	1.000	0.999	0.996	0.991	0.980
9	8	1.000	1.000	1.000	1.000	1.000	1.000	1.000	1.000	1.000	1.000	1.000	1.000	1.000	1.000	1.000	1.000	0.999	0.998
10	0	0.904	0.817	0.737	0.665	0.599	0.539	0.484	0.434	0.389	0.349	0.197	0.107	0.056	0.028	0.013	0.006	0.003	0.001
10	1	0.996	0.984	0.965	0.942	0.914	0.882	0.848	0.812	0.775	0.736	0.544	0.376	0.244	0.149	0.086	0.046	0.023	0.011
10	2	1.000	0.999	0.997	0.994	0.988	0.981	0.972	0.960	0.946	0.930	0.820	0.678	0.526	0.383	0.262	0.167	0.100	0.055
10	3	1.000	1.000	1.000	1.000	0.999	0.998	0.996	0.994	0.991	0.987	0.950	0.879	0.776	0.650	0.514	0.382	0.266	0.172
10	4	1.000	1.000	1.000	1.000	1.000	1.000	1.000	0.999	0.999	0.998	0.990	0.967	0.922	0.850	0.751	0.633	0.504	0.377
10	5	1.000	1.000	1.000	1.000	1.000	1.000	1.000	1.000	1.000	1.000	0.999	0.994	0.980	0.953	0.905	0.834	0.738	0.623

Appendix J
Chi-Square Distribution

Chi-square distribution

df	$\chi^2_{0.995}$	$\chi^2_{0.99}$	$\chi^2_{0.975}$	$\chi^2_{0.95}$	$\chi^2_{0.90}$	$\chi^2_{0.10}$	$\chi^2_{0.05}$	$\chi^2_{0.025}$	$\chi^2_{0.01}$	$\chi^2_{0.005}$
1	0.000	0.000	0.001	0.004	0.016	2.706	3.841	5.024	6.635	7.879
2	0.010	0.020	0.051	0.103	0.211	4.605	5.991	7.378	9.210	10.597
3	0.072	0.115	0.216	0.352	0.584	6.251	7.815	9.348	11.345	12.838
4	0.207	0.297	0.484	0.711	1.064	7.779	9.488	11.143	13.277	14.860
5	0.412	0.554	0.831	1.145	1.610	9.236	11.070	12.832	15.086	16.750
6	0.676	0.872	1.237	1.635	2.204	10.645	12.592	14.449	16.812	18.548
7	0.989	1.239	1.690	2.167	2.833	12.017	14.067	16.013	18.475	20.278
8	1.344	1.647	2.180	2.733	3.490	13.362	15.507	17.535	20.090	21.955
9	1.735	2.088	2.700	3.325	4.168	14.684	16.919	19.023	21.666	23.589
10	2.156	2.558	3.247	3.940	4.865	15.987	18.307	20.483	23.209	25.188
11	2.603	3.053	3.816	4.575	5.578	17.275	19.675	21.920	24.725	26.757
12	3.074	3.571	4.404	5.226	6.304	18.549	21.026	23.337	26.217	28.300
13	3.565	4.107	5.009	5.892	7.041	19.812	22.362	24.736	27.688	29.819
14	4.075	4.660	5.629	6.571	7.790	21.064	23.685	26.119	29.141	31.319
15	4.601	5.229	6.262	7.261	8.547	22.307	24.996	27.488	30.578	32.801
16	5.142	5.812	6.908	7.962	9.312	23.542	26.296	28.845	32.000	34.267
17	5.697	6.408	7.564	8.672	10.085	24.769	27.587	30.191	33.409	35.718
18	6.265	7.015	8.231	9.390	10.865	25.989	28.869	31.526	34.805	37.156
19	6.844	7.633	8.907	10.117	11.651	27.204	30.144	32.852	36.191	38.582
20	7.434	8.260	9.591	10.851	12.443	28.412	31.410	34.170	37.566	39.997
21	8.034	8.897	10.283	11.591	13.240	29.615	32.671	35.479	38.932	41.401
22	8.643	9.542	10.982	12.338	14.041	30.813	33.924	36.781	40.289	42.796
23	9.260	10.196	11.689	13.091	14.848	32.007	35.172	38.076	41.638	44.181
24	9.886	10.856	12.401	13.848	15.659	33.196	36.415	39.364	42.980	45.558
25	10.520	11.524	13.120	14.611	16.473	34.382	37.652	40.646	44.314	46.928
26	11.160	12.198	13.844	15.379	17.292	35.563	38.885	41.923	45.642	48.290
27	11.808	12.878	14.573	16.151	18.114	36.741	40.113	43.195	46.963	49.645
28	12.461	13.565	15.308	16.928	18.939	37.916	41.337	44.461	48.278	50.994

Continued

Chi-square distribution *(continued)*

df	$\chi^2_{0.995}$	$\chi^2_{0.99}$	$\chi^2_{0.975}$	$\chi^2_{0.95}$	$\chi^2_{0.90}$	$\chi^2_{0.10}$	$\chi^2_{0.05}$	$\chi^2_{0.025}$	$\chi^2_{0.01}$	$\chi^2_{0.005}$
29	13.121	14.256	16.047	17.708	19.768	39.087	42.557	45.722	49.588	52.335
30	13.787	14.953	16.791	18.493	20.599	40.256	43.773	46.979	50.892	53.672
31	14.458	15.655	17.539	19.281	21.434	41.422	44.985	48.232	52.191	55.002
32	15.134	16.362	18.291	20.072	22.271	42.585	46.194	49.480	53.486	56.328
33	15.815	17.073	19.047	20.867	23.110	43.745	47.400	50.725	54.775	57.648
34	16.501	17.789	19.806	21.664	23.952	44.903	48.602	51.966	56.061	58.964
35	17.192	18.509	20.569	22.465	24.797	46.059	49.802	53.203	57.342	60.275
40	20.707	22.164	24.433	26.509	29.051	51.805	55.758	59.342	63.691	66.766
45	24.311	25.901	28.366	30.612	33.350	57.505	61.656	65.410	69.957	73.166
50	27.991	29.707	32.357	34.764	37.689	63.167	67.505	71.420	76.154	79.490
55	31.735	33.571	36.398	38.958	42.060	68.796	73.311	77.380	82.292	85.749
60	35.534	37.485	40.482	43.188	46.459	74.397	79.082	83.298	88.379	91.952
65	39.383	41.444	44.603	47.450	50.883	79.973	84.821	89.177	94.422	98.105
70	43.275	45.442	48.758	51.739	55.329	85.527	90.531	95.023	100.425	104.215
75	47.206	49.475	52.942	56.054	59.795	91.061	96.217	100.839	106.393	110.285
80	51.172	53.540	57.153	60.391	64.278	96.578	101.879	106.629	112.329	116.321
85	55.170	57.634	61.389	64.749	68.777	102.079	107.522	112.393	118.236	122.324
90	59.196	61.754	65.647	69.126	73.291	107.565	113.145	118.136	124.116	128.299
95	63.250	65.898	69.925	73.520	77.818	113.038	118.752	123.858	129.973	134.247
100	67.328	70.065	74.222	77.929	82.358	118.498	124.342	129.561	135.807	140.170

Appendix K
Exponential Distribution

Exponential distribution

X	Area to left of X	Area to right of X
0	0.00000	1.00000
0.1	0.09516	0.90484
0.2	0.18127	0.81873
0.3	0.25918	0.74082
0.4	0.32968	0.67032
0.5	0.39347	0.60653
0.6	0.45119	0.54881
0.7	0.50341	0.49659
0.8	0.55067	0.44933
0.9	0.59343	0.40657
1	0.63212	0.36788
1.1	0.66713	0.33287
1.2	0.69881	0.30119
1.3	0.72747	0.27253
1.4	0.75340	0.24660
1.5	0.77687	0.22313
1.6	0.79810	0.20190
1.7	0.81732	0.18268
1.8	0.83470	0.16530
1.9	0.85043	0.14957
2	0.86466	0.13534
2.1	0.87754	0.12246
2.2	0.88920	0.11080
2.3	0.89974	0.10026
2.4	0.90928	0.09072
2.5	0.91792	0.08208
2.6	0.92573	0.07427

Continued

Exponential distribution *(continued)*

X	Area to left of X	Area to right of X
2.7	0.93279	0.06721
2.8	0.93919	0.06081
2.9	0.94498	0.05502
3	0.95021	0.04979
3.1	0.95495	0.04505
3.2	0.95924	0.04076
3.3	0.96312	0.03688
3.4	0.96663	0.03337
3.5	0.96980	0.03020
3.6	0.97268	0.02732
3.7	0.97528	0.02472
3.8	0.97763	0.02237
3.9	0.97976	0.02024
4	0.98168	0.01832
4.1	0.98343	0.01657
4.2	0.98500	0.01500
4.3	0.98643	0.01357
4.4	0.98772	0.01228
4.5	0.98889	0.01111
4.6	0.98995	0.01005
4.7	0.99090	0.00910
4.8	0.99177	0.00823
4.9	0.99255	0.00745
5	0.99326	0.00674
5.1	0.99390	0.00610
5.2	0.99448	0.00552
5.3	0.99501	0.00499
5.4	0.99548	0.00452
5.5	0.99591	0.00409
5.6	0.99630	0.00370
5.7	0.99665	0.00335
5.8	0.99697	0.00303
5.9	0.99726	0.00274
6	0.99752	0.00248

Appendix L
Poisson Distribution

Probability of x or fewer occurrences of an event

Poisson distribution

$x\downarrow$ $n\rightarrow$	0	1	2	3	4	5	6	7	8	9	10	11	12	13	14	15	16	17
0.005	0.995	1.000	1.000	1.000	1.000	1.000	1.000	1.000	1.000	1.000	1.000	1.000	1.000	1.000	1.000	1.000	1.000	1.000
0.01	0.990	1.000	1.000	1.000	1.000	1.000	1.000	1.000	1.000	1.000	1.000	1.000	1.000	1.000	1.000	1.000	1.000	1.000
0.02	0.980	1.000	1.000	1.000	1.000	1.000	1.000	1.000	1.000	1.000	1.000	1.000	1.000	1.000	1.000	1.000	1.000	1.000
0.03	0.970	1.000	1.000	1.000	1.000	1.000	1.000	1.000	1.000	1.000	1.000	1.000	1.000	1.000	1.000	1.000	1.000	1.000
0.04	0.961	0.999	1.000	1.000	1.000	1.000	1.000	1.000	1.000	1.000	1.000	1.000	1.000	1.000	1.000	1.000	1.000	1.000
0.05	0.951	0.999	1.000	1.000	1.000	1.000	1.000	1.000	1.000	1.000	1.000	1.000	1.000	1.000	1.000	1.000	1.000	1.000
0.06	0.942	0.998	1.000	1.000	1.000	1.000	1.000	1.000	1.000	1.000	1.000	1.000	1.000	1.000	1.000	1.000	1.000	1.000
0.07	0.932	0.998	1.000	1.000	1.000	1.000	1.000	1.000	1.000	1.000	1.000	1.000	1.000	1.000	1.000	1.000	1.000	1.000
0.08	0.923	0.997	1.000	1.000	1.000	1.000	1.000	1.000	1.000	1.000	1.000	1.000	1.000	1.000	1.000	1.000	1.000	1.000
0.09	0.914	0.996	1.000	1.000	1.000	1.000	1.000	1.000	1.000	1.000	1.000	1.000	1.000	1.000	1.000	1.000	1.000	1.000
0.1	0.905	0.995	1.000	1.000	1.000	1.000	1.000	1.000	1.000	1.000	1.000	1.000	1.000	1.000	1.000	1.000	1.000	1.000
0.15	0.861	0.990	0.999	1.000	1.000	1.000	1.000	1.000	1.000	1.000	1.000	1.000	1.000	1.000	1.000	1.000	1.000	1.000
0.2	0.819	0.982	0.999	1.000	1.000	1.000	1.000	1.000	1.000	1.000	1.000	1.000	1.000	1.000	1.000	1.000	1.000	1.000
0.25	0.779	0.974	0.998	1.000	1.000	1.000	1.000	1.000	1.000	1.000	1.000	1.000	1.000	1.000	1.000	1.000	1.000	1.000
0.3	0.741	0.963	0.996	1.000	1.000	1.000	1.000	1.000	1.000	1.000	1.000	1.000	1.000	1.000	1.000	1.000	1.000	1.000
0.35	0.705	0.951	0.994	1.000	1.000	1.000	1.000	1.000	1.000	1.000	1.000	1.000	1.000	1.000	1.000	1.000	1.000	1.000
0.4	0.670	0.938	0.992	0.999	1.000	1.000	1.000	1.000	1.000	1.000	1.000	1.000	1.000	1.000	1.000	1.000	1.000	1.000
0.5	0.607	0.910	0.986	0.998	1.000	1.000	1.000	1.000	1.000	1.000	1.000	1.000	1.000	1.000	1.000	1.000	1.000	1.000
0.6	0.549	0.878	0.977	0.997	1.000	1.000	1.000	1.000	1.000	1.000	1.000	1.000	1.000	1.000	1.000	1.000	1.000	1.000
0.7	0.497	0.844	0.966	0.994	0.999	1.000	1.000	1.000	1.000	1.000	1.000	1.000	1.000	1.000	1.000	1.000	1.000	1.000
0.8	0.449	0.809	0.953	0.991	0.999	1.000	1.000	1.000	1.000	1.000	1.000	1.000	1.000	1.000	1.000	1.000	1.000	1.000
0.9	0.407	0.772	0.937	0.987	0.998	1.000	1.000	1.000	1.000	1.000	1.000	1.000	1.000	1.000	1.000	1.000	1.000	1.000
1	0.368	0.736	0.920	0.981	0.996	0.999	1.000	1.000	1.000	1.000	1.000	1.000	1.000	1.000	1.000	1.000	1.000	1.000
1.2	0.301	0.663	0.879	0.966	0.992	0.998	1.000	1.000	1.000	1.000	1.000	1.000	1.000	1.000	1.000	1.000	1.000	1.000
1.4	0.247	0.592	0.833	0.946	0.986	0.997	0.999	1.000	1.000	1.000	1.000	1.000	1.000	1.000	1.000	1.000	1.000	1.000
1.6	0.202	0.525	0.783	0.921	0.976	0.994	0.999	1.000	1.000	1.000	1.000	1.000	1.000	1.000	1.000	1.000	1.000	1.000
1.8	0.165	0.463	0.731	0.891	0.964	0.990	0.997	0.999	1.000	1.000	1.000	1.000	1.000	1.000	1.000	1.000	1.000	1.000
2	0.135	0.406	0.677	0.857	0.947	0.983	0.995	0.999	1.000	1.000	1.000	1.000	1.000	1.000	1.000	1.000	1.000	1.000

Continued

Poisson distribution *(continued)*

$x\downarrow\ n\rightarrow$	0	1	2	3	4	5	6	7	8	9	10	11	12	13	14	15	16	17
2.2	0.111	0.355	0.623	0.819	0.928	0.975	0.993	0.998	1.000	1.000	1.000	1.000	1.000	1.000	1.000	1.000	1.000	1.000
2.4	0.091	0.308	0.570	0.779	0.904	0.964	0.988	0.997	0.999	1.000	1.000	1.000	1.000	1.000	1.000	1.000	1.000	1.000
2.6	0.074	0.267	0.518	0.736	0.877	0.951	0.983	0.995	0.999	1.000	1.000	1.000	1.000	1.000	1.000	1.000	1.000	1.000
2.8	0.061	0.231	0.469	0.692	0.848	0.935	0.976	0.992	0.998	0.999	1.000	1.000	1.000	1.000	1.000	1.000	1.000	1.000
3	0.050	0.199	0.423	0.647	0.815	0.916	0.966	0.988	0.996	0.999	1.000	1.000	1.000	1.000	1.000	1.000	1.000	1.000
3.2	0.041	0.171	0.380	0.603	0.781	0.895	0.955	0.983	0.994	0.998	1.000	1.000	1.000	1.000	1.000	1.000	1.000	1.000
3.4	0.033	0.147	0.340	0.558	0.744	0.871	0.942	0.977	0.992	0.997	0.999	1.000	1.000	1.000	1.000	1.000	1.000	1.000
3.6	0.027	0.126	0.303	0.515	0.706	0.844	0.927	0.969	0.988	0.996	0.999	1.000	1.000	1.000	1.000	1.000	1.000	1.000
3.8	0.022	0.107	0.269	0.473	0.668	0.816	0.909	0.960	0.984	0.994	0.998	0.999	1.000	1.000	1.000	1.000	1.000	1.000
4	0.018	0.092	0.238	0.433	0.629	0.785	0.889	0.949	0.979	0.992	0.997	0.999	1.000	1.000	1.000	1.000	1.000	1.000
4.5	0.011	0.061	0.174	0.342	0.532	0.703	0.831	0.913	0.960	0.983	0.993	0.998	0.999	1.000	1.000	1.000	1.000	1.000
5	0.007	0.040	0.125	0.265	0.440	0.616	0.762	0.867	0.932	0.968	0.986	0.995	0.998	0.999	1.000	1.000	1.000	1.000
5.5	0.004	0.027	0.088	0.202	0.358	0.529	0.686	0.809	0.894	0.946	0.975	0.989	0.996	0.998	0.999	1.000	1.000	1.000
6	0.002	0.017	0.062	0.151	0.285	0.446	0.606	0.744	0.847	0.916	0.957	0.980	0.991	0.996	0.999	0.999	1.000	1.000
6.5	0.002	0.011	0.043	0.112	0.224	0.369	0.527	0.673	0.792	0.877	0.933	0.966	0.984	0.993	0.997	0.999	1.000	1.000
7	0.001	0.007	0.030	0.082	0.173	0.301	0.450	0.599	0.729	0.830	0.901	0.947	0.973	0.987	0.994	0.998	0.999	1.000
7.5	0.001	0.005	0.020	0.059	0.132	0.241	0.378	0.525	0.662	0.776	0.862	0.921	0.957	0.978	0.990	0.995	0.998	0.999
8	0.000	0.003	0.014	0.042	0.100	0.191	0.313	0.453	0.593	0.717	0.816	0.888	0.936	0.966	0.983	0.992	0.996	0.998
8.5	0.000	0.002	0.009	0.030	0.074	0.150	0.256	0.386	0.523	0.653	0.763	0.849	0.909	0.949	0.973	0.986	0.993	0.997
9	0.000	0.001	0.006	0.021	0.055	0.116	0.207	0.324	0.456	0.587	0.706	0.803	0.876	0.926	0.959	0.978	0.989	0.995
9.5	0.000	0.001	0.004	0.015	0.040	0.089	0.165	0.269	0.392	0.522	0.645	0.752	0.836	0.898	0.940	0.967	0.982	0.991
10	0.000	0.000	0.003	0.010	0.029	0.067	0.130	0.220	0.333	0.458	0.583	0.697	0.792	0.864	0.917	0.951	0.973	0.986
10.5	0.000	0.000	0.002	0.007	0.021	0.050	0.102	0.179	0.279	0.397	0.521	0.639	0.742	0.825	0.888	0.932	0.960	0.978

Appendix M
Median Ranks

Median ranks

n	1	2	3	4	5	6	7	8	9	10	11	12
1	0.500	0.292	0.206	0.159	0.130	0.109	0.095	0.083	0.074	0.067	0.061	0.056
2		0.708	0.500	0.386	0.315	0.266	0.230	0.202	0.181	0.163	0.149	0.137
3			0.794	0.614	0.500	0.422	0.365	0.321	0.287	0.260	0.237	0.218
4				0.841	0.685	0.578	0.500	0.440	0.394	0.356	0.325	0.298
5					0.870	0.734	0.635	0.560	0.500	0.452	0.412	0.379
6						0.891	0.770	0.679	0.606	0.548	0.500	0.460
7							0.905	0.798	0.713	0.644	0.588	0.540
8								0.917	0.819	0.740	0.675	0.621
9									0.926	0.837	0.763	0.702
10										0.933	0.851	0.782
11											0.939	0.863
12												0.944

n	13	14	15	16	17	18	19	20	21	22	23	24
1	0.052	0.049	0.045	0.043	0.040	0.038	0.036	0.034	0.033	0.031	0.030	0.029
2	0.127	0.118	0.110	0.104	0.098	0.092	0.088	0.083	0.079	0.076	0.073	0.070
3	0.201	0.188	0.175	0.165	0.155	0.147	0.139	0.132	0.126	0.121	0.115	0.111
4	0.276	0.257	0.240	0.226	0.213	0.201	0.191	0.181	0.173	0.165	0.158	0.152
5	0.351	0.326	0.305	0.287	0.270	0.255	0.242	0.230	0.220	0.210	0.201	0.193
6	0.425	0.396	0.370	0.348	0.328	0.310	0.294	0.279	0.266	0.254	0.244	0.234
7	0.500	0.465	0.435	0.409	0.385	0.364	0.345	0.328	0.313	0.299	0.286	0.275
8	0.575	0.535	0.500	0.470	0.443	0.418	0.397	0.377	0.360	0.344	0.329	0.316
9	0.649	0.604	0.565	0.530	0.500	0.473	0.448	0.426	0.407	0.388	0.372	0.357
10	0.724	0.674	0.630	0.591	0.557	0.527	0.500	0.475	0.453	0.433	0.415	0.398
11	0.799	0.743	0.695	0.652	0.615	0.582	0.552	0.525	0.500	0.478	0.457	0.439
12	0.873	0.813	0.760	0.713	0.672	0.636	0.603	0.574	0.547	0.522	0.500	0.480

Continued

Median ranks *(continued)*

n	13	14	15	16	17	18	19	20	21	22	23	24
13	0.948	0.882	0.825	0.774	0.730	0.690	0.655	0.623	0.593	0.567	0.543	0.520
14		0.951	0.890	0.835	0.787	0.745	0.706	0.672	0.640	0.612	0.585	0.561
15			0.955	0.896	0.845	0.799	0.758	0.721	0.687	0.656	0.628	0.602
16				0.957	0.902	0.853	0.809	0.770	0.734	0.701	0.671	0.643
17					0.960	0.908	0.861	0.819	0.780	0.746	0.714	0.684
18						0.962	0.912	0.868	0.827	0.790	0.756	0.725
19							0.964	0.917	0.874	0.835	0.799	0.766
20								0.966	0.921	0.879	0.842	0.807
21									0.967	0.924	0.885	0.848
22										0.969	0.927	0.889
23											0.970	0.930
24												0.971

Appendix N
Normal Scores

Normal scores

$n =$	4	5	6	7	8	9	10	11	12	13	14	15	16	17
1	-1.05	-1.18	-1.28	-1.36	-1.43	-1.50	-1.55	-1.59	-1.64	-1.68	-1.71	-1.74	-1.77	-1.80
2	-0.30	-0.50	-0.64	-0.76	-0.85	-0.93	-1.00	-1.06	-1.11	-1.16	-1.20	-1.24	-1.28	-1.32
3	0.30	0.00	-0.20	-0.35	-0.47	-0.57	-0.65	-0.73	-0.79	-0.85	-0.90	-0.94	-0.99	-1.03
4	1.05	0.50	0.20	0.00	-0.15	-0.27	-0.37	-0.46	-0.53	-0.60	-0.66	-0.71	-0.76	-0.80
5		1.18	0.64	0.35	0.15	0.00	-0.12	-0.22	-0.31	-0.39	-0.45	-0.51	-0.57	-0.62
6			1.28	0.76	0.47	0.27	0.12	0.00	-0.10	-0.19	-0.27	-0.33	-0.39	-0.45
7				1.36	0.85	0.57	0.37	0.22	0.10	0.00	-0.09	-0.16	-0.23	-0.29
8					1.43	0.93	0.65	0.46	0.31	0.19	0.09	0.00	-0.08	-0.15
9						1.50	1.00	0.73	0.53	0.39	0.27	0.16	0.08	0.00
10							1.55	1.06	0.79	0.60	0.45	0.33	0.23	0.15
11								1.59	1.11	0.85	0.66	0.51	0.39	0.29
12									1.64	1.16	0.90	0.71	0.57	0.45
13										1.68	1.20	0.94	0.76	0.62
14											1.71	1.24	0.99	0.80
15												1.74	1.28	1.03
16													1.77	1.32
17														1.80
18														
19														
20														
21														
22														
23														
24														
25														
26														
27														
28														
29														
30														

Continued

Normal scores *(continued)*

n =	18	19	20	21	22	23	24	25	26	27	28	29	30
1	-1.82	-1.85	-1.87	-1.89	-1.91	-1.93	-1.95	-1.97	-1.98	-2.00	-2.01	-2.03	-2.04
2	-1.35	-1.38	-1.40	-1.43	-1.45	-1.48	-1.50	-1.52	-1.54	-1.56	-1.58	-1.59	-1.61
3	-1.06	-1.10	-1.13	-1.16	-1.18	-1.21	-1.24	-1.26	-1.28	-1.30	-1.32	-1.34	-1.36
4	-0.84	-0.88	-0.92	-0.95	-0.98	-1.01	-1.04	-1.06	-1.09	-1.11	-1.13	-1.15	-1.17
5	-0.66	-0.70	-0.74	-0.78	-0.81	-0.84	-0.87	-0.90	-0.93	-0.95	-0.98	-1.00	-1.02
6	-0.50	-0.54	-0.59	-0.63	-0.66	-0.70	-0.73	-0.76	-0.79	-0.82	-0.84	-0.87	-0.89
7	-0.35	-0.40	-0.45	-0.49	-0.53	-0.57	-0.60	-0.63	-0.66	-0.69	-0.72	-0.75	-0.77
8	-0.21	-0.26	-0.31	-0.36	-0.40	-0.44	-0.48	-0.52	-0.55	-0.58	-0.61	-0.64	-0.67
9	-0.07	-0.13	-0.19	-0.24	-0.28	-0.33	-0.37	-0.41	-0.44	-0.48	-0.51	-0.54	-0.57
10	0.07	0.00	-0.06	-0.12	-0.17	-0.22	-0.26	-0.30	-0.34	-0.38	-0.41	-0.44	-0.47
11	0.21	0.13	0.06	0.00	-0.06	-0.11	-0.15	-0.20	-0.24	-0.28	-0.31	-0.35	-0.38
12	0.35	0.26	0.19	0.12	0.06	0.00	-0.05	-0.10	-0.14	-0.18	-0.22	-0.26	-0.29
13	0.50	0.40	0.31	0.24	0.17	0.11	0.05	0.00	-0.05	-0.09	-0.13	-0.17	-0.21
14	0.66	0.54	0.45	0.36	0.28	0.22	0.15	0.10	0.05	0.00	-0.04	-0.09	-0.12
15	0.84	0.70	0.59	0.49	0.40	0.33	0.26	0.20	0.14	0.09	0.04	0.00	-0.04
16	1.06	0.88	0.74	0.63	0.53	0.44	0.37	0.30	0.24	0.18	0.13	0.09	0.04
17	1.35	1.10	0.92	0.78	0.66	0.57	0.48	0.41	0.34	0.28	0.22	0.17	0.12
18	1.82	1.38	1.13	0.95	0.81	0.70	0.60	0.52	0.44	0.38	0.31	0.26	0.21
19		1.85	1.40	1.16	0.98	0.84	0.73	0.63	0.55	0.48	0.41	0.35	0.29
20			1.87	1.43	1.18	1.01	0.87	0.76	0.66	0.58	0.51	0.44	0.38
21				1.89	1.45	1.21	1.04	0.90	0.79	0.69	0.61	0.54	0.47
22					1.91	1.48	1.24	1.06	0.93	0.82	0.72	0.64	0.57
23						1.93	1.50	1.26	1.09	0.95	0.84	0.75	0.67
24							1.95	1.52	1.28	1.11	0.98	0.87	0.77
25								1.97	1.54	1.30	1.13	1.00	0.89
26									1.98	1.56	1.32	1.15	1.02
27										2.00	1.58	1.34	1.17
28											2.01	1.59	1.36
29												2.03	1.61
30													2.04

Appendix O
Values of *t* Distribution

Values of *t* distribution

df	$t_{0.10}$	$t_{0.05}$	$t_{0.025}$	$t_{0.01}$	$t_{0.005}$	df
1	3.078	6.314	12.706	31.821	63.656	1
2	1.886	2.920	4.303	6.965	9.925	2
3	1.638	2.353	3.182	4.541	5.841	3
4	1.533	2.132	2.776	3.747	4.604	4
5	1.476	2.015	2.571	3.365	4.032	5
6	1.440	1.943	2.447	3.143	3.707	6
7	1.415	1.895	2.365	2.998	3.499	7
8	1.397	1.860	2.306	2.896	3.355	8
9	1.383	1.833	2.262	2.821	3.250	9
10	1.372	1.812	2.228	2.764	3.169	10
11	1.363	1.796	2.201	2.718	3.106	11
12	1.356	1.782	2.179	2.681	3.055	12
13	1.350	1.771	2.160	2.650	3.012	13
14	1.345	1.761	2.145	2.624	2.977	14
15	1.341	1.753	2.131	2.602	2.947	15
16	1.337	1.746	2.120	2.583	2.921	16
17	1.333	1.740	2.110	2.567	2.898	17
18	1.330	1.734	2.101	2.552	2.878	18
19	1.328	1.729	2.093	2.539	2.861	19
20	1.325	1.725	2.086	2.528	2.845	20
21	1.323	1.721	2.080	2.518	2.831	21
22	1.321	1.717	2.074	2.508	2.819	22
23	1.319	1.714	2.069	2.500	2.807	23
24	1.318	1.711	2.064	2.492	2.797	24
25	1.316	1.708	2.060	2.485	2.787	25
26	1.315	1.706	2.056	2.479	2.779	26
27	1.314	1.703	2.052	2.473	2.771	27
28	1.313	1.701	2.048	2.467	2.763	28

Continued

Values of *t* distribution *(continued)*

df	$t_{0.10}$	$t_{0.05}$	$t_{0.025}$	$t_{0.01}$	$t_{0.005}$	df
29	1.311	1.699	2.045	2.462	2.756	29
30	1.310	1.697	2.042	2.457	2.750	30
31	1.309	1.696	2.040	2.453	2.744	31
32	1.309	1.694	2.037	2.449	2.738	32
33	1.308	1.692	2.035	2.445	2.733	33
34	1.307	1.691	2.032	2.441	2.728	34
35	1.306	1.690	2.030	2.438	2.724	35
40	1.303	1.684	2.021	2.423	2.704	40
45	1.301	1.679	2.014	2.412	2.690	45
50	1.299	1.676	2.009	2.403	2.678	50
55	1.297	1.673	2.004	2.396	2.668	55
60	1.296	1.671	2.000	2.390	2.660	60
70	1.294	1.667	1.994	2.381	2.648	70
80	1.292	1.664	1.990	2.374	2.639	80
90	1.291	1.662	1.987	2.368	2.632	90
100	1.290	1.660	1.984	2.364	2.626	100
200	1.286	1.653	1.972	2.345	2.601	200
400	1.284	1.649	1.966	2.336	2.588	400
600	1.283	1.647	1.964	2.333	2.584	600
800	1.283	1.647	1.963	2.331	2.582	800
999	1.282	1.646	1.962	2.330	2.581	999

Glossary

#

2^k **designs**—A factorial design with k factors, each with two levels. These designs are referred to as "two-to-the-k" designs. See also *factorial design*.

5S—A lean methodology of visual control based on five Japanese words, each beginning with the letter *s*: *seiri* (sort), *seiton* (straighten), *seiso* (shine), *seiketsu* (standardize), and *shitsuke* (sustain).

5-why analysis—A problem-solving tool in which the question "why" is asked multiple times to drill down to the root cause.

A

acceptance quality limit (AQL)—The maximum percentage or proportion of variant units in a lot or batch that, for purposes of acceptance sampling, can be considered satisfactory as a process average.

acceptance sampling—Sampling inspection in which decisions are made to accept or not accept a product or service; also, the methodology that deals with procedures by which decisions to accept or not accept are based on the results of the inspection of samples.

accuracy—A qualitative term that describes the closeness of alignment between an observed value and an accepted reference value.

action plan—The detailed plan to implement the actions needed to achieve strategic goals and objectives.

activity network diagram (AND) (arrow diagram)—A management and planning tool used to develop the best possible schedule and appropriate controls to accomplish the schedule; the critical path method (CPM) and the program evaluation review technique (PERT) make use of arrow diagrams.

advanced product quality planning (APQP) and control plan—APQP is a comprehensive quality planning and control system specifying protocols for product and process design and development, validation, assessment, and corrective action.

advanced quality planning (AQP)—A comprehensive system of applying quality disciplines during a product or process development effort.

affinity diagram—A quality management tool used to help collect, organize, summarize, and communicate facts, opinions, and ideas based on natural relationships.

aliasing—See *confounding*.

alternative hypothesis (H_a)—In statistical hypothesis testing, this is the hypothesis that the null hypothesis is tested against. The hypothesis test is conducted under the assumption that the null hypothesis is true. If evidence is found against the null hypothesis, the null hypothesis is rejected.

American National Standards Institute (ANSI)—An organization that creates and promotes guidelines and standards across many industries.

American Society for Quality (ASQ)—An organization that provides the community with training, professional certifications, and knowledge related to quality.

analysis of variance (ANOVA)—A partitioning of total variability into components due to factors or other sources of variation. The sources of variation as well as their corresponding sums of squares and degrees of freedom are usually given in an *analysis of variance table*.

appraisal costs—The costs associated with measuring, evaluating, or auditing products or services to ensure conformance to quality standards and performance requirements.

assignable causes—See *special causes*.

assumptions—Conditions that must be true for a statistical procedure to be valid.

attributes data—Data that are categorized for analysis or evaluation. Attributes data may involve measurements if the measurements are used only to place a given piece of data in a category for further analysis or evaluation. Contrast with *variables data*.

audit—A systematic and independent evaluation of the quality system and its execution.

auditee—The individual or organization being audited.

autocorrelation—A measure of the linear relationship between sequential observations, typically associated with time series.

availability—The probability that a system is properly operating at time t.

average run length (ARL)—In process monitoring and statistical process control, the average number of time periods or samples that elapse until the process signals out-of-control or produces an out-of-control signal.

average sample number (ASN)—The average number of sample units per lot used for making decisions (acceptance or nonacceptance).

B

bathtub curve—A general failure rate model for the life cycle of a system with the failure rate plotted against time. Named because of its shape, the curve has a decreasing failure rate (see *infant mortality phase*), followed by constant failure rate, followed by an increasing failure rate (see *wear-out phase*).

benchmark—An organization, part of an organization, or measurement that serves as a reference point or point of comparison.

benefit-cost analysis—A collection of the dollar value of benefits derived from an initiative, divided by the associated costs incurred.

Bernoulli trial—A trial that results in one of two possible outcomes, usually defined as "success" and "failure."

bias—A quantitative term representing the systematic difference between results or measurements obtained and the true quantity of interest. In measurement system analysis, bias describes the difference between the average of measurements made on the same unit and its reference or master value.

binomial distribution—A discrete distribution describing the number of successes in a set or series of n independent Bernoulli trials where the probability of a success is constant from trial to trial.

block diagram—A diagram that describes the operation, interrelationships, and interdependencies of components in a system. Boxes, or blocks (hence the name), represent the components; connecting lines between the blocks represent interfaces. See also *functional block diagram* and *reliability block diagram.*

blocking—A principle of experimental design used to group experiments into relatively homogenous experimental conditions to reduce the variability transmitted from nuisance factors.

brainstorming—A problem-solving tool that teams use to generate as many ideas as possible related to a particular subject. Team members begin by offering all their ideas; the ideas are not discussed or reviewed until after the brainstorming session.

C

c **chart**—A control chart that monitors the number of nonconformities in a process. Compare with *u chart.*

calibrate—To determine whether an instrument is functioning within prescribed accuracy objectives.

calibration—The disciplines necessary to compare and/or control a measurement instrument or system of unverified accuracy with a measurement instrument or system of known accuracy. Calibration can also be used to detect any variation from the true value.

categorical variable—A variable whose possible outcomes are categories that have no numerical significance.

causation—The principle that a change in a factor or regressor variable causes a change in the response. Can only be determined by a designed experiment. Contrast with *correlation.*

cause-and-effect diagram—A graphical aid used to organize and identify possible causes of a problem or effect. The causal factors are variables that when changed or manipulated may result in an effect. Also known as a *fishbone diagram* or *Ishikawa diagram.*

central limit theorem—The principle that the distribution of the sum of independent, identically distributed random variables approaches a normal distribution as the sample size increases toward infinity. Often used to approximate the distribution of sample means.

certified quality engineer (CQE)—A professional who understands the application of the quality principles of product and service quality evaluation and control, which are outlined by the American Society for Quality.

chance cause variation—Variation due to an inherent part of the process. Also known as *common cause variation*.

change agent—The person who takes the lead in transforming a company into a quality organization by providing guidance during the planning phase, facilitating implementation, and supporting those who pioneer the changes.

check sheet—One of the seven quality control tools; used to count event occurrences when collecting data. Check sheets are often used to summarize types of defects.

chi-square distribution—A continuous probability distribution that results from the sum of k squared independent normal random variables.

coefficient of determination (R^2)—The proportion of the total variability in the response that can be explained by the regression line. Provides a measure (between 0 and 1 inclusive) of how adequate the current regression model is for a particular set of data.

complement—In probability, an event that contains all the outcomes in the sample space that are not in the event itself. The complement of an event A is denoted A' or A^C.

confidence interval—An interval of values (L, U) that is believed to contain the true parameter value of interest. The probability level refers only to the interval constructed and its properties and not the unknown parameter being estimated.

confidence level—Is equal to 100 multiplied by (1 – significance level). The interpretation of a 99% confidence interval would be that if the estimation procedure is repeated multiple times, 99% of all the constructed intervals would contain the true parameter of interest.

conflict resolution—A process for resolving disagreements in a manner acceptable to all parties.

confounding—A design of experiments term that refers to indistinguishable effects. Two factors that are confounded means that their effects cannot be distinguished from one another. Mathematically, this means that the effect calculations are computed by the same linear combination.

consumer's risk (β)—For a sampling plan, refers to the probability of acceptance of a lot, the quality of which has a designated numerical value representing a level that is seldom desirable. Usually the value will be the *lot tolerance percent defective* (LTPD). Also known as the *beta risk* or probability of a type II error.

contingency table—A table for grouping data from two or more categorical variables. Categories can be represented as rows and columns. The values in the table cells represent counts.

continuous variable—A numerical variable that can take on any possible value inside a provided interval.

contour plot—A graph that displays the predicted response over a range of the variables in a regression equation. Can be used to determine optimal or robust settings of factors.

control chart—A chart used to monitor a critical-to-quality characteristic of interest. A control chart generally consists of three horizontal lines: one representing the mean or target level, one representing an upper limit, and one representing a lower limit (although there are many instances when only an upper limit or only a lower limit is of interest). The limits are statistically determined.

control factor—In design of experiments, a factor or process input that can be manipulated by the experimenter and is presumed to affect the output of a process.

control plan—A document used to communicate the procedures used to monitor and control a process.

coordinate measuring machine (CMM)—A machine used to calculate a physical representation of a three-dimensional rectilinear coordinate system. CMMs are used for defining the geometry of different-shaped workpieces.

corrective action—Action taken to eliminate the root cause(s) and symptom(s) of an existing deviation or nonconformity to prevent recurrence.

correlation—A general term describing the degree of interdependence between two or more variables.

correlation coefficient—A measure of the linear relationship between two random variables. The correlation coefficient is dimensionless and can take on any value between –1 and 1 inclusive.

cost-benefit analysis—A project management tool in which financial inputs and outputs are weighed against each other to estimate the strengths and weaknesses of alternative courses of action and determine the best use of investment.

cost of quality—A methodology that allows an organization to determine the extent to which its resources are used for activities that prevent poor quality, that appraise the quality of the organization's products or services, and that result from internal and external failures.

Crawford slip method—A method of gathering and presenting anonymous data from a group by using various voting schemes.

critical defect—A defect that may lead to severe injury or catastrophic loss.

critical path—The sequence of tasks that take the longest time and determine a project's completion date.

critical path method (CPM)—An activity-oriented project management technique that uses arrow-diagramming techniques to demonstrate both the time and the cost required to complete a project. It provides one time estimate—normal (most likely) time.

critical region—In hypothesis testing, it is the value of the test statistic that will lead to rejection of the null hypothesis.

critical value—In hypothesis testing, the value (or values) with which the value of the test statistic is compared to determine whether the null hypothesis can be rejected. The critical value is determined from the significance level of the test.

criticality—An indication of the consequences that are expected to result from a failure.

critical-to-quality (CtQ) characteristic—The most important or key features of a product, process, or service.

cumulative distribution function (cdf)—Used to describe a probability distribution for a random variable. For a random variable X, the cumulative distribution function would be given by $P(X \leq x)$, where x is some numeric value.

cycle time—The time that it takes to complete a process from beginning to end.

D

dashboard—A visual display that shows at-a-glance key business indicators.

decision tree—A planning tool used to help estimate the expected value of gain or loss in a project. The tree lists potential outcomes and the financial payout for each outcome, with a probability assigned to each branch.

defect—A nonconformity severe enough to cause the product to not satisfy normal usage requirements.

defining relation—In design of experiments, an expression for a fractional factorial design that contains all possible combinations of columns in the design matrix that do not change (are equal to the identity column).

density function—See *probability density function.*

dependent events—Two events A and B are dependent if the probability of one event occurring is affected by the occurrence of the other event. Contrast with *independent events.*

descriptive statistics—Techniques for displaying and summarizing data. Examples include histograms, run charts, and summary statistics such as the mean and standard deviation.

design of experiments (DOE)—A formal method including pre-experimental planning, setting up and running an experiment, analyzing the data, and drawing objective conclusions.

design review—A documented, comprehensive, and systematic examination of a design to evaluate its capability to fulfill the requirements for quality.

designed experiment—A formal statistical process for determining the test or series of runs in which the experimenter manipulates the factor levels to determine potential causal effects on the response.

detection—A criterion for risk used in the risk priority number and is defined as the likelihood of detecting a failure once it has occurred. Detection is evaluated based on a 10-point scale. At the lowest end of the scale (1) it is assumed that a design control will detect a failure with certainty. At the highest end of the scale (10) it is assumed that a design control will not detect a failure if a failure occurs.

dial indicator—A measurement tool that magnifies the dimension deviation from a standard to which a gage is set.

discrete variable—A numeric variable whose possible values form a finite or at most countably infinite set.

disjoint events—See *mutually exclusive events.*

distribution function—See *cumulative distribution function.*

DMAIC—An acronym denoting a sequence used in the methodology most often associated with Six Sigma: define, measure, analyze, improve, control.

E

effect estimate—In design of experiments, the difference in the average response at the high and low levels of a factor or combination of factors.

environmental stress screening—A process designed to trigger burgeoning defects into detectable failures by applying environmental stresses, such as temperature or vibration, to hardware.

error—1. The difference between the estimated value and the true value of a measured quantity. 2. A fault resulting from defective judgment, deficient knowledge, or carelessness. It is not to be confused with measurement error, which is the difference between a computed or measured value and the true or theoretical value.

error-proofing—See *foolproofing.*

estimate—A numerical value for a population parameter based on information collected from a sample. Also known as a *point estimate.*

estimator—A statistic used to compute estimates of a parameter.

event—In probability, a subset of the sample space.

expected frequency—In the chi-squared goodness-of-fit test, the number of nonconforming units that would be expected in each category if the sample exactly followed the historical percentages.

expected value—The mean of a random variable.

experiment—See *designed experiment.*

experimental error—See *random error.*

exponential distribution—A continuous probability distribution often used to model problems in reliability that have a constant failure rate.

external failure costs—Costs of quality associated with defects found during or after delivery of the product or service.

extract, load, transform—See *extract, transform, load.* A framework for high-volume data management.

extract, transform, load—See *extract, load, transform.* A framework for high-volume data management.

extrapolation—In regression analysis, the process of predicting new observations with predictor values outside the range of the original data. Contrast with *interpolation.*

F

F **distribution**—A continuous probability distribution defined by the ratio of two independent chi-square random variables divided by their respective degrees of freedom.

facilitator—An individual who is responsible for creating favorable conditions that will enable a team to reach its purpose or achieve its goals by bringing together the necessary tools, information, and resources to get the job done. Provides support to the team while allowing the team to maintain ownership of its decisions.

factor—In design of experiments, an independent variable chosen by the experimenter to determine what effect, if any, it has on the response in an experiment.

factorial design—In design of experiments, a type of design where all possible combinations of factor levels are examined.

fail-safe device—A method of preventive action to ensure problems or abnormalities in a process are discovered in a manner that maintains a safe working environment and ensures that quality is not compromised.

failure—The termination, due to one or more defects, of the ability of an item, product, or service to perform its required function when called on to do so. A failure may be partial, complete, or intermittent.

failure density function—A probability density function that represents the distribution of failure time.

failure mode effects and criticality analysis (FMECA)—A failure modes and effects analysis (FMEA) that includes a criticality metric in the evaluation of potential failure modes of a system, subsystem, product, or process.

failure modes and effects analysis (FMEA)—A team-based problem-solving procedure for helping users identify and eliminate or reduce the negative effects of potential failures by evaluating a risk priority number of potential failure modes of a system, subsystem, product, or process.

fault tree—A top-down technique for analyzing complex systems to determine potential failure modes and the probabilities of their occurrence. Some of the symbols in the fault tree include AND gate, OR gate, basic fault events, and priority AND gate.

filters—Relative to human-to-human communication, those perceptions (based on culture, language, demographics, experience, etc.) that affect how a message is transmitted by the sender and how a message is interpreted by the receiver.

fishbone diagram—See *cause-and-effect diagram.*

fixed effect—In analysis of variance, an effect is fixed if the factor levels included in the test or experiment are the only levels of interest. That is, the levels of the factor included in the experiment are the only ones to which the results of testing will apply.

flowchart—One of the seven tools of quality; a graphical representation of the elements, components, or tasks associated with a process.

foolproofing—A process in preventive action to make a product or process immune to errors on the part of the user or operator. Synonymous with *error-proofing.*

force field analysis—A quality management method for organizing ideas based on driving and opposing forces associated with a desired change in an organization. Compare with *affinity diagram.*

fraction nonconforming—In quality control, the proportion of the total number of units under study that do not meet specifications. Also known as *fraction defective.*

fractional factorial design—In design of experiments, a design consisting of only a subset or fraction of all possible combinations of a factorial design.

functional block diagram—A block diagram that shows a system's subsystems and lower-level products, their interrelationships, and interfaces with other systems.

G

gage block—A system for producing precision lengths; may be used as a reference when calibrating dial indicators.

gage repeatability and reproducibility (gage R&R)—Measures the capability of a gage to determine whether it is suitable for use in its intended application. Repeatability represents the gage variability when the gage is used to measure the same unit with the same setup or operator. Reproducibility refers to the variability arising from different setups or operators.

Gantt chart—A type of bar chart used in process or project planning and control to display planned and finished work in relation to time. Also called a *milestone chart*.

gauging—A procedure that determines product conformance with specifications with the aid of measuring instruments such as calipers, micrometers, templates, and other mechanical, optical, and electronic devices.

Gaussian distribution—See *normal distribution*.

go/no-go gage—A tool to measure inspection by attributes, made to sizes identical to the design specification limits of the dimension to be inspected. The "go" end checks the characteristic at the maximum material condition while the "no-go" end detects conditions of excessive clearance. Also called a *limit gage*.

H

hazard analysis and critical control points (HACCP)—A process analysis tool used prevent known hazards and reduce the risk of them occurring at points in the production cycle.

hazard and operability analysis (HAZOP)—A technique used to identify operability issues and potential hazards that may lead to unacceptable products, processes, services, or risk to personnel.

hazard rate function—A function defined by the limit of the failure rate as the time interval approaches zero; provides an instantaneous failure rate at time t.

heredity—In design of experiments, the principle that if an interaction between two main effects is significant, then both main effects are also significant.

hierarchical relationship—A set of relationships that can be ordered or arranged from general to specific.

hierarchy—In design of experiments, the principle that if a higher-order term is significant, then a lower-order term also containing that factor should be included in the model.

histogram—A graphical display of observations from a sample where the class frequencies are represented by areas of rectangles over the interval for each class.

hold point—A point, defined in an appropriate document, beyond which an activity must not proceed without the approval of a designated organization or authority.

hypothesis testing—A formal statistical procedure for testing a statement about a population using sample data. The statement to be tested may also concern a distributional form of a quality characteristic of interest.

I

I and MR chart—A pair of control charts used to monitor a variable in which the sample size is one (also called individual measurements). The MR values are typically calculated by computing the difference between sequential pairs of individual observations (see *moving range* [MR]) and are representative of sample variability.

independent events—Two events A and B are said to be independent if the occurrence of one event does not depend on the occurrence or lack of occurrence of another (or preceding) event. If two events are independent, then the probability that they both occur is the product of the probabilities of their individual occurrence.

Industry 4.0—A concept that refers to a fourth industrial revolution in manufacturing, often characterized by big data, advanced analytics, and human-machine interfaces.

infant mortality phase—In reliability, represents the first phase in a bathtub curve. It is often characterized by a decreasing failure rate where failures are typically attributed to defects in the manufacturing processes, assemblies, and shipping of the product.

inferential statistics—Techniques for reaching conclusions about a population based on analysis of data from a sample.

information system—Technology-based system used to support operations, aid day-to-day decision making, and support strategic analysis (other names often used include *management information system, decision system, information technology* [IT], and *data processing*).

inspection—The process of measuring, examining, testing, gauging, or otherwise comparing a unit with the applicable requirements.

interaction—A term used to describe that the relationship between a response variable and an input variable may change in the presence of one or more other variables.

interaction plot—A graph in which the average response (y-axis) is plotted against a factor (x-axis) over various levels of a second factor, used to determine the presence of an interaction between two factors.

internal failure costs—Costs associated with defects found before the product or service is delivered; including scrap, rework, and material review.

International Organization for Standardization (ISO)—The organization responsible for the ISO 9000 and other management standard series.

Internet of things (IoT)—A multitude of intelligent devices connected to the Internet.

interpolation—In regression analysis, the process of predicting new observations with predictor values inside the range of the original data. Contrast with *extrapolation*.

interquartile range—The difference between the 75th and the 25th quantiles.

interrelationship digraph—A tool used to help discover, visualize, and communicate a high-level sequential and/or cause-and-effect relationship.

intersection—In probability, the event consisting of all outcomes that are contained in both A and B.

Ishikawa diagram—See *cause-and-effect diagram.*

J

joint distribution—A probability distribution representing two or more variables that are involved in a random experiment. Also known as *joint probability distribution.*

just-in-time—A lean principle that refers to the delivery of material, components, or parts just prior to their use to minimize inventory costs.

K

kaizen—A Japanese word for the philosophy that defines management's role in continuously encouraging small improvements involving everyone in an organization.

kaizen blitz—An intense team approach to employing the concepts and techniques of continuous improvement in a short time frame (e.g., to reduce cycle time or increase throughput).

kanban—A system to simplify and improve inventory resupply procedures.

k-out-of-n system—A system with n components or subcomponents where k of the components must be functioning for the system to operate properly.

L

lean—A process for eliminating waste from a system, such that only value-added activities remain.

least squares estimation—In regression analysis, a method for estimating parameters by minimizing the sum of the squared differences between the actual or observed responses and the values predicted by the fitted model.

level of significance (α)—See *significance level.*

levels—In experimental design, the chosen values of a factor of interest to be varied in an experiment.

limit gage—See *go/no-go gage.*

linear regression—See *regression analysis.*

linearity—A measure of how changes in the size of the part being measured will affect measurement system bias over the expected process range.

lognormal distribution—A continuous probability distribution often used to model product life spans. It is the distribution of a random variable whose logarithm follows the normal distribution.

lot tolerance percent defective (LTPD)—Expressed in percent defective, the poorest quality in an individual lot that should be accepted.

M

main effect—The effect on a response due to a change in a factor or variable independent of all other factors or variables in the system.

main effect plot—A plot that represents the average change in the response (plotted on the *y*-axis) over the values of a particular factor (plotted on the *x*-axis).

maintainability—The measure of the ability of an item to be retained or restored to a specified condition when maintenance is performed by personnel having specified skill levels and using prescribed procedures and resources at each prescribed level of maintenance and repair.

major defect—A defect that interferes with normal or reasonable foreseeable use but does not cause a risk of damage or injury.

material control—A broad collection of tools for managing the items and lots in a production process.

materials review board—A quality control committee or team, usually employed in manufacturing or other materials-processing installations, that has the responsibility and authority to deal with items or materials that do not conform to fitness-for-use specifications.

matrix diagram—A tool used to help people discover, visualize, and communicate relationships within a single set of factors or between two or more sets of factors.

mean—A measure of central tendency. For random variables, it is also the expected value. For a sample of data of size n, it is the sum of the observations divided by n.

mean squares—In analysis of variance, mean squares are estimates of variances. In general, they are found by dividing the sum of squares by the appropriate degrees of freedom.

mean time between failures (MTBF)—The expected time between two successive failures when the system is repairable.

mean time to failure (MTTF)—The expected time to failure between two successive failures when the system is nonrepairable.

mean time to repair (MTTR)—The expected time to repair a failure, not including waiting time for parts or tools to start the repair.

measurement—1. The process of evaluating a property or characteristic of an object and describing it with a numerical or nominal value. 2. A series of manipulations of physical objects or systems according to a defined protocol that results in a number.

measurement process—Repeated application of a test method using a measuring system.

measurement system—The entire process for obtaining measurement on some quality characteristic of interest, including standards, personnel, and methods of measurement.

measurement system analysis (MSA)—Qualifying the measurement process, determining the adequacy of the measurement system for use, and identifying and estimating the process error.

measuring system—In general, the elements of a measuring system include the instrumentation, calibration standards, environmental influences, human operator limitations, and features of the workpiece or object being measured.

median—A measure of central tendency that divides an ordered data set in half; 50% of the data are at or below this value and 50% of the data are above this value.

metrology—The science of precision measurement.

milestone—A specific time when a critical event is to occur; a symbol placed on a milestone chart to locate the point when a critical event is to occur.

milestone chart—See *Gantt chart*.

minor defect—A defect that may cause difficulty in assembly or use of a product but does not prevent the product from being properly used and does not pose any hazard to users.

mode—The value in a data set that occurs most often. There can be more than one mode for a sample.

moving average—An unweighted average of observations in a series of data over a specified span. Contrast with *exponentially weighted moving average*.

moving range (MR)—The difference between two successive observations.

muda—The seven classes of waste: overproduction, delay, transportation, processing, inventory, wasted motion, and defective parts.

multivoting—A decision-making tool that enables a group to sort through a long list of ideas to identify priorities.

mutually exclusive events—Events that do not have outcomes in common or that do not occur jointly.

Myers-Briggs Type Indicator—A method and instrument for assessing personality that can be used for building a team with complementary skills. Based on Carl Jung's theory of personality preferences.

N

National Institute of Standards and Technology (NIST)—An organization for the standards of measurement, established by an act of Congress. NIST maintains the base units of measurements that are used in calibration.

natural tolerance limits—Limits based on the natural variation of the process (measured by the process standard deviation).

noise factor—See *nuisance factor*.

nominal group technique—A technique similar to brainstorming, used by teams to generate and make a selection from ideas on a particular subject based on group prioritization.

nominal variable—A categorical variable with no order implied in the values.

nonconformity—A failure of a quality characteristic to meet its intended level or state, occurring with severity sufficient to cause the product to not meet a specification. Sometimes the specification is based on fitness-for-use requirements.

non-value-added activity—Activities that the customer is not willing to pay for and/or do not change the form or function of the product or service.

normal distribution—A symmetric, bell-shaped continuous probability distribution. Another name for the *Gaussian distribution*, often attributed to Karl Gauss.

normal probability plot—See *probability plot*.

np **chart**—A control chart used to monitor the number of nonconforming units in a sample. Compare with *p chart*.

nuisance factor—A factor that may influence the response in an experiment (see *designed experiment*) but is not of direct interest to the experimenter.

null hypothesis—In hypothesis testing, a statement about a population parameter or distributional form of a quality characteristic that is to be tested. It is often the statement of no difference.

O

observation—The process of determining the presence or absence of attributes or making measurements of a variable. Also, the result of the process of determining the presence or absence of attributes or making a measurement of a variable.

observational study—Analysis of data collected from a process without imposing changes on the process.

occurrence—A criterion for risk used in the risk priority number and is defined as the likelihood of a failure occurring. Occurrence is evaluated based on a 10-point scale. At the lowest end of the scale (1) it is assumed that the probability of a failure is unlikely. At the highest end of the scale (10) it is assumed that the probability of a failure is nearly inevitable.

one-way ANOVA—See *analysis of variance*.

operating characteristic (OC) curve—For a sampling plan, a plot that indicates the probability of accepting a lot based on the sample size to be taken and the fraction defective in the batch.

opportunity—A positive risk.

ordinal variable—A categorical variable for which the levels that the variable takes on have an inherent or natural order (e.g., shirt size of small, medium, or large).

outlier—One or more observations that deviate significantly from the majority of the sample from which they came.

overall equipment effectiveness (OEE)—A rate metric that is calculated to determine how well a manufacturing unit, for example a machine, is operating when compared against its full potential in terms of operating time, performance and quality performance.

P

p **chart**—A control chart that monitors the fraction nonconforming in a process. Compare with *np chart*.

paired data—Data in which observations from two samples are dependent, where an observation from one sample is paired with an observation from the other sample.

parallel system—A system where the components are connected in such a way that failure of one or more units still allows the remaining units to perform properly. The system fails when all units fail.

parameter—A constant or coefficient that describes some characteristic of a population.

Pareto diagram—One of the seven quality control tools; used to rank causes of problems from most significant to least significant.

percentile—See *quantile.*

Phase 1 analysis—In statistical process control, the development of trial control limits based on preliminary samples of data.

Phase 2 analysis—In statistical process control, the development of reliable control chart limits that can be used for monitoring future production.

plan-do-check-act (PDCA)—A continuous improvement methodology developed by Shewhart that is made up of a four-stage improvement process. Also called *plan-do-study-act (PDSA).*

point estimate—See *estimate.*

Poisson distribution—A discrete probability distribution where values take on integer values, often used to model count data such as the number of nonconformities.

poka-yoke—A term that means to mistake-proof a process by building safeguards into the system that avoid or immediately find errors. The term comes from the Japanese terms *poka,* which means "error," and *yokeru,* which means "to avoid."

pooled variance—An estimator for the variance of the difference between two population means; used when the population variances are unknown but assumed roughly equal.

population—All possible outcomes or objects of interest.

power—In statistical inference, the probability of rejecting a false null hypothesis.

practical significance—In statistical inference, identifying a meaningful difference associated with a parameter of interest. Compare with *statistical significance.*

precision—The closeness of agreement between randomly selected individual measurements or test results.

prediction—Estimation of new or future observations using a statistical model.

predictor variable—See *regressor.*

prevention costs—Costs of quality related to activities specifically designed to prevent poor quality in products or services.

probability—A numerical measure assigned to events in a sample space that represents the likelihood that a particular outcome will occur. It takes on values between 0 and 1 inclusive.

probability density function (pdf)—A function that describes the probability distribution of a continuous random variable.

probability mass function (pmf)—A function that describes the probability distribution of a discrete random variable.

probability plot—A graphical display that shows the actual data on the x-axis plotted against percentiles based on the hypothesized or assumed distribution of interest on the y-axis; used to assess whether a data set follows a specified distribution, for example, with a normal probability plot.

process capability—The ability of a process to meet its intended purpose. It is a measure of how well the process produces outcomes that meet specifications.

process decision program chart (PDPC)—A planning tool to help organize and evaluate process-related events and contingencies with respect to implementation and/or early operations.

process map—A flowchart of a work process in detail, including key measurements.

process stability—See *stable process.*

process value chain diagram—A planning tool that depicts a sequence of cause-to-effect and effect-to-cause relationships between business results and outcomes and basic physical, economic, and social variables.

producer's risk (α)—For a sampling plan, refers to the probability of not accepting a lot, the quality of which has a designated numerical value representing a level that is generally desirable. Usually the designated value will be the acceptable quality level. Also called *alpha risk* or *probability of a type I error.*

product identification—A means of marking parts with a label, etching, engraving, ink, or other means so that different part numbers and other key attributes can be identified.

programmable logic controller (PLC)—A computer system used for the control of a manufacturing process.

pull system—A lean concept for continuous flow manufacturing. A process where each activity moves a component through the value stream so that it arrives at the next activity at the time it is needed. See also *just-in-time.*

push system—A system in manufacturing where production is driven by forecasts of demand for a product. Contrast with *pull system.*

p-value—The probability of getting a value of the test statistic as extreme as or more extreme than that observed if the null hypothesis is true. The p-value is the actual or observed significance level for a test.

Q

qualitative variable—A variable whose possible outcomes are nonnumeric or categorical. See also *categorical variable.*

quality—A term with many interpretations and definitions, including fitness for use and conformance to specifications.

quality assurance—All the planned or systematic actions necessary to provide adequate confidence that a product or service will satisfy given needs.

quality audit—A systematic, independent examination and review to determine whether quality activities and related results comply with planned arrangements and whether these arrangements are implemented effectively and are suitable to achieve the objectives.

quality control—The operational techniques and the activities that sustain a quality of a product or service that will satisfy given needs; also, the use of such techniques and activities.

quality control tools—Seven common tools used in statistical process control: flowcharts, cause-and-effect diagrams, check sheets, histograms, Pareto charts, control charts, and scatter diagrams.

quality cost—See *cost of quality.*

quality council—The group driving the quality improvement effort and usually having oversight responsibility for the implementation and maintenance of the quality management system; it is operated in parallel with the normal operation of the business. Sometimes referred to as a *quality steering committee.*

quality function deployment (QFD)—A structured method in which customer requirements are translated into appropriate technical requirements for each stage of product development and production. The QFD process is often referred to as *listening to the voice of the customer.*

quality information system—A collection of data, rules, and equipment that creates information about quality in a systematic way. The system will collect, store, analyze, and manage quality-related data from customers, suppliers, and internal processes.

quality manual—A document stating the quality policy and describing the quality system of an organization.

quality policy—Top management's formally stated intentions and direction for the organization pertaining to quality.

quality surveillance—Continual monitoring and verification of the status of an entity and analysis of records to ensure that specified requirements are being fulfilled.

quality system—The organizational structure, procedures, processes, and resources needed to implement quality management.

quantile—A value x such that $100q\%$ of the sample is less than x.

quantitative variable—A variable whose outcomes are numeric, continuous or discrete.

quartile—A boundary point of a sorted data set divided into four approximately equal subsets. The second quartile is also called the median.

R

random effect—In analysis of variance, an effect is random if the factor levels included in the test or experiment are randomly selected from a larger population of possible levels. The results of the test conducted would then apply to the entire population of factor levels and not just those included in the experiment.

random error—Error that occurs as a result of natural variation in a process or system. It is variation that occurs when taking repeated measurements on the same unit or item under identical conditions. Also referred to as *experimental error.*

random experiment—An experiment that has more than one possible outcome.

random sampling—The process of selecting units for a sample such that all combinations of units under consideration have an equal or ascertainable chance of being selected as the sample.

random variable—A function that associates a real number to each outcome in an experiment.

range—The difference between the largest and smallest value or observation in a data set. It provides a measure of dispersion in a set of data.

rational subgrouping—A method for collecting data that will allow for minimizing the chance of variability due to assignable causes while maximizing the chance of variability due to chance or natural causes. A fundamental and nontrivial concept in statistical process control.

readability—The ease of reading the instrument scale when a dimension is being measured.

regression analysis—Statistical techniques for determining and modeling the relationship between a dependent variable and one or more independent variables. The response variable is also referred to as a *response,* and the independent variables are also referred to as *regressors* or *predictors.*

regression coefficient—The parameters in a linear regression model that define the mathematical relationship between the response and regressors.

regressor—In regression analysis, it is the independent variable. Also known as the *predictor variable.*

rejection region—In significance testing, the values of the test statistic that will lead to rejection of the null hypothesis. Sometimes referred to as the *critical region.*

reliability—The probability that an item can perform its intended function for a specified interval under stated conditions.

reliability block diagram—A block diagram that is similar to the functional block diagram except that it is modified to emphasize those aspects influencing reliability.

repeatability—Variability due to the gage or test instrument used to measure the same part under identical measuring conditions.

replication—The repetition of the set of all the treatment combinations to be compared in an experiment. Each of the repetitions is called a *replicate.*

reproducibility—Variability due to different operators or setup measuring the same parts using the same measuring device. Thus, reproducibility represents the variability due to the measurement system.

residual—The difference between the actual or observed response and the predicted response for the variable of interest.

residual analysis—An examination of the residuals used to determine the adequacy of a fitted model and to check the validity of assumptions made in model fitting.

resolution—A design is of resolution R if no p-factor effect is aliased with another effect containing less than $R - p$ factors. For example, a resolution III design is one in which the main effects are aliased with two-factor interactions.

resource requirements matrix—A tool to relate the resources required to the project tasks requiring them (used to indicate types of individuals needed, material needed, subcontractors, etc.).

response surface plot—A three-dimensional plot of the response variable versus two of the regressors, generated by a regression model.

response variable—The variable that shows the observed results of an experimental treatment. It is the dependent variable in regression analysis.

responsible, accountable, consulted, and informed (RACI) matrix—A project management tool to identify levels of responsibility and authority and clarify ownership of assignments.

return on investment (ROI)—An umbrella term for a variety of ratios measuring an organization's business performance, calculated by dividing some measure of return by a measure of investment and then multiplying by 100 to provide a percentage. In its most basic form, ROI indicates what remains from all money taken in after all expenses are paid.

risk—Effect of uncertainty on objectives, or combination of the probability of occurrence of harm and the severity of that harm.

risk analysis—The process for comprehending the nature of risk and determining the level of risk.

risk appetite—The willingness of an organization to seek risk in anticipation of realization of opportunities.

risk assessment—A key part of the risk management process that consists of risk identification, risk analysis, and risk evaluation.

risk attitude—An organization's approach to assess, and eventually pursue, retain, take, or turn away from risk.

risk-based thinking—A mindset that leads us to foresee threats and opportunities and estimate them with an objective level of certainty such that targeted modifications and controls can be built into the design and surveillance of systems. A structured process for identifying necessary and appropriate courses of action based on analysis of relevant information and evaluation of known or anticipated risks associated with each alternative action.

risk control—The utilization of measures to reduce or mitigate risk.

risk evaluation—The final phase of risk assessment, where the results of risk analysis are compared with criteria and assigned a level of acceptability based on which additional actions to modify or maintain risk are determined.

risk identification—The process of finding, recognizing, describing, and recording risks. Risk identification involves the identification of risk sources, events, their causes, and their potential consequences.

risk management—Systematic application of management policies, procedures, and practices to the tasks of analyzing, evaluating, controlling, and monitoring risk.

risk monitoring—The use of data to track risks and/or their constituents to ensure that the risks are behaving in the manner anticipated during risk treatment and response planning.

risk tolerance—An organization's or stakeholder's readiness to bear the risk after risk treatment in order to achieve its objectives.

risk treatment—A set of actions to be applied to the evaluated and prioritized risks to ensure that the organizational objectives are successfully achieved by attempting to change the existing risk profile or exposure.

risk priority number (RPN)—The multiplication of the three scores for severity (S), occurrence (O), and detection (D) to assess risk. Because each scale (S, O, and D) ranges from 1 to 10, the minimum RPN is 1 and the maximum is 1000.

robust designs—Products or processes that continue to perform as intended in spite of manufacturing variation and extreme environmental conditions during use.

robustness—The condition of a product or process design that remains relatively stable with a minimum of variation even though factors that influence operations or usage, such as environment and wear, are constantly changing.

run chart—See *time series plot.*

S

sample—A subset of units or observations selected from a population of interest. A sample can provide information that may be used as a basis for making a decision concerning the larger quantity.

sample integrity—Procedures implemented so that samples are maintained in a unique manner to avoid corruption or confusion with others.

sample space—The set of all possible outcomes of a random process or random experiment.

sample standard deviation—A measure of dispersion for a set of observations in the same unit of measure as the original data. It is the positive square root of the sample variance.

sample variance—See *variance.*

sampling distribution—The probability distribution of a statistic calculated from a random sample of a given size.

sampling plan—A plan used for acceptance sampling defined by the sample size and acceptance number. The plan may contain multiple sample sizes and acceptance numbers if double or multiple sampling is used.

scatter diagram—A two-dimensional plot of data resulting from two random variables (bivariate data). The scatter diagram is a tool that can reveal associations between two variables. Also known as a *scatter plot.*

sensitivity—The least perceptible change in dimension detected by the measuring instrument and shown by the indicator.

series system—A system composed of *n* components or subsystems connected end-to-end such that a failure of any component results in the failure of the entire system.

serious defect—A defect that may lead to injury or significant economic loss.

severity—A criterion for risk used in the risk priority number and is an indicator of the severity of a failure should a failure occur. Severity can be evaluated based on a 10-point scale. At the lowest end of the scale (1) it is assumed that a failure will have no noticeable effect. At the highest end of the scale (10) it is assumed that a failure will impact safe operation or violate compliance with a regulatory mandate.

significance level—A stated or fixed probability of wrongly rejecting a true null hypothesis that the practitioner is willing to accept. It is the probability of committing a type I error.

simple random sampling—See *random sampling.*

single minute exchange of dies (SMED)—A system used to reduce changeover time and improve timely response to demand.

SIPOC diagram—A high-level process map used to identify the important aspects of the current process (suppliers, inputs, process, outputs, and customers); often used in quality planning activities.

Six Sigma—A continuous improvement methodology; a collection of techniques and tools for use in reducing variation; a program of improvement that focuses on strong leadership tools and emphasizes bottom-line financial results.

sparsity-of-effects principle—The belief that the system under investigation is dominated by the main effects and low-order interactions. The assumption made in typical designed experiments is that some higher-order interactions (orders higher than two-factor interactions) are negligible.

special causes—Causes of variation that arise because of special circumstances or unusual events. They are not an inherent part of a process. Special causes are also referred to as *assignable causes.*

specification limits—Limits of a quality characteristic determined externally, for example, by the customer.

stable process—A process in which no special causes of variation are present.

stakeholders—People, departments, and/or parties that have an investment or interest in the success of or actions taken by the organization.

standard—A statement, specification, or quantity of material against which measured outputs from a process may be judged as acceptable or unacceptable.

standard deviation—A measure of dispersion or spread in the same units as the unit of measure. It is equal to the positive square root of the variance.

standard error—The standard deviation of the sampling distribution of a statistic. In general, it is the standard deviation of any estimator of a parameter and provides a measure of precision of the estimate.

standardized work—A lean tool that states that each activity should be performed the same way every time.

standby system—A form of a redundant system where standby components function only upon the failure of the main component.

statistic—A quantity calculated from a sample of observations, most often to form an estimate of some population parameter.

statistical control—See *stable process*.

statistical process control (SPC)—The application of formal statistical methods that seek to improve process performance and reduce/understand variability in critical-to-quality metrics. A control chart is one of the primary SPC techniques.

statistical quality control (SQC)—The use of statistical and engineering technology for quality improvement within an organization. Three primary areas of statistical quality control are statistical process control, design of experiments, and acceptance sampling.

statistical significance—The rejection of the null hypothesis at a prespecified level. A statistically significant result (one in favor of the alternative hypothesis) may not have practical significance in some cases (e.g., if two mean values are different with statistical significance, but their difference is smaller than 0.001 of their value, this might not be of practical importance).

stratified sampling—A method of sampling used when the population is divided into groups. Items are randomly selected within each group and each group makes up a proportional part of the stratified sample.

sum of squares—The sum of squared observations between two values.

supervisory control and data acquisition (SCADA) system—A large-scale networked control system that uses programmable logic controllers for the management of a manufacturing process.

supply chain—The series of processes and/or organizations that are involved in producing and delivering a product to the final user.

surface metrology—The measurement of the difference between what a surface actually is and what it is intended to be. It may involve other terms such as *surface roughness* and *surface finish*.

survival function—A reliability function used to model the probability that an object of interest (or component) will survive beyond a specified time.

SWOT analysis—An assessment of an organization's key strengths, weaknesses, opportunities, and threats. It considers factors such as the organization's industry, competitive position, functional areas, and management.

system—A composite of equipment, skills, and techniques capable of performing or supporting an operational role, or both. A complete system includes all equipment, related facilities, material, software, services, and personnel required for its operation and support to the degree that it can be considered self-sufficient in its intended operating environment.

systematic error—Error that remains the same over repeated measurements taken under assumed identical conditions.

T

t **distribution**—The distribution of the ratio of two independent random variables. The random variable in the numerator is a standard normal random variable. The random variable in the denominator is the square root of a chi-square random variable divided by its degrees of freedom. Also known as *Student's* t *distribution*.

takt time—The rate needed to complete a product to meet customer demand.

tally sheet—See *check sheet*.

test for significance of regression—An analysis of variance procedure used to determine whether any of the regression coefficients in the linear regression model (except for the intercept) is different from a value of zero.

test statistic—A quantity calculated from a sample of data, which is based on the null hypothesis in a statistical hypothesis test and used to make a statistical decision (reject or fail to reject the null hypothesis).

testing—A means of determining the capability of an item to meet specified requirements by subjecting the item to a set of physical, chemical, environmental, or operating actions and conditions.

threat—A negative risk.

time series analysis—The use of mathematical modeling and statistical inference to summarize and predict observations dependent on time and/or each other.

time series plot—A graphical depiction of data (observations) over time.

tolerance interval—A statistical interval that contains a stated percentage of a population with a specified level of confidence.

total quality management (TQM)—A structured approach to managing quality improvement methods within an organization, with a focus on the customer, employee empowerment, and leadership.

total sum of squares—The sum of the squared differences between each observation in a data set and the overall mean of the data set.

traceability—The ability to trace the history, application, or location of an item or activity and like items or activities by means of recorded identification.

treatment—Levels of a factor in an experiment.

tree diagram—A planning tool to visualize hierarchical relationships between critical events. See *fault tree*.

type I error—The failure to reject the null hypothesis given that the null is true. The probability of type I error is called the significance level (α).

type II error—The rejection of the null hypothesis given that the null is false. The probability of type II error is referred to as β.

U

u chart—A control chart used to measure the average number of nonconformities. Compare with *c chart*.

unbiased estimator—An estimator whose expected value is equal to the parameter for which it is an estimator.

uniform distribution—A distribution whose values are equally distributed over an interval. Each possible outcome is assigned equal probability. The uniform distribution is defined for both continuous and discrete random variables.

union—The union of two events A and B is that event consisting of all outcomes contained in A, in B, or in both.

utility function—A mathematical equation in which alternatives are ranked based on their utility to an individual.

V

validation—Confirmation, through the provision of objective evidence, that the requirements for a specific intended use or application have been fulfilled.

value added—Work activities in a process that change the form and/or function of the product or service.

value stream mapping—A tool based on the principles of lean, used to identify opportunities for improvement of a process and track performance.

variables data—Data resulting from the measurement of a parameter or a variable. The resulting measurements may be recorded on a continuous scale. Contrast with *attributes data.*

variables sampling plan—The use of the actual measurements of sample products for decision making rather than classifying products as conforming or nonconforming Compare with *sampling plans.*

variance—A measure of dispersion. For a set of data, it is the sum of the squared differences between the individual observations and the mean of the observations divided by the degrees of freedom. For population variance, the degrees of freedom is the total population size; for sample variance, the degrees of freedom is the sample size minus one.

verification—Confirmation, through the provision of objective evidence, that specified requirements have been fulfilled.

visual control—A lean tool used to create a visual factory, a facility in which locations for tools, inventory, safety equipment, etc. are clearly marked and identified.

voice of the customer—The customer's expectations and preferences, commonly captured using quality function deployment and SIPOC diagrams.

W

wear-out phase—In reliability, represents the final phase in a bathtub curve. It is often characterized by an increasing failure rate due to examples such as fatigue loading and friction between mating surfaces.

Weibull distribution—A continuous probability distribution, typically used to model failure rates, including non-constant failure rates.

work breakdown structure (WBS)—A project management technique by which a project is divided into tasks, subtasks, and units of work to be performed.

X

$\bar{x}$ **and** R **charts**—A pair of control charts for variables (continuous) subgroup data, where the $\bar{x}$ chart (pronounced "x-bar") is used to monitor the process mean and the R chart is used to monitor the process variability. R is computed as the subgroup range. $\bar{x}$ and R charts are typically used when the subgroup size is less than or equal to 10.

$\bar{x}$ **and** s **charts**—A pair of control charts for variables (continuous) subgroup data, where the $\bar{x}$ chart (pronounced "x-bar") is used to monitor the process mean and the s chart is used to monitor the process variability. s is computed as the subgroup sample standard deviation. $\bar{x}$ and s charts are typically used when the subgroup size is greater than 10 or of variable size.

References

Agresti, A. 1988. "A Model for Agreement between Ratings on an Ordinal Scale." *Biometrics* 44: 539–48.

———. 1992. "Modeling Patterns of Agreement and Disagreement." *Statistical Methods in Medical Research* 1: 201–18.

Agresti, A., and B. Coull. 1998. "Approximate Is Better Than Exact for Interval Estimation of Binomial Proportions." *American Statistician* 52: 119–26.

Agresti, A., and J. B. Lang. 1993. "Quasi-symmetric Latent Class Models, with Application to Rater Agreement." *Biometrics* 49: 131–39.

Akao, Y., ed. 1990. *Quality Function Deployment*. Portland, OR: Productivity Press.

AlMaian, R. Y., K. L. Needy, K. D. Walsh, T. D. C. Alves, and N. M. Scala. 2016. "Analyzing Supplier Quality Management Practices in the Construction Industry." *Quality Engineering* 28 (2): 175–83.

Anderson, N. C., and J. V. Kovach. 2014. "Reducing Welding Defects in Turnaround Projects: A Lean Six Sigma Case Study." *Quality Engineering* 26 (2): 168–81.

Anderson-Cook, C. M. 2017. "Optimizing in a Complex World: A Statistician's Role in Decision Making." *Quality Engineering* 29 (1): 27–41.

Anderson-Cook, C. M., and L. Lu. 2015. "Much-Needed Structure: A New 5-Step Decision-Making Process Helps You Evaluate, Balance Competing Objectives." ASQ *Quality Progress* 48 (10): 42–50.

ANSI/ASQ Z1.4-2003 (R2013). 2013. *Sampling Procedures and Tables for Inspection by Attributes*. Milwaukee, WI: ASQ Quality Press.

Atzori, L., Iera, A., and Morabito, G. "The Internet of Things: A Survey." *Comput. Netw.* 54 (15): 2787–2805.

Automotive Industry Action Group (AIAG). 2006. *Production Part Approval Process Manual*. Detroit, MI: AIAG.

———. 2010. *Measurement System Analysis Reference Manual*. Detroit, MI: AIAG.

———. 2019. *AIAG & VDA FMEA Handbook*. Berlin, Germany: VDA, Verband der Automobilindustrie.

Badiru, A. B., and P. S. Pulat. 1995. *Comprehensive Project Management*. Englewood Cliffs, NJ: Prentice Hall.

Banerjee, M., M. Capozzoli, L. McSweeney, and D. Sinha. 1999. "Beyond Kappa: A Review of Interrater Agreement Measures." *Canadian Journal of Statistics* 27: 3–23.

Barnes, R. M. 1980. *Motion and Time Study Design and Measurement of Work*. 7th ed. New York: John Wiley & Sons.

Barrentine, L. 2003. *Concepts for R&R Studies*. Milwaukee, WI: ASQ Quality Press.

Baur, C., and D. Wee. 2015. "Manufacturing's Next Act." *McKinsey Quarterly*, June.

Belanger, B. C. 1980. *Measurement of Quality Control and the Use of NBS Measurement Assistance Program*. NBS Special Publication 620-A. Washington, DC: US Department of Commerce.

Besterfield, D. H. 1999. *Total Quality Management*. 2nd ed. Englewood Cliffs, NJ: Prentice Hall.

———. 2001. *Quality Control*. 6th ed. Englewood Cliffs, NJ: Prentice Hall.

Biru, A., Minerva, R., and Rotandi, D. "Towards a definition of the Internet of Things (IoT)." *IEEE Tech. Rep.* 2015. http://iot.ieee.org/definition.html.

Bisgaard, S. 2008. "Must a Process Be in Statistical Control before Conducting Designed Experiments?" *Quality Engineering* 20 (2): 143–50. doi: 10.1080/08982110701826721.

Bisgaard, S., and M. Kulahci. 2011. *Time Series Analysis and Forecasting by Example*. Hoboken, NJ: Wiley & Sons.

Bloch, D. A., and H. C. Kraemer. 1989. "2 × 2 Kappa Coefficients: Measures of Agreement or Association." *Biometrics* 45: 269–87.

Bond, T. P. 1983. "Basics of an MRB." *Quality* (November): 48.

Borror, C. M., D. C. Montgomery, and G. C. Runger. 1997. "Confidence Intervals for Variance Components from Gauge Capability Studies." *Quality and Reliability Engineering International* 13: 361–69.

Bosch, J. A. 1984. *66 Centuries of Measurement*. Dayton, OH: Sheffield Measurement Division.

Bothe, D. R. 1997. *Measuring Process Capability: Techniques and Calculations for Quality and Manufacturing Engineers*. New York: McGraw-Hill Companies.

———. 2001. "Back to Basics: Use Check Sheets to Identify the Causes of Downtime." ASQ *Quality Progress* 34 (4): 136.

Boulanger, M., M. E. Johnson, and S. N. Luko. 2012. "Reviews of Standards and Related Material: Statistical Standards and ISO, Part 1." *Quality Engineering* 24 (1): 94–101.

Box, G. E. 1954. "Some Theorems on Quadratic Forms Applied in the Study of Analysis of Variance Problems, I. Effect of Inequality of Variance in the One-Way Classification." *The Annals of Mathematical Statistics* 25 (2): 290–302.

Box, G. E. P., W. Hunter, and J. S. Hunter. 2005. *Statistics for Experimenters: Design, Innovation, and Discovery*. 2nd ed. Hoboken, NJ: John Wiley & Sons.

Box, G. E. P., and W. H. Woodall. 2012. "Innovation, Quality Engineering, and Statistics." *Quality Engineering* 24 (1): 20–29.

Boyles, R. A. 2001. "Gauge Capability for Pass-Fail Inspection." *Technometrics* 43: 223–29.

Brassard, M. 1989. *The Memory Jogger Plus+*. Methuen, MA: Goal/QPC Press.

Brettel, M., N. Friederichsen, M. Keller, and M. Rosenberg. 2014. "How Virtualization, Decentralization and Network Building Change the Manufacturing Landscape: An Industry 4.0 Perspective." *International Journal of Mechanical, Industrial Science and Engineering* 8 (1) : 37–44.

Breyfogle, F. W. 1999. *Implementing Six Sigma: Smarter Solutions Using Six Sigma*. New York: John Wiley & Sons.

———. 2003. "Control Charting at the 30,000-Foot-Level." ASQ *Quality Progress* (November): 66–70.

Breyfogle, F. W., J. Cupello, and B. Meadows. 2000. *Managing Six Sigma: A Practical Guide to Understanding, Assessing, and Implementing the Strategy That Yields Bottom-Line Success*. New York: John Wiley & Sons.

Britz, G. C., and D. W. Emerling. 2000. *Improving Performance through Statistical Thinking*. Milwaukee, WI: ASQ Quality Press.

Burdick, R. K., E. Allen, and G. Larsen. 2002. "Comparing Variability of Two Measurement Processes Using R&R Studies." *Journal of Quality Technology* 34: 97–105.

Burdick, R. K., C. M. Borror, and D. C. Montgomery. 2003. "A Review of Methods for Measurement Systems Capability Analysis." *Journal of Quality Technology* 35: 342–54.

———. 2005. *Design and Analysis of Gauge R&R Studies: Making Decisions with Confidence Intervals in Random and Mixed ANOVA Models*. Philadelphia: ASA-SIAM Series on Statistics and Applied Probability.

Burdick, R. K., and G. Larsen. 1997. "Confidence Intervals on Measures of Variability in Gauge R&R Studies." *Journal of Quality Technology* 29: 261–73.

Burnett, R. E. 2005. *Technical Communication*. 6th ed. Boston: Wadsworth/ITP.

Camgoz-Akdag, H., I. H. Pinar, and E. K. Nazli. 2016. "Internal Customer Satisfaction Improvement with QFD Technique." *Business Process Management Journal* 22 (5): 957–68.

Camp, R. C. 1989. *Benchmarking: The Search for Industry Best Practices That Lead to Superior Performance*. Milwaukee, WI: ASQC Quality Press.

———. 1995. *Business Process Benchmarking*. Milwaukee, WI: ASQC Quality Press.

Capizzi, G. 2015. "Recent Advances in Process Monitoring: Nonparametric and Variable-Selection Methods for Phase I and Phase II." *Quality Engineering* 27 (1): 44–67.

Chakraborti, S., S. W. Human, and M. A. Graham. 2008. "Phase I Statistical Process Control Charts: An Overview and Some Results." *Quality Engineering* 21 (1): 52–62.

Champ, C. W., and W. H. Woodall. 1987. "Exact Results for Shewhart Control Charts with Supplementary Runs Rules." *Technometrics* 29 (4): 393–99.

Cianfrani, C. A., and J. E. West. 2015. *ISO 9001:2015 Explained*. 4th ed. Milwaukee, WI: ASQ Quality Press.

Cicchetti, D. V., and A. R. Feinstein. 1990. "High Agreement but Low Kappa: II. Resolving the Paradoxes." *Journal of Clinical Epidemiology* 43: 551–58.

Cohen, J. 1960. "Coefficient of Agreement for Nominal Scales." *Educational and Psychological Measurement* 20: 37–46.

Cole, B. 2011. "Back To Basics: An Eye for Design." *Quality Progress*. 44, No. 9: 72.

Collins, J. C., and J. I. Porras. 1997. *Built to Last: Successful Habits of Visionary Companies*. New York: Harper Business.

Conger, A. J. 1980. "Integration and Generalization of Kappas for Multiple Raters." *Psychological Bulletin* 88: 322–28.

Cox, L. A. T. 2008. "What's Wrong with Risk Matrices?" *Risk Analysis* 28 (2): 497–512.

Creasy, T., and S. Ramey. 2013. "Don't Lose Patients." ASQ *Quality Progress* 46 (2): 42–49.

Crosby, P. B. 1979. *Quality Is Free*. New York: McGraw-Hill.

Daepp, M. I., M. J. Hamilton, G. B. West, and L. M. Bettencourt. 2015. "The Mortality of Companies." *Journal of The Royal Society Interface* 12 (106): 20150120.

Dalkey, N. C. 1967. *Analysis of the Future: The Delphi Method*. Santa Monica, CA: RAND Corporation. http://www.rand.org/pubs/papers/P3558.html.

Daniel, C. 1959. "Use of Half-Normal Plots in Interpreting Factorial Two Level Experiments." *Technometrics* 1: 311–42.

Darmody, W. J. 1967. "Elements of a Generalized Measuring System." In *Handbook of Industrial Metrology*. Englewood Cliffs, NJ: Prentice-Hall (ASTME).

Day, R. G. 1993. *Quality Function Deployment: Linking a Company with Its Customers*. Milwaukee, WI: ASQC Quality Press.

De Mast, J., and W. N. van Wieringen. 2004. "Measurement System Analysis for Bounded Ordinal Data." *Quality and Reliability Engineering International* 20: 383–95.

———. 2007. "Measurement System Analysis for Categorical Measurements: Agreement and Kappa-Type Indices." *Journal of Quality Technology* 39: 191–202.

DeBono, E. 1992. *Serious Creativity: Using the Power of Lateral Thinking to Create New Ideas.* New York: HarperCollins.

Defense Acquisition University (DAU). 2017. "Introduction to Systems Engineering." In *Defense Acquisition Guidebook.* https://www.dau.mil/tools/dag.

Defeo, J. A. 2016. *Juran's Quality Handbook: The Complete Guide to Performance Excellence.* 7th ed. New York: McGraw-Hill Professional.

Deming, W. E. 1982. *Quality, Productivity, and Competitive Position.* Cambridge, MA: M.I.T. Center for Advanced Engineering Study.

———. 1986. *Out of the Crisis.* Cambridge, MA: M.I.T. Center for Advanced Engineering Study.

Devore, J. 2016. *Probability and Statistics for Engineering and the Sciences.* 9th ed. Pacific Grove, CA: Duxbury Press.

Dodson, B., and D. Nolan. 1999. *Reliability Engineering Handbook.* Tucson, AZ: QA Publishing, LLC.

Doganaksoy, N., and G. J. Hahn. 2012. "Getting the Right Data Up Front: A Key Challenge." *Quality Engineering* 24 (4): 446–59.

Doiron, T. 2007. "20 °C—A Short History of the Standard Reference Temperature for Industrial Dimensional Measurements." *Journal of Research of the National Institute of Standards and Technology* 112 (1): 1–23.

Dolezal, K. K., R. K. Burdick, and N. J. Birch. 1998. "Analysis of a Two-Factor R&R Study with Fixed Operators." *Journal of Quality Technology* 30: 163–70.

Drews, W. E. 1978. "How to Measure Roundness." *Tooling and Production* (June): 156–60.

Duffy, G. L. 2014. *Modular Kaizen: Continuous and Breakthrough Improvement.* Milwaukee, WI: ASQ Quality Press.

Duncan, A. J. 1986. *Quality Control and Industrial Statistics.* 5th ed. Homewood, IL: Richard D. Irwin.

Durivage, M. A. 2016. *Practical Process Validation.* Milwaukee, WI: ASQ Quality Press.

———. 2017. "Work Smarter, Not Harder." ASQ *Quality Progress* 50 (3): 41–43.

Ebeling, C. E. 2009. *Introduction to Reliability and Maintainability Engineering.* Long Grove, IL: Waveland Press.

Elsayed, E. A. 1996. *Reliability Engineering.* Reading, PA: Addison Wesley.

———. 2000. "Perspectives and Challenges for Research in Quality and Reliability Engineering." *International Journal of Production Research* 38 (9): 1953–76.

Engel, J., and B. deVries. 1997. "Evaluating a Well-Known Criterion for Measurement Precision." *Journal of Quality Technology* 29: 469–76.

Erdmann, T. P., R. J. M. M. Does, and S. Bisgaard. 2009. "Quality Quandaries: A Gage R&R Study in a Hospital." *Quality Engineering* 22 (1): 46–53.

Feigenbaum, A. V. 2004. *Total Quality Control.* 4th ed. New York: McGraw-Hill.

Feinstein, A. R., and D. V. Cicchetti. 1990. "High Agreement but Low Kappa: I. The Problems of Two Paradoxes." *Journal of Clinical Epidemiology* 43: 543–49.

Filho, M. G., A. Boschi, A. F. Rentes, M. Thurer, and T. M. Bertani. 2015. "Improving Hospital Performance by Use of Lean Techniques: An Action Research Project in Brazil." *Quality Engineering* 27 (2): 196–211.

Fisher, R. A. 1925. *Statistical Methods for Research Workers.* London: Oliver and Boyd.

Fleiss, J. L. 1971. "Measuring Nominal Scale Agreement among Many Raters." *Psychological Bulletin* 76: 378–82.

Foster, S. T. 1998. "The Ups and Downs of Customer-Driven Quality." ASQ *Quality Progress* (October): 67–72.

Freedman, D., and P. Diaconis. 1981. "On the Histogram as a Density Estimator: L_2 Theory." *Zeit. Wahr. ver. Geb.* 57: 453–76.

Gale, B. T., with R. C. Wood. 1994. *Managing Customer Value: Creating Quality and Service That Customers Can See.* New York: The Free Press.

Garrett, D. F., and J. Lee. 2011. "Lean Construction Submittal Process—A Case Study." *Quality Engineering* 23 (1): 83–93.

Garvey, P. R. 2009. *Analytical Methods for Risk Management.* Boca Raton, FL: Taylor & Francis Group.

Garvin, D. A. 1987. "Competing in the Eight Dimensions of Quality." *Harvard Business Review* 87 (6): 101–9.

Gee, G., P. McGrath, and M. Izadi. 1996. "A Team Approach to Kaizen." *Journal of Industrial Technology* (Fall): 45–48.

George, M. L., D. Rowlands, M. Price, and J. Maxey. 2005. *The Lean Six Sigma Pocket Tool Book.* New York: McGraw-Hill.

Gilbreth, F., and L. M. Gilbreth. 1921. *Process Charts.* New York: American Society of Mechanical Engineers.

Gillette, B., R. Johnson, E. Polashek, J. Thornburg, and C. White. 1993. *The Art of Working Together: A Guide to Effective Collaboration.* Ames, IA: C. I. White and Associates.

Godfrey, A. J. R., G. K. G. Russell, and B. D. Betz-Stablein. 2016. "Monitoring Acute and Chronic Kidney Failure Using Statistical Process Control Techniques." *Quality Engineering* 28 (2): 184–92.

Goldratt, E. M. 1997. *Critical Chain.* Great Barrington, MA: The North River Press.

Gosavi, A., and E. Cudney. 2012. "Form Errors in Precision Metrology: A Survey of Measurement Techniques." *Quality Engineering* 24 (3): 369–80.

Gryna, F. M. 1988a. "Manufacturing Planning." In *Juran's Quality Control Handbook,* 1–59. 4th ed. New York: McGraw-Hill.

———. 1988b. "Training for Quality." In *Juran's Quality Control Handbook.* 4th ed. New York: McGraw-Hill.

Gryna, F. M., R. C. H. Chua, and J. A. Defeo. 2007. *Juran's Quality Planning and Analysis for Enterprise Quality.* 5th ed. New York: McGraw-Hill.

Hahn, G., N. Doganaksoy, and C. Stanard. 2001. "Statistical Tools for Six Sigma." ASQ *Quality Progress* (September): 78–82.

Hallock, M. L., S. J. Alper, and B. Karsh. 2006. "A Macroergonomic Work System Analysis of the Diagnostic Testing Process in an Outpatient Health Care Facility for Process Improvement and Patient Safety." *Ergonomics* 49 (5–6): 544–66.

Hawkins, D. M., and Q. Wu. 2014. "The CUSUM and the EWMA Head-to-Head." *Quality Engineering* 26 (2): 215–22.

Hayes, B. E. 2008. *Measuring Customer Satisfaction: Survey Design, Use, and Statistical Analysis Methods.* 3rd ed. Milwaukee, WI: ASQ Quality Press.

Hellier, C. 2012. *Handbook of Nondestructive Evaluation.* 2nd ed. New York: McGraw Hill.

Hill, H. M., and D. J. McClaskey. 1980. "Developing Awareness of Quality Responsibilities." In *ASQC Technical Conference Transactions.* Milwaukee, WI: ASQC Quality Press.

Hoerl, R. 2001. "Six Sigma Black Belts: What Do They Need to Know?" (with discussion). *Journal of Quality Technology* 33: 391–435.

Hoerl, R., and R. D. Snee. 2012. *Statistical Thinking: Improving Business Performance.* Hoboken, NJ: John Wiley & Sons.

Hogg, R. V., E. A. Tanis, and D. Zimmerman. 2014. *Probability and Statistical Inference.* Englewood Cliffs, NJ: Pearson Higher Ed.

Houf, R., and D. Berman. 1988. "Statistical Analysis of Power Module Thermal Test Equipment Performance." *IEEE Transactions on Components, Hybrids, and Manufacturing Technology* 22: 516–20.

Hughes, T. A. 1995. *Measurement and Control Basics*. 2nd ed. Research Triangle Park, NC: Instrument Society of America.

Imai, M. 1986. *Kaizen*. New York: McGraw-Hill.

Ishikawa, K. 1985. *What Is Total Quality Control? The Japanese Way*. Englewood Cliffs, NJ: Prentice Hall.

ISO. 2015. *Moving from ISO 9001:2008 to ISO 9001:2015*. Geneva: International Organization for Standardization.

ISO 9001:2015. 2015. *Quality Management Systems—Requirements*. Geneva: International Organization for Standardization.

ISO 9004:2009. 2009. *Managing for the Sustained Success of an Organisation: A Quality Management Approach*. Geneva: International Organization for Standardization.

ISO 31000:2018. 2018. *Risk Management—Principles and Guidelines*. Geneva: International Organization for Standardization.

Jardine, A. K. S., and J. A. Buzacott. 1983. "Equipment Reliability and Maintenance." *European Journal of Operational Research* 19: 285–96.

Jensen, C. R. 2002. "Variance Component Calculations: Common Methods and Misapplications in the Semiconductor Industry." *Quality Engineering* 14: 645–57.

Johnson, R. H., and R. T. Webber. 1985. *Buying Quality: How Purchasing, Quality Control, and Suppliers Work Together*. New York: Franklin Watts.

Juran, J. M. 1988. *Juran's Quality Handbook*. 4th ed. New York: McGraw-Hill.

———. 1989. *Juran on Leadership for Quality*. New York: Free Press.

Juran, J. M., and A. Godfrey. 1999. *Juran's Quality Handbook*. 5th ed. New York: McGraw Hill.

Juran, J. M., and F. N. Gryna Jr. 1980. *Quality Planning and Analysis*. New York: McGraw-Hill.

Kaplan, R. S., and D. Norton. 1992. "The Balanced Scorecard: Measures That Drive Performance." *Harvard Business Review* 70 (1): 71–79.

Kerns, D. T., and D. T. Nadler. 1992. *Prophets in the Dark: How Xerox Reinvented Itself and Beat Back the Japanese*. New York: Harper Business.

Kilmann, R. H., and K. W. Thomas. 1977. "Developing a Forced Choice Measure of Conflict-Handling Behavior: The 'MODE' Instrument." *Educational and Psychological Measurement* 37 (2): 309–25.

Kim, S., Y. Yoon, and G. Zeon. 2004. "Combine Quality and Speed To Market." *Six Sigma Forum Magazine* 3 (4): 26–31.

King, B. 1987. *Better Designs in Half the Time*. Methuen, MA: Goal/QPC Press.

Kirkpatrick, D. L. 2006. *Evaluating Training Programs: The Four Levels*. 3rd ed. San Francisco: Berrett-Koehler.

Knowles, M. S. 1996. "Adult Learning." In *The ASTD Training and Development Handbook*. 4th ed. New York: McGraw-Hill.

Kolarik, W. J. 1995. *Creating Quality: Concepts, Systems, Strategies, and Tools*. New York: McGraw-Hill.

———. 1999. *Creating Quality: Process Design for Results*. New York: McGraw-Hill.

Kotz, S., and C. Lovelace. 1998. *Process Capability Indices in Theory and Practice*. London: Arnold Press.

Kubiak, T. M. 2009. "Perusing Process Performance Metrics." ASQ *Quality Progress* (August): 42.

Kutner, M. H., C. J. Nachtsheim, J. Neter, and W. Li. 2004. *Applied Linear Statistical Models.* 5th ed. Boston: McGraw-Hill Irwin.

Laford, R. J. 1986. *Ship-to-Stock: An Alternative to Incoming Inspection.* Milwaukee, WI: ASQC Quality Press.

Langdon, D. J. 1994. "A New Language of Work." *Quality Digest* (October): 44–48.

Larsen, G. A. 2002. "Measurement System Analysis—The Usual Metrics Can Be Noninformative." *Quality Engineering* 15: 293–98.

Ledolter, J., and A. Swersey. 2007. *Testing 1-2-3: Experimental Design with Applications in Marketing and Service Operations.* Los Angeles: Stanford University Press.

Lee, H., and H. Awbi. 2004. "Effect of Internal Partitioning on Room Air Quality with Mixing Ventilation—Statistical Analysis." *Renewable Energy* 29: 1721–32.

Long, C. S., and F. M. Gryna. 1999. *Preferred Practices in Developing a Quality Information System.* Report No. 907. Tampa, FL: College of Business.

Luceño, A. 1996. "A Process Capability Ratio with Reliable Confidence Intervals." *Communication in Statistics—Simulation and Computation* 25: 235–46.

Luko, S. N. 2013. "Risk Management Terminology." *Quality Engineering* 25 (3): 292–97.

Machinability Data Center. 1980. *Machining Data Handbook.* Cincinnati, OH: TechSolve.

Mader, D. P., J. Prins, and R. E. Lampe. 1999. "The Economic Impact of Measurement Error." *Quality Engineering* 15: 293–98.

Majeske, K. D., and R. W. Andrews. 2002. "Evaluating Measurement Systems and Manufacturing Processes Using Three Quality Measures." *Quality Engineering* 15 (2): 243–51.

Makino, T. 1984. "Mean Hazard Rate and Its Application to the Normal Approximation of the Weibull Distribution." *Naval Research Logistics Quarterly* 31: 1–8.

Mallette, P. 1993. "Improving Through Creativity." *Quality Digest* (May): 81–85.

Malshe, A., K. Rajurkar, A. Samant, H. N. Hansen, S. Bapat, and W. Jiang. 2013. "Bio-inspired Functional Surfaces for Advanced Applications." *CIRP Annals-Manufacturing Technology* 62 (2): 607–28.

Manos, T. 2006. "Value Stream Mapping—An Introduction." ASQ *Quality Progress* (June): 64–69.

McCaslin, J. A., and G. F. Gruska. 1976. "Analysis of Attribute Gage Systems." *ASQC Technical Conference Transactions* 30: 392–99.

McNish, A. 1967. "The Nature of Measurement." In *Handbook of Industrial Metrology.* Englewood Cliffs, NJ: Prentice Hall.

Menesatti, P., C. Beni, G. Paglia, S. Marcelli, and S. D'Andrea. 1999. "Predictive Statistical Model for the Analysis of Drop Impact Damage on Peach." *Journal of Agricultural Engineering Research* 73 (3): 275–82.

MIL-HDBK-61A(SE). 2001. *Military Handbook: Configuration Management Guidance.* Washington, DC: Department of Defense.

MIL-STD-1629A. 1980. *Procedures for Performing a Failure Mode, Effects, and Criticality Analysis.* Washington, DC: Department of Defense.

Mizuno, S., ed. 1988. *Management for Quality Improvement.* Portland, OR: Productivity Press.

Montgomery, D. C. 2013. *Introduction to Statistical Quality Control.* 7th ed. Hoboken, NJ: John Wiley & Sons.

———. 2017. *Design and Analysis of Experiments.* 9th ed. New York: John Wiley & Sons.

Montgomery, D. C., C. Jennings, and M. Kulahci. 2015. *Introduction to Time Series Analysis and Forecasting.* 2nd ed. New York: John Wiley & Sons.

Montgomery, D. C., and G. C. Runger. 2013. *Applied Statistics and Probability for Engineers.* 6th ed. Hoboken, NJ: John Wiley & Sons.

Montgomery, D. C., G. C. Runger, and N. F. Hubele. 2010. *Engineering Statistics*. 5th ed. Hoboken, NJ: John Wiley & Sons.

Moon, J. 2020. *Foundations of Quality Risk Management*. Milwaukee, WI: Quality Press.

Myers, R. H., D. C. Montgomery, and C. M. Anderson-Cook. 2016. *Response Surface Methodology*. 4th ed. New York: John Wiley & Sons.

Nadler, G., and S. Hibino. 1994. *Breakthrough Thinking*. 2nd ed. Rocklin, CA: Prima Publishing.

Nakajima, S. 1988. *Introduction to TPM*. New York: Productivity Press.

Nakajima, S. 1989. *TPM Development Program*. New York: Productivity Press.

Nepal, B., S. Mohanty, and L. Kay. 2013. "Quality Improvement of Medical Wire Manufacturing Process." *Quality Engineering* 25 (2): 151–63.

NIST (National Institute for Standards and Technology). 1981. *A Brief History of Measurement Systems*. Special Publication 304A. Washington, DC: US Department of Commerce.

Page, E. S. 1961. "Cumulative Sum Control Charts." *Technometrics* 3: 1–9.

Palady, P. 1997. *Failure Modes and Effects Analysis: Practical Applications*. Ann Arbor, MI: Library of Congress.

Park, C. S. 2007. *Contemporary Engineering Economics*. 4th ed. New Jersey: Prentice Hall.

Parsowith, B. S. 1995. *Fundamentals of Quality Auditing*. Milwaukee, WI: ASQC Quality Press.

Pearlson, K. E., and C. S. Saunders. 2004. *Managing and Using Information Systems: A Strategic Approach*. New York: John Wiley & Sons.

Perez-Wilson, M. 1997. "Process Capability: Minding Your Cpk's." *Quality Digest*. Accessed December 20, 2016. http://www.qualitydigest.com/magazine/1997/dec/article/process-capability-minding-your-cpks.html.

Perry, B. 1998. "Seeing Your Customers in a Whole New Light." *Journal for Quality and Participation* 21 (6): 38–43.

Phillips, J. J. 2003. *Return on Investment in Training and Performance Improvement Programs*. New York: Butterworth Heinemann.

Pinto, C. A., and P. R. Garvey. 2012. *Advanced Risk Analysis in Engineering Enterprise Systems*. Boca Raton, FL: CRC Press.

Reason, R. E. 1960. *The Measurement of Surface Texture*. London: CleaverHume Press.

ReVelle, J. B. 2004. *Quality Essentials: A Reference Guide from A to Z*. Milwaukee, WI: ASQ Quality Press.

Rice, G. O. 1986. "Metrology." In *Quality Management Handbook*, edited by L. Walsh, R. Wurster, and R. J. Kimber. Milwaukee, WI: ASQC Quality Press; New York: Marcel Dekker.

Robbins, S. P., and T. Judge. 2012. *Essentials of Organizational Behavior*. Upper Saddle River, NJ: Pearson.

Roberts, S. W. 1959. "Control Chart Tests Based on Geometric Moving Averages." *Technometrics* 1: 97–102.

Rodriguez-Perez, J. 2012. *Quality Risk Management in the FDA-Regulated Industry*. Milwaukee, WI: ASQ Quality Press.

Rother, M., and J. Shook. 1999. *Learning to See*. Brookline, MA: The Lean Enterprise Institute.

Russell, J. P., ed. 2013. *The ASQ Auditing Handbook*. 4th ed. Milwaukee, WI: ASQ Quality Press.

Saaty, T. 1982. *Decision Making for Leaders*. Belmont, CA: Lifetime Learning Publications.

Salegna, G., and F. Fazel. 2000. "Obstacles to Implementing Quality." ASQ *Quality Progress* (July): 53–57.

Schall, S. O. 2012. "Variability Reduction: A Statistical Engineering Approach to Engage Operations Teams in Process Improvement." *Quality Engineering* 24 (2): 264–79.

Schoonhoven, M., C. Lubbers, and R. J. M. M. Does. 2013. "Quality Quandaries: Shortening the Throughput Time at a Hospital's Billing Process." *Quality Engineering* 25 (2): 188–93.

Scott, D. 1979. "On Optimal and Data-Based Histograms." *Biometrika* 66: 605–10.

Shewhart, W. A. 1980. *Economic Control of Quality Manufactured Product*. Milwaukee, WI: ASQC Quality Press.

Shingo, S. 1986. *Zero Quality Control: Source Inspection and the Poka-Yoke System*. Portland, OR: Productivity Press.

Simon, J. 2022. *Risk Management for Medical Device Manufacturers*. Milwaukee, WI: ASQ Quality Press.

Simpson, J. A. 1981. "Foundations of Metrology." *Journal of Research of the National Bureau of Standards* 86 (3): 36–42.

Simpson, J. R., C. M. Listak, and G. T. Hutto. 2013. "Guidelines for Planning and Evidence for Assessing a Well-Designed Experiment." *Quality Engineering* 25 (4): 333–55.

Snee, R. D., and R. W. Hoerl. 2003. *Leading Six Sigma: A Step-by-Step Guide Based on Experience with GE and Other Six Sigma Companies*. Upper Saddle River, NJ: Financial Times Prentice Hall.

———. 2012. "Leadership—Essential for Developing the Discipline of Statistical Engineering." *Quality Engineering* 24: 162–70.

Society for Automotive Engineers. 2014. Aerospace First Article Inspection Requirement.

Standard AS9102b.

Somerville, S. E., and D. C. Montgomery. 1996. "Process Capability Indices and Nonnormal Distributions." *Quality Engineering* 9 (2): 305–16.

Spragg, R. C. 1976. "Advanced System for the Measurement of Errors of Form." SME Paper No. IQ 76-807.

Stamatis, D. 2003. *Failure Mode and Effect Analysis: FMEA Theory to Execution*. 2nd ed. Milwaukee, WI: ASQ Quality Press.

Stephens, K. S. 2016. "Practitioner Advice: Dodge and Romig Sampling Tables: Revisited, Refined, and Extended-Practitioner Advice." *Quality Engineering* 28 (2): 238–44.

Stevenson, W. 2000. "Supercharging Your Pareto Analysis." ASQ *Quality Progress* (October): 51–55.

Stolovitch, H. D., and E. J. Keeps, eds. 1992. *The Handbook of Human Performance Technology*. San Francisco: Jossey-Bass.

Sturges, H. A. 1926. "The Choice of a Class Interval." *Journal of the American Statistical Association* 21: 65–66.

Sullivan, L. P. 1986. "Quality Function Deployment." ASQC *Quality Progress* (June): 39–50.

Sumithra, B., and S. Bhattacharya. 2008. "Toasting of Corn Flakes: Product Characteristics as a Function of Processing Conditions." *Journal of Food Engineering* 88: 419–28.

Sweet, A. L., S. Tjokrodjojo, and P. Wijaya. 2005. "An Investigation of the Measurements Systems Analysis 'Analytic Method' for Attribute Gages." *Quality Engineering* 17: 219–26.

Taguchi, G. 1986. *Introduction to Quality Engineering: Designing Quality into Products and Processes*. White Plains, NY: Kraus International; UNIPUB (Asian Productivity Organization).

Tague, N. 2005. *The Quality Toolbox*. 2nd ed. Milwaukee, WI: ASQ Quality Press.

Tan, R. Y. C., M. Met-Domestici, K. Zhou, A. B. Guzman, S. T. Lim, K. C. Soo, T. W. Feeley, and J. Ngeow. 2016. "Using Quality Improvement Methods and Time-Driven Activity-Based Costing to Improve Value-Based Cancer Care Delivery at a Cancer Genetics Clinic." *Journal of Oncology Practice* 12 (3): e320–31. JOPR007765.

Taylor, B. N., and A. Thompson, eds. 2008. *The International System of Units (SI).* NIST Special Publication SP 330-2008. Washington, DC: Government Printing Office.

Tobias, P. A., and D. C. Trindade. 2011. *Applied Reliability.* 3rd ed. Boca Raton, FL: CRC Press.

Townsend, A., N. Senin, L. Blunt, R. K. Leach, and J. S. Taylor. 2016. "Surface Texture Metrology for Metal Additive Manufacturing: A Review." *Precision Engineering* 46: 34–47.

Trip, A., and R. J. Does. 2010. "Quality Quandaries: Interpretation of Signals from Runs Rules in Shewhart Control Charts." *Quality Engineering* 22 (4): 351–57.

Tuckman, B. W. 1965. "Developmental Sequence in Small Groups." *Psychological Bulletin* 63 (6): 384–99.

Tuckman, B. W., and M. A. C. Jensen. 1977. "Stages of Small-Group Development Revisited." *Group & Organizational Studies* 2 (4): 419–27.

Uebersax, J. S., and W. M. Grove. 1990. "Latent Class Analysis of Diagnostic Agreement." *Statistical Methods* 9: 559–72.

Van Patten, J. 2006. "A Second Look at 5S." ASQ *Quality Progress* 39 (10): 55–59.

Van Wieringen, W. N., and E. R. van Heuvel. 2005. "A Comparison of Methods for the Evaluation of Binary Measurement Systems." *Quality Engineering* 17: 495–507.

Vardeman, S. B., and E. S. VanValkenburg. 1999. "Two-Way Random-Effects Analyses and Gauge R&R Sudies." *Technometrics* 41: 202–11.

Vendor-Vendee Technical Committee. 1977. *How to Conduct a Supplier Survey.* Milwaukee, WI: ASQC Quality Press.

Vining, G. 2009. "Technical Advice: Phase I and Phase II Control Charts." *Quality Engineering* 21: 478–79.

———. 2011. "Technical Advice: Essential Elements for Quality Improvement Programs," *Quality Engineering* 23: 395–97.

———. 2013. "Technical Advice: Scientific Method and Approaches for Collecting Data." *Quality Engineering* 25 (2): 194–201.

Vining, G. G., and S. Kowalski. 2011. *Statistical Methods for Engineers.* 3rd ed. Pacific Grove, CA: Brooks-Cole.

Vogt, T. L. 1980. *Optimizing Calibration Recall Intervals and Algorithms.* NIST Publication NBS-GCR-80-283.

Wang, J. X., and M. L. Roush. 2000. *What Every Engineer Should Know about Risk Engineering and Management.* Boca Raton, FL: CRC Press.

Watson, G. H. 1993. *Strategic Benchmarking.* New York: John Wiley & Sons.

Weaver, B. P., M. S. Hamada, S. B. Vardeman, and A. G. Wilson. 2012. "A Bayesian Approach to the Analysis of Gauge R&R Data." *Quality Engineering* 24 (4): 486–500.

Westcott, R. T. 2003. *Stepping Up to ISO 9004:2000.* Chico, CA: Paton Press.

Western Electric Company. 1956. *Statistical Quality Control Handbook.* Indianapolis, IN: Western Electric Co.

Wheeler, D. J. 2004. *The Six Sigma Practitioner's Guide to Data Analysis.* Knoxville, TN: SPC Press.

Wheeler, D. J., and R. W. Lyday. 1989. *Evaluating the Measurement Process.* 2nd ed. Knoxville, TN: SPC Press.

Whitehouse, D. 2002. *Surfaces and Their Measurements.* London: Kogan Page Science.

———. 2010. *Handbook of Surface and Nanometrology.* 2nd ed. Boca Raton, FL: Taylor and Francis Group.

Wijma, J., A. Trip, R. J. M. M. Does, and S. Bisgaard. 2009. "Quality Quandaries: Efficiency Improvement in a Nursing Department," *Quality Engineering* 21 (2): 222–28.

Windsor, S. E. 2003. "Attribute Gage R&R." *Six Sigma Forum Magazine* 2 (4): 23–28.

Woodall, W. 2017. "Bridging the Gap between Theory and Practice in Basic Statistical Process Monitoring." *Quality Engineering* 21 (1): 2–15.

Woodall, W. H., and C. M. Borror. 2008. "Some Relationships between Gage R&R Criteria." *Quality and Reliability Engineering International* 24: 99–104.

Woodall, W., and D. C. Montgomery. 1999. "Research Issues and Ideas in Statistical Process Control." *Journal of Quality Technology* 31 (4): 376–86.

———. 2014. "Some Current Directions in the Theory and Application of Statistical Process Monitoring." *Journal of Quality Technology* 46 (1): 78–94.

Zwetsloot, I. M., and R. J. M. M. Does. 2015. "Quality Quandaries: Improving Revenue by Attracting More Clients Online." *Quality Engineering* 27 (1): 130–38.

Index

Note: Page numbers followed by *f* or *t* refer to figures or tables, respectively.

O